A SUBTREASURY OF AMERICAN HUMOR

A Subtreasury of
AMERICAN
HUMOR

E. B. White *and* Katharine S. White

EDITORS

COWARD-McCANN, INC · NEW YORK

21109

817.08
W583su

PJ

MANUFACTURED IN THE UNITED STATES OF AMERICA
Van Rees Press • New York

ACKNOWLEDGMENTS

THE EDITORS are grateful to the many authors who have allowed their work to be reprinted in this book. Every care has been taken to obtain permission from the owners to reprint material which is in copyright; any errors are unintentional and will be gladly corrected in future printings if notification is sent to the publishers, Coward-McCann, Inc., who wish to acknowledge with thanks the courtesy of the following for permission to reprint as indicated:

George Ade for "The Professor Who Wanted to Be Alone" from his *Fables in Slang*.

George P. Anderson for "Lengthy Symphony" by Persis Greely Anderson.

D. Appleton-Century Company for a selection from *The Casting Away of Mrs. Lecks and Mrs. Aleshine* by Frank R. Stockton, copyright, 1886, 1913 by The Century Company.

Morris Bishop for "A Worm-Chorus" and "Ozymandias Revisited" from *Paramount Poems*.

Roark Bradford for "The Adulteration of Old King David" from his *Ol' Man Adam an' His Chillun*.

Brandt & Brandt, agents, for "Whitey" from *Penrod and Sam* by Booth Tarkington, copyright, 1916 by Booth Tarkington, and "For City Spring" from *Burning City,* copyright, 1935 by Stephen Vincent Benét, and published by Farrar & Rinehart, Inc.

Dodd, Mead & Company for "Death in the Rumble Seat," "Ring Out, Wild Bells," and "Time . . . Fortune . . . Life . . . Luce . . ." from *A Bed of Neuroses* by Wolcott Gibbs, copyright, 1929-1937 by Wolcott Gibbs; "It's a Wise Parent" from *Dithers and Jitters* by Cornelia Otis Skinner, copyright, 1938 by Cornelia Otis Skinner; and selections from *Dere Mable* by Edward Streeter, copyright, 1918, 1941 by Edward Streeter. Used by Permission of Dodd, Mead & Company, Inc.

Doubleday, Doran and Company, Inc. for "The Waist-Band That Was Taut Up to the Moment It Gave Way" and "The Ninny Who Swam Away from the Life Preserver" from *Hand-Made Fables* by George Ade, copyright, 1920; reprinted by permission of Doubleday,

v

Doran and Company; "Fable of the Iron Dogs" from *The Almost Perfect State,* "the coming of archy," "mehitabel was once cleopatra," "the song of mehitabel," and "the old trouper" from *archy and mehitabel* by Don Marquis, copyright, 1927 by Doubleday, Doran and Company, Inc.; "Sonnets to a Red-Haired Lady" from *Sonnets to a Red-Haired Lady* by Don Marquis, copyright, 1922 by Doubleday, Doran and Company, Inc.; and "The Whisky Rebellion" from *A Parody Outline of History* by Donald Ogden Stewart, copyright, 1921 by Doubleday, Doran and Company, Inc.

Duell, Sloan & Pearce, Inc. for "A Hobby a Day Keeps the Doldrums Away," "Ode to the End of Summer" and "Public Journal" from *A Pocketful of Wry* by Phyllis McGinley. Reprinted by permission of the publishers.

E. P. Dutton & Co., Inc. for "Sea Chill" from *Gaily the Troubadour* by Arthur Guiterman and "Anthologistics" from *Lyric Laughter* by Arthur Guiterman, both volumes published and copyright by E. P. Dutton & Co., Inc., New York.

Irwin Edman and *Harper's Magazine* for "Intermission, Please!"

Farrar & Rinehart, Inc. for "A Fish Fry" from *The Green Pastures* by Marc Connelly, copyright, 1929 and reprinted by permission of Farrar & Rinehart, Inc., Publishers.

Lee Furman, Inc. for "In Mulberry Street" and "Natural History" from *Back Where I Came From* by A. J. Liebling, and "Tanya" from *My Ears Are Bent* by Joseph Mitchell.

Milt Gross for "Ferry-Tail from Keeng Mitas for Nize Baby" from his *Nize Baby.*

Harcourt, Brace and Company, for "Mrs. Heywood Cox Broun" from *The Collected Works of Heywood Broun,* copyright, 1941 by Heywood Hale Broun; "the Cambridge ladies" from *Collected Poems by e. e. cummings,* published by Harcourt Brace & Company. Copyright, 1923, 1925, 1931, 1935, 1938 by E. E. Cummings; copyright, 1926 by Boni & Liveright; a selection from *Babbitt* by Sinclair Lewis; copyright, 1922 by Harcourt, Brace and Company, Inc.; "The Sock Hunt" from *My Sister Eileen,* copyright, 1938 by Ruth McKenney; "The Summer of the Beautiful White Horse" from *My Name is Aram,* copyright, 1940 by William Saroyan; and "A. E. Housman Turns 'Georgey Porgey' Into a Shropshire Lad" from *Selected Poems and Parodies of Louis Untermeyer,* copyright, 1935 by Harcourt, Brace and Company, Inc. All reprints by permission of the publishers.

Harper & Brothers, for the following by Robert Benchley: "Christmas Afternoon" from *Of All Things,* copyright, 1921 by Harper & Brothers; "Happy Childhood Tales" from *No Poems,* copyright, 1932 by Robert Benchley; "More Songs for Meller" from *The Early Worm,* copyright, 1927 by Harper & Brothers; "The Blue Sleeve Garter" from *Pluck and Luck,* copyright, 1925 by Harper & Brothers; "Confessions of a Gallomaniac," "Novels and Hats," "The Loeb Classics," and "When Nature Lovers Write Books" from *The Colby Essays* by Frank Moore Colby, copyright, 1926 by Harper & Brothers; "If Grant Had Been Drinking at Appomattox" and "The Greatest Man in the World" from *The Middle-Aged Man on the Flying Trapeze* by James Thurber, copyright, 1935 by James Thurber; "The Night the Bed Fell" from *My Life and Hard Times* by James Thurber, copyright, 1933 by James Thurber; "The Owl Who Was God," "The Shrike and the Chipmunks," "The Moth and the Star," and "The Unicorn in the Garden" from *Fables for Our Time* by James Thurber, copyright, 1939 by James Thurber; "A Mississippi Pilot," from *Life on the Mississippi* by Mark Twain; "Fenimore Cooper's Literary Offenses" from *In Defense of Harriet Shelley and Other Essays* by Mark Twain, copyright, 1918 by The Mark Twain Company; "His Grandfather's Old Ram," from *Roughing It* by Mark Twain; "Huck and Jim Talk about Kings," from *The Adventures of Huckleberry Finn* by Mark Twain; "The Hunting of the Cow" from *Mark Twain in Eruption* by Mark Twain, edited by Bernard de Voto, copyright, 1940 by The Mark Twain Company; "Dusk in Fierce Pajamas" and "The Parable of the Family Which Dwelt Apart" from *Quo Vadimus* by E. B. White, copyright, 1934 by E. B. White; and "Harper to Mifflin to Chance" from *The Fox of Peapack,* copyright, 1932 by E. B. White. All titles published by Harper & Brothers.

Lucien Harris for "Miss Cow Falls a Victim to Mr. Rabbit" from *Uncle Remus* by Joel Chandler Harris.

Holiday House, Inc. for "Why There Are No Trees on the Desert" from *Ol' Paul, the Mighty Logger,* by Glen Rounds.

Houghton Mifflin Company for "Sunthin' in the Pastoral Line" from *Lowell's Complete Poetical Works;* "Jungle Folk" from *Condensed Novels (Second Series)* by Bret Harte; "The Peterkins Celebrate the Fourth of July" from *The Peterkin Papers* by Lucretia P. Hale and "Cacoëthes Scribendi" from Holmes' *Complete Poetical Works.* All selections used by permission of the authorized publishers, Houghton Mifflin Company.

Alva Johnston and *The Saturday Evening Post* for "How to Become a Great Writer."

Alfred A. Knopf, Inc. for "The Governor" from *Our Government* by James M. Cain; selections from *Thoughts without Words* and illustrations by Clarence Day; "The Noblest Instrument" reprinted from *Life With Father* by Clarence Day; "Going to Bed Before a Young Lady" by "M" contained in *Tall Tales of the Southwest,* edited by Franklin J. Meine; "Brief Gust of Glory" reprinted from *Happy Days* by H. L. Mencken; "The Wedding: A Stage Direction" reprinted from *A Book of Burlesque* by H. L. Mencken and "Back to Methuselah" reprinted from *The Intimate Notebooks of George Jean Nathan.* All selections used by permission of and special arrangement with Alfred A. Knopf, Inc., authorized publishers.

John Lardner for "Sit Still" by Ring Lardner.

Little, Brown & Company for "Doucement, Doucement!" from *The Mott Family in France* by Donald Moffat; "Let's Stay Home and Make Friends" from *Free Wheeling* by Ogden Nash; "The Song of Songs" from *I'm a Stranger Here Myself* by Ogden Nash; "Bankers Are Just Like Anybody Else, Except Richer," "Cat Naps Are Too Good for Cats," "First Families, Move Over!", " 'My Child Is Phlegmatic . . .' Anxious Parent," "Requiem," "The Strange Case of Mr. Fortague's Disappointment," and "To a Small Boy Standing on My Shoes While I am Wearing Them," from *The Face Is Familiar* by Ogden Nash; and "A Weekend at Lady Astor's" from *A Pearl in Every Oyster* by Frank Sullivan. All selections reprinted by permission of Little, Brown & Company.

Liveright Publishing Corp. for "A Short History of Man" from *How to Tell Your Friends from the Apes* by Will Cuppy; selections from *Poems in Praise of Practically Nothing* by Samuel Hoffenstein; a selection from *Gentlemen Prefer Blondes* by Anita Loos; "In Old Chinatown" from *Dawn Ginsbergh's Revenge* by S. J. Perelman; and "The Vanderbilt Convention" from *Broccoli and Old Lace* by Frank Sullivan. All titles published by Liveright.

Phyllis McGinley for "Song from New Rochelle" from *On the Contrary.*

Paul McPharlin and The Fine Book Circle for "Three Love Letters" by Benjamin Franklin, translated from the French by Paul McPharlin. Selection taken from *Satires and Bagatelles* by Benjamin Franklin, edited by Paul McPharlin, published by The Fine Book Circle, Detroit, 1937.

G. P. Putnam's Sons for "The Disinterested Arbiter," "The Party Over There," "Cat and King," "Revenge," "Officer and Thug," and "Saint and Soul" from *Fantastic Fables* by Ambrose Bierce; "Ain't There at Least One Gen'leman Here?" from *I'm Sorry if I Have Offended and Other Sob Ballads* by C. Knapp; and "Farewell, My Lovely!" from *Farewell to Model T* by Lee Strout White.

Random House, Inc. for "Appreciation of Art" from *Junior Miss* by Sally Benson, copyright, 1941 by Random House, Inc., 1939-1941 by Sally Benson; "Portrait" from *Dead Reckoning* by Kenneth Fearing, copyright, 1938 by Random House, Inc.; "Lady's Room" from *Celibate at Twilight* by John Mosher, copyright, 1940 by Random House, Inc., 1926-1940 by John Mosher; "The Idol's Eye" and "Waiting for Santy" from *Strictly from Hunger* by S. J. Perelman, copyright, 1937 by Random House, Inc., and "Down with the Restoration!" from *Look Who's Talking* by S. J. Perelman. All selections reprinted by permission of Random House, Inc.

Charles Scribner's Sons for "Mr. Dooley on the Education of the Young" from *Mr. Dooley at His Best* by Finley Peter Dunne, edited by Elmer Ellis; "Mr. Dooley on the Power of Music" and "Mr. Dooley on Golf" from *Mr. Dooley on Making a Will and Other Necessary Evils* by Finley Peter Dunne; "The Norris Plan" from *In the Worst Possible Taste,* copyright, 1922 by Corey Ford and published by Charles Scribner's Sons; "The Horse," "The Hen," "The Cow," and "The Gnu" with the accompanying illustrations, from *More Animals* by Oliver Herford; "Large Coffee," "Odd's Bodkins," and "On Conversation" from *First and Last* by Ring Lardner; "Alibi Ike" from *Round Up* by Ring Lardner; "Sonnets to Baedeker" from *Bay Window Ballads* by David McCord; and "Benny and the Bird-Dogs" from *When the Whippoorwill* by Marjorie Kinnan Rawlings.

Simon & Schuster, Inc. for selections from *The Diary of Our Own Samuel Pepys* by Franklin P. Adams, copyright, 1935 by Franklin P. Adams and "Boggains in the Bronx" from *Thunder in the Bronx* by Arthur Kober, copyright, 1935 by Arthur Kober, and published by Simon & Schuster, Inc.

Frederick A. Stokes Company, Inc. for "The Man from Yellowhouse" reprinted by permission of Frederick A. Stokes Company, Inc., from *Wolfville* by Alfred Henry Lewis, copyright, 1897.

Mrs. Bert Leston Taylor for "The Passionate Professor" by Bert Leston Taylor.

The Viking Press, Inc. for "To a Thesaurus," "Advice to Young

Men," and "Lines to Three Boys" from *The Melancholy Flute* by Franklin P. Adams, copyright, 1936 by Franklin P. Adams; "The Ballet Visits the Splendide's Magician" from *Hotel Splendide* by Ludwig Bemelmans, copyright, 1941 by Ludwig Bemelmans; "Glory in the Daytime" from *Here Lies* by Dorothy Parker; "Little Words," "Tombstone for an Actress," and "The Searched Soul" from *Not So Deep as a Well* by Dorothy Parker, copyright, 1926, 1928, 1931, 1936 and "The Highly Recurrent Mr. Hamilton" and "Re-enter Margot Asquith" by Dorothy Parker from *The New Yorker;* "Capsule Criticism" from *Shouts and Murmurs* by Alexander Woollcott; and "Manhattan" from *Enchanted Aisles* by Alexander Woollcott. All selections by permission of The Viking Press, Inc.

The Yale University Press for selections and illustrations from *Scenes from the Mesozoic* by Clarence Day.

The following selections were first printed in *The New Yorker* and "to the best of our knowledge" have not been published since in book form except in a few cases in *New Yorker* anthologies. The editors and publishers are grateful to both the magazine and the authors and artists for allowing them to be used in this volume: Nine selections from "The Talk of the Town"; "Memoirs of a Master"—M. R. A.; "La Presse Perverse"—Robert Benchley; drawing of Henry Luce—Will Cotton; "Woman Out of Taxi"—Angela Cypher (Marjorie Allen Seiffert); two book reviews—Clifton Fadiman; "Limericks Long After Lear"—Morris Bishop and Richard Taylor; two theater reviews and "Shakespeare, Here's Your Hat"—Wolcott Gibbs; "Boy Meets Bullfinch" and "Mother Taft's Chickens"—Geoffrey Hellman; "Dr. C-dm-n's Daily"—Nunnally Johnson; "At Home with the Paleys"—E. J. Kahn Jr.; "Who Is This King of Glory?"—A. J. Liebling and St. Clair McKelway; "What Did You Do, Grandfather?"—Richard Lockridge; "An Affix for Birds"—St. Clair McKelway; "Atheist Hit by Truck"—John McNulty; "Inflexible Logic"—Russell Maloney; "The Downfall of Fascism in Black Ankle County"—Joseph Mitchell; "Savage Homecoming"—Clifford Orr; "The Mesecks"—Kenneth Allan Robinson; "Christopher K*a*p*l*a*n"—Leonard Q. Ross (Leo C. Rosten); "A Ride With Ralph"—Francis Steegmuller; "A Garland of Ibids" and "The Jukes Family"—Frank Sullivan; illustrations for "Fables for Our Time"—James Thurber; "Owl Man"—Sanderson Vanderbilt; "Fpafm"—Frances Warfield; "Famous Baths and Bathers" —Carolyn Wells.

A COLLECTION, whether of birds' eggs or of funny pieces, is likely to reveal more about the collector than about the subject. I know this to be true, because there was a cabinet of birds' eggs in the attic of the house I lived in as a child, and although I learned very little about birds from this early and fascinating anthology, I caught quite a glimpse of the cousin who had assembled all those eggs under one roof. They were arranged according to a plan which struck me as admirable: they were placed according to size—starting with an ostrich egg and ending with a hummingbird's. I'm sure that even at that date there must have been a more scientific way of grouping birds' eggs, but there was no lovelier. It was a memorable collection. The cousin died in a gun accident before I ever encountered him in the flesh, the only anthologist with whose taste I have been in complete agreement. There was not one egg that was not a perfect work of art.

In this collection of American humor, Katharine S. White (who shall hereafter be known as my wife) and I have tried to select some things we like ourselves, and have made no attempt to throw in anything to please anybody else. This is a subtreasury designed for the safekeeping of our own valuables. Anyone else who wants to pay his way in is at liberty to wander about, criticizing the contents of the vaults and looking for trouble. That is part of your money's worth. There are some well-known pieces in here, and some that are not well known, and two or three old chestnuts for roasting over an open fire these crisp fall nights. One thing you may *not* find in here is your favorite humorist, and we strongly advise you not to look for him, poor fellow. We passed him on the street the other day and he seemed far from well.

However, there is a little more to this book (we hope) than pure prejudice, and there is a little more to it than may be suggested by so sudden a mobilization of funny stuff, as though an emergency had arisen in humor. We have looked up some authors whose works were not familiar to us, and we have gone to some trouble to arrange things sensibly, according to their nature. (I would have arranged them ac-

xi

cording to size, remembering the ostrich egg, if there hadn't been a steadier hand to lead me.) Parodists are here lined up, with their victims, under the same chapter heading. Story tellers are bunched, and moralists, and critics, and so on. I think you will find this a convenience, and possibly even interesting.

In one sense, any deliberate compilation of reading matter is a dubious project for anyone in his right mind to undertake, and some anthologies I have seen have reminded me strongly of the shell collections of ladies who have just come in from their first day on a Florida beach—a lot of broken-down pectens and some damaged sea worms. This anthology should be more resourceful and prettier than that, if only because our period of collection has been a long one and we have conscientiously discarded many specimens that turned out to be defective or that grew dull after they had lain around.

It will be apparent immediately that the book contains only humor which is, so to speak, "literary"—that is, it has been written down on paper, in words, to be read. The only drawings are drawings which are inseparable from the text. There are no jokes, as such, in the book. There is no unconscious humor, as far as we know. Vast fields of American humor are here untouched—the radio gag, the anecdote, the newsbreak, the after-dinner speech, the pun, the epigram, the humor that ripples in the subway and explodes in the ball park, the quip, the crack, the nifty, the wow, the wonderful stuff that the stenographer with her pad upon her knee tosses to the stockroom boy coming in with a fresh supply of paper clips, the humor of Mickey and Pluto, of blackface minstrels, of newspaper comic strips, of Benny Goodman playing Bach, the coinage of Winchell, the pantomime of Chaplin, the red curls of Harpo, the vast unwritten satires of Ed Wynn and Ethel Merman and Ray Bolger and W. C. Fields and the rest. There is nothing that can be done about them in a book. The melodious and collaborative humor of Merman-Porter is not distributable through the ordinary channels of book publishing, short of a pop-up containing a concealed Victrola. No subtreasury of American humor is complete today without a scene from *Of Thee I Sing* and the night-club parody from *Pal Joey,* but you simply can't present them without all those girls. I never realized how confining a book could be till we got going on this one.

We had our fair share of disillusionment in assembling it. It seemed like a gay idea, to begin with, but it soon began to ride us hard and we developed some nasty saddle sores before we got through. There was quite a period when we entertained the notion that we would include what we fondly called "newspaper humor." We were going to collect a lot of terribly funny stories from the press. We collected them, all right, and some of them were funny, too, but we soon had to keep them in a separate icebox on account of the way the cream was beginning to taste. Old newspaper stories have an odor all their own; they are extremely hard to run down, and after you find them, you wish you hadn't. Something has happened to them in the meantime. Ask any newspaperman to name a funny story that he has written or that he has read, and he will direct you to within about three months of a certain issue of a certain newspaper (except it wasn't the *Times* it was the *Tribune*), and at last you discover the exact date and the very paper and you coax the library into letting you examine this immortal yet crumbling relic, this sere and yellow specimen, and as it trickles into your lap, particle by particle, you read with glassy eyes and set jaw the howlingly funny news story of long ago. It is a bad moment.

This is not said in disparagement of the humor of the press, or of reporters, plenty of whom are first-class humorists and are daily performing a brilliant feat in gathering news and transmitting it somewhat humorously. It simply means that even the perfect newspaper story, by the most expert and gifted reporter, dies like a snake with the setting of the sun. The news goes out of it (though some humor may remain), and when the news goes out of it the heart goes out of it. It doesn't bear reprinting except in a textbook, and this is not a textbook.*

So we ended by deleting from the "Reporters at Work" section of our book all the daily stuff, leaving only the magazine stuff, including a few pieces from "The Talk of the Town" in *The New Yorker*. In a way this seems unjust: the best reporting (including the best humorous reporting) is to be found in newspapers, not in magazines; but an anthologist has to take material which can go into type a second time with some effect, regardless of how good or even distinguished it may have been in its first appearance. The "Talk of the Town" pieces, although they had grown whiskers as timely articles do, stood up a little better, we found, than the daily paper pieces, probably because the prime purpose of a daily story is to acquaint you with the facts, whereas the prime purpose of a *New Yorker* story is to enter-

* *Note to Professors of English: Pay no attention to this sentence.*

tain you with the facts. As far as possible we picked pieces which, though they were not out of newspapers, at least had been written by men who had been (or are now) newspaper reporters: Joseph Mitchell, Alva Johnston, Sanderson Vanderbilt, John McNulty, A. J. Liebling, St. Clair McKelway.

At any rate, in this section as in all the others, the editors decided not to include anybody or anything just for the sake of being inclusive or of getting coverage. We asked simply that we be amused, now in 1941. Our motto throughout was:

> If it be not droll to we,
> What care us how droll it be!

A lot of the humor of fifty to one hundred years ago was dialect humor. Then was the heyday of the crackerbarrel philosopher, sometimes wise, always wise-seeming, and nowadays rather dreary. We plunged into this period with willing hearts and open minds, and came out of it exhausted and not greatly enriched. While I was in there it occurred to me that a certain basic confusion often exists in the use of tricky or quaint or illiterate spelling to achieve a humorous effect. I mean, it is not always clear whether the author intends his character to be writing or speaking—and I, for one, feel that unless I know at least this much about what I am reading, I am off to a bad start. For instance, here are some spellings from the works of Petroleum V. Nasby: he spells "would" *wood,* "of" *uv,* "you" *yoo,* "hence" *hentz,* "office" *offis.*

Now, it happens that I pronounce "office" *offis.* And I pronounce "hence" *hentz,* and I even pronounce "of" *uv.* Therefore, I infer that Nasby's character is supposed not to be speaking but to be writing. Yet in either case, justification for this perversion of the language is lacking; for if the character is speaking, the queer spelling is unnecessary, since the pronunciation is impossible to distinguish from the natural or ordinary pronunciation, and if the character is writing, the spelling is most unlikely. Who ever wrote "uv" for "of"? Nobody. Anyone who knows how to write at all, knows how to spell a simple word like "of." If you can't spell "of" you wouldn't be able to spell anything and wouldn't be attempting to set words to paper—much less words like "solissitood." A person who can't spell "of" is an illiterate, and the only time such a person attempts to write anything down is in a great crisis. He doesn't write political essays or diaries or letters or satirical paragraphs.

In *Dere Mabel*, which is patently offered as "written" material, since it is a book of letters, some of the spelling seems highly questionable. All "ing" words are spelled "in" without the "g." This is rare, I think, in real life. Even partially or badly educated persons know the ending "ing." All schoolboys know it. It is one of the first things you learn when you learn to spell in school.

Obviously, some of the pieces by the dialect writers seemed funny to us in spite of the handicap of spelling. In the case of Dooley, the Irish dialect is difficult but worth the effort, and it smooths out after the first hundred miles. Finley Peter Dunne was a sharp and gifted humorist, who wrote no second-rate stuff, and he had the sympathetic feeling for his character which is indispensable. This same sympathy is discernible in Jewish humor—in the work of Gross, Kober, Ross. It is sympathy, not contempt or derision, that makes their characters live. Lardner's ball player was born because the author had a warm feeling for ballplayers, however boyish or goofy. The spelling in all these cases is not a device for gaining a humorous effect, but is a necessary tool for working the material, which is itself inherently humorous.

I suspect that the popularity of all dialect stuff derives in part from flattery of the reader—giving him a pleasant sensation of superiority which he gets from working out the intricacies of misspelling, and the satisfaction of detecting boorishness or illiteracy in someone else. This is not the whole story, but it has some bearing in the matter. Incidentally, I am told by an authority on juvenile literature that dialect is tops with children. They like to study out the words. When they catch on to the thing, they must feel that first fine glow of maturity—the ability to exercise higher intellectual powers than those of the character they are looking at.

Since this book is an arbitrary selection, we do not feel obliged to explain anything or to apologize for anything. The inclusion of any item can be ascribed to the editors' jaundiced taste, the omission of any item to their sheer vindictiveness.

There are some admirable American humorists who are absent from the book through no fault of their own or of ours either. One of them is Harry Leon Wilson, whose stories are too long to reprint in a volume of this sort. We tried breaking off a limb of *Merton* and of *Bunker*

Bean, but they didn't seem to do well, separated from the main trunk. Another man is Henry Thoreau. There is hardly a paragraph of *Walden* which does not seem humorous to me; but we didn't include any of it, having no wish to attitudinize, and because it, too, is unsatisfactory when broken up. Nevertheless, Thoreau makes me laugh the inaudible, the enduring laugh. Oliver Wendell Holmes is present in the book but is inadequately represented; the humor in the *Autocrat* is in such dilution as to be unsuitable for a concentrated pill.

Tall stories are commonly regarded as the rockbed of American humor, and we have included a few of them that we liked. We found, however, that tall stories can be unspeakably boring. It is possible to be quite tall without being a bit funny. We also found (or rather we verified the fact) that we had no taste for the Genial School of humor—a large school with some rather impressive pupils. Geniality is not, per se, humorous, in spite of the illusion of humor it often gives, and too often geniality turns out to be long-windedness in sheep's clothing. Verbosity is an occupational disease in America, and writing can be as dangerous as painting the luminous dials of watches. Many a humorist has been stricken fatally at an early age—you will find their dry bones in the magazines whose principal literary requirement is that every story be long enough to break over into the back pages among the advertisements.

Among those absent from this book are the Canadians. We kept the Canadians out simply because we were getting crowded for space and the Canadian border made a convenient place to stop. And while I am on the delicate subject of who is in this book and who isn't, it will be observed by the more observant readers that there are certain items in here which I wrote myself. This is an unsavory episode upon which I shall not dwell.

It will also be observed that quite a large amount of the material in here was published first in *The New Yorker.* This discovery should surprise nobody. My wife and I happen to own a complete file of the bound volumes of *The New Yorker,* and after a long evening with George Horatio Derby or somebody or other who wrote the best light verse during the McKinley administration, it would often be our stealthy custom to pull out a volume at random and dip up a nice funny piece before going to bed. We could easily have assembled the whole book from this invaluable shelf of ours, but it would have been a little tough on Washington Irving and Mark Twain and a few others who had the misfortune to be doing their work before the magazine got well under way.

A great deal of modern humor has been born and is growing up which would never have seen the light and would still be in the kept-under stage if it had not been for the receptive attitude of *The New Yorker* toward new writers, and for its solid conviction that humor is an art form and not a barber shop fitting. We have a speaking acquaintance with *New Yorker* pieces, a parental feeling about some of them, and a high regard for the magazine and its editor and its contributors. It would be odd indeed if our book didn't show this attachment.

As for the pieces themselves, we do not pretend that they are thoroughly representative of *New Yorker* humor; we have not even included some of our favorite writers, confident that they will endure their horrid fate with characteristic poise. And my wife thinks it would be well to add, also, that where we have used two pieces by one writer and one piece by another writer, it doesn't mean that we think the first man is twice as good as the second. We may think he is only half as good and are trying to cover up.

In the back of the book you will find an alphabetical list of authors, with their dates. An author with *no* birth date can be assumed to be living. It appears that some authors elect to keep the fact of their birth a secret from the world, although it is clear from the color of their jackets that they are alive and hearty.

The same list will help you identify the many authors who used, or use, pseudonyms. There was hardly a writer prior to the Twentieth Century who signed his own name to his stuff. They must all either have been ashamed or in debt.

Analysts have had their go at humor, and I have read some of this interpretative literature, but without being greatly instructed. Humor can be dissected, as a frog can, but the thing dies in the process and the innards are discouraging to any but the pure scientific mind.

A certain type of humor has come to be big business in the United States. The gag factories are as impressive as Allis Chalmers, and will probably soon be taken over for defense purposes. Radio comedians employ their own corps of geniuses, who sit and think and think of something funny to say. It is sometimes rather grim business, this production for the big markets. In a newsreel theater the other day I saw a picture of a man who had developed the soap bubble to a higher point than it had ever before reached. He had become the ace soap bubble blower of America, had perfected the business of blowing bubbles, refined it, doubled it, squared it, and had even worked himself up into a convenient lather. The effect was not pretty. Some of the bubbles were too big to be beautiful, and the blower was always jumping into them or out of them, or playing some sort of unattractive trick with them. It was, if anything, a rather repulsive sight. Humor is a little like that: it won't stand much blowing up, and it won't stand much poking. It has a certain fragility, an evasiveness, which one had best respect. Essentially, it is a complete mystery. A human frame convulsed with laughter, and the laughter becoming hysterical and uncontrollable, is as far out of balance as one shaken with the hiccoughs or in the throes of a sneezing fit.

One of the things commonly said about humorists is that they are really very sad people—clowns with a breaking heart. There is some truth in it, but it is badly stated. It would be more accurate, I think, to say that there is a deep vein of melancholy running through everyone's life and that a humorist, perhaps more sensible of it than some others, compensates for it actively and positively. Practically everyone is a manic depressive of sorts, with his up moments and his down moments, and you certainly don't have to be a humorist to taste the sadness of situation and mood. But, as everyone knows, there is often a rather fine line between laughing and crying, and if a humorous piece of writing brings a person to the point where his emotional responses are untrustworthy and seem likely to break over into the opposite realm, it is because humorous writing, like poetical writing, has an extra content. It plays, like an active child, close to the big hot fire which is Truth. And sometimes the reader feels the heat.

The world likes humor, but it treats it patronizingly. It decorates its serious artists with laurel, and its wags with Brussels sprouts. It feels that if a thing is funny it can be presumed to be something less than great, because if it were truly great it would be wholly serious. Writers know this, and those who take their literary selves with great seriousness are at considerable pains never to associate their name with anything funny or flippant or nonsensical or "light." They suspect it would hurt their reputation, and they are right. Many a poet writing today signs his real name to his serious verse and a pseudonym to his comical verse, being unwilling to have the public discover him in any but a pensive and heavy moment. It is a wise precaution. (It is often a bad poet, too.)

When I was reading over some of the parody diaries of Franklin P. Adams, I came across this entry, for April 28, 1926:

"Read H. Canby's book, *Better Writing,* very excellent. But when he says, 'A sense of humour is worth gold to any writer,' I disagree with him vehemently. For the writers who amass the greatest gold have, it seems to me, no sense of humour; and I think also that if they had, it would be a terrible thing for them, for it would paralyze them so that they would not write at all. For in writing, emotion is more to be treasured than a sense of humour, and the two are often in conflict."

That is a sound observation. The conflict is fundamental. There constantly exists, for a certain sort of person of high emotional content, at work creatively, the danger of coming to a point where something cracks within himself or within the paragraph under construction —cracks and turns into a snicker. Here, then, is the very nub of the conflict: the careful form of art, and the careless shape of life itself. What a man does with this uninvited snicker (which may closely resemble a sob, at that) decides his destiny. If he resists it, conceals it, destroys it, he may keep his architectural scheme intact and save his building, and the world will never know. If he gives in to it, he becomes a humorist, and the sharp brim of the fool's cap leaves a mark forever on his brow.

I'm sure there isn't a humorist alive but can recall the day, in the early stages of his career, when someone he loved and respected took him anxiously into a corner and asked him when he was "going to write something serious." That day is memorable, for it gives a man pause to realize that the bright star he is following is held to be not of the first magnitude.

I think the stature of humor must vary some with the times. The court fool in Shakespeare's day had no social standing and was no better than a lackey, but he did have some artistic standing and was listened to with considerable attention, there being a well-founded belief that he had the truth hidden somewhere about his person. Artistically he stood probably higher than the humorist of today, who has gained social position but not the ear of the mighty. (Think of the trouble the world would save itself if it would pay some attention to nonsense!) A narrative poet at court, singing of great deeds, enjoyed a higher standing than the fool and was allowed to wear fine clothes; yet I suspect that the ballad singer was more often than not a second-rate stooge, flattering his monarch lyrically, while the fool must often have been a first-rate character, giving his monarch good advice in bad puns.

In the British Empire of our time, satirical humor of the Gilbert and Sullivan sort enjoys a solid position in the realm, and *Punch,* which is as British as vegetable marrow, is socially acceptable everywhere an Englishman is to be found. The *Punch* editors not only write the jokes but they help make the laws of England. Here in America we have an immensely humorous people in a land of milk and honey and wit, who cherish the ideal of the "sense" of humor and at the same time are highly suspicious of anything which is nonserious. Whatever else an American believes or disbelieves about himself, he is absolutely sure he has a sense of humor.

Frank Moore Colby, one of the most intelligent humorists operating in this country in the early years of the century, in an essay called "The Pursuit of Humor" described how the American loves and guards his most precious treasure:

"... Now it is the commonest thing in the world to hear people call the absence of a sense of humor the one fatal defect. No matter how owlish a man is, he will tell you that. It is a miserable falsehood, and it does incalculable harm. A life without humor is like a life without legs. You are haunted by a sense of incompleteness, and you cannot go where your friends go. You are also somewhat of a burden. But the only really fatal thing is the shamming of humor when you have it not. There are people whom nature meant to be solemn from their cradle to their grave. They are under bonds to remain so. In so far as they are true to themselves they are safe company for any one; but outside their proper field they are terrible. Solemnity is relatively a blessing, and the man who was born with it should never be encouraged to wrench himself away.

"We have praised humor so much that we have started an insincere cult, and there are many who think they must glorify it when they hate it from the bottom of their hearts. False humor-worship is the deadliest of social sins, and one of the commonest. People without a grain of humor in their composition will eulogize it by the hour. Men will confess to treason, murder, arson, false teeth, or a wig. How many of them will own up to a lack of humor? The courage that could draw this confession from a man would atone for everything."

Relatively few American humorists have become really famous, so

that their name is known to everyone in the land in the way that many
novelists and other solemn literary characters have become famous.
Mark Twain made it. He had, of course, an auspicious start, since he
was essentially a story teller and his humor was an added attraction.
(It was also very, very good.) In this century Ring Lardner is the idol
of professional humorists and of plenty of other people, too; but I
think I am correct in saying that at the height of his career he was not
one of the most widely known literary figures in this country, and the
name Lardner was not known to the millions but only to the thousands.
Even today he has not reached Mr. and Mrs. America and all the clip-
pers at sea, to the extent that Mark Twain reached them, and I doubt
if he ever will. On the whole, the humorists who contribute pleasure
to a wide audience are the ones who create characters and tell tales,
the ones who are story tellers at heart. Lardner told stories and gave
birth to some characters, but I think he was a realist and a parodist
and a satirist first of all, not essentially a writer of fiction. The general
public needs something to get a grip on—a Penrod, a Huck Finn, a
Brer Rabbit, or a Father Day. The subtleties of satire and burlesque
and nonsense and parody and criticism are no dish for the masses;
they are only for the top (or, if you want, for the bottom) layer of
intellect. Clarence Day, for example, was relatively inconspicuous when
he was oozing his incomparable "Thoughts without Words," which
are his best creations; he became generally known and generally loved
only after he had brought Father to life. (Advice to young writers who
want to get ahead without any annoying delays: don't write about
Man, write about *a* man.)

I was interested, in reading DeVoto's *Mark Twain in Eruption,* to
come across some caustic remarks of Mr. Clemens's about an anthology
of humor which his copyright lawyer had sent him and which Mark
described as "a great fat, coarse, offensive volume." He was not amused.
"This book is a cemetery," he wrote.

"In this mortuary volume I find Nasby, Artemus Ward, Yawcob
Strauss, Derby, Burdette, Eli Perkins, the Danbury News Man,
Orpheus C. Kerr, Smith O'Brien, Josh Billings, and a score of others,
maybe two score, whose writings and sayings were once in everybody's
mouth but are now heard of no more and are no longer mentioned.
Seventy-eight seems an incredible crop of well-known humorists for
one forty-year period to have produced, and yet this book has not
harvested the entire crop—far from it. It has no mention of Ike
Partington, once so welcome and so well known; it has no mention

of Doesticks, nor of the Pfaff crowd, nor of Artemus Ward's numerous and perishable imitators, nor of three very popular Southern humorists whose names I am not able to recall, nor of a dozen other sparkling transients whose light shone for a time but has now, years ago, gone out.

"Why have they perished? Because they were merely humorists. Humorists of the 'mere' sort cannot survive. Humor is only a fragrance, a decoration. Often it is merely an odd trick of speech and of spelling, as in the case of Ward and Billings and Nasby and the 'Disbanded Volunteer,' and presently the fashion passes and the fame along with it. There are those who say a novel should be a work of art solely, and you must not preach in it, you must not teach in it. That may be true as regards novels but it is not true as regards humor. Humor must not professedly teach, and it must not professedly preach, but it must do both if it would live forever. By forever, I mean thirty years. With all its preaching it is not likely to outlive so long a term as that. The very things it preaches about, and which are novelties when it preaches about them, can cease to be novelties and become commonplaces in thirty years. Then that sermon can thenceforth interest no one.

"I have always preached. That is the reason that I have lasted thirty years. If the humor came of its own accord and uninvited, I have allowed it a place in my sermon, but I was not writing the sermon for the sake of humor. I should have written the sermon just the same, whether any humor applied for admission or not. I am saying these vain things in this frank way because I am a dead person speaking from the grave. Even I would be too modest to say them in life. I think we never become really and genuinely our entire and honest selves until we are dead—and not then until we have been dead years and years. People ought to start dead, and then they would be honest so much earlier."

Well, I didn't intend to get off onto the broad subject of humor, or even to let Mark Twain get off onto it. I don't think I agree that humor must preach in order to live; it need only speak the truth—and I notice it always does. As for this book, I think the truth is in it. We, the compilers, hope that there will be spots, here and there, where our taste will coincide with the taste of the reader, and that enjoyment and profit will result.

——E. B. W.

CONTENTS

ALL SORTS OF DILEMMAS

HISTORY, POLITICS, AND AFFAIRS
OF STATE

PARODIES AND BURLESQUES

FOR (OR AGAINST) CHILDREN

SATIRE—BROAD AND OTHERWISE

FOLKLORE AND TALL STORIES

NONSENSE

THE CRITICS AT WORK

THE REPORTERS AT WORK

VERSE

REMINISCENCE

A SUBTREASURY OF AMERICAN HUMOR

STORIES AND PEOPLE

The first section of this book is a fiction section, but a great deal of fiction will be found elsewhere in the book, too. In classifying material, it was sometimes a toss-up whether a piece fitted more appropriately under one head or under another.

The Frank Stockton contribution to the following group of stories has been slightly tampered with, as explained in a note. Mostly we have done no tampering, and any piece appearing in the Subtreasury may be presumed to be exactly as written by its author, unless otherwise noted.

In general, we have resisted the temptation to use chapters or excerpts from novels or long stories, but there are exceptions and this fictional department happens to contain three notable ones. We didn't, for the sake of sticking to our principles, want to miss such a plum as the first chapter of "Babbitt," which, although a fragment of a novel, stands by itself as a little work of art and is written with good humor as well as with great compassion. We did not want to omit "Mrs. Lecks and Mrs. Aleshine," either, or Miss Loos's lady-like blonde.

Neither Sinclair Lewis nor Marjorie Kinnan Rawlings is classified in the library as a humorist, but if that didn't stop us it needn't stop you.

Marjorie Kinnan Rawlings

BENNY AND THE BIRD-DOGS

You can't change a man, no-ways. By the time his mammy turns him
loose and he takes up with some innocent woman and marries her,
he's what he is. If it's his nature to set by the hearthfire and scratch
hisself, you just as good to let him set and scratch. If it's his nature,
like Will Dover, my man, to go to the garage in his Sunday clothes
and lay down under some backwoods Cracker's old greasy Ford and
tinker with it, you just as good to let him lay and tinker. And if it's
his nature, like Uncle Benny, to prowl; if it's his nature to cut the
fool; why, it's interfering in the ways of Providence even to stop to
quarrel with him about it. Some women is born knowing that. Sometimes a woman, like the Old Hen (Uncle Benny's wife, poor soul!),
has to quarrel a lifetime before she learns it. Then when it does come
to her, she's like a cow has tried to jump a high fence and has got
hung up on it—she's horn-swoggled.

The Old Hen's a mighty fine woman—one of the finest I know.
She looks just the way she did when she married Uncle Benny
Mathers thirty years ago, except her hair has turned gray, like the
feathers on an Irish Gray game hen. She's plump and pretty and kind
of pale from thirty years' fretting about Uncle Benny. She has a disposition, by nature, as sweet as new cane syrup. When she settled down
for a lifetime's quarrelling at him, it was for the same reason syrup
sours—the heat had just been put to her too long.

I can't remember a time when the Old Hen wasn't quarrelling at
Uncle Benny. It begun a week after they was married. He went off
prowling by hisself, to a frolic or such as that, and didn't come home
until four o'clock in the morning. She was setting up waiting for him.
When she crawled him about it, he said, "Bless Katy, wife, let's sleep
now and quarrel in the morning." So she quarrelled in the morning
and just kept it up. For thirty years. Not for meanness—she just kept
hoping she could change him.

3

Change him? When he takened notice of the way she was fussing and clucking and ruffling her feathers, he quit calling her by her given name and began calling her the Old Hen. That's all I could ever see she changed him.

Uncle Benny's a sight. He's been constable here at Oak Bluff, Florida, for twenty years. We figure it keeps him out of worse trouble to let him be constable. He's the quickest shot in three counties and the colored folks is all as superstitious of him as if he was the devil hisself. He's a comical-appearing somebody. He's small and quick and he don't move—he prances. He has a little bald sun-tanned head with a rim of white hair around the back of it. Where the hair ends at the sides of his head, it sticks straight up over his ears in two little white tufts like goat-horns. He's got bright blue eyes that look at you quick and wicked, the way a goat looks. That's exactly what he looks and acts like—a mischievous little old billy-goat. And he's been popping up under folks' noses and playing tricks on them as long as Oak Bluff has knowed him. Doc in particular. He loved to torment Doc.

And stay home? Uncle Benny don't know what it is to stay home. The Old Hen'll cook hot dinner for him and he won't come. She'll start another fire in the range and warm it up for him about dusk-dark and he won't come. She'll set up till midnight, times till day-break, and maybe just about the time the east lightens and the birds gets to whistling good, he'll come home. Where's he been? He's been with somebody 'gatoring, or with somebody catching crabs to Salt Springs; he's been to a square-dance twenty miles away in the flat-woods; he's been on the highway in that Ford car, just rambling as long as his gas held out—and them seven pieded bird-dogs setting up in the back keeping him company.

It was seven years ago, during the Boom, that he bought the Model-T and begun collecting bird-dogs. Everybody in Florida was rich for a whiles, selling gopher holes to the Yankees. Now putting an automobile under Uncle Benny was like putting wings on a wild-cat—it just opened up new territory. Instead of rambling over one county, he could ramble over ten. And the way he drove—like a bat out of Torment. He's one of them men just loves to cover the ground. And that car and all them bird-dogs worked on the Old Hen like a quart of gasoline on a camp-fire. She really went to raring. I tried to tell her then 'twasn't no use to pay him no mind, but she wouldn't listen.

I said, "It's just his nature. You can't do a thing about it but take it for your share and go on. You and Uncle Benny is just made different. You want him home and he don't want to be home. You're a barn-yard fowl and he's a wild fowl."

"Mis' Dover," she said, "it's easy for you to talk. Your man runs a garage and comes home nights. You don't know how terrible it is to have a man that prowls."

I said, "Leave him prowl."

She said, "Yes, but when he's on the prowl, I don't no more know where to look for him than somebody's tom-cat."

I said, "If 'twas me, I wouldn't look for him."

She said, "Moonlight nights he's the worst. Just like the varmints."

I said, "Don't that tell you nothing?"

She said, "If he'd content hisself with prowling— But he ain't content until he cuts the fool. He takes that Ford car and them seven bird-dogs and maybe a pint of moonshine, and maybe picks up Doc to prowl with him, and he don't rest until he's done something crazy. What I keep figuring is, he'll kill hisself in that Ford car, cutting the fool."

I said, "You don't need to fret about him and that Ford. What's un-natural for one man is plumb natural for another. And cutting the fool is so natural for Uncle Benny, it's like a bird in the air or a fish in water—there won't no harm come to him from it."

She said, "Mis' Dover, what the devil throws over his back has got to come down under his belly."

I said, "Uncle Benny Mathers is beyond rules and sayings. I know men-folks, and if you'll listen to me, you'll settle down and quit quar-relling and leave him go his way in quiet."

I happened to be in on it this spring, the last time the Old Hen ever quarrelled at Uncle Benny. Me and Doc was both in on it. It was the day of old lady Weller's burying. Doc carried me in his car to the cemetery. My Will couldn't leave the garage, because the trucks hauling the Florida oranges north was bringing in pretty good business. Doc felt obliged to go to the burying. He's a patent-medicine salesman—a big fat fellow with a red face and yellow hair. He sells the Little Giant line of remedies. Old lady Weller had been one of his best customers. She'd taken no nourishment the last week of her life except them remedies, and Doc figured he ought to pay her the proper respect and show everybody he was a man was always grateful to his customers.

Uncle Benny and the Old Hen went to the burying in the Model-T.

And the seven bird-dogs went, setting up in the back seat. They always went to the buryings.

Uncle Benny said, "Walls nor chains won't hold 'em. Better to have 'em go along riding decent and quiet, than to bust loose and foller the Model-T like a daggone pack of bloodhounds."

That was true enough. Those bird-dogs could hear that old Ford crank up and go off in low gear, clear across the town. They'd always hope it was time to go bird-hunting again, and here they'd come, trailing it. So there were the bird-dogs riding along to old lady Weller's burying, with their ears flopping and their noses in the air for quail. As constable, Uncle Benny sort of represented the town, and he was right in behind the hearse. I mean, that car was a pain, to be part of a funeral procession. In the seven years he'd had it, he'd all but drove it to pieces, and it looked like a rusty, mangy razor-back hog. The hood was thin and narrow, like a shoat's nose—you remember the way all Model-T Fords were built. It had no top to it, nor no doors to the front seat, and the back seat rose up in a hump where the bird-dogs had squeezed the excelsior chitlin's out of it.

The Old Hen sat up stiff and proud, not letting on she minded. Doc and I figured she's been quarrelling at Uncle Benny about the bird-dogs, because when one of them put his paws on her shoulders and begun licking around her ears, she turned and smacked the breath out of him.

The funeral procession had just left the Oak Bluff dirt road and turned onto No. 9 Highway, when the garage keeper at the bend ran out.

He hollered, "I just got a 'phone call for Uncle Benny Mathers from the high sheriff!"

So Uncle Benny cut out of the procession and drove over to the pay station by the kerosene tank to take the message. He caught up again in a minute and called to Doc, "A drunken nigger is headed this way in a Chevrolet and the sheriff wants I should stop him."

About that time here comes the Chevrolet and started to pass the procession, wobbling back and forth as if it had the blind staggers. You may well know the nigger was drunk or he wouldn't have passed a funeral. Uncle Benny cut out of line and took out after him. When he saw who was chasing him, the nigger turned around and headed back the way he'd come from. Uncle Benny was gaining on him when they passed the hearse. The bird-dogs begun to take an interest and rared up, barking. What does Uncle Benny do but go to the side of the Chevrolet so the nigger turns around—and then Uncle Benny crowded him so all he could do was to shoot into line in the funeral procession. Uncle Benny cut right in after him and the nigger shot out of line and Uncle Benny crowded him in again.

I'll declare, I was glad old lady Weller wasn't alive to see it. She'd had no use for Uncle Benny, she'd hated a nigger, and she'd despised dogs so to where she kept a shotgun by her door to shoot at them if one so much as crossed her cornfield. And here on the way to her burying, where you'd figure she was entitled to have things the way she liked them, here was Uncle Benny chasing a nigger in and out of line, and seven bird-dogs were going Ki-yippity-yi! Ki-yippity-yi! Ki-yippity-yi! I was mighty proud the corpse was no kin to me.

The Old Hen was plumb mortified. She put her hands over her face and when the Ford would swerve by or cut in ahead of us, Doc and me could see her swaying back and forth and suffering. I don't scarcely need to say Uncle Benny was enjoying hisself. If he'd looked sorrowful-like, as if he was just doing his duty, you could of forgive him. Near a filling-station the Chevrolet shot ahead and stopped and the nigger jumped out and started to run. Uncle Benny stopped and climbed out of the Ford and drew his pistol and called "Stop!" The nigger kept on going.

Now Uncle Benny claims that shooting at niggers in the line of duty is what keeps him in practice for bird-shooting. He dropped a ball to the right of the nigger's heel and he dropped a ball to the left of it. He called "Stop!" and the nigger kept on going. Then Uncle Benny took his pistol in both hands and took a slow aim and he laid the third ball against the nigger's shin-bone. He dropped like a string-haltered mule.

Uncle Benny said to the man that ran the filling-station, "Get your gun. That there nigger is under arrest and I deputize you to keep him that-a-way. The sheriff'll be along to pick him up direckly."

He cut back into the funeral procession between us and the hearse, and we could tell by them wicked blue eyes he didn't know when he'd enjoyed a burying like old lady Weller's. When we got back from the burying, he stopped by Will's garage. The Old Hen was giving him down-the-country.

She said, "That was the most scandalous thing I've ever knowed you to do, chasing that nigger in and out of Mis' Weller's funeral."

Uncle Benny's eyes begun to dance and he said, "I know it, wife, but I couldn't help it. 'Twasn't me done the chasing—it was the Model-T."

Doc got in to it then and sided with the Old Hen. He gets excited, the way fat men do, and he swelled up like a spreading adder.

"Benny," he said, "you shock my modesty. This ain't no occasion for laughing or lying."

Uncle Benny said, "I know it, Doc. I wouldn't think of laughing nor lying. You didn't know I've got that Ford trained? I've got it trained to where it'll do two things. It's helped me chase so many niggers, I've got it to where it just naturally takes out after 'em by itself."

Doc got red in the face and asked, real sarcastic, "And what's the other piece of training?"

Uncle Benny said, "Doc, that Ford has carried me home drunk so many times, I've got it trained to where it'll take care of me and carry me home safe when I ain't fitten."

Doc spit halfway across the road and he said, "You lying old jaybird."

Uncle Benny said, "Doc, I've got a pint of moonshine and if you'll come go camping with me to Salt Springs this evening, I'll prove it."

The Old Hen spoke up and she said, "Benny, Heaven forgive you for I won't, if you go on the prowl again before you've cleared the weeds out of my old pindar field. I'm a month late now, getting it planted."

Doc loves Salt Springs crab and mullet as good as Uncle Benny does, and I could see he was tempted.

But he said, "Benny, you go along home and do what your wife wants, and when you're done—when she says you're done—then we'll go to Salt Springs."

So Uncle Benny and the Old Hen drove off. Doc watched after them.

He said, "Anyways, cutting the fool at a burying had ought to last Benny quite a while."

I said, "You don't know him. Cutting the fool don't last him no time at all."

I was right. I ain't so special wise a woman, but if I once know a man, I can come right close to telling you what he'll do. Uncle Benny hadn't been gone hardly no time, when somebody come by the garage hollering that he'd done set the Old Hen's pindar field on fire.

I said to Doc, "What did I tell you? The last thing in the world was safe for that woman to do, was to turn him loose on them weeds. He figured firing was the quickest way to get shut of them."

Doc said, "Let's go see."

We got in his car and drove out to Uncle Benny's place. Here was smoke rolling up back of the house, and the big live oak in the yard was black with soldier blackbirds the grass fire had drove out of the pindar field. The field hadn't had peanuts in it since fall, but bless Katy, it was full of something else. Uncle Benny's wife had it plumb full of setting guinea-hens. She hadn't told him, because he didn't like guineas.

Far off to the west corner of the field was the Old Hen, trying to run the guineas into a coop. They were flying every which-a-way and hollering *Pod-rac! Pod-rac!* the way guineas holler. All the young uns in the neighborhood were in the middle of the field, beating out the grass fire with palmettos. And setting up on top of the east gate, just as unconcerned, was Uncle Benny, with them two little horns of white hair curling in the heat. Now what do you reckon he was doing? He had all seven of them bird-dogs running back and forth retrieving guinea eggs. He'd say now and again, "Dead—fetch!" and they'd wag their tails and go hunt up another nest and here they'd come, with guinea eggs carried gentle in their mouths. He was putting the eggs in a basket.

When the commotion was over, and the fire out, and everybody gone on but Doc and me, we went to the front porch to set down and rest. The Old Hen was wore out. She admitted it was her fault not letting Uncle Benny know about the setting guinea-hens. She was about to forgive him setting the field a-fire, because him and the bird-dogs had saved the guinea eggs. But when we got to the porch, here lay the bird-dogs in the rocking chairs. There was one to every chair, rocking away and cutting their eyes at her. Their coats and paws were smuttied from the burnt grass—and the Old Hen had put clean sugar-sacking covers on every blessed chair that morning. That settled it. She was stirred up anyway about the way he'd cut the fool at the burying, and she really set in to quarrel at Uncle Benny. And like I say, it turned out to be the last piece of quarrelling she ever done.

She said to him, "You taught them bird-dogs to rock in a rocking-chair just to torment me. Ever' beast or varmint you've brought home, you've learned to cut the fool as bad as you do."

"Now wife, what beast or varmint did I ever learn to cut the fool?"

"You learned the 'coon to screw the tops off my syrup cans. You learned the 'possum to hang upside down in my cupboards, and I'd go for a jar of maybe pepper relish and put my hand on him.... There's been plenty of such as that. I've raised ever'thing in the world for you but a stallion horse."

Doc said, "Give him time, he'll have one of them stabled in the kitchen."

"Bird-dogs is natural to have around," she said. "I was raised to bird-dogs. But it ain't natural for 'em to rock in a rocking-chair. There's so terrible many of them, and when they put in the night on the porch laying in the rocking-chairs and rocking, I don't close my eyes for the fuss."

Uncle Benny said, "You see, Doc? You see, Mis' Dover? She's always quarrelling that me and the dogs ain't never home at night. Then when we do come in, she ain't willing we should all be comf'table.

"We just as good to go on to Salt Springs, Doc. Wait while I go in the house and get my camping outfit and we'll set out."

He went in the house and came out with his camping stuff. She knowed he was gone for nobody knew how long.

We walked on down to the gate and the Old Hen followed, sniffling a little and twisting the corner of her apron.

"Benny," she said, "please don't go to Salt Springs. You always lose your teeth in the Boil."

"I ain't lost 'em but three times," he said, and he cranked up the Model-T and climbed in. "I couldn't help losing 'em the first time. That was when I was laughing at the Yankee casting for bass, and his plug caught me in the open mouth and lifted my teeth out. Nor I couldn't help it the second time, when Doc and me was rassling in the rowboat and he pushed me in."

"Yes," she said, "an how'd you lose 'em the third time?"

His eyes twinkled and he shoved the Ford in low. "Cuttin' the fool," he said.

"That's just it," she said, and the tears begun to roll out of her eyes. "Anybody with false teeth hadn't ought to cut the fool!"

Now I always thought it was right cute, the way Uncle Benny fooled Doc about the trained Ford. You know how the old-timey Fords get the gas—it feeds from the hand-throttle on the wheel. Well, Uncle

Benny had spent the day before old lady Weller's funeral at Will's garage, putting in a foot accelerator. He didn't say a word to anybody, and Will and me was the only ones knowed he had it. Doc and Uncle Benny stayed three-four days camping at Salt Springs. Now the night they decided to come home, they'd both had something to drink, but Uncle Benny let on like he was in worse shape than he was.

Doc said, "Benny, you better leave me drive."

Uncle Benny pretended to rock on his feet and roll his head and he said, "I've got that Model-T trained to carry me home, drunk or sober."

Doc said, "Never mind that lie again. You get up there in the seat and whistle in the dogs. I'm fixing to drive us home."

Well, I'd of give a pretty to of been in the back seat with them bird-dogs that night when Doc drove the Ford back to Oak Bluff. It's a treat, any ways, to see a fat man get excited. The first thing Doc knowed, the Ford was running away with him. The Ford lights were none too good, and Doc just did clear a stump by the roadside, and he run clean over a blackjack sapling. He looked at the hand-throttle on the wheel and here it was where the car had ought to be going about twenty miles an hour and it was going forty-five. That rascal of an Uncle Benny had his foot on the foot accelerator.

Doc shut off the gas altogether and the Ford kept right on going.

He said, "Something's the matter."

Uncle Benny seemed to be dozing and didn't pay no mind. The Ford whipped back and forth in the sand road like a 'gator's tail. Directly they got on to the hard road and the Model-T put on speed. They begun to get near a curve. It was a dark night and the carlights wobbling, but Doc could see it coming. He took a tight holt of the wheel and begun to sweat. He felt for the brakes, but Uncle Benny never did have any.

He said, "We'll all be kilt."

When they started to take the curve, the Model-T was going nearly fifty-five—and then just as they got there, all of a sudden it slowed down as if it knowed what it was doing, and went around the curve as gentle as a day-old kitten. Uncle Benny had eased his foot off the accelerator. Doc drawed a breath again.

It's a wonder to me that trip didn't make Doc a nervous wreck. On every straightaway the Ford would rare back on its haunches and stretch out like a greyhound. Every curve they come to, it would go to it like a jack-rabbit. Then just as the sweat would pour down Doc's face and the drops would splash on the wheel, and he'd gather hisself together ready to jump, the Ford would slow down. It was a hot spring night, but Uncle Benny says Doc's teeth were chattering. The Model-T made the last mile lickety-brindle with the gas at the hand-throttle shut off entirely—and it coasted down in front of Will's garage and of its own free will come to a dead stop.

It was nine o'clock at night. Will was just closing up and I had locked the candy and cigarette counter and was waiting for him. There was a whole bunch of the men and boys around, like always, because the garage is the last place in Oak Bluff to put the lights out. Doc climbed out of the Ford trembling like a dish of custard. Uncle Benny eased out after him and I looked at him and right away I knowed he'd been up to mischief.

Doc said, "I don't know how he done it—but dogged if he wasn't telling the truth when he said he had that blankety-blank Model-T trained to carry him home when he ain't fitten."

Will asked, "How come?" and Doc told us. Will looked at me and begun to chuckle and we knowed what Uncle Benny had done to him. I think maybe I would of let Uncle Benny get away with it, but Will couldn't keep it.

"Come here, Doc," he said. "Here's your training."

I thought the bunch would laugh Doc out of town. He swelled up like a toadfish and he got in his car without a word and drove away.

It's a wonderful thing just to set down and figure out how many different ways there are to be crazy. We never thought of Uncle Benny as being really crazy. We'd say, "Uncle Benny's cutting the fool again," and we'd mean he was just messing around some sort of foolishness like a daggone young un. We figured his was what you might call the bottom kind of craziness. The next would be the half-witted. The next would be the senseless. The next would be what the colored folks call "mindless." And clear up at the top would be what you'd call cold-out crazy. With all his foolishness, we never figured Uncle Benny was cold-out crazy.

Well, we missed Uncle Benny from Oak Bluff a day or two. When I came to ask questions, I found he'd gone on a long prowl and was over on the Withlacoochie River camping with some oyster fishermen. I didn't think much about it, because he was liable to stay off that-a-way. But time rocked on and he didn't show up. I dropped by his house to ask the Old Hen about him. She didn't know a blessed thing.

She said, "Ain't it God's mercy we've got no young uns? The pore things would be as good as fatherless."

And then a few days later Doc came driving up to the garage. He got out and blew his nose and we could see his eyes were red.

He said, "Ain't it awful! I can't hardly bear to think about it."

Will said, "Doc, if you know bad news, you must be carrying it. Ain't nothing sorrowful I know of, except the Prohi's have found Philbin's still."

Doc said, "Don't talk about such little accidents at a time like this. You don't mean you ain't heerd about Benny?"

The bunch was there and they all perked up, interested. They knowed if it was Uncle Benny, they could expect 'most any news.

I said, "We ain't heerd a word since he went off to the west coast."

"You ain't heerd about him going crazy?"

I said, "Doc, you mean being crazy. He's always been that-a-way."

"I mean being crazy and going crazy, pore ol' Benny Mathers has gone really cold-out crazy."

Well, we all just looked at him and we looked at one another. And it came over the whole bunch of us that we weren't surprised. A nigger setting by the free air hose said, "Do, Jesus!" and eased away to tell the others.

Doc blew his nose and wiped his eyes and he said, "I'm sure we all forgive the pore ol' feller all the things he done. He wasn't responsible. I feel mighty bad, to think the hard way I've often spoke to him."

Will asked, "How come it to finally happen?"

Doc said, "He'd been up to some foolishness all night, raring through some of them Gulf coast flat-woods. Him and the fellers he was camping with was setting on the steps of the camp-house after breakfast. All of a sudden Uncle Benny goes to whistling, loud and shrill like a jay-bird. Then he says, 'I'm Sampson,' and he begun to tear down the camp-house."

Will asked, "What'd they do with him?"

Doc said, "You really ain't heerd? I declare, I can't believe the news has come so slow. They had a terrible time holding him and tying him. They got in the doctors and the sheriff and they takened pore ol' Uncle Benny to the lunatic asylum at Chattahoochie."

Doc wiped his eyes and we all begun to sniffle and our eyes to burn. I declare, it was just as if Uncle Benny Mathers had died on us.

I said, "Oh, his pore wife—"

Will said, "We'll have to be good to him and go see him and take him cigarettes and maybe slip him a pint of 'shine now and again."

I said, "The way he loved his freedom—shutting him up in the crazy-house will be like putting a wild-cat in a crocus sack."

Doc said, "Oh, he ain't in the asylum right now. He's broke loose. That's what makes me feel so bad. He's headed this way, and no telling the harm he'll do before he's ketched again."

Everybody jumped up and begun feeling in their hip pockets for their guns.

Doc said, "No use to try to put no guns on him. He's got his'n and they say he's shooting just as accurate as ever."

That was enough for me. I ran back of the counter at the garage and begun locking up.

I said, "Doc, you're a sight. 'Tain't no time to go to feeling sorry for Uncle Benny and our lives and property in danger."

Doc said, "I know, but I knowed him so long and I knowed him so good. I can't help feeling bad about it."

I said, "Do something about it. Don't just set there, and him liable to come shooting his way in any minute."

Doc said, "I know, but what can anybody do to stop him? Pore man, with all them deputies after him."

Will said, "Deputies?"

Doc said, "Why, yes. The sheriff at Ocala asked me would I stop along the road and leave word for all the deputies to try and ketch him. Pore ol' Benny, I'll swear. I hated doing it the worst way."

I scooped the money out of the cash register and I told them, "Now, men, I'm leaving. I've put up with Uncle Benny Mathers when he was drunk and I've put up with him when he was cutting the fool. But the reckless way he drives that Ford and the way he shoots a pistol, I ain't studying on messing up around him and him gone cold-out crazy."

Doc said, "Ain't a thing in the world would stop him when he goes by, and all them deputies after him, but a barricade acrost the road."

I said, "Then for goodness' sake, you sorry, low-down, no-account, varminty white men, tear down the wire fence around my chicken yard and fix Uncle Benny a barricade."

Doc said, "I just hated to suggest it."

Will said, "He'd slow down for the barricade and we could come in from behind and hem him in."

Doc said, "It'll be an awful thing to hem him in and have to see him sent back to Chattahoochie."

Will said, "I'll commence pulling out the posts and you-all can wind up the fencing."

They worked fast and I went out and looked up the road now and again to see if Uncle Benny was coming. Doc had stopped at the Standard filling-station on his way, to leave the news, and we could see the people there stirring around and going out to look, the same as we were doing. When we dragged the roll of wire fencing out into the road we hollered to them so they could see what we were doing and they all cheered and waved their hats. The word had spread, and the young uns begun traipsing barefooted down to the road, until some of their mammies ran down and cuffed them and hurried them back home out of the way of Uncle Benny. The men strung the fencing tight across the road between the garage on one side and our smoke-house on the other. They nailed it firm at both ends.

Doc said, "Leave me drive the last nail, men—it may be the last thing I can do for Benny this side of Chattahoochie."

I talked the men into unloading their guns.

"He'll have to stop when he sees the barricade," I said, "and then you can all go in on him with your guns drawed and capture him. I just can't hear to a loaded gun being drawed on him, for fear of somebody getting excited and shooting him."

Doc wiped the sweat off his forehead and he said, "Men, this is a mighty serious occasion. I'd be mighty proud if you'd all have a little snort on me," and he passed the bottle.

"Here's to Uncle Benny, the way we all knowed him before he went cold-out crazy," he said.

And then we heerd a shouting up the dirt road and young uns whistling and women and girls screaming and chickens scattering.

"Yonder comes Uncle Benny!"

And yonder he came.

The Model-T was swooping down like a bull-bat after a mosquito. The water was boiling up out of the radiator in a foot-high stream. The seven pieded bird-dogs were hanging out of the back seat and trembling as if they craved to tell the things they'd seen. And behind Uncle Benny was a string of deputy sheriffs in Fords and Chevrolets and motorcycles that had gathered together from every town between Oak Bluff and Ocala. And Uncle Benny was hunched over the steering wheel with them two tufts of goat-horn hair sticking up in the breeze —and the minute I laid eyes on him I knowed he wasn't one mite crazier than he ever had been. I knowed right then Doc had laid out to get even with him and had lied on him all the way down the road.

It was too late then. I knowed, whatever happened, there'd be people to the end of his life would always believe it. I knowed there'd be young uns running from him and niggers hiding. And I knowed there wasn't a thing in the world now could keep him out of Chattahoochie for the time being. I knowed he'd fight when he was taken, and all them mad and hot and dusty deputies would get him to the lunatic asylum quicker than a black snake can cross hot ashes. And once a man that has cut the fool all his life, like Uncle Benny, is in the crazy-house, there'll be plenty of folks to say to keep him there.

It was too late. Uncle Benny was bearing down toward the garage and right in front of him was the barricade.

Doc hollered, "Be ready to jump on him when he stops!"

Stop? Uncle Benny stop? He kept right on coming. The sight of that chicken-wire barricade was no more to him than an aggravation. Uncle Benny and the Model-T dived into the barricade like a water-turkey into a pool. The barricade held. And the next thing we knowed, the Ford had somersaulted over the fencing and crumpled up like a paper shoe-box and scattered bird-dogs over ten acres and laid Uncle Benny in a heap over against the wall of the smoke-house. I was raised to use the language of a lady, but I could hold in.

"Doc," I said, "you low-down son of a ——"

He said, "Mis' Dover, the name's too good. I've killed my friend."

Killed him? Killed Uncle Benny? It can't be done until the Almighty Hisself hollers "Sooey!" Uncle Benny was messed up considerable, but him nor none of the bird-dogs was dead.

The doctor took a few stitches in him at the garage before he come to, and tied up his head right pretty in a white bandage. We left Will to quiet the deputies and we put Uncle Benny in Doc's car and carried him home to the Old Hen. Naturally, I figured it would set her to quarrelling. Instead, it just brought out all her sweetness. I can guess a man, but I can't guess another woman.

"The pore ol' feller," she said. "I knowed he had it coming to him. What the devil throws over his back—. I knowed he'd kill hisself in that Ford car, cutting the fool and prowling. The biggest load is off my mind. Now," she said, "now, by God's mercy, when it did come to him, he got out alive."

She begun fanning him with a palmetto fan where he lay on the bed, and Doc poured out a drink of 'shine to have ready for him when he come to. Doc's hand was trembling. Uncle Benny opened his eyes. He eased one hand up to the bandage across his head and he groaned and grunted. He looked at Doc as if he couldn't make up his mind whether or not to reach for his pistol. Doc put the 'shine to his mouth and Uncle Benny swallowed. Them wicked blue eyes begun to dance.

"Doc," he said, "how will I get home when I'm drunk, now you've tore up my trained Ford?"

Doc broke down and cried like a little baby.

"I ain't got the money to replace it," he said, "but I'll give you my car. I'll carry the Little Giant line of remedies on foot."

Uncle Benny said, "I don't want your car. It ain't trained."

Doc said, "Then I'll tote you on my back, anywheres you say."

The Old Hen let in the bird-dogs, some of them limping a little, and they climbed on the bed and beat their tails on the counterpane and licked Uncle Benny. We felt mighty relieved things had come out that way.

Uncle Benny was up and around in a few days, with his head bandaged, and him as pert as a woodpecker. He just about owned Oak Bluff—all except the people that did like I figured, never did get over the idea he'd gone really crazy. Most people figured he'd had a mighty good lesson and it would learn him not to cut the fool. The Old Hen was as happy as a bride. She was so proud to have the Ford torn up, and no money to get another, that she'd even now and again pet one of the bird-dogs. She waited on Uncle Benny hand and foot and couldn't do enough to please him.

She said to me, "The pore ol' feller sure stays home nights now."

Stay home? Uncle Benny stay home? Two weeks after the accident the wreck of the Model-T disappeared from behind the garage where Will had dragged it. The next day the seven bird-dogs disappeared. The day after that Doc and Uncle Benny went to Ocala in Doc's car. Will wouldn't answer me when I asked him questions. The Old Hen stopped by the garage and got a Coca-Cola and she didn't know any more than I did. Then Will pointed down the road.

He said, "Yonder he comes."

And yonder he came. You could tell him way off by the white bandage with the tufts of hair sticking up over it. He was scrooched down behind the wheel of what looked like a brand-new automobile. Doc was following behind him. They swooped into the garage.

Will said, "It's a new second-hand body put on the chassis and around the engine of the old Ford."

Uncle Benny got out and he greeted us.

He said, "Will, it's just possible it was the motor of the Model-T that had takened the training. The motor ain't hurt, and me and Doc are real hopeful."

The Old Hen said, "Benny, where'd you get the money to pay for it?"

He said, "Why, a daggone bootlegger in a truck going from Miami to New York bought the bird-dogs for twenty-five dollars apiece. The low-down rascal knowed good and well they was worth seventy-five."

She brightened some. Getting shut of the bird-dogs was a little progress. She walked over to the car and begun looking around it.

"Benny," she said, and her voice come kind of faintified, "if you sold the bird-dogs, what's this place back here looks like it was fixed for 'em?"

We all looked, and here was a open compartment-like in the back, fixed up with seven crocus sacks stuffed with corn shucks. About that time here come a cloud of dust down the road. It was the seven bird-dogs. They were about give out. Their tongues were hanging out and their feet looked blistered.

Uncle Benny said, "I knowed they'd jump out of that bootlegger's truck. I told him so."

I tell you, what's in a man's nature you can't change. It takened the Old Hen thirty years and all them goings-on to learn it. She went and climbed in the front seat of the car and just sat there waiting for Uncle Benny to drive home for his dinner. He lifted the bird-dogs up and set them down to rest on the corn-shucks cushions, and he brought them a pan of water.

He said, "I figure they busted loose just about Lawtey."

The Old Hen never opened her mouth. She hasn't quarrelled at him from that day to this. She was hornswoggled.

Leonard Q. Ross

CHRISTOPHER K*A*P*L*A*N

Mr. Parkhill considered the beginners' grade as more than a group of scholars eager to master the English language. He took a larger view of his responsibilities; to Mr. Parkhill the American Night Preparatory School for Adults was not merely a place where foreigners could learn the English language—it was an incubator of Americans, a kind of intellectual Ellis Island. To imbue the men and women of a dozen nations with the meaning of America—its past, its traditions, its aspirations—this, to Mr. Parkhill, was the greater work to which he had dedicated himself.

So it was that on the eve of any national holiday, Mr. Parkhill devoted at least half an hour to a foray into the patriotic sentiments of the occasion. One Monday night, therefore, two nights before Columbus Day, Mr. Parkhill opened the class session with these ringing words, "Tonight, let us—er—consider the work of the man whose achievement the world will celebrate Wednesday."

A happy murmur ran through the room.

"To this man," said Mr. Parkhill earnestly, "the United States owes its very existence. For he—"

"Jawdge Vashington!" Miss Fanny Gidwitz promptly guessed.

"No, no, Miss Gidwitz. *Not* George Washington—watch that 'w,' Miss Gidwitz. I'm referring to—"

"Paul Rewere!" cried Oscar Trabish impetuously. Mr. Parkhill adjusted his spectacles. Mr. Trabish had formed some strange psychic union with "Paul Rewere": he had already written two compositions and made one fiery speech on his historical alter ego. The compositions had been called "Paul Revere's Horse Makes History" and "Paul Revere. One by the Land, Two by the Seashore." The title of the speech had been announced by Mr. Trabish as "Paul Rewere! Vhy He Vasn't Prazidant?" He had been quite indignant about it.

But now Mr. Parkhill shook his head. "Not Paul Re*were*—it's a 'v,'

19

Mr. Trabish. Let's not *guess,* class. What date is next Wednesday?"

"Mine boitday!" an excited voice rang out.

Mr. Parkhill ignored this comment. "Next Wednesday," he continued firmly, "is October twelfth. And on October twelfth, 1492—"

He got no further.

"Det's mine boitday! Mine *boit*day! I should live so! Honist!"

Mr. Parkhill recognized that voice. It was Hyman Kaplan's. Mr. Parkhill took a deep breath, a slow, deep breath, and said cautiously, "Mr. Kaplan, is October twelfth—er—really your birthday?"

Mr. Kaplan's eyes widened with hurt. *"Mister* Pockheel." Mr. Parkhill felt ashamed of himself.

Stanislaus Wilkomirski growled, "Kaplan too old for have bir-day." (Mr. Wilkomirski was a member of the Opposition.)

"October tvalf I'm born; October tvalf I'm tsalebratink!" Mr. Kaplan retorted. "All mine *life* I'm hevink boitdays October tvalf. No haxceptions!"

Mr. Parkhill said, "Well, well, well. That *is* a coincidence. October twelfth. Hmm." He smiled politely. "I'm sure we all wish Mr. Kaplan many happy returns."

Mr. Kaplan beamed, jumped to his feet, bowed, and sat down, beaming.

Miss Mitnick, feeling the occasion called for good will and peace among men, said, "Congratulations."

Mr. Kaplan said, "Denks."

"However," Mr. Parkhill went on resolutely, "the historical anniversary is that of Christopher Columbus. On October twelfth, 1492—"

*"Colom*biss!" Mr. Kaplan's rapture positively exploded.

Excitement seized the beginners' grade. "Colombus!" "Aha!" "Columbia Day!" "Colombos discovert America!"

"On October twelfth, 1492—"

Mr. Trabish dropped a sneer in the general direction of Fanny Gidwitz. "And you sad Jawdge Vashington!"

"You said Paul Rewere!"

"On October twelfth, 1492," persevered Mr. Parkhill.

"By me is avery day in year somthing about Paul Rewere!"

"And by *me* is our foist Prazident vert ten hoss-riders!"

"On October twelfth, 1492"—Mr. Parkhill's voice had risen until it was commanding—"Christopher Columbus discovered a new continent!"

The class quieted down at last, and Mr. Parkhill launched upon the saga of Christopher Columbus. He spoke slowly, impressively, almost with fervor. They listened to him closely, caught by the drama of the great voyage. "The food ran low. Water was scarce. The sailors began to grumble. . . ."

Goldie Pomeranz leaned forward and sighed moistly into Mr. Kaplan's ear, "You soitinly locky, Mr. Kaplan. Born same day Columbus did."

Mr. Kaplan was in a world of dreams. *"Christover Colombiss!"* He kept whispering the name to himself. "My!" He had closed his eyes to be alone with his hero. "October tvalf I'm arrivink in de voild—an' October tvalf Colombiss picks ot for discoverink U.S.! Dastiny."

"Mutiny faced Christopher Columbus," Mr. Parkhill said with feeling.

"My boitday is Motch toity," Miss Pomeranz whispered to Mr. Kaplan with sad envy. "Not iven a soborb vas discovered Motch toity."

Mr. Kaplan gave Miss Pomeranz a modest murmur. "Ufcawss, Colombiss discovert lonk bafore I arrived."

"October twalf is October twalf!" cried Mr. Pinsky, a true-blue Kaplan supporter.

Mr. Kaplan sighed, nodded, and let the mantle of history fall upon his shoulders.

Mr. Parkhill, driven to greater efforts by the Pomeranz-Kaplan-Pinsky symposium, told the class of the geographical boundaries in 1492, of the then current belief that the world was flat, of the mockery to which Columbus had been subjected. He described the singular confluence of events which had led to the new continent's being named after Amerigo Vespucci. ("A *mistake!*" Mr. Kaplan cried indignantly.) Mr. Parkhill outlined the immortal voyage of three tiny ships across an ocean infested in men's minds by monstrous things. When he said, "And because Columbus thought he was really in India, he called the natives Indians," the amazement of the beginners' grade of the American Night Preparatory School for Adults burst its bonds.

"Vun mistake on ton de odder!" Mr. Kaplan moaned.

"So dey called Hindyans by *mistake?*" asked Mrs. Moskowitz, wide-eyed. Mrs. Moskowitz could scarcely believe that of history.

"Yes, Mrs. Moskowitz, by mistake," said Mr. Parkhill quietly.

Mr. Kaplan shook his head three times. "Dose poor Hindyans."

Mr. Parkhill hurried on to details about Ferdinand and Isabella.

Just before he had completed the absorbing tale, Mr. Kaplan announced, without warning, "Ectual ve ain't Americans!"

Mr. Parkhill paused. " 'Actual*ly*, we *are*n't Americans,' Mr. Kaplan. There is no such word as—"

"Ectual ve all Colombians!" Mr. Kaplan cried. A passion for justice flamed in his eyes.

Mr. Parkhill turned the class over to Miss Mitnick for General Discussion. General Discussion, Mr. Parkhill had found, was a particularly fruitful exercise, and he occasionally invited one of the more competent students, like Miss Mitnick, to lead the discussion. It was even better training than the more formal Recitation and Speech periods and aroused fewer anxieties in the breasts of the timid.

Miss Mitnick struck the keynote for the evening with a touching if half-embarrassed eulogy of explorers in general and Columbus in particular. She ended her comments with a deft comparison of Columbus with Admiral Byrd. "Both men fond new places for humanity. Natchelly, in different places."

"Edmiral Boyd?" Mr. Kaplan sniffed at once. It was clear that henceforth anyone drawing comparisons between Columbus and lesser spirits would have to answer to Hyman Kaplan. "Vat kind finder new tings is dis Edmiral Boyd?"

"It's '*Ad*miral *Byrd*,' " Mr. Parkhill suggested from the seat he had taken next to Mr. Studniczka.

"Admiral Byrd is a kind *modern* Columbus," Miss Mitnick said, blushing.

"Vat he discovert should compare Colombiss's vunderful didd?" There was hauteur in Mr. Kaplan's tone.

"Admiral Byrd discovered Sout Pole," Miss Mitnick said. She looked a little frightened.

"Som discoverink!" said Mr. Kaplan, dismissing Antarctica scornfully.

"Sout Pole is important, Mr. Kaplan! It has—"

"It's to leff! Averybody *knew* vas Sot Pole, no? All Edmiral Boyd did vas *go* dere!"

Miss Mitnick turned pale.

"*Ad*miral *Byrd*, Mr. Kaplan," said Mr. Parkhill.

"Admiral Byrd is big *hero*," Miss Mitnick insisted, wetting her lips. "He went through terrible things for humanity—cold, icebergs, alone, freezings."

"Edmiral Boyd *vent mit all modinn conweniences!*"

Miss Mitnick shot a wild S.O.S. to Mr. Parkhill.

"Er—it's *Ad*miral *Byrd!*" Mr. Parkhill said. No one paid any attention to him.

Miss Caravello plunged into the controversy with a passionate "Is only da one Columbus! No more lak!" It was clear that to Miss Caravello Columbus was a peculiarly Italian phenomenon, unparalleled, incomparable. Admiral Byrd, she said flatly, was a "copying cat." For Columbus, Miss Caravello concluded hotly, nothing short of a thousand *"Viva"*s would do. She proceeded to give three of them: *"Viva! Viva! Viva!"*

Mr. Kaplan broke into furious applause.

Now Mr. Gus Matsoukas demanded the floor. "Colomb' good man, no doubts about," he began magnanimously. Columbus was, indeed, worth all that Mr. Kaplan and Miss Caravello had claimed for him. But after all, Mr. Matsoukas insinuated, should one not regard Columbus as no more than a sort of descendant of the first and *greatest* explorer—Ulysses? Ulysses, it turned out, was born in a town no more than seventeen kilometres from Mr. Matsoukas's birthplace.

"Boit*days* is more important den boit*places!*" Mr. Kaplan said.

Mr. Matsoukas, crestfallen, could think of no answer to this proposition. He fell back into his normal coma.

"Anybody else wants to say few words?" asked Miss Mitnick.

There were vague mumblings. Mr. Kaplan raised his hand.

"Floor is *open,*" Miss Mitnick announced. She kept her eyes away from Mr. Kaplan. *"Any*body can talk."

Mr. Kaplan rose at once, said "Foidinand an' Isabel. Ha!" and sat down.

There was a nervous silence. Miss Mitnick twisted her handkerchief around her fingers. "Mr. Kaplan, please," she stammered. "I didn't catch."

Mr. Kaplan got up again. "Foidinand an' Isabel. Ha!" He sat down.

Miss Mitnick looked to Mr. Parkhill in anguish.

"Er—Mr. Kaplan . . ."

"Axplain, Keplen!" Mr. Plonsky called out.

Mr. Kaplan said nothing.

"Keplen wants to talk or Keplen *not* wants to talk?" Mr. Plonsky asked the elements ironically.

Mr. Parkhill recognized his responsibility and decided to intervene.

"Y-yes, Mr. Kaplan. I do think the class is entitled to some explanation of your brief—er—comment."

"All of a sodden Mr. Kaplan makes fun Foidinand, Isabel!" Mrs. Moskowitz snickered. "Not even sayink 'Axcuse!' he makes 'Ha, ha!' on kinks and quinns!"

This frontal attack stirred the royalists into action.

"Talk, Kaplan!"

"You got the floor, no?"

"Tell awreddy! Tell!"

A more formal dialectician cried, "Give your meanink dose remocks!"

Mr. Kaplan faced his attackers calmly, almost apologetically. "Ladies an gantlemen, Mr. Pockheel—an' chairlady." Miss Mitnick lowered her eyes. "Ve all agreeink Colombiss's joiney vas vun de most movvellous tings in de voild." There were murmurs of affirmation. "*Tink* abot det treep, jost *tink*. Viks an' viks Colombiss vas sailink—tru storm, lighteninks, tonder. Tru vafes high like Ampire State Buildink. Fodder an' fodder Colombiss vent—alone!" Mr. Kaplan paused to let the drama sink home. "Vell, in *vat kind boats* Colombiss made det vunderful voyitch?" Mr. Kaplan's eyes narrowed. "I esk—*in vat kind boats?* Leetle, teentsy sheeps! Chizz boxes! Boats full likks! Boats full doit, joims, vater commink in! *Som* boats for discoverink America! An' det's vy I'm sayink '*Shame* on you, Foidinand an' Isabel!'" Mr. Kaplan's eyes flashed. "Couldn't dey give a man like Colombiss batter transportation?"

Fury broke in the classroom.

"Bravo!" cried Miss Caravello. "Bravo!"

"Crazy talk," muttered Mr. Matsoukas, thinking of the raft of Ulysses.

"Maybe dey should builded in 1492 a S.S. Quinn Marie?" asked Mr. Plonsky sarcastically.

Attacks, defences, taunts filled the scholastic air. Miss Mitnick, charged with the duties of arbitration, kept stammering, "Mr. Kaplan please. Mr. Kaplan please." Her voice shook. "Mr. Kaplan please. The ships Ferdinand and Isabella gave were fine for that *time*."

"For de *time?* But not for de *man!*"

"But in those days—"

"A man like Colombiss should have averyting fromm de bast!"

Mr. Parkhill got up. It seemed to be the only thing to do. "Well, class, I think—"

"Colombiss desoived more den a Senta Maria, a Nina, an' a Pintele!" Mr. Kaplan, soulmate of Columbus, plunged on in his passion, hacking right and left without mercy in the service of his historical partner. "I say det ven a man stotts ot to discover America—"

"Columbus didn't go to discover a specifical *place*," Miss Mitnick objected.

"He didn't go for axercise!" cried Hyman Kaplan.

Miss Mitnick bit her lip. "I mean Columbus didn't *know* was America. He didn't know was a continent in Atlentic Ocean. Columbus just went out . . ."

Mr. Kaplan regarded Miss Mitnick with tolerance. "*Vy* he vent ot, plizz?"

"To—to discover," Miss Mitnick said feebly.

"*Vat* to discover?"

Tears were in Miss Mitnick's eyes. "Just to *discover.*"

Mr. Kaplan looked from side to side, nodding. "Colombiss vent 'jost to discover,' " he repeated softly. " '*Jost* to discover.' " He sighed and shook his head, mourning man's naïveté. And then, his face lit with fervor, he struck. "Som people tink det if a man goes ot to mail a latter he *hopes* he'll find a mailbox!"

And now the battle raged once more—with shouts and cries and accusations; with lusty assaults on Mr. Kaplan's logic, and hot defences of Rose Mitnick.

In the corridors the bell rang, but no one heard it. The bell rang again, loud and long, but no one cared.

Mr. Parkhill said, "That's all for tonight, class." He said it calmly, but he had a worried look. For Mr. Parkhill felt that General Discussion had not been a complete success this evening. If only Columbus had discovered America on October eleventh; if only Hyman Kaplan had been born on October thirteenth.

Frank R. Stockton

THE CASTING AWAY OF MRS. LECKS AND MRS. ALESHINE *

I was on my way from San Francisco to Yokohama, when in a very desultory and gradual manner I became acquainted with Mrs. Lecks and Mrs. Aleshine. The steamer, on which I was making a moderately rapid passage toward the land of the legended fan and the lacquered box, carried a fair complement of passengers, most of whom were Americans; and, among these, my attention was attracted from the very first day of the voyage to two middle-aged women who appeared to me very unlike the ordinary traveler or tourist. At first sight they might have been taken for farmers' wives who, for some unusual reason, had determined to make a voyage across the Pacific; but, on closer observation, one would have been more apt to suppose that they belonged to the families of prosperous tradesmen in some little country town, where, besides the arts of rural housewifery, there would be opportunities of becoming acquainted in some degree with the ways and manners of the outside world. They were not of that order of persons who generally take first-class passages on steamships, but the stateroom occupied by Mrs. Lecks and Mrs. Aleshine was one of the best in the vessel.

Mrs. Lecks was a rather tall woman, large-boned and muscular, and her well-browned countenance gave indications of that conviction of superiority which gradually grows up in the minds of those who for a long time have had absolute control of the destinies of a state, or the multifarious affairs of a country household. Mrs. Aleshine was somewhat younger than her friend, somewhat shorter, and a great deal fatter. She had the same air of reliance upon her individual

* This is Part I of the Stockton novel "The Casting Away of Mrs. Lecks and Mrs. Aleshine." A few cuts have been made, and a few sentences from Part II have been added—this last for the purpose of getting the ladies into smooth water and within reach of land. It seemed the decent thing to do.

26

worth that characterized Mrs. Lecks, but there was a certain geniality about her which indicated that she would have a good deal of forbearance for those who never had had the opportunity or the ability of becoming the thoroughly good housewife which she was herself.

These two worthy dames spent the greater part of their time on deck, where they always sat together in a place at the stern of the vessel which was well sheltered from wind and weather. As they sat thus they were generally employed in knitting, although this occupation did not prevent them from keeping up what seemed to me, as I passed them in my walks about the deck, a continuous conversation. From a question which Mrs. Lecks once asked me about a distant sail, our acquaintance began. There was no one on board for whose society I particularly cared, and as there was something quaint and odd about these countrywomen on the ocean which interested me, I was glad to vary my solitary promenades by an occasional chat with them. They were not at all backward in giving me information about themselves. They were both widows, and Mrs. Aleshine was going out to Japan to visit a son who had a position there in a mercantile house. Mrs. Lecks had no children, and was accompanying her friend because, as she said, she would not allow Mrs. Aleshine to make such a voyage as that by herself, and because, being quite able to do so, she did not know why she should not see the world as well as other people.

These two friends were not educated women. They made frequent mistakes in their grammar, and a good deal of Middle States provincialism showed itself in their pronunciation and expressions. But although they brought many of their rural ideas to sea with them, they possessed a large share of that common sense which is available anywhere, and they frequently made use of it in a manner which was very amusing to me. I think, also, that they found in me a quarry of information concerning nautical matters, foreign countries, and my own affairs, the working of which helped to make us very good ship friends.

Our steamer touched at the Sandwich Islands; and it was a little more than two days after we left Honolulu that, about nine o'clock in the evening, we had the misfortune to come into collision with an eastern-bound vessel. This vessel, which appeared to be a small steamer, struck us with great force near our bows, and then, backing, disappeared into the fog, and we never saw or heard of her again.

It was soon discovered that our injuries were serious and, indeed, disastrous. The hull of our steamer had been badly shattered on the port bow, and the water came in at a most alarming rate. For nearly two hours the crew and many of the passengers worked at the pumps, and everything possible was done to stop the enormous leak; but all labor to save the vessel was found to be utterly unavailing, and a little before midnight the captain announced that it was impossible to keep the steamer afloat, and that we must all take to the boats. The night was now clear, the stars were bright, and, as there was but little wind, the sea was comparatively smooth. With all these advantages, the captain assured us that there was no reason to apprehend danger, and he thought that by noon of the following day we could easily make a small inhabited island, where we could be sheltered and cared for until we should be taken off by some passing vessel.

There was plenty of time for all necessary preparations, and these were made with much order and subordination. Everybody obeyed the captain's orders, and all prepared themselves for the transfer to the boats. The first officer came among us, and told each of us what boats we were to take, and where we were to place ourselves on deck. I was•assigned to a large boat which was to be principally occupied by steerage passengers; and as I came up from my stateroom, where I had gone to secure my money and some portable valuables, I met on the companionway Mrs. Lecks and Mrs. Aleshine, who expressed considerable dissatisfaction when they found that I was not going in the boat with them. They, however, hurried below, and I went on deck, where in about ten minutes I was joined by Mrs. Lecks, who apparently had been looking for me. She told me she had something very particular to say to me, and conducted me toward the stern of the vessel, where, behind one of the deck-houses, we found Mrs. Aleshine.

"Look here," said Mrs. Lecks, leading me to the rail, and pointing downward; "do you see that boat there? It has been let down, and there is nobody in it. The boat on the other side has just gone off, full to the brim. I never saw so many people crowded into a boat. The other ones will be just as packed, I expect. I don't see why we shouldn't take this empty boat, now we've got a chance, instead of squeezin' ourselves into those crowded ones. If any of the other people come afterward, why, we shall have our choice of seats, and that's considerable of a p'int, I should say, in a time like this."

"That's so," said Mrs. Aleshine; "and me and Mrs. Lecks would 'a' got right in when we saw the boat was empty, if we hadn't been afraid to be there without any man, for it might have floated off, and neither of us don't know nothin' about rowin'. And then Mrs. Lecks she thought of you, supposin' a young man who knew so much about the sea would know how to row."

"Oh, yes," said I; "but I cannot imagine why this boat should have been left empty. I see a keg of water in it, and the oars, and some tin cans, and so I suppose it has been made ready for somebody. Will you wait here a minute until I run forward and see how things are going on there?"

Amidships and forward I saw that there was some confusion among the people who were not yet in their boats, and I found that there was to be rather more crowding than at first was expected. People who had supposed that they were to go in a certain boat found there no place, and were hurrying to other boats. It now became plain to me that no time should be lost in getting into the small boat which Mrs. Lecks had pointed out, so I slipped quietly aft, and joined Mrs. Lecks and Mrs. Aleshine.

"We must get in as soon as we can," said I, in a low voice, "for this boat may be discovered, and then there will be a rush for it. I suspect it may have been reserved for the captain and some of the officers, but we have as much right in it as they."

"And more too," replied Mrs. Lecks; "for we had nothin' to do with the steerin' and smashin'."

"But how are we goin' to get down there?" said Mrs. Aleshine. "There's no steps."

"That is true," said I. "I shouldn't wonder if this boat is to be taken forward when the others are filled. We must scramble down as well as we can by the tackle at the bow and stern. I'll get in first and keep her close to the ship's side."

"That's goin' to be a scratchy business," said Mrs. Lecks, "and I'm of the opinion we ought to wait till the ship has sunk a little more, so we'll be nearer to the boat."

"It won't do to wait," said I, "or we shall not get in it at all."

"And goodness gracious!" exclaimed Mrs. Aleshine, "I can't stand here and feel the ship sinkin' cold-blooded under me, till we've got where we can make an easy jump!"

"Very well, then," said Mrs. Lecks, "we won't wait. But the first thing to be done is for each one of us to put on one of these life-preservers. Two of them I brought from Mrs. Aleshine's and my cabin, and the other one I got next door, where the people had gone off and left it on the floor. I thought if anythin' happened on the way to the island, these would give us a chance to look about us; but it seems to me we'll need 'em more gettin' down them ropes than anywhere else. I did intend puttin' on two myself to make up for Mrs. Aleshine's fat; but you must wear one of 'em, sir, now that you are goin' to join the party."

As I knew that two life-preservers would not be needed by Mrs. Lecks, and would greatly inconvenience her, I accepted the one offered me, but declined to put it on until it should be necessary, as it would interfere with my movements.

"Very well," said Mrs. Lecks, "if you think you are safe in gettin' down without it. But Mrs. Aleshine and me will put ours on before we begin sailor-scramblin'. We know how to do it, for we tried 'em on soon after we started from San Francisco. And now, Barb'ry Aleshine, are you sure you've got everythin' you want? for it'll be no use thinkin' about anythin' you've forgot after the ship has sunk out of sight."

"There's nothin' else I can think of," said Mrs. Aleshine; "at least, nothin' I can carry; and so I suppose we may as well begin, for your talk of the ship sinkin' under our feet gives me a sort o' feelin' like an oyster creepin' up and down my back."

Mrs. Lecks looked over the side at the boat, into which I had already descended. "I'll go first, Barb'ry Aleshine," said she, "and show you how."

The sea was quiet, and the steamer had already sunk so much that Mrs. Lecks's voice sounded frightfully near me, although she spoke in a low tone.

"Watch me," said she to her companion. "I'm goin' to do just as he did, and you must follow in the same way."

So saying, she stepped on a bench by the rail; then, with one foot on the rail itself, she seized the ropes which hung from one of the davits to the bow of the boat. She looked down for a moment, and then she drew back.

"It's no use," she said. "We must wait until she sinks more, and I can get in easier."

This remark made me feel nervous. I did not know at what moment there might be a rush for this boat, nor when, indeed, the steamer might go down. The boat amidships on our side had rowed away some minutes before, and through the darkness I could distinguish another boat, near the bows, pushing off. It would be too late now for us to try to get into any other boat, and I did not feel that there was time enough for me to take this one to a place where the two women could more easily descend to her. Standing upright, I urged them not to delay.

"You see," said I, "I can reach you as soon as you swing yourself off the ropes, and I'll help you down."

"If you're sure you can keep us from comin' down too sudden, we'll try it," said Mrs. Lecks; "but I'd as soon be drowned as to get to an island with a broken leg. And as to Mrs. Aleshine, if she was to slip she'd go slam through that boat to the bottom of the sea. Now, then, be ready! I'm comin' down."

So saying, she swung herself off, and she was then so near me that I was able to seize her and make the rest of her descent comparatively easy. Mrs. Aleshine proved to be a more difficult subject. Even after I had a firm grasp of her capacious waist she refused to let go the ropes, for fear that she might drop into the ocean instead of the boat. But the reproaches of Mrs. Lecks and the downward weight of myself made her loosen her nervous grip; and, although we came very near going overboard together, I safely placed her on one of the thwarts.

I now unhooked the tackle from the stern; but before casting off at the bow I hesitated, for I did not wish to desert any of those who might be expecting to embark in this boat. But I could hear no approaching footsteps, and from my position, close to the side of the steamer, I could see nothing. Therefore I cast off, and, taking the oars, I pushed away and rowed to a little distance, where I could get whatever view was possible of the deck of the steamer. Seeing no forms moving about, I called out, and, receiving no answer, I shouted again at the top of my voice. I waited for nearly a minute, and, hearing nothing and seeing nothing, I became convinced that no one was left on the vessel.

"They are all gone," said I, "and we will pull after them as fast as we can."

And I began to row toward the bow of the steamer, in the direction which the other boats had taken.

"It's a good thing you can row," said Mrs. Lecks, settling herself comfortably in the stern-sheets, "for what Mrs. Aleshine and me would ha' done with them oars I am sure I don't know."

"I'd never have got into this boat," said Mrs. Aleshine, "if Mr. Craig hadn't been here."

"No, indeed," replied her friend. "You'd ha' gone to the bottom, hangin' for dear life to them ropes."

When I had rounded the bow of the steamer, which appeared to me to be rapidly settling in the water, I perceived at no great distance several lights, which of course belonged to the other boats, and I rowed as hard as I could, hoping to catch up with them, or at least to keep sufficiently near. It might be my duty to take off some of the people who had crowded into the other boats, probably supposing that this one had been loaded and gone. How such a mistake could have taken place I could not divine, and it was not my business to do so. Quite certain that no one was left on the sinking steamer, all I had to do was to row after the other boats, and to overtake them as soon as possible. I thought it would not take me very long to do this, but after rowing for half an hour, Mrs. Aleshine remarked that the lights seemed as far off, if not farther, than when we first started after them. Turning, I saw that this was the case, and was greatly surprised. With only two passengers I ought soon to have come up with those heavily laden boats. But after I had thought over it a little, I considered that as each of them was probably pulled by half a dozen stout sailors, it was not so very strange that they should make as good or better headway than I did.

It was not very long after this that Mrs. Lecks said that she thought that the lights on the other boats must be going out, and that this, most probably, was due to the fact that the sailors had forgotten to fill their lanterns before they started. "That sort of thing often happens," she said, "when people leave a place in a hurry."

But when I turned around, and peered over the dark waters, it was quite plain to me that it was not want of oil, but increased distance, which made those lights so dim. I could now perceive but three of them. We were being left behind, that was certain, and all I could do was to row on as long and as well as I could in the direction which the other boats had taken.

"I don't believe this boat has been emptied out since the last rain," said Mrs. Aleshine, "for my feet are wet, though I didn't notice it before."

At this I shipped my oars, and began to examine the boat. The bottom was covered with a movable floor of slats, and as I put my hand down I could feel the water welling up between the slats. The flooring was in sections, and lifting the one beneath me, I felt under it, and put my hand into six or eight inches of water.

The exact state of the case was now as plain to me as if it had been posted up on a bulletin-board. This boat had been found to be unseaworthy, and its use had been forbidden, all the people having been crowded into the others. This had caused confusion at the last moment, and, of course, we were supposed to be on some one of the other boats.

And now here was I, in the middle of the Pacific Ocean, in a leaky boat, with two middle-aged women!

"Anythin' the matter with the floor?" asked Mrs. Lecks.

I let the section fall back into its place, and looked aft. By the starlight I could see that my two companions had each fixed upon me a steadfast gaze. They evidently felt that something was the matter, and wanted to know what it was. I did not hesitate for a moment to inform them. They appeared to me to be women whom it would be neither advisable nor possible to deceive in a case like this.

"This boat has a leak in it," I said. "There is a lot of water in her already, and that is the reason we have got along so slowly."

"And that is why," said Mrs. Aleshine, "it was left empty. We ought to have known better than to expect to have a whole boat just for three of us. It would have been much more sensible, I think, if we had tried to squeeze into one of the others."

"Now, Barb'ry Aleshine," said Mrs. Lecks, "don't you begin findin' fault with good fortune, when it comes to you. Here we've got a comfortable boat, with room enough to set easy and stretch out if we want to. If the water is comin' in, what we've got to do is to get it out again just as fast as we can. What's the best way to do that, Mr. Craig?"

"We must bail her out, and lose no time about it," said I. "If I can find the leak I may be able to stop it."

I now looked about for something to bail with, and the two women aided actively in the search. I found one leather scoop in the bow; but as it was well that we should all go to work, I took two tin cans that had been put in by some one who had begun to provision the boat, and proceeded to cut the tops from them with my jack-knife.

"Don't lose what's in 'em," said Mrs. Lecks; "that is, if it's anythin' we'd be likely to want to eat. If it's tomatoes, pour it into the sea, for nobody ought to eat tomatoes put up in tins."

I hastily passed the cans to Mrs. Lecks, and I saw her empty the contents of one into the sea, and those of the other on a newspaper which she took from her pocket and placed in the stern.

I pulled up the movable floor and threw it overboard, and then began to bail.

"I thought," said Mrs. Aleshine, "that they always had pumps for leaks."

"Now, Barb'ry Aleshine," said Mrs. Lecks, "just gether yourself up on one of them seats, and go to work. The less talkin' we do, and the more scoopin', the better it'll be for us."

I soon perceived that it would have been difficult to find two more valuable assistants in the bailing of a boat than Mrs. Lecks and Mrs. Aleshine. They were evidently used to work, and were able to accommodate themselves to the unusual circumstances in which they were placed. We threw out the water very rapidly, and every little while I stopped bailing and felt about to see if I could discover where it came in. As these attempts met with no success, I gave them up after a time, and set about bailing with new vigor, believing that if we could get the boat nearly dry I should surely be able to find the leak.

But, after working half an hour more, I found that the job would be a long one; and if we all worked at once we would all be tired out at once, and that might be disastrous. Therefore I proposed that we should take turns in resting, and Mrs. Aleshine was ordered to stop work for a time. After this Mrs. Lecks took a rest, and when she went to work I stopped bailing and began again to search for the leak.

For about two hours we worked in this way, and then I concluded it was useless to continue any longer this vain exertion. With three of us bailing we were able to keep the water at the level we first found it; but with only two at work, it slightly gained upon us, so that now there was more water in the boat than when we first discovered it. The boat was an iron one, the leak in it I could neither find nor remedy, and it was quite plain that the water was now coming in more rapidly than it did at first. We were very tired, and even Mrs. Lecks, who had all along counseled us to keep at work, and not to waste one breath in talking, now admitted that it was of no use to try to get the water out of that boat.

It had been some hours since I had used the oars, but whether we had drifted, or remained where we were when I stopped rowing, of course I could not know; but this mattered very little; our boat was slowly sinking beneath us, and it could make no difference whether we went down in one spot or another. I sat and racked my brain to think what could be done in this fearful emergency. To bail any longer was useless labor, and what else was there that we could do?

"When will it be time," asked Mrs. Lecks, "for us to put on the life-preservers? When the water gets nearly to the seats?"

I answered that we should not wait any longer than that, but in my own mind I could not see any advantage in putting them on at all. Why should we wish to lengthen our lives by a few hours of helpless floating upon the ocean?

"Very good," said Mrs. Lecks; "I'll keep a watch on the water. One of them cans was filled with lobster, which would be more than likely to disagree with us, and I've throwed it out; but the other had baked beans in it, and the best thing we can do is to eat some of these right away. They are mighty nourishin', and will keep up strength as well as anythin', and then, as you said there's a keg of water in the boat, we can all take a drink of that, and it'll make us feel like new cre'tur's. You'll have to take the beans in your hands, for we've got no spoons nor forks."

Mrs. Lecks and Mrs. Aleshine were each curled up out of reach of the water, the first in the stern, and the other on the aft thwart. The day was now beginning to break, and we could see about us very distinctly. Before reaching out her hands to receive her beans, Mrs. Aleshine washed them in the water in the boat, remarking at the same time that she might as well make use of it since it was there. Having then wiped her hands on some part of her apparel, they were filled with beans from the newspaper held by Mrs. Lecks, and these were passed over to me. I was very hungry, and when I had finished my beans I agreed with my companions that although they would have been a great deal better if heated up with butter, pepper, and salt, they were very comforting as they were. One of the empty cans was now passed to me, and after having been asked by Mrs. Lecks to rinse it out very carefully, we all satisfied our taste from the water in the keg.

"Cold baked beans and lukewarm water ain't exactly company vittles," said Mrs. Aleshine, "but there's many a poor wretch would be glad to get 'em."

I could not imagine any poor wretch who would be glad of the food together with the attending circumstances; but I did not say so.

"The water is just one finger from the bottom of the seat," said Mrs. Lecks, who had been stooping over to measure, "and it's time to put on the life-preservers."

"Very good," said Mrs. Aleshine; "hand me mine."

Each of us now buckled on a life-preserver, and as I did so I stood up upon a thwart and looked about me. It was quite light now, and I could see for a long distance over the surface of the ocean, which was gently rolling in wide, smooth swells. As we rose upon the summit of one of these I saw a dark spot upon the water, just on the edge of our near horizon. "Is that the steamer?" I thought; "and has she not yet sunk?"

At this there came to me a glimmering of courageous hope. If the steamer had remained afloat so long, it was probable that on account of water-tight compartments, or for some other reason, her sinking had reached its limit, and that if we could get back to her we might be saved. But, alas, how were we to get back to her? This boat would sink long, long before I could row that distance.

However, I soon proclaimed the news to my companions, whereupon Mrs. Aleshine prepared to stand upon a thwart and see for herself. But Mrs. Lecks restrained her.

"Don't make things worse, Barb'ry Aleshine," said she, "by tumblin' overboard. If we've got to go into the water, let us do it decently and in order. If that's the ship, Mr. Craig, don't you suppose we can float ourselves to it in some way?"

I replied that by the help of a life-preserver a person who could swim might reach the ship.

"But neither of us can swim," said Mrs. Lecks, "for we've lived where the water was never more'n a foot deep, except in time of freshets, when there's no swimmin' for man or beast. But if we see you swim, perhaps we can follow, after a fashion. At any rate, we must do the best we can, and that's all there is to be done."

"The water now," remarked Mrs. Aleshine, "is so near to the bottom of my seat that I've got to stand up, tumble overboard or no."

"All right," remarked Mrs. Lecks; "we'd better all stand up, and let the boat sink under us. That will save our jumpin' overboard, or rollin' out any which way, which might be awkward."

"Goodness gracious me!" exclaimed Mrs. Aleshine. "You set the oysters creepin' over me again! First you talk of the ship sinkin' under us, and now it's the boat goin' to the bottom under our feet. Before any sinkin' 's to be done I'd ruther get out."

"Now, Barb'ry Aleshine," said Mrs. Lecks, "stand up straight, and don't talk so much. It'll be a great deal better to be let down gradual than to flop into the water all of a bunch."

"Very well," said Mrs. Aleshine; "it may be best to get used to it by degrees; but I must say I wish I was home."

As for me, I would have much preferred to jump overboard at once, instead of waiting in this cold-blooded manner; but as my companions had so far preserved their presence of mind, I did not wish to do anything which might throw them into a panic. I believed there would be no danger from the suction caused by the sinking of a small boat like this, and if we took care not to entangle ourselves with it in any way, we might as well follow Mrs. Lecks's advice as not. So we all stood up, Mrs. Lecks in the stern, I in the bow, and Mrs. Aleshine on a thwart between us. The last did not appear to have quite room enough for a steady footing, but, as she remarked, it did not matter very much, as the footing, broad or narrow, would not be there very long.

I am used to swimming, and have never hesitated to take a plunge into river or ocean, but I must admit that it was very trying to my nerves to stand up this way and wait for a boat to sink beneath me. How the two women were affected I do not know. They said nothing, but their faces indicated that something disagreeable was about to happen, and that the less that was said about it the better.

The boat had now sunk so much that the water was around Mrs. Aleshine's feet, her standing-place being rather lower than ours. I made myself certain that there were no ropes nor any other means of entanglement near my companions or myself, and then I waited. There seemed to be a good deal of buoyancy in the bow and stern of the boat, and it was a frightfully long time in sinking. The suspense became so utterly unendurable that I was tempted to put one foot on the edge of the boat, and, by tipping it, put an end to this nerve-rack; but I refrained, for I probably would throw the women off their balance, when they might fall against some part of the boat, and do themselves a hurt. I had just relinquished this intention, when two little waves seemed to rise one on each side of Mrs. Aleshine, and gently flowing over the side of the boat, they flooded her feet with water.

"Hold your breaths!" I shouted. And now I experienced a sensation which must have been very like that which comes to a condemned criminal at the first indication of the pulling of the drop. Then there was a horrible sinking, a gurgle, and a swash, and the ocean over which I had been gazing appeared to rise up and envelop me.

In a moment, however, my head was out of the water, and, looking hastily about me, I saw, close by, the heads and shoulders of Mrs. Lecks and Mrs. Aleshine. The latter was vigorously winking her eyes and blowing from her mouth some sea-water that had got into it; but as soon as her eyes fell upon me she exclaimed: "That was ever so much more suddint than I thought it was goin' to be!"

"Are you both all right?"

"I suppose I am," said Mrs. Aleshine, "but I never thought that a person with a life-preserver on would go clean under the water."

"But since you've come up again, you ought to be satisfied," said Mrs. Lecks. "And now," she added, turning her face toward me, "which way ought we to try to swim? and have we got everythin' we want to take with us?"

"What we haven't got we can't get," remarked Mrs. Aleshine; "and as for swimmin', I expect I'm goin' to make a poor hand at it."

I had a hope, which was not quite strong enough to be a belief, that, supported by their life-preservers, the two women might paddle themselves along; and that, by giving them in turn a helping hand, I might eventually get them to the steamer. There was a strong probability that I would not succeed, but I did not care to think of that.

I now swam in front of my companions, and endeavored to instruct them in the best method of propelling themselves with their arms and their hands. If they succeeded in this, I thought I would give them some further lessons in striking out with their feet. After watching me attentively, Mrs. Lecks did manage to move herself slowly through the smooth water, but poor Mrs. Aleshine could do nothing but splash.

"If there was anythin' to take hold of," she said to me, "I might get along; but I can't get any grip on the water, though you seem to do it well enough. Look there!" she added in a higher voice. "Isn't that an oar floatin' over there? If you can get that for me, I believe I can row myself much better than I can swim."

This seemed an odd idea, but I swam over to the floating oar, and brought it her. I was about to show her how she could best use it, but she declined my advice.

"If I do it at all," she said, "I must do it in my own way." And taking the oar in her strong hands, she began to ply it on the water very much in the way in which she would handle a broom. At first she dipped the blade too deeply, but, correcting this error, she soon began to paddle herself along at a slow but steady rate.

"Capital!" I cried. "You do that admirably!"

"Anybody who's swept as many rooms as I have," she said, "ought to be able to handle anythin' that can be used like a broom."

"Isn't there another oar?" cried Mrs. Lecks, who had now been left a little distance behind us. "If there is, I want one."

Looking about me, I soon discovered another floating oar, and brought it to Mrs. Lecks, who, after holding it in various positions, so as to get "the hang of it," as she said, soon began to use it with as much skill as that shown by her friend. If either of them had been obliged to use an oar in the ordinary way, I fear they would have had a bad time of it; but, considering the implement in the light of a broom, its use immediately became familiar to them, and they got on remarkably well.

I now took a position a little in advance of my companions, and as I swam slowly they were easily able to keep up with me. Mrs. Aleshine, being so stout, floated much higher out of the water than either Mrs. Lecks or I, and this permitted her to use her oar with a great deal of freedom. Sometimes she would give such a vigorous brush to the water that she would turn herself almost entirely around, but after a little practice she learned to avoid undue efforts of this kind.

I was not positively sure that we were going in the right direction, for my position did not allow me to see very far over the water; but I remembered that when I was standing up in the boat, and made my discovery, the sun was just about to rise in front of me, while the dark spot on the ocean lay to my left. Judging, therefore, from the present position of the sun, which was not very high, I concluded that we were moving toward the north, and therefore in the right direction. How far off the steamer might be I had no idea, for I was not accustomed to judging distances at sea; but I believed that if we were careful of our strength, and if the ocean continued as smooth as it now was, we might eventually reach the vessel, provided she were yet afloat.

"After you are fairly in the water," said Mrs. Aleshine, as she swept along, although without the velocity which that phrase usually implies, "it isn't half so bad as I thought it would be. For one thing, it don't feel a bit salt, although I must say it tasted horribly that way when I first went into it."

"You didn't expect to find pickle-brine, did you?" said Mrs. Lecks. "Though, if it was, I suppose we could float on it settin'."

"And as to bein' cold," said Mrs. Aleshine, "the part of me that's in is actually more comfortable than that which is out."

"There's one thing I would have been afraid of," said Mrs. Lecks, "if we hadn't made preparations for it, and that's sharks."

"Preparations!" I exclaimed. "How in the world did you prepare for sharks?"

"Easy enough," said Mrs. Lecks. "When we went down into our room to get ready to go away in the boats we both put on black stockin's. I've read that sharks never bite colored people, although if they see a white man in the water they'll snap him up as quick as lightnin'; and black stockin's was the nearest we could come to it. You see, I thought as like as not we'd have some sort of an upset before we got through."

"It's a great comfort," remarked Mrs. Aleshine, "and I'm very glad you thought of it, Mrs. Lecks. After this I shall make it a rule: Black stockin's for sharks."

"I suppose in your case," said Mrs. Lecks, addressing me, "dark trousers will do as well."

To which I answered that I sincerely hoped they would.

"Another thing I'm thankful for," said Mrs. Aleshine, "is that I thought to put on a flannel skeert."

"And what's the good of it," said Mrs. Lecks, "when it's soppin' wet?"

"Flannel's flannel," replied her friend, "whether it's wet or dry; and if you'd had the rheumatism as much as I have, you'd know it."

To this Mrs. Lecks replied with a sniff, and asked me how soon I thought we would get sight of the ship; for if we were going the wrong way, and had to turn round and go back, it would certainly be very provoking.

I should have been happy indeed to be able to give a satisfactory answer to this question. Every time that we rose upon a swell I threw a rapid glance around the whole circle of the horizon; and at last, not a quarter of an hour after Mrs. Lecks's question, I was rejoiced to see, almost in the direction in which I supposed it ought to be, the dark spot which I had before discovered. I shouted the glad news, and as we rose again my companions strained their eyes in the direction to which I pointed. They both saw it, and were greatly satisfied.

"Now, then," said Mrs. Aleshine, "it seems as if there was somethin' to work for"; and she began to sweep her oar with great vigor.

"If you want to tire yourself out before you get there, Barb'ry Aleshine," said Mrs. Lecks, "you'd better go on in that way. Now what I advise is that we stop rowin' altogether, and have somethin' to eat; for I'm sure we need it to keep up our strength."

"Eat!" I cried. "What are you going to eat? Do you expect to catch fish?"

"And eat 'em raw?" said Mrs. Lecks. "I should think not. But do you suppose, Mr. Craig, that Mrs. Aleshine and me would go off and leave that ship without takin' somethin' to eat by the way? Let's all gether here in a bunch, and see what sort of a meal we can make. And now, Barb'ry Aleshine, if you lay your oar down there on the water, I recommend you to tie it to one of your bonnet-strings, or it'll be floatin' away, and you won't get it again."

As she said this, Mrs. Lecks put her right hand down into the water, and fumbled about, apparently in search of a pocket. I could not but smile as I thought of the condition of food when, for an hour or more, it had been a couple of feet under the surface of the ocean; but my ideas on the subject were entirely changed when I saw Mrs. Lecks hold up in the air two German sausages, and shake the briny drops from their smooth and glittering surfaces.

"There's nothin'," she said, "like sausages for shipwreck and that kind o' thing. They're very sustainin', and bein' covered with a tight skin, water can't get at 'em, no matter how you carry 'em. I wouldn't bring these out in the boat, because, havin' the beans, we might as well eat them. Have you a knife about you, Mr. Craig?"

I produced a dripping jack-knife, and after the open blade had been waved in the air to dry it a little, Mrs. Lecks proceeded to divide one of the sausages, handing the other to me to hold meanwhile.

"Now don't go eatin' sausages without bread, if you don't want 'em to give you dyspepsy," said Mrs. Aleshine, who was tugging at a submarine pocket.

"I'm very much afraid your bread is all soaked," said Mrs. Lecks.

To which her friend replied that that remained to be seen, and forthwith produced, with a splash, a glass preserve-jar with a metal top.

"I saw this nearly empty, as I looked into the ship's pantry, and I stuffed into it all the soft biscuits it would hold. There was some sort of jam left at the bottom, so that the one who gets the last biscuit will have somethin' of a little spread on it. And now, Mrs. Lecks," she continued triumphantly, as she unscrewed the top, "that rubber ring has kept 'em as dry as chips. I'm mighty glad of it, for I had trouble enough gettin' this jar into my pocket, and gettin' it out, too, for that matter."

Floating thus, with our hands and shoulders above the water, we made a very good meal from the sausages and soft biscuit.

"Barb'ry Aleshine," said Mrs. Lecks, as her friend proceeded to cut the second sausage, "don't you lay that knife down, when you've done with it, as if 't was an oar; for if you do it'll sink, as like as not, about six miles. I've read that the ocean is as deep as that in some places."

"Goodness gracious me!" exclaimed Mrs. Aleshine, "I hope we are not over one of them deep spots."

"There's no knowin'," said Mrs. Lecks, "but if it's more comfortin' to think it's shallerer, we'll make up our minds that way. Now, then," she continued, "we'll finish off this meal with a little somethin' to drink. I'm not given to takin' spirits, but I never travel without a little whisky, ready mixed with water, to take if it should be needed."

So saying, she produced from one of her pockets a whisky-flask tightly corked, and of its contents we each took a sip, Mrs. Aleshine remarking that, leaving out being chilled or colicky, we were never likely to need it more than now.

Thus refreshed and strengthened, Mrs. Lecks and Mrs. Aleshine took up their oars, while I swam slightly in advance, as before. When, with occasional intermissions of rest, and a good deal of desultory conversation, we had swept and swam for about an hour, Mrs. Lecks suddenly exclaimed: "I can see that thing ever so much plainer now, and I don't believe it's a ship at all. To me it looks like bushes."

"You're mighty long-sighted without your specs," said Mrs. Aleshine, "and I'm not sure but what you're right."

For ten minutes or more I had been puzzling over the shape of the dark spot, which was now nearly all the time in sight. Its peculiar form had filled me with a dreadful fear that it was the steamer, bottom upward, although I knew enough about nautical matters to have no good reason to suppose that this could be the case. I am not far-sighted, but when Mrs. Lecks suggested bushes, I gazed at the distant object with totally different ideas, and soon began to believe that it was not a ship, either right side up or wrong side up, but that it might be an island. This belief I proclaimed to my companions, and for some time we all worked with increased energy in the desire to get near enough to make ourselves certain in regard to this point.

"As true as I'm standin' here," said Mrs. Lecks, who, although she could not read without spectacles, had remarkably good sight at long range, "them is trees and bushes that I see before me, though they do seem to be growin' right out of the water."

"There's an island under them; you may be sure of that!" I cried. "Isn't this ever so much better than a sinking ship?"

"I'm not so sure about that," said Mrs. Aleshine. "I'm used to the ship, and as long as it didn't sink I'd prefer it. There's plenty to eat on board of it, and good beds to sleep on, which is more than can be expected on a little bushy place like that ahead of us. But then, the ship might sink all of a suddint, beds, vittles, and all."

"Do you suppose that is the island the other boats went to?" asked Mrs. Lecks.

This question I had already asked of myself. I had been told that the island to which the captain intended to take his boats lay about thirty miles south of the point where we left the steamer. Now I knew very well that we had not come thirty miles, and had reason to believe, moreover, that the greater part of the progress we had made had been toward the north. It was not at all probable that the position of this island was unknown to our captain; and it must, therefore, have been considered by him as an unsuitable place for the landing of his passengers. There might be many reasons for this unsuitableness: the island might be totally barren and desolate; it might be the abode of unpleasant natives; and, more important than anything else, it was, in all probability, a spot where steamers never touched.

But, whatever its disadvantages, I was most wildly desirous to reach it.

"I do not believe," I said, in answer to Mrs. Lecks, "that that is the island to which the captain would have taken us; but, whatever it is, it is dry land, and we must get there as soon as we can."

"That's true," said Mrs. Aleshine, "for I'd like to have ground nearer to my feet than six miles; and if we don't find anything to eat and any place to sleep when we get there, it's no more than can be said of the place where we are now."

"You're too particular, Barb'ry Aleshine," said Mrs. Lecks, "about your comforts. If you find the ground too hard to sleep on, when you get there, you can put on your life-preserver, and go to bed in the water."

"Very good," said Mrs. Aleshine; "and if these islands are made of coral, as I've heard they are, and if they're as full of small p'ints as some coral I've got at home, you'll be glad to take a berth by me, Mrs. Lecks."

I counseled my companions to follow me as rapidly as possible, and we all pushed vigorously forward. When we had approached near enough to the island to see what sort of place it really was, we perceived that it was a low-lying spot, apparently covered with verdure, and surrounded, as far as we could see as we rose on the swells, by a rocky reef, against which a tolerably high surf was running.

Before us we could see a continuous line of white-capped breakers, and so I led my little party to the right, hoping that we would soon see signs of an opening in the reef.

We swam and paddled, however, for a long time and still the surf rolled menacingly on the rocks before us. At last we perceived, at no great distance, a spot where there seemed to be no breakers; and when we reached it we found, to our unutterable delight, that here was smooth water flowing through a wide opening in the reef.

I swam through into an open lagoon followed closely by Mrs. Lecks and Mrs. Aleshine.

The first thing that arrested our attention was a little wharf or landing-stage, erected upon the narrow beach of the island, almost opposite to us.

"As sure as I stand here," exclaimed Mrs. Lecks, who never seemed to forget her upright position, "somebody lives in this place!"

"And it isn't a stickery coral island, either," cried Mrs. Aleshine, "for that sand's as smooth as any I ever saw."

"Whoever does live here," resumed Mrs. Lecks, "has got to take us in, whether they like it or not, and the sooner we get over there the better."

Anita Loos

GENTLEMEN PREFER BLONDES *

March 16th:

A gentleman friend and I were dining at the Ritz last evening and he said that if I took a pencil and a paper and put down all of my thoughts it would make a book. This almost made me smile as what it would really make would be a whole row of encyclopediacs. I mean I seem to be thinking practically all of the time. I mean it is my favorite recreation and sometimes I sit for hours and do not seem to do anything else but think. So this gentleman said a girl with brains ought to do something else with them besides think. And he said he ought to know brains when he sees them, because he is in the senate and he spends quite a great deal of time in Washington, d. c., and when he comes into contract with brains he always notices it. So it might have all blown over but this morning he sent me a book. And so when my maid brought it to me, I said to her, "Well, Lulu, here is another book and we have not read half the ones we have got yet." But when I opened it and saw that it was all a blank I remembered what my gentleman acquaintance said, and so then I realized that it was a diary. So here I am writing a book instead of reading one.

But now it is the 16th of March and of course it is to late to begin with January, but it does not matter as my gentleman friend, Mr. Eisman, was in town practically all of January and February, and when he is in town one day seems to be practically the same as the next day.

I mean Mr. Eisman is in the wholesale button profession in Chicago and he is the gentleman who is known practically all over Chicago as Gus Eisman the Button King. And he is the gentleman who is interested in educating me, so of course he is always coming down to New York to see how my brains have improved since the last time. But when Mr. Eisman is in New York we always seem to do the

---

* *This is the first chapter of Anita Loos's novel.*

same thing and if I wrote down one day in my diary, all I would have to do would be to put quotation marks for all other days. I mean we always seem to have dinner at the Colony and see a show and go to the Trocadero and then Mr. Eisman shows me to my apartment. So of course when a gentleman is interested in educating a girl, he likes to stay and talk about the topics of the day until quite late, so I am quite fatigued the next day and I do not really get up until it is time to dress for dinner at the Colony.

It would be strange if I turn out to be an authoress. I mean at my home near Little Rock, Arkansas, my family all wanted me to do something about my music. Because all of my friends said I had talent and they all kept after me and kept after me about practising. But some way I never seemed to care so much about practising. I mean I simply could not sit for hours and hours at a time practising just for the sake of a career. So one day I got quite tempermental and threw the old mandolin clear across the room and I have really never touched it since. But writing is different because you do not have to learn or practise and it is more tempermental because practising seems to take all the temperment out of me. So now I really almost have to smile because I have just noticed that I have written clear across two pages onto March 18th, so this will do for today and tomorrow. And it just shows how tempermental I am when I get started.

March 19th:

Well last evening Dorothy called up and Dorothy said she has met a gentleman who gave himself an introduction to her in the lobby of the Ritz. So then they went to luncheon and tea and dinner and then they went to a show and then they went to the Trocadero. So Dorothy said his name was Lord Cooksleigh but what she really calls him is Coocoo. So Dorothy said why don't you and I and Coocoo go to the Follies tonight and bring Gus along if he is in town? So then Dorothy and I had quite a little quarrel because every time that Dorothy mentions the subject of Mr. Eisman she calls Mr. Eisman by his first name, and she does not seem to realize that when a gentle-man who is as important as Mr. Eisman, spends quite a lot of money educating a girl, it really does not show reverence to call a gentleman by his first name. I mean I never even think of calling Mr. Eisman by his first name, but if I want to call him anything at all, I call him

"Daddy" and I do not even call him "Daddy" if a place seems to be public. So I told Dorothy that Mr. Eisman would not be in town until day after tomorrow. So then Dorothy and Coocoo came up and we went to the Follies.

So this morning Coocoo called up and he wanted me to luncheon at the Ritz. I mean these foreigners really have quite a nerve. Just because Coocoo is an Englishman and a Lord he thinks a girl can waste hours on him just for a luncheon at the Ritz, when all he does is talk about some exposition he went on to a place called Tibet and after talking for hours I found out that all they were was a lot of Chinamen. So I will be quite glad to see Mr. Eisman when he gets in. Because he always has something quite interesting to talk about, as for instants the last time he was here he presented me with quite a beautiful emerald bracelet. So next week is my birthday and he always has some delightful surprise on holidays.

I did intend to luncheon at the Ritz with Dorothy today and of course Coocoo had to spoil it, as I told him that I could not luncheon with him today, because my brother was in town on business and had the mumps, so I really could not leave him alone. Because of course if I went to the Ritz now I would bump into Coocoo. But I sometimes almost have to smile at my own imagination, because of course I have not got any brother and I have not even thought of the mumps for years. I mean it is no wonder that I can write.

So the reason I thought I would take luncheon at the Ritz was because Mr. Chaplin is at the Ritz and I always like to renew old acquaintances, because I met Mr. Chaplin once when we were both working on the same lot in Hollywood and I am sure he would remember me. Gentlemen always seem to remember blondes. I mean the only career I would like to be besides an authoress is a cinema star and I was doing quite well in the cinema when Mr. Eisman made me give it all up. Because of course when a gentleman takes such a friendly interest in educating a girl as Mr. Eisman does, you like to show that you appreciate it, and he is against a girl being in the cinema because his mother is authrodox.

March 20th:

Mr. Eisman gets in tomorrow to be here in time for my birthday. So I thought it would really be delightful to have at least one good time before Mr. Eisman got in, so last evening I had some literary gentlemen in to spend the evening because Mr. Eisman always likes me to have literary people in and out of the apartment. I mean he is quite anxious for a girl to improve her mind and his greatest interest in me is because I always seem to want to improve my mind and not waste any time. And Mr. Eisman likes me to have what the French people call a "salo" which means that people all get together in the evening and improve their minds. So I invited all of the brainy gentlemen I could think up. So I thought up a gentleman who is the proffessor of all of the economics up at Columbia College, and the editor who is the famous editor of the New York Transcript and another gentleman who is a famous playright who writes very, very famous plays that are all about Life. I mean anybody would recognize his name but it always seems to slip my memory because all of we real friends of his only call him Sam. So Sam asked if he could bring a gentleman who writes novels from England, so I said yes, so he brought him. And then we all got together and I called up Gloria and Dorothy and the gentleman brought their own liquor. So of course the place was a wreck this morning and Lulu and I worked like proverbial dogs to get it cleaned up, but Heaven knows how long it will take to get the chandelier fixed.

March 22nd:

Well my birthday has come and gone but it was really quite depressing. I mean it seems to me a gentleman who has a friendly interest in educating a girl like Gus Eisman, would want her to have the biggest square cut diamond in New York. I mean I must say I was quite disappointed when he came to the apartment with a little thing you could hardly see. So I told him I thought it was quite cute, but I had quite a headache and I had better stay in a dark room all day and I told him I would see him the next day, perhaps. Because even Lulu thought it was quite small and she said, if she was I, she really would do something definite and she said she always believed in the old addage, "Leave them while you're looking good." But he came in at dinner time with really a very very beautiful bracelet of square cut diamonds so I was quite cheered up. So then we had dinner at the Colony and we went to a show and supper at the Trocadero as usual whenever he is in town. But I will give him credit that he realized how small it was. I mean he kept talking about how bad business was and the button profession was full of bolshevicks who make nothing but trouble. Because Mr. Eisman feels that the country is really on the verge of the bolshevicks and I become quite worried. I mean if the bolshevicks do get in, there is only one gentleman who could handle them and that is Mr. D. W. Griffith. Because I will never forget when Mr. Griffith was directing Intolerance. I mean it was my last cinema just before Mr. Eisman made me give up my career and I was playing one of the girls that fainted at the battle when all of the gentlemen fell off the tower. And when I saw how Mr. Griffith handled all of those mobs in Intolerance I realized that he could do anything, and I really think that the government of America ought to tell Mr. Griffith to get all ready if the bolshevicks start to do it.

Well I forgot to mention that the English gentleman who writes novels seems to have taken quite an interest in me, as soon as he found out that I was literary. I mean he has called up every day and I went to tea twice with him. So he has sent me a whole complete set of books for my birthday by a gentleman called Mr. Conrad. They all seem to be about ocean travel although I have not had time to more than glance through them. I have always liked novels about ocean travel ever since I posed for Mr. Christie for the front cover of a novel about ocean travel by McGrath because I always say that a girl never really looks as well as she does on board a steamship, or even a yacht.

So the English gentleman's name is Mr. Gerald Lamson as those who have read his novels would know. And he also sent me some of his own novels and they all seem to be about middle age English gentlemen who live in the country over in London and seem to ride bicycles, which seems quite different from America, except at Palm Beach. So I told Mr. Lamson how I write down all of my thoughts and he said he knew I had something to me from the first minute he saw me and when we become better acquainted I am going to let him read my diary. I mean I even told Mr. Eisman about him and he is quite pleased. Because of course Mr. Lamson is quite famous and it seems Mr. Eisman has read all of his novels going to and fro on the trains and Mr. Eisman is always anxious to meet famous people and take them to the Ritz to dinner on Saturday night. But of course I did not tell Mr. Eisman that I am really getting quite a little crush on Mr. Lamson, which I really believe I am, but Mr. Eisman thinks my interest in him is more literary.

March 30th:

At last Mr. Eisman has left on the 20th Century and I must say I am quite fatigued and a little rest will be quite welcome. I mean I do not mind staying out late every night if I dance, but Mr. Eisman is really not such a good dancer so most of the time we just sit and drink some champagne or have a bite to eat and of course I do not dance with anyone else when I am out with Mr. Eisman. But Mr. Eisman and Gerry, as Mr. Lamson wants me to call him, became quite good friends and we had several evenings, all three together. So now that Mr. Eisman is out of town at last, Gerry and I are going out together this evening and Gerry said not to dress up, because Gerry seems to like me more for my soul. So I really had to tell Gerry that if all the gentlemen were like he seems to be, Madame Frances' whole dress making establishment would have to go out of business. But Gerry does not like a girl to be nothing else but a doll, but he likes her to bring in her husband's slippers every evening and make him forget what he has gone through.

But before Mr. Eisman went to Chicago he told me that he is going to Paris this summer on professional business and I think he intends to present me with a trip to Paris as he says there is nothing so educational as traveling. I mean it did worlds of good to Dorothy when she went abroad last spring and I never get tired of hearing her telling how the merry-go-rounds in Paris have pigs instead of horses. But I really do not know whether to be thrilled or not because, of course, if I go to Paris I will have to leave Gerry and both Gerry and I have made up our minds not to be separated from one another from now on.

March 31st:

Last night Gerry and I had dinner at quite a quaint place where we had roast beef and baked potato. I mean he always wants me to have food which is what he calls "nourishing," which most gentlemen never seem to think about. So then we took a hansom cab and drove for hours around the park because Gerry said the air would be good for me. It is really very sweet to have some one think of all those things that gentlemen hardly ever seem to think about. So then we talked quite a lot. I mean Gerry knows how to draw a girl out and I told him things that I really would not even put in my diary. So when he heard all about my life he became quite depressed and we both had tears in our eyes. Because he said he never dreamed a girl could go through so much as I, and come out so sweet and not made bitter by it all. I mean Gerry thinks that most gentlemen are brutes and hardly ever think about a girl's soul.

So it seems that Gerry has had quite a lot of trouble himself and he can not even get married on account of his wife. He and she have never been in love with each other but she was a suffragette and asked him to marry her, so what could he do? So we rode all around the park until quite late talking and philosophizing quite a lot and I finally told him that I thought, after all, that bird life was the highest form of civilization. So Gerry calls me his little thinker and I really would not be surprised if all of my thoughts will give him quite a few ideas for his novels. Because Gerry says he has never seen a girl of my personal appearance with so many brains. And he had almost given up looking for his ideal when our paths seemed to cross each other and I told him I really thought a thing like that was nearly always the result of fate.

So Gerry says that I remind him quite a lot of Helen of Troy, who was of Greek extraction. But the only Greek I know is a Greek gentleman by the name of Mr. Georgopolis who is really quite wealthy and he is what Dorothy and I call a "Shopper" because you can always call him up at any hour and ask him to go shopping and he is always quite delighted, which very few gentlemen seem to be. And he never seems to care how much anything costs. I mean Mr. Georgopolis is also quite cultured, as I know quite a few gentlemen who can speak to a waiter in French but Mr. Georgopolis can also speak to a waiter in Greek which very few gentlemen seem to be able to do.

April 1st:
I am taking special pains with my diary from now on as I am really writing it for Gerry. I mean he and I are going to read it together some evening in front of the fireplace. But Gerry leaves this evening for Boston as he has to lecture about all of his works at Boston, but he will rush right back as soon as possible. So I am going to spend all of my time improving myself while he is gone. And this afternoon we are both going to a museum on 5th Avenue, because Gerry wants to show me a very very beautiful cup made by an antique jeweler called Mr. Cellini and he wants me to read Mr. Cellini's life which is a very very fine book and not dull while he is in Boston.

So the famous playright friend of mine who is called Sam called up this morning and he wanted me to go to a literary party tonight that he and some other literary gentlemen are giving to Florence Mills in Harlem but Gerry does not want me to go with Sam as Sam always insists on telling riskay stories. But personally I am quite broad minded and I always say that I do not mind a riskay story as long as it is really funny. I mean I have a great sense of humor. But Gerry says Sam does not always select and choose his stories and he just as soon I did not go out with him. So I am going to stay home and read the book by Mr. Cellini instead, because, after all, the only thing I am really interested in, is improving my mind. So I am going to do nothing else but improve my mind while Gerry is in Boston. I mean I just received a cable from Willie Gwynn who arrives from Europe tomorrow, but I am not even going to bother to see him. He is a sweet boy but he never gets anywhere and I am not going to waste my time on such as him, after meeting a gentleman like Gerry.

April 2nd:

I seem to be quite depressed this morning as I always am when there is nothing to put my mind to. Because I decided not to read the book by Mr. Cellini. I mean it was quite amuseing in spots because it was really quite riskay but the spots were not so close together and I never seem to like to always be hunting clear through a book for the spots I am looking for, especially when there are really not so many spots that seem to be so amuseing after all. So I did not waste my time on it but this morning I told Lulu to let all of the house work go and spend the day reading a book entitled "Lord Jim" and then tell me all about it, so that I would improve my mind while Gerry is away. But when I got her the book I nearly made a mistake and gave her a book by the title of "The Nigger of the Narcissus" which really would have hurt her feelings. I mean I do not know why authors cannot say "Negro" instead of "Nigger" as they have their feelings just the same as we have.

Well I just got a telegram from Gerry that he will not be back until tomorrow and also some orchids from Willie Gwynn, so I may as well go to the theatre with Willie tonight to keep from getting depressed, as he really is a sweet boy after all. I mean he never really does anything obnoxious. And it is quite depressing to stay at home and do nothing but read, unless you really have a book that is worth bothering about.

April 3rd:

I was really so depressed this morning that I was even glad to get a letter from Mr. Eisman. Because last night Willie Gwynn came to take me to the Follies, but he was so intoxicated that I had to telephone his club to send around a taxi to take him home. So that left me alone with Lulu at nine o'clock with nothing to do, so I put in a telephone call for Boston to talk to Gerry but it never went through. So Lulu tried to teach me how to play mah jong, but I really could not keep my mind on it because I was so depressed. So today I think I had better go over to Madame Frances and order some new evening gowns to cheer me up.

Well Lulu just brought me a telegram from Gerry that he will be in this afternoon, but I must not meet him at the station on account of all of the reporters who always meet him at the station wherever he comes from. But he says he will come right up to see me as he has something to talk about.

April 4th:

What an evening we had last evening. I mean it seems that Gerry is madly in love with me. Because all of the time he was in Boston lecturing to the womens clubs he said, as he looked over the faces of all those club women in Boston, he never realized I was so beautiful. And he said that there was only one in all the world and that was me. But it seems that Gerry thinks that Mr. Eisman is terrible and that no good can come of our friendship. I mean I was quite surprised, as they both seemed to get along quite well together, but it seems that Gerry never wants me to see Mr. Eisman again. And he wants me to give up everything and study French and he will get a divorce and we will be married. Because Gerry does not seem to like the kind of life all of us lead in New York and he wants me to go home to papa in Arkansas and he will send me books to read so that I will not get lonesome there. And he gave me his uncle's Masonic ring, which came down from the time of Soloman and which he never even lets his wife wear, for our engagement ring, and this afternoon a lady friend of his is going to bring me a new system she thought up of how to learn French. But some way I still seem to be depressed. I mean I could not sleep all night thinking of the terrible things. Gerry said about New York and about Mr. Eisman. Of course I can understand Gerry being jealous of any gentleman friend of mine and of course I never really thought that Mr. Eisman was Rudolph Valentino, but Gerry said it made him cringe to think of a sweet girl like I having a friendship with Mr. Eisman. So it really made me feel quite depressed. I mean Gerry likes to talk quite a lot and I always think a lot of talk is depressing and worries your brains with things you never even think of when you are busy. But so long as Gerry does not mind me going out with other gentlemen when they have something to give you mentally, I am going to luncheon with Eddie Goldmark of the Goldmark Films who is always wanting me to sign a contract to go into the cinema. Because Mr. Goldmark is madly in love with Dorothy and Dorothy is always wanting me to go back in the cinema because Dorothy says that she will go if I will go.

April 6th:
Well I finally wrote Mr. Eisman that I was going to get married and it seems that he is coming on at once as he would probably like to give me his advice. Getting married is really quite serious and Gerry talks to me for hours and hours about it. I mean he never seems to get tired of talking and he does not seem to even want to go to shows or dance or do anything else but talk, and if I don't really have something definite to put my mind on soon I will scream.

April 7th:
Well Mr. Eisman arrived this morning and he and I had quite a long talk, and after all I think he is right. Because here is the first real opportunity I have ever really had. I mean to go to Paris and broaden out and improve my writing, and why should I give it up to marry an author, where he is the whole thing and all I would be would be the wife of Gerald Lamson? And on top of that I would have to be dragged into the scandal of a divorce court and get my name smirched. So Mr. Eisman said that opportunities come to seldom in a girls life for me to give up the first one I have really ever had. So I am sailing for France and London on Tuesday and taking Dorothy with me and Mr. Eisman says that he will see us there later. So Dorothy knows all of the ropes and she can get along in Paris just as though she knew French and besides she knows a French gentleman who was born and raised there, and speaks it like

a native and knows Paris like a book. And Dorothy says that, when we get to London nearly everybody speaks English anyway. So it is quite lucky that Mr. Lamson is out lecturing in Cincinnati and he will not be back until Wednesday and I can send him a letter and tell him that I have to go to Europe now but I will see him later perhaps. So anyway I will be spared listening to any more of his depressing conversation. So Mr. Eisman gave me quite a nice string of pearls and he gave Dorothy a diamond pin and we all went to the Colony for dinner and we all went to a show and supper at the Trocadero and we all spent quite a pleasant evening.

Sinclair Lewis

GEORGE F. BABBITT STARTS THE DAY*

The towers of Zenith aspired above the morning mist; austere towers of steel and cement and limestone, sturdy as cliffs and delicate as silver rods. They were neither citadels nor churches, but frankly and beautifully office-buildings.

The mist took pity on the fretted structures of earlier generations: the Post Office with its shingle-tortured mansard, the red brick minarets of hulking old houses, factories with stingy and sooted windows, wooden tenements colored like mud. The city was full of such grotesqueries, but the clean towers were thrusting them from the business center, and on the farther hills were shining new houses, homes—they seemed—for laughter and tranquillity.

Over a concrete bridge fled a limousine of long sleek hood and noiseless engine. These people in evening clothes were returning from an all-night rehearsal of a Little Theater play, an artistic adventure considerably illuminated by champagne. Below the bridge curved a railroad, a maze of green and crimson lights. The New York Flyer boomed past, and twenty lines of polished steel leaped into the glare.

In one of the skyscrapers the wires of the Associated Press were closing down. The telegraph operators wearily raised their celluloid eye-shades after a night of talking with Paris and Peking. Through the building crawled the scrubwomen, yawning, their old shoes slapping. The dawn mist spun away. Cues of men with lunch-boxes clumped toward the immensity of new factories, sheets of glass and hollow tile, glittering shops where five thousand men worked beneath one roof, pouring out the honest wares that would be sold up the Euphrates and across the veldt. The whistles rolled out in greeting a chorus cheerful as the April dawn; the song of labor in a city built—it seemed—for giants.

*This is the first chapter of Sinclair Lewis's novel "Babbitt."

There was nothing of the giant in the aspect of the man who was beginning to awaken on the sleeping-porch of a Dutch Colonial house in that residential district of Zenith known as Floral Heights.

His name was George F. Babbitt. He was forty-six years old now, in April, 1920, and he made nothing in particular, neither butter nor shoes nor poetry, but he was nimble in the calling of selling houses for more than people could afford to pay.

His large head was pink, his brown hair thin and dry. His face was babyish in slumber, despite his wrinkles and the red spectacle-dents on the slopes of his nose. He was not fat but he was exceedingly well fed; his cheeks were pads, and the unroughened hand which lay helpless upon the khaki-colored blanket was slightly puffy. He seemed prosperous, extremely married and unromantic; and altogether unromantic appeared this sleeping-porch, which looked on one sizable elm, two respectable grass-plots, a cement driveway, and a corrugated iron garage. Yet Babbitt was again dreaming of the fairy child, a dream more romantic than scarlet pagodas by a silver sea.

For years the fairy child had come to him. Where others saw but Georgie Babbitt, she discerned gallant youth. She waited for him, in the darkness beyond mysterious groves. When at last he could slip away from the crowded house he darted to her. His wife, his clamoring friends, sought to follow, but he escaped, the girl fleet beside him, and they crouched together on a shadowy hillside. She was so slim, so white, so eager! She cried that he was gay and valiant, that she would wait for him, that they would sail—

Rumble and bang of the milk-truck.

Babbitt moaned, turned over, struggled back toward his dream. He could see only her face now, beyond misty waters. The furnace-man slammed the basement door. A dog barked in the next yard. As Babbitt sank blissfully into a dim warm tide, the paper-carrier went by whistling, and the rolled-up *Advocate* thumped the front door. Babbitt roused, his stomach constricted with alarm. As he relaxed, he was pierced by the familiar and irritating rattle of some one cranking a Ford: snap-ah-ah, snap-ah-ah, snap-ah-ah. Himself a pious motorist, Babbitt cranked with the unseen driver, with him waited through taut hours for the roar of the starting engine, with him agonized as the roar ceased and again began the infernal patient snap-ah-ah—a round, flat sound, a shivering cold-morning sound, a sound infuriating and inescapable. Not till the rising voice of the motor told him that the Ford was moving was he released from the panting tension. He glanced once at his favorite tree, elm twigs against the gold patina of sky, and fumbled for sleep as for a drug. He who had been a boy very credulous of life was no longer greatly interested in the possible and improbable adventures of each new day.

He escaped from reality till the alarm-clock rang, at seven-twenty.

It was the best of nationally advertised and quantitatively produced alarm-clocks, with all modern attachments, including cathedral chime, intermittent alarm, and a phosphorescent dial. Babbitt was proud of being awakened by such a rich device. Socially it was almost as creditable as buying expensive cord tires.

He sulkily admitted now that there was no more escape, but he lay and detested the grind of the real-estate business, and disliked his family, and disliked himself for disliking them. The evening before, he had played poker at Vergil Gunch's till midnight, and after such holidays he was irritable before breakfast. It may have been the tremendous home-brewed beer of the prohibition-era and the cigars to which that beer enticed him; it may have been resentment of return from this fine, bold man-world to a restricted region of wives and stenographers, and of suggestions not to smoke so much.

From the bedroom beside the sleeping-porch, his wife's detestably cheerful "Time to get up, Georgie boy," and the itchy sound, the brisk and scratchy sound, of combing hairs out of a stiff brush.

He grunted; he dragged his thick legs, in faded baby-blue pajamas, from under the khaki blanket; he sat on the edge of the cot, running his fingers through his wild hair, while his plump feet mechanically felt for his slippers. He looked regretfully at the blanket—forever a suggestion to him of freedom and heroism. He had bought it for a camping trip which had never come off. It symbolized gorgeous loafing, gorgeous cursing, virile flannel shirts.

He creaked to his feet, groaning at the waves of pain which passed behind his eyeballs. Though he waited for their scorching recurrence, he looked blurrily out at the yard. It delighted him, as always; it was the neat yard of a successful business man of Zenith, that is, it was perfection, and made him also perfect. He regarded the corrugated iron garage. For the three-hundred-and-sixty-fifth time in a year he reflected, "No class to that tin shack. Have to build me a frame garage. But by golly it's the only thing on the place that isn't up-to-date!" While he stared he thought of a community garage for his acreage development, Glen Oriole. He stopped puffing and jiggling. His arms were akimbo. His petulant, sleep-swollen face was set in harder lines. He suddenly seemed capable, an official, a man to contrive, to direct, to get things done.

On the vigor of his idea he was carried down the hard, clean, unused-looking hall into the bathroom.

Though the house was not large it had, like all houses on Floral Heights, an altogether royal bathroom of porcelain and glazed tile and metal sleek as silver. The towel-rack was a rod of clear glass set in nickel. The tub was long enough for a Prussian Guard, and above the set bowl was a sensational exhibit of tooth-brush holder, shaving-brush holder, soap-dish, sponge-dish, and medicine-cabinet, so glittering and so ingenious that they resembled an electrical instrument-board. But the Babbitt whose god was Modern Appliances was not pleased. The air of the bathroom was thick with the smell of a heathen toothpaste. "Verona been at it again! 'Stead of sticking to Lilidol, like I've re-peat-ed-ly asked her, she's gone and gotten some confounded stinkum stuff that makes you sick!"

The bath-mat was wrinkled and the floor was wet. (His daughter Verona eccentrically took baths in the morning, now and then.) He slipped on the mat, and slid against the tub. He said "Damn!" Furiously he snatched up his tube of shaving-cream, furiously he lathered, with a belligerent slapping of the unctuous brush, furiously he raked his plump cheeks with a safety-razor. It pulled. The blade was dull. He said, "Damn—oh—oh—damn it!"

He hunted through the medicine-cabinet for a packet of new razor-blades (reflecting, as invariably, "Be cheaper to buy one of these dinguses and strop your own blades,") and when he discovered the packet, behind the round box of bicarbonate of soda, he thought ill of his wife for putting it there and very well of himself for not saying "Damn." But he did say it, immediately afterward, when with wet and soap-slippery fingers he tried to remove the horrible little envelope and crisp clinging oiled paper from the new blade.

Then there was the problem, oft-pondered, never solved, of what to do with the old blade, which might imperil the fingers of his young. As usual, he tossed it on top of the medicine-cabinet, with a mental note that some day he must remove the fifty or sixty other blades that were also, temporarily, piled up there. He finished his shaving in a growing testiness increased by his spinning headache and by the emptiness in his stomach. When he was done, his round face smooth and streamy and his eyes stinging from soapy water, he reached for a towel. The family towels were wet, wet and clammy and vile, all of them wet, he found, as he blindly snatched them—his own face-towel, his wife's, Verona's, Ted's, Tinka's, and the lone bath-towel with the huge welt of initial. Then George F. Babbitt did a dismaying thing. He wiped his face on the guest-towel! It was a pansy-embroidered trifle which always hung there to indicate that the Babbitts were in the best Floral Heights society. No one had ever used it. No guest had ever dared to. Guests secretively took a corner of the nearest regular towel.

He was raging, "By golly, here they go and use up all the towels, every doggone one of 'em, and they use 'em and get 'em all wet and sopping, and never put out a dry one for me—of course, I'm the goat!—and then I want one and—I'm the only person in the doggone house that's got the slightest doggone bit of consideration for other people and thoughtfulness and consider there may be others that may want to use the doggone bathroom after me and consider—"

He was pitching the chill abominations into the bath-tub, pleased by the vindictiveness of that desolate flapping sound; and in the midst his wife serenely trotted in, observed serenely, "Why Georgie dear, what are you doing? Are you going to wash out the towels? Why, you needn't wash out the towels. Oh, Georgie, you didn't go and use the guest-towel, did you?"

It is not recorded that he was able to answer.

For the first time in weeks he was sufficiently roused by his wife to look at her.

Myra Babbitt—Mrs. George F. Babbitt—was definitely mature. She had creases from the corners of her mouth to the bottom of her chin, and her plump neck bagged. But the thing that marked her as having passed the line was that she no longer had reticences before her husband, and no longer worried about not having reticences. She was in a petticoat now, and corsets which bulged, and unaware of being seen in bulgy corsets. She had become so dully habituated to married life that in her full matronliness she was as sexless as an anemic nun. She was a good woman, a kind woman, a diligent woman, but no one, save perhaps Tinka her ten-year-old, was at all interested in her or entirely aware that she was alive.

After a rather thorough discussion of all the domestic and social aspects of towels she apologized to Babbitt for his having an alcoholic headache; and he recovered enough to endure the search for a B.V.D. undershirt which had, he pointed out, malevolently been concealed among his clean pajamas.

He was fairly amiable in the conference on the brown suit.

"What do you think, Myra?" He pawed at the clothes hunched on a chair in their bedroom, while she moved about mysteriously adjusting and patting her petticoat and, to his jaundiced eye, never seeming to get on with her dressing. "How about it? Shall I wear the brown suit another day?"

"Well, it looks awfully nice on you."

"I know, but gosh, it needs pressing."

"That's so. Perhaps it does."

"It certainly could stand being pressed, all right."

"Yes, perhaps it wouldn't hurt it to be pressed."

"But gee, the coat doesn't need pressing. No sense in having the whole darn suit pressed, when the coat doesn't need it."

"That's so."

"But the pants certainly need it, all right. Look at them—look at those wrinkles—the pants certainly do need pressing."

"That's so. Oh, Georgie, why couldn't you wear the brown coat with the blue trousers we were wondering what we'd do with them?"

"Good Lord! Did you ever in all my life know me to wear the coat of one suit and the pants of another? What do you think I am? A busted bookkeeper?"

"Well, why don't you put on the dark gray suit to-day, and stop in at the tailor and leave the brown trousers?"

"Well, they certainly need— Now where the devil is that gray suit? Oh, yes, here we are."

He was able to get through the other crises of dressing with comparative resoluteness and calm.

His first adornment was the sleeveless dimity B.V.D. undershirt, in which he resembled a small boy humorlessly wearing a cheese-cloth tabard at a civic pageant. He never put on B.V.D.'s without thanking the God of Progress that he didn't wear tight, long, old-fashioned undergarments, like his father-in-law and partner, Henry Thompson. His second embellishment was combing and slicking back his hair. It gave him a tremendous forehead, arching up two inches beyond the former hair-line. But most wonder-working of all was the donning of his spectacles.

There is character in spectacles—the pretentious tortoise-shell, the meek pince-nez of the school teacher, the twisted silver-framed glasses of the old villager. Babbitt's spectacles had huge, circular, frameless lenses of the very best glass; the ear-pieces were thin bars of gold. In them he was the modern business man; one who gave orders to clerks and drove a car and played occasional golf and was scholarly in regard to Salesmanship. His head suddenly appeared not babyish but weighty, and you noted his heavy, blunt nose, his straight mouth and thick, long upper lip, his chin overfleshy but strong; with respect you beheld him put on the rest of his uniform as a Solid Citizen.

The gray suit was well cut, well made, and completely undistinguished. It was a standard suit. White piping on the V of the vest added a flavor of law and learning. His shoes were black laced boots, good boots, honest boots, standard boots, extraordinarily uninteresting boots. The only frivolity was in his purple knitted scarf. With considerable comment on the matter to Mrs. Babbitt (who, acrobatically fastening the back of her blouse to her skirt with a safety-pin, did not hear a word he said) he chose between the purple scarf and a tapestry effect with stringless brown harps among blown palms, and into it he thrust a snake-head pin with opal eyes.

A sensational event was changing from the brown suit to the gray the contents of his pockets. He was earnest about these objects. They were of eternal importance, like baseball or the Republican Party. They included a fountain pen and a silver pencil (always lacking a supply of new leads) which belonged in the right-hand upper vest pocket. Without them he would have felt naked. On his watch-chain were a gold penknife, silver cigar cutter, seven keys (the use of two of which he had forgotten), and incidentally a good watch. Depending from the chain was a large, yellowish elk's-tooth—proclamation of his membership in the Benevolent and Protective Order of Elks. Most significant of all was his loose-leaf pocket note-book, that modern and efficient note-book which contained the addresses of people whom he had forgotten, prudent memoranda of postal money-orders which had reached their destinations months ago, stamps which had lost their mucilage, clippings of verse by T. Cholmondeley Frink and of the newspaper editorials from which Babbitt got his opinions and his polysyllables, notes to be sure and do things which he did not intend to do, and one curious inscription—D.S.S.D.M.Y.P.D.F.

But he had no cigarette-case. No one had ever happened to give him one, so he hadn't the habit, and people who carried cigarette-cases he regarded as effeminate.

Last, he stuck in his lapel the Boosters' Club button. With the conciseness of great art the button displayed two words: "Boosters—Pep!" It made Babbitt feel loyal and important. It associated him with Good Fellows, with men who were nice and human, and important in business circles. It was his V.C., his Legion of Honor ribbon, his Phi Beta Kappa key.

With the subtleties of dressing ran other complex worries. "I feel kind of punk this morning," he said. "I think I had too much dinner last evening. You oughtn't to serve those heavy banana fritters."

"But you asked me to have some."

"I know, but— I tell you, when a fellow gets past forty he has to look after his digestion. There's a lot of fellows that don't take proper care of themselves. I tell you at forty a man's a fool or his doctor—I mean, his own doctor. Folks don't give enough attention to this matter of dieting. Now I think— Course a man ought to have a good meal after the day's work, but it would be a good thing for both of us if we took lighter lunches."

"But Georgie, here at home I always do have a light lunch."

"Mean to imply I make a hog of myself, eating down-town? Yes, sure! You'd have a swell time if you had to eat the truck that new steward hands out to us at the Athletic Club! But I certainly do feel out of sorts, this morning. Funny, got a pain down here on the left side —but no, that wouldn't be appendicitis, would it? Last night, when I was driving over to Verg Gunch's, I felt a pain in my stomach, too. Right here it was—kind of a sharp shooting pain. I— Where'd that dime go to? Why don't you serve more prunes at breakfast? Of course I eat an apple every evening—an apple a day keeps the doctor away—but still, you ought to have more prunes, and not all these fancy doodads."

"The last time I had prunes you didn't eat them."

"Well, I didn't feel like eating 'em, I suppose. Matter of fact, I think I did eat some of 'em. Anyway— I tell you it's mighty important to—

I was saying to Verg Gunch, just last evening, most people don't take sufficient care of their diges—"

"Shall we have the Gunches for our dinner, next week?"

"Why sure; you bet."

"Now see here, George: I want you to put on your nice dinner-jacket that evening."

"Rats! The rest of 'em won't want to dress."

"Of course they will. You remember when you didn't dress for the Littlefields' supper-party, and all the rest did, and how embarrassed you were."

"Embarrassed, hell! I wasn't embarrassed. Everybody knows I can put on as expensive a Tux. as anybody else, and I should worry if I don't happen to have it on sometimes. All a darn nuisance, anyway. All right for a woman, that stays around the house all the time, but when a fellow's worked like the dickens all day, he doesn't want to go and hustle his head off getting into the soup-and-fish for a lot of folks that he's seen in just reg'lar ordinary clothes that same day."

"You know you enjoy being seen in one. The other evening you admitted you were glad I'd insisted on your dressing. You said you felt a lot better for it. And oh, Georgie, I do wish you wouldn't say 'Tux.' It's 'dinner-jacket.'"

"Rats, what's the odds?"

"Well, it's what all the nice folks say. Suppose Lucile McKelvey heard you calling it a 'Tux.'"

"Well, that's all right now! Lucile McKelvey can't pull anything on me! Her folks are common as mud, even if her husband and her dad are millionaires! I suppose you're trying to rub in *your* exalted social position! Well, let me tell you that your revered paternal ancestor, Henry T., doesn't even call it a 'Tux'! He calls it a 'bob-tail jacket for a ringtail monkey,' and you couldn't get him into one unless you chloroformed him!"

"Now don't be horrid, George."

"Well, I don't want to be horrid, but Lord! you're getting as fussy as Verona. Ever since she got out of college she's been too ram-bunctious to live with—doesn't know what she wants—well, I know what she wants!—all she wants is to marry a millionaire, and live in Europe, and hold some preacher's hand, and simultaneously at the same time stay right here in Zenith and be some blooming kind of a socialist agitator or boss charity-worker or some damn thing!

Lord, and Ted is just as bad! He wants to go to college, and he doesn't want to go to college. Only one of the three that knows her own mind is Tinka. Simply can't understand how I ever came to have a pair of shillyshallying children like Rone and Ted. I may not be any Rockefeller or James J. Shakespeare, but I certainly do know my own mind, and I do keep right on plugging along in the office and— Do you know the latest? Far as I can figure out, Ted's new bee is he'd like to be a movie actor and— And here I've told him a hundred times, if he'll go to college and law-school and make good, I'll set him up in business and— Verona just exactly as bad. Doesn't know what she wants. Well, well, come on! Aren't you ready yet? The girl rang the bell three minutes ago."

Before he followed his wife, Babbitt stood at the westernmost window of their room. This residential settlement, Floral Heights, was on a rise; and though the center of the city was three miles away— Zenith had between three and four hundred thousand inhabitants now—he could see the top of the Second National Tower, an Indiana limestone building of thirty-five stories.

Its shining walls rose against April sky to a simple cornice like a streak of white fire. Integrity was in the tower, and decision. It bore its strength lightly as a tall soldier. As Babbitt stared, the nervousness was soothed from his face, his slack chin lifted in reverence. All he articulated was "That's one lovely sight!" but he was inspired by the rhythm of the city; his love of it renewed. He beheld the tower as a temple-spire of the religion of business, a faith passionate, exalted, surpassing common men; and as he clumped down to breakfast he whistled the ballad "Oh, by gee, by gosh, by jingo" as though it were a hymn melancholy and noble.

John Mosher

LADY'S ROOM

Cousin Millicent Opal was the immediate cause of Mr. Opal's new room. Cousin Millicent was an elderly maiden lady of independent means and somewhat mystical tastes, and she had several times indicated a curiosity about his Fire Island hideaway. The politest and most tentative woman in the world, she could yet manage to make her whims imperative. Early in the spring, Mr. Opal found himself enclosing what had been an upstairs porch and with discretion furnishing a room which, he decided, would be primarily designed for female guests. It was by no means a large room—only one female guest could be accommodated at a time—and yet, as he went on with his arrangements, he became amazed at the magnitude of this seemingly simple undertaking.

"My approach to the whole problem," he said to his neighbor, Miss Penelope Asia, "is the psychological rather than the decorative. I have a number of lady friends and they are all different. I am trying to adapt this small room to the needs of each one."

Miss Asia's dachshund, Aspiration, was barking madly at the catbirds and she had to shout at him to stop. "Try to get used to the birds," she exclaimed. "God knows, all the rest of us have to."

"I hope you won't say anything like that to Cousin Millicent," said Mr. Opal. "She is a member of the Audubon Society. I want you ladies to keep on good terms down here. After all, we are on an island."

"That's why you have that Audubon print on the wall, I suppose," said Miss Asia. "Well, it's cheerful. And I like the white walls."

"White seemed to me suitable for all women," said Mr. Opal. "A general cool effect. Calming to the nerves. I always dread tantrums."

"It's light," remarked Miss Asia. "Some women like to sleep late. I can imagine your Cousin Millicent will be up at the crack of dawn from what you say, but what about the other types? That little Miss

67

Bailey you like so much—I am sure she doesn't go in for the dawn. At least from the wrong end, so to speak."

Mr. Opal pointed out the heavy dark shades which should, he thought, reconcile even Miss Bailey and her kind to the hardships of beach life. It was obvious that he had made an intensive study of all the peculiarities of the female sex. As he looked about the finished room, he felt confident that he had not overlooked any caprice of his imminent guests. He had, he told Miss Asia, searched all over town for this wicker chair, placed now in the most appropriate corner. It was a rather old-fashioned affair, with a large side pocket built into it, convenient for magazines, books, and knitting. Beside it, for a more sportive character, he had placed a trim little table with a bright-blue top of some modernistic resistant material that wouldn't develop rings.

"I am not unaware," said Mr. Opal, "that one or two of the ladies I know enjoy a little private sip of something."

"Miss Bailey?" said Miss Asia.

Mr. Opal ventured to remark that perhaps Miss Asia was not really devoted to Miss Bailey, but conceded that he could visualize Miss Bailey spread out in the armchair for an afternoon of reflection with a tall glass on the table beside her.

"And after two or three hours of reflection," said Miss Asia, "I can visualize her, too, pulling the dunes down."

Evading useless argument, Mr. Opal pointed to the writing table, which he had placed with care for the lighting. It was the smallest writing table he had been able to unearth in any of the shops, and it was the ideal morsel of furniture for a lady's epistolary needs—the penning of occasional checks, the notations in a diary, the answers to invitations, and the tender notes, on scented paper, of exquisite sentiment. For a letter of condolence it was surely perfect. That some women might demand more he knew and was prepared for. The lady with a portable typewriter and a briefcase could, of course, be accommodated. Such special products could make use of a folding table, concealed at the moment in the closet. Or literary types might prefer to move the mirror off the dressing table and make use of that for their work. Such women were generally husky and resourceful, and Mr. Opal felt no great concern about them. "To any woman of enterprise or creative ability," he explained, "I shall just hand over the whole house at once. I might as well do it at the beginning as a bit later."

Even Miss Asia had to concede that he had thought of practically everything and that the room was really rather attractive, too, though decoration had not been his aim. He was, she could see, prepared now for the intellectual woman, the homebody, the flibbertigibbet, the dreamer, the dressy and active type, the young, and those beyond their first youth. She herself could think of nothing that he need add.

Being thus so beautifully ready for guests—or a guest, rather—Mr. Opal suddenly discovered that no one was turning up. Cousin Millicent wrote that she had changed her mind and was going to the mountains; she would come next year; she couldn't possibly manage the beach this summer; she was so disappointed. Mr. Opal made a tentative grab for Miss Bailey, but Miss Bailey was having the time of her life, curiously enough, in the steamy environs of Nyack and couldn't be lured away. For a while it seemed that this studied sanctuary, this room that was a valentine to womanhood itself, would remain unoccupied, unappreciated. Then, all at once, it was Miss Asia who came to Mr. Opal's rescue.

She came running, breathless. "You've got to help me out," she cried. "My house is absolutely crammed. There isn't even a single free couch. And I've just got this telegram, sent up from Ocean Beach —they kept it there overnight—they always do—sleep on them. Cora Wind is coming on the next boat. She'll be here in ten minutes."

Mr. Opal had never heard of Cora Wind, but he said he would be delighted to place his guest room at her disposal, and then he began to sense from a word or two of Miss Asia's that there was something mysterious in the air. The last person on earth, it seemed, that Miss Asia expected to see out here on Fire Island, just at this time, was Mrs. Wind. "The woman must be insane to make such a trip now," Miss Asia said. "But, of course, that is the way some women are affected."

Miss Asia didn't stop to explain but rushed off to meet the boat, promising to bring Mrs. Wind straight back with her from the dock. The whole thing seemed ominous. Mr. Opal hoped his first guest would not be a mental case. With a vague sense of approaching calamity, he went to the room, opened a window or two, saw that it was ready. He was glad the room was far enough from his own so that if Mrs. Wind had an acute melancholia he wouldn't hear her crying all night.

Mrs. Wind was not melancholy. She was, on the other hand, simply beaming with health and good humor, but even to Mr. Opal, a bachelor, no family man at all, it was perfectly apparent why Miss Asia had been amazed to find Mrs. Wind coming to Fire Island. Naturally, Mrs. Wind must know what she is doing, he thought. And, of course, a woman in her condition must have had expert medical advice. People couldn't be certain, though, about such things. Dates got mixed. Wasn't there supposed to be some mental state which accompanied the physical manifestations and led women to all sorts of unreasonable behavior? Like this, for instance? Like coming on this wild trip?

Pale, he threw open the door and showed his guest her room. Somehow they would have to, come what might, get through the night.

"And I thought," Mr. Opal said to himself, "that I was ready for everything."

Edward Streeter

TWO LETTERS FROM A ROOKIE TO HIS GIRL*

Dere Mable:

Having nothin better to do I take up my pen to rite.

We have been here now three weeks. As far as I am concerned I am all ready to go. I told the Captin that I was ready any time. He said yes, but that wed have to wait for the slow ones cause they was all goin together. I says was I to go out to drill with the rest. He said yes more for the example than anything else. Its kind of maddening to be hangin round here when I might be over there helpin the Sammies put a stop to this thing.

In the mean time I been doin guard duty. Seems like I been doin it every night but I know what there up against and I dont say nothin. Guard duty is something like extemperaneus speakin. You got to know everything your goin to say before you start. Its very tecknickle. For instance you walk a post but there aint no post. An you mount guard but you dont really mount nothin. An you turn out the guard but you dont really turn em out. They come out them selves. Just the other night I was walkin along thinkin of you Mable an my feet which was hurtin. It made me awful lonesome. An officer come up and he says why dont you draw your pistol when you here someone comin. An I says I dont wait till the sheep is stole I drew it this afternoon from the Supply sargent. An I showed it to him tucked inside my shirt where noone could get it away from me without some tussel, you bet, Mable. But it seems that you got to keep on drawin it all the time. Then later I here footsteps. I was expectin the relief so I was right on the job. An a man come up and I poked my pistol right in his face and says Halt. Who goes there? And he says Officer of the day. An bein disappointed as who wouldnt be I says Oh hell I thought it was the relief. And he objected to that. The relief, Mable—but whats the use you wouldn't understand it.

From "Dere Mable."

71

Theres some mistake up north Mable about the way were built, Mable. Its kind of depresin to think that you could forget about us so quick. Everyones gettin sweters without sleeves and gloves without fingers. We still got everything we started with Mable. Why not sox without feet and pants without legs. If your makin these things for after the war I think your anticipatin a little. Besides its depresin for the fellos to be reminded all the time. Its like givin a fello a life membership to the Old Soldiers home to cheer him up when he sails. I was sayin the other day that if the fellos at Washington ever get onto this theyll be issuin soleles shoes and shirtles sleves.

Its gettin awful cold. No wonder this is a healthy place. All the germs is froze. I guess there idea of the hardenin proces is to freeze a fello stiff. The Captin said the other day we was gettin in tents of trainin. Thats all right but Id kind of like to see those steam heated barraks. Youve red about those fellos that go swimmin in the ice in winter. I guess thed like our shouer baths. They say Cleanliness is next to Godliness, Mable. I say its next to impossible.

I started this letter almost a weak ago. I just found it in my bakin can. They call it a bakin can but its too small to bake nothin. I keep my soap in it. I got some news for you. The regiment is to be dismantled. The Captin called me over this mornin and asked me where Id like to be transferred. I said home if it was the same to him. So there goin to send me to the artillery. This is a very dangerous and useful limb of the servus, Mable. I dont kno my address. Just write me care of the General.

I got the red muffler that your mother sent me. Give her my love just the same

yours relentlessly,
Bill.

Dere Mable:

I havnt rote for some time I had such sore feet lately. When they broke up our regiment and sent me over to the artillery I thought I was goin to quit usin my feet. That was just another roomor.

Thanks for the box of stuff you sent me. I guess the brakeman must have used it for a chair all the way. It was pretty well baled but that dont matter. And thanks for the fudge too. That was fudge wasnt it, Mable? And the sox. They dont fit but I can use them for somethin. A good soldier never throws nothin away. An thank your mother for the half pair of gloves she sent me. I put them away. Maybe sometime shell get a chance to nit the other half. Or if I ever get all my fingers shot off theyll come in very handy.

The artillerys a little different from the infantry. They make us work harder. At least theres more work on the skedule. I know now what they mean when they say that the "artillerys active on the western front."

They got a drill over here called the standin gun drill. The names misleadin. I guess it was invented by a troop of Jap akrobats. They make you get up and sit on the gun. Before you can get settled comfortable they make you get down again. It looks like they didnt know just what they did want you to do.

I dont like the sargent. I dont like any sargent but this one particular. The first day out he kept sayin "Prepare to mount" and then "Mount." Finally I went up to him and told him that as far as I was concerned he could cut that stuff for I was always prepared to do what I was told even though it was the middle of the night. He said, Fine, then I was probably prepared to scrub pans all day Sunday.

I dont care much for horses. I think they feels the same way about me. Most of them are so big that the only thing there good for is the view of the camp you get when you climb up. They are what they call hors de combat in French. My horse died the other day. I guess it wasnt much effort for him. If it had been he wouldnt have done it.

They got a book they call Drill Regulations Field and Light. Thats about as censible as it is all the way through. For instance they say that when the command for action is given one man jumps for the wheel and another springs for the trail an another leaps for the muzzle. I guess the fellow that rote the regulations thought we was a bunch of grass hoppers.

Well I got to quit now an rite a bunch of other girls. Thanks again for the box although it was so busted that it wasnt much good but that dont matter.

Yours till you here otherwise,

Bill.

Dorothy Parker

GLORY IN THE DAYTIME

Mr. Murdock was one who carried no enthusiasm whatever for plays and their players, and that was too bad, for they meant so much to little Mrs. Murdock. Always she had been in a state of devout excitement over the luminous, free, passionate elect who serve the theater. And always she had done her wistful worshiping, along with the multitudes, at the great public altars. It is true that once, when she was a particularly little girl, love had impelled her to write Miss Maude Adams a letter beginning "Dearest Peter," and she had received from Miss Adams a miniature thimble inscribed "A kiss from Peter Pan." (That was a day!) And once, when her mother had taken her holiday shopping, a limousine door was held open and there had passed her, as close as *that,* a wonder of sable and violets and round red curls that seemed to tinkle on the air; so, forever after, she was as good as certain that she had been not a foot away from Miss Billie Burke. But until some three years after her marriage, these had remained her only personal experiences with the people of the lights and the glory.

Then it turned out that Miss Noyes, new-come to little Mrs. Murdock's own bridge club, knew an actress. She actually knew an actress; the way you and I know collectors of recipes and members of garden clubs and amateurs of needlepoint.

The name of the actress was Lily Wynton, and it was famous. She was tall and slow and silvery; often she appeared in the rôle of a duchess, or of a Lady Pam or an Honorable Moira. Critics recurrently referred to her as "that great lady of our stage." Mrs. Murdock had attended, over years, matinée performances of the Wynton successes. And she had no more thought that she would one day have opportunity to meet Lily Wynton face to face than she had thought— well, than she had thought of flying!

Yet it was not astounding that Miss Noyes should walk at ease among the glamorous. Miss Noyes was full of depths and mystery, and she could talk with a cigarette still between her lips. She was always doing something difficult, like designing her own pajamas, or reading Proust, or modeling torsos in plasticine. She played excellent bridge. She liked little Mrs. Murdock. "Tiny one," she called her.

"How's for coming to tea tomorrow, tiny one?" she said, at a therefore memorable meeting of the bridge club. "Lily Wynton's going to drop up. You might like to meet her."

The words fell so easily that she could not have realized their weight. Lily Wynton was coming to tea. Mrs. Murdock might like to meet her. Little Mrs. Murdock walked home through the early dark, and stars sang in the sky above her.

Mr. Murdock was already at home when she arrived. It required but a glance to tell that for him there had been no singing stars that evening in the heavens. He sat with his newspaper opened at the financial page, and bitterness had its way with his soul. It was not the time to cry happily to him of the impending hospitalities of Miss Noyes; not the time, that is, if one anticipated exclamatory sympathy. Mr. Murdock did not like Miss Noyes. When pressed for a reason, he replied that he just plain didn't like her. Occasionally he added, with a sweep that might have commanded a certain admiration, that all those women made him sick. Usually when she told him of the temperate activities of the bridge club meetings, Mrs. Murdock kept any mention of Miss Noyes's name from the accounts. She had found that this omission made for a more agreeable evening. But now she was caught in such a sparkling swirl of excitement that she had scarcely kissed him before she was off on her story.

"Oh, Jim," she cried. "Oh, what do you think! Hallie Noyes asked me to tea tomorrow to meet Lily Wynton!"

"Who's Lily Wynton?" he said.

"Ah, Jim," she said. "Ah, really, Jim. Who's Lily Wynton! Who's Greta Garbo, I suppose!"

"She some actress or something?" he said.

Mrs. Murdock's shoulders sagged. "Yes, Jim," she said. "Yes. Lily Wynton's an actress."

She picked up her purse and started slowly toward the door. But before she had taken three steps, she was again caught up in her sparkling swirl. She turned to him, and her eyes were shining.

"Honestly," she said, "it was the funniest thing you ever heard in your life. We'd just finished the last rubber—oh, I forgot to tell you, I won three dollars, isn't that pretty good for me?—and Hallie Noyes said to me, 'Come on in to tea tomorrow. Lily Wynton's going to drop up,' she said. Just like that, she said it. Just as if it was anybody."

"Drop up?" he said. "How can you drop *up?*"

"Honestly, I don't know what I said when she asked me," Mrs. Murdock said. "I suppose I said I'd love to—I guess I must have. But I was so simply—Well, you know how I've always felt about Lily Wynton. Why, when I was a little girl, I used to collect her pictures. And I've seen her in, oh, everything she's ever been in, I should think, and I've read every word about her, and interviews and all. Really and truly, when I think of *meeting* her—Oh, I'll simply die. What on earth shall I say to her?"

"You might ask her how she'd like to try dropping down, for a change," Mr. Murdock said.

"All right, Jim," Mrs. Murdock said. "If that's the way you want to be."

Wearily she went toward the door, and this time she reached it before she turned to him. There were no lights in her eyes.

"It—it isn't so awfully nice," she said, "to spoil somebody's pleasure in something. I was so thrilled about this. You don't see what it is to me, to meet Lily Wynton. To meet somebody like that, and see what they're like, and hear what they say, and maybe get to know them. People like that mean—well, they mean something different to me. They're not like this. They're not like me. Who do I ever see? What do I ever hear? All my whole life, I've wanted to know—I've almost prayed that some day I could meet—Well. All right, Jim."

She went out, and on to her bedroom.

Mr. Murdock was left with only his newspaper and his bitterness for company. But he spoke aloud.

" 'Drop up!' " he said. " 'Drop *up,*' for God's sake!"

The Murdocks dined, not in silence, but in pronounced quiet. There was something straitened about Mr. Murdock's stillness; but little Mrs. Murdock's was the sweet, far quiet of one given over to dreams. She had forgotten her weary words to her husband, she had passed through her excitement and her disappointment. Luxuriously she floated on innocent visions of days after the morrow. She heard her own voice in future conversations. . . .

I saw Lily Wynton at Hallie's the other day, and she was telling me all about her new play—no, I'm terribly sorry, but it's a secret, I promised her I wouldn't tell anyone the name of it. . . . Lily Wynton dropped up to tea yesterday, and we just got to talking, and she told me the most interesting things about her life; she said she'd never dreamed of telling them to anyone else. . . . Why, I'd love to come, but I promised to have lunch with Lily Wynton. . . . I had a long, long letter from Lily Wynton. . . . Lily Wynton called me up this morning. . . . Whenever I feel blue, I just go and have a talk with Lily Wynton, and then I'm all right again. . . . Lily Wynton told me. . . . Lily Wynton and I . . . "Lily," I said to her . . .

The next morning, Mr. Murdock had left for his office before Mrs. Murdock rose. This had happened several times before, but not often. Mrs. Murdock felt a little queer about it. Then she told herself that it was probably just as well. Then she forgot all about it, and gave her mind to the selection of a costume suitable to the afternoon's event. Deeply she felt that her small wardrobe included no dress adequate to the occasion; for, of course, such an occasion had never before arisen. She finally decided upon a frock of dark blue serge with fluted white muslin about the neck and wrists. It was her style, that was the most she could say for it. And that was all she could say for herself. Blue serge and little white ruffles—that was she.

The very becomingness of the dress lowered her spirits. A nobody's frock, worn by a nobody. She blushed and went hot when she recalled the dreams she had woven the night before, the mad visions of intimacy of equality with Lily Wynton. Timidity turned her heart liquid, and she thought of telephoning Miss Noyes and saying she had a bad cold and could not come. She steadied, when she planned a course of conduct to pursue at teatime. She would not try to say anything; if she stayed silent, she could not sound foolish. She would listen and watch and worship and then come home, stronger, braver, better for an hour she would remember proudly all her life.

Miss Noyes's living-room was done in the early modern period. There were a great many oblique lines and acute angles, zigzags of aluminium and horizontal stretches of mirror. The color scheme was sawdust and steel. No seat was more than twelve inches above the floor, no table was made of wood. It was, as has been said of larger places, all right for a visit.

Little Mrs. Murdock was the first arrival. She was glad of that; no, maybe it would have been better to have come after Lily Wynton;

no, maybe this was right. The maid motioned her toward the living-room, and Miss Noyes greeted her in the cool voice and the warm words that were her special combination. She wore black velvet trousers, a red cummerbund, and a white silk shirt, opened at the throat. A cigarette clung to her lower lip, and her eyes, as was her habit, were held narrow against its near smoke.

"Come in, come in, tiny one," she said. "Bless its little heart. Take off its little coat. Good Lord, you look easily eleven years old in that dress. Sit ye doon, here beside of me. There'll be a spot of tea in a jiff."

Mrs. Murdock sat down on the vast, perilously low divan, and, be-cause she was never good at reclining among cushions, held her back straight. There was room for six like her, between herself and her hostess. Miss Noyes lay back, with one ankle flung upon the other knee, and looked at her.

"I'm a wreck," Miss Noyes announced. "I was modeling like a mad thing, all night long. It's taken everything out of me. I was like a thing bewitched."

"Oh, what were you making?" cried Mrs. Murdock.

"Oh, Eve," Miss Noyes said. "I always do Eve. What else is there to do? You must come pose for me some time, tiny one. You'd be nice to do. Ye-es, you'd be very nice to do. My tiny one."

"Why, I—" Mrs. Murdock said, and stopped. "Thank you very much, though," she said.

"I wonder where Lily is," Miss Noyes said. "She said she'd be here early—well, she always says that. You'll adore her, tiny one. She's really rare. She's a real person. And she's been through perfect hell. God, what a time she's had!"

"Ah, what's been the matter?" said Mrs. Murdock.

"Men," Miss Noyes said. "Men. She never had a man that wasn't a louse." Gloomily she stared at the toe of her flat-heeled patent leather pump. "A pack of lice, always. All of them. Leave her for the first little floozie that comes along."

"But—" Mrs. Murdock began. No, she couldn't have heard right. How could it be right? Lily Wynton was a great actress. A great actress meant romance. Romance meant Grand Dukes and Crown Princes and diplomats touched with gray at the temples and lean, bronzed, reckless Younger Sons. It meant pearls and emeralds and chinchilla and rubies red as the blood that was shed for them. It meant a grim-faced boy sitting in the fearful Indian midnight, beneath the dreary whirring of the *punkahs,* writing a letter to the lady he had seen but once; writing his poor heart out, before he turned to the service revolver that lay beside him on the table. It meant a golden-locked poet, floating face downward in the sea, and in his pocket his last great sonnet to the lady of ivory. It meant brave, beautiful men, living and dying for the lady who was the pale bride of art, whose eyes and heart were soft with only compassion for them.

A pack of lice. Crawling after little floozies; whom Mrs. Murdock swiftly and hazily pictured as rather like ants.

"But—" said little Mrs. Murdock.

"She gave them all her money," Miss Noyes said. "She always did. Or if she didn't, they took it anyway. Took every cent she had, and then spat in her face. Well, maybe she's beginning to learn a little sense now. Oh, there's the bell—that'll be Lily. No, sit ye doon, tiny one. You belong there."

Miss Noyes rose and made for the archway that separated the living-room from the hall. As she passed Mrs. Murdock, she stooped suddenly, cupped her guest's round chin, and quickly, lightly kissed her mouth.

"Don't tell Lily," she murmured, very low.

Mrs. Murdock puzzled. Don't tell Lily what? Could Hallie Noyes think that she might babble to the Lily Wynton of these strange confidences about the actress's life? Or did she mean—But she had no more time for puzzling. Lily Wynton stood in the archway. There she stood, one hand resting on the wooden molding and her body swayed toward it, exactly as she stood for her third-act entrance of her latest play, and for a like half-minute.

You would have known her anywhere, Mrs. Murdock thought. Oh, yes, anywhere. Or at least you would have exclaimed, "That woman looks something like Lily Wynton." For she was somehow different in the daylight. Her figure looked heavier, thicker, and her face—there was so much of her face that the surplus sagged from the strong, fine bones. And her eyes, those famous dark, liquid eyes. They were dark, yes, and certainly liquid, but they were set in little hammocks of folded flesh, and seemed to be set but loosely, so readily did they roll. Their whites, that were visible all around the irises, were threaded with tiny scarlet veins.

"I suppose footlights are an awful strain on their eyes," thought little Mrs. Murdock.

Lily Wynton wore, just as she should have, black satin and sables, and long white gloves were wrinkled luxuriously about her wrists. But there were delicate streaks of grime in the folds of her gloves, and down the shining length of her gown there were small, irregularly shaped dull patches; bits of food or drops of drink, or perhaps both, sometime must have slipped their carriers and found brief sanctuary there. Her hat—oh, her hat. It was romance, it was mystery, it was strange, sweet sorrow; it was Lily Wynton's hat, of all the world, and no other could dare it. Black it was, and tilted, and a great, soft plume drooped from it to follow her cheek and curl across her throat. Beneath it, her hair had the various hues of neglected brass. But oh, her hat.

"Darling!" cried Miss Noyes.

"Angel," said Lily Wynton. "My sweet."

It was that voice. It was that deep, soft, glowing voice. "Like purple velvet," someone had written. Mrs. Murdock's heart beat visibly.

Lily Wynton cast herself upon the steep bosom of her hostess, and murmured there. Across Miss Noyes's shoulder she caught sight of little Mrs. Murdock.

"And who is this?" she said. She disengaged herself.

"That's my tiny one," Miss Noyes said. "Mrs. Murdock."

"What a clever little face," said Lily Wynton. "Clever, clever little face. What does she do, sweet Hallie? I'm sure she writes, doesn't she? Yes, I can feel it. She writes beautiful, beautiful words. Don't you, child?"

"Oh, no, really I—" Mrs. Murdock said.

"And you must write me a play," said Lily Wynton. "A beautiful, beautiful play. And I will play in it, over and over the world, until I am a very, very old lady. And then I will die. But I will never be forgotten, because of the years I played in your beautiful, beautiful play."

She moved across the room. There was a slight hesitancy, a seeming insecurity, in her step, and when she would have sunk into a chair, she began to sink two inches, perhaps, to its right. But she swayed just in time in her descent, and was safe.

"To write," she said, smiling sadly at Mrs. Murdock, "to write. And such a little thing, for such a big gift. Oh, the privilege of it. But the anguish of it, too. The agony."

"But, you see, I—" said little Mrs. Murdock.

"Tiny one doesn't write, Lily," Miss Noyes said. She threw herself back upon the divan. "She's a museum piece. She's a devoted wife."

"A wife!" Lily Wynton said. "A wife. Your first marriage, child?"

"Oh, yes," said Mrs. Murdock.

"How sweet," Lily Wynton said. "How sweet, sweet, sweet. Tell me, child, do you love him very, very much?"

"Why, I—" said little Mrs. Murdock, and blushed. "I've known him for ages," she said.

"You love him," Lily Wynton said. "You love him. And is it sweet to go to bed with him?"

"Oh—" said Mrs. Murdock, and blushed till it hurt.

"The first marriage," Lily Wynton said. "Youth, youth. Yes, when I was your age I used to marry, too. Oh, treasure your love, child, guard it, live in it. Laugh and dance in the love of your man. Until you find out what he's really like."

There came a sudden visitation upon her. Her shoulders jerked upward, her cheeks puffed, her eyes sought to start from their hammocks. For a moment she sat thus, then slowly all subsided into place. She lay back in her chair, tenderly patting her chest. She shook her head sadly, and there was grieved wonder in the look with which she held Mrs. Murdock.

"Gas," said Lily Wynton, in the famous voice. "Gas. Nobody knows what I suffer from it."

"Oh, I'm so sorry," Mrs. Murdock said. "Is there anything—"

"Nothing," Lily Wynton said. "There is nothing. There is nothing that can be done for it. I've been everywhere."

"How's for a spot of tea, perhaps?" Miss Noyes said. "It might help." She turned her face toward the archway and lifted up her voice. "Mary! Where the hell's the tea?"

"You don't know," Lily Wynton said, with her grieved eyes fixed on Mrs. Murdock, "you don't know what stomach distress is. You can never, never know, unless you're a stomach sufferer yourself. I've been one for years. Years and years and years."

"I'm terribly sorry," Mrs. Murdock said.

"Nobody knows the anguish," Lily Wynton said. "The agony."

The maid appeared, bearing a triangular tray upon which was set an heroic-sized tea service of bright white china, each piece a hectagon. She set it down on a table within the long reach of Miss Noyes and retired, as she had come, bashfully.

"Sweet Hallie," Lily Wynton said, "my sweet. Tea—I adore it. I worship it. But my distress turns it to gall and wormwood in me. Gall and wormwood. For hours, I should have no peace. Let me have a little, tiny bit of your beautiful, beautiful brandy, instead."

"You really think you should, darling?" Miss Noyes said. "You know—"

"My angel," said Lily Wynton, "it's the only thing for acidity."

"Well," Miss Noyes said. "But do remember you've got a performance tonight." Again she hurled her voice at the archway. "Mary! Bring the brandy and a lot of soda and ice and things."

"Oh, no, my saint," Lily Wynton said. "No, no, sweet Hallie. Soda and ice are rank poison to me. Do you want to freeze my poor, weak stomach? Do you want to kill poor, poor Lily?"

"Mary!" roared Miss Noyes. "Just bring the brandy and a glass." She turned to little Mrs. Murdock. "How's for your tea, tiny one? Cream? Lemon?"

"Cream, if I may, please," Mrs. Murdock said. "And two lumps of sugar, please, if I may."

"Oh, youth, youth," Lily Wynton said. "Youth and love."

The maid returned with an octagonal tray supporting a decanter of brandy and a wide, squat, heavy glass. Her head twisted on her neck in a spasm of diffidence.

"Just pour it for me, will you, my dear?" said Lily Wynton. "Thank you. And leave the pretty, pretty decanter here, on this enchanting little table. Thank you. You're so good to me."

The maid vanished, fluttering. Lily Wynton lay back in her chair, holding in her gloved hand the wide, squat glass, colored brown to the brim. Little Mrs. Murdock lowered her eyes to her teacup, carefully carried it to her lips, sipped, and replaced it on its saucer. When she raised her eyes, Lily Wynton lay back in her chair, holding in her gloved hand the wide, squat, colorless glass.

"My life," Lily Wynton said, slowly, "is a mess. A stinking mess. It always has been, and it always will be. Until I am a very, very old lady. Ah, little Clever-Face, you writers don't know what struggle is."

"But really I'm not—" said Mrs. Murdock.

"To write," Lily Wynton said. "To write. To set one word beautifully beside another word. The privilege of it. The blessed, blessed peace of it. Oh, for quiet, for rest. But do you think those Jew bastards would close that play while it's doing a nickel's worth of business?

Oh, no. Tired as I am, sick as I am, I must drag along. Oh, child, child, guard your precious gift. Give thanks for it. It is the greatest thing of all. It is the only thing. To write."

"Darling, I told you tiny one doesn't write," said Miss Noyes. "How's for making more sense? She's a wife."

"Ah, yes, she told me. She told me she had perfect, passionate love," Lily Wynton said. "Young love. It is the greatest thing. It is the only thing." She grasped the decanter; and again the squat glass was brown to the brim.

"What time did you start today, darling?" said Miss Noyes.

"Oh, don't scold me, sweet love," Lily Wynton said. "Lily hasn't been naughty. Her wuzzunt naughty dirl 't all. I didn't get up until late, late, late. And though I parched, though I burned, I didn't have a drink until after my breakfast. 'It is for Hallie,' I said." She raised the glass to her mouth, tilted it, and brought it away, colorless.

"Good Lord, Lily," Miss Noyes said. "Watch yourself. You've got to walk on that stage tonight, my girl."

"All the world's a stage," said Lily Wynton. "And all the men and women merely players. They have their entrance and their exitses, and each man in his time plays many parts, his act being seven ages. At first, the infant, mewling and puking—"

"How's the play doing?" Miss Noyes said.

"Oh, lousily," Lily Wynton said. "Lousily, lousily, lousily. But what isn't? What isn't, in this terrible, terrible world? Answer me that." She reached for the decanter.

"Lily, listen," said Miss Noyes. "Stop that. Do you hear?"

"Please, sweet Hallie," Lily Wynton said. "Pretty please. Poor, poor Lily."

"Do you want me to do what I had to do last time?" Miss Noyes said. "Do you want me to strike you, in front of tiny one, here?"

Lily Wynton drew herself high. "You do not realize," she said, icily, "what acidity is." She filled the glass and held it, regarding it as though through a lorgnon. Suddenly her manner changed, and she looked up and smiled at little Mrs. Murdock.

"You must let me read it," she said. "You mustn't be so modest."

"Read—" said little Mrs. Murdock.

"Your play," Lily Wynton said. "Your beautiful, beautiful play. Don't think I am too busy. I always have time. I have time for everything. Oh, my God, I have to go to the dentist tomorrow. Oh, the suffering I have gone through with my teeth. Look!" She set down her glass, inserted a gloved forefinger in the corner of her mouth, and dragged it to the side. "Oogh!" she insisted. "Oogh!"

Mrs. Murdock craned her neck shyly, and caught a glimpse of shining gold.

"Oh, I'm so sorry," she said.

"As wah ee id a me ass ime," Lily Wynton said. She took away her forefinger and let her mouth resume its shape. "That's what he did to me last time," she repeated. "The anguish of it. The agony. Do you suffer with your teeth, little Clever-Face?"

"Why, I'm afraid I've been awfully lucky," Mrs. Murdock said. "I—"

"You don't know," Lily Wynton said. "Nobody knows what it is. You writers—you don't know." She took up her glass, sighed over it, and drained it.

"Well," Miss Noyes said. "Go ahead and pass out, then, darling. You'll have time for a sleep before the theater."

"To sleep," Lily Wynton said. "To sleep, perchance to dream. The privilege of it. Oh, Hallie, sweet, sweet Hallie, poor Lily feels so terrible. Rub my head for me, angel. Help me."

"I'll go get the eau de Cologne," Miss Noyes said. She left the room, lightly patting Mrs. Murdock's knee as she passed her. Lily Wynton lay in her chair and closed her famous eyes.

"To sleep," she said. "To sleep, perchance to dream."

"I'm afraid," little Mrs. Murdock began. "I'm afraid," she said, "I really must be going home. I'm afraid I didn't realize how awfully late it was."

"Yes, go, child," Lily Wynton said. She did not open her eyes. "Go to him. Go to him, live in him, love him. Stay with him always. But when he starts bringing them into the house—get out."

"I'm afraid—I'm afraid I didn't quite understand," Mrs. Murdock said.

"When he starts bringing his fancy women into the house," Lily Wynton said. "You must have pride, then. You must go. I always did. But it was always too late then. They'd got all my money. That's all they want, marry them or not. They say it's love, but it isn't. Love is the only thing. Treasure your love, child. Go back to him. Go to bed with him. It's the only thing. And your beautiful, beautiful play."

"Oh, dear," said little Mrs. Murdock. "I—I'm afraid it's really terribly late."

There was only the sound of rhythmic breathing from the chair where Lily Wynton lay. The purple voice rolled along the air no longer.

Little Mrs. Murdock stole to the chair upon which she had left her coat. Carefully she smoothed her white muslin frills, so that they would be fresh beneath the jacket. She felt a tenderness for her frock; she wanted to protect it. Blue serge and little ruffles—they were her own.

When she reached the outer door of Miss Noyes's apartment, she stopped a moment and her manners conquered her. Bravely she called in the direction of Miss Noyes's bedroom.

"Good-by, Miss Noyes," she said. "I've simply got to run. I didn't realize it was so late. I had a lovely time—thank you ever so much."

"Oh, good-by, tiny one," Miss Noyes called. "Sorry Lily went by-by. Don't mind her—she's really a real person. I'll call you up, tiny one. I want to see you. Now where's that damned cologne?"

"Thank you ever so much," Mrs. Murdock said. She let herself out of the apartment.

Little Mrs. Murdock walked homeward, through the clustering dark. Her mind was busy, but not with memories of Lily Wynton. She thought of Jim; Jim, who had left for his office before she had arisen that morning, Jim, whom she had not kissed good-by. Darling Jim. There were no others born like him. Funny Jim, stiff and cross and silent; but only because he knew so much. Only because he knew the silliness of seeking afar for the glamour and beauty and romance of living. When they were right at home all the time, she thought. Like the Blue Bird, thought little Mrs. Murdock.

Darling Jim. Mrs. Murdock turned in her course, and entered an enormous shop where the most delicate and esoteric of foods were sold for heavy sums. Jim liked red caviar. Mrs. Murdock bought a jar of the shiny, glutinous eggs. They would have cocktails that night, though they had no guests, and the red caviar would be served with them for a surprise, and it would be a little, secret party to celebrate her return to contentment with her Jim, a party to mark her happy renunciation of all the glory of the world. She bought, too, a large, foreign cheese. It would give a needed touch to dinner. Mrs. Murdock had not given much attention to ordering dinner, that morning. "Oh, anything you want, Signe," she had said to the maid. She did not want to think of that. She went on home with her packages.

Mr. Murdock was already there when she arrived. He was sitting with his newspaper opened to the financial page. Little Mrs. Murdock ran in to him with her eyes a-light. It is too bad that the light in a person's eyes is only the light in a person's eyes, and you cannot tell at a look what causes it. You do not know if it is excitement about you, or about something else. The evening before, Mrs. Murdock had run in to Mr. Murdock with her eyes a-light.

"Oh, hello," he said to her. He looked back at his paper, and kept his eyes there. "What did you do? Did you drop up to Hank Noyes's?"

Little Mrs. Murdock stopped right where she was.

"You know perfectly well, Jim," she said, "that Hallie Noyes's first name is Hallie."

"It's Hank to me," he said. "Hank or Bill. Did what's-her-name show up? I mean drop up. Pardon me."

"To whom are you referring?" said Mrs. Murdock, perfectly.

"What's-her-name," Mr. Murdock said. "The movie star."

"If you mean Lily Wynton," Mrs. Murdock said, "she is not a movie star. She is an actress. She is a great actress."

"Well, did she drop up?" he said.

Mrs. Murdock's shoulders sagged. "Yes," she said. "Yes, she was there, Jim."

"I suppose you're going on the stage now," he said.

"Ah, Jim," Mrs. Murdock said. "Ah, Jim, please. I'm not sorry at all I went to Hallie Noyes's today. It was—it was a real experience to meet Lily Wynton. Something I'll remember all my life."

"What did she do?" Mr. Murdock said. "Hang by her feet?"

"She did no such thing!" Mrs. Murdock said. "She recited Shakespeare, if you want to know."

"Oh, my God," Mr. Murdock said. "That must have been great."

"All right, Jim," Mrs. Murdock said. "If that's the way you want to be."

Wearily she left the room and went down the hall. She stopped at the pantry door, pushed it open, and spoke to the pleasant little maid.

"Oh, Signe," she said. "Oh, good evening, Signe. Put these things somewhere, will you? I got them on the way home. I thought we might have them some time."

Wearily little Mrs. Murdock went on down the hall to her bedroom.

Arthur Kober

BOGGAINS IN THE BRONX

Bella looked at her watch, quickly drew her napkin across her mouth, pushed the plate away, and rose. Ma Gross saw her rise and frowned.

"Come on, Pa," said Bella. "Help me clear the table."

Mr. Gross had his newspaper propped up against a sugar bowl and was too deep in a news item to pay any attention to his daughter. The latter now started stacking the dishes.

"Come on, Ma," she said. "I'll wash the dishes and you can dry them."

"Look, look, how she rushes!" Mrs. Gross was obviously suspicious of such eager and unsolicited aid. "So who you rushing to see, Miss Hurry-Shmurry? Maybe you rushing to see Pressident-Rosenvelt, he's waiting donnstairs in the hall?"

Mrs. Gross's rasping voice managed to spear her husband. "Awways talk, talk, talk with the tongue," he shouted. "Give the poor tongue a couple minutes' rest!"

"Look who's talking!" Mrs. Gross curled her lip contemptuously as she addressed her husband. "He comes home fomm woik, puts by him the nose in newspaper, and now alluva sudden Mr. Boss, he's talking. Put better back the nose in newspaper, Mr. Boss."

"Aw, please help me with the dishes, will ya?" Bella pleaded. "Kitty Shapiro and her intended, Dr. Rappaport, they're coming here to pick me up. We're gonna take in a pickcha show."

Bella's parents suddenly came to life. Pa dropped the newspaper and began to empty the remains of the evening's dinner into one large platter. Ma carefully folded the napkins and placed them in the top drawer of the bureau.

"So is coming here Kitty's intendit, the-docteh?" Mrs. Gross asked with great interest.

"The denttist!" Pa was more explicit.

"Where comes a fine boy like a denttist to Kitty Shapiro?" Ma wanted to know.

"What'sa metta with Kitty Shapiro?" Mr. Gross didn't like or dislike Kitty—he hardly knew her, but because he habitually challenged anything his wife said, he found himself in the position of defending his daughter's friend. "A nice girl, Kitty."

"Eh, she ain't so extra," his wife said, disparagingly. "She got no shape, she got no good looks, and still in all she's engaged. She got luck, that's all."

Bella removed the fruit bowl from the mantelpiece and took it into the kitchen. The bowl was a prize Mrs. Gross had captured on one of her vacations. It bore the inscription, burnt on the surface, "Souvenir of Flugelman Manor, Catskill Mts., Greene Co., N. Y." She found some oranges in the icebox and placed these in the bowl.

Mrs. Gross took advantage of her daughter's momentary absence to ask a question which had long disturbed her and which she asked with annoying regularity. "What is with our Bella? Such a nice girl can't catch a fine, steady boy who knows how to put by a dolleh? She got a good head on her," she added, listing her daughter's virtues. "She's ten times smott like Kitty Shapiro, and still in all Kitty, she can catch a nice boy, a docteh—"

"A denttist-docteh," Pa interrupted.

"Awright, a denttist-docteh, and our Bella can't find a steady boy who makes heavy wages."

"Oh, so you're off on that again!" said Bella, coming out of the kitchen. No subject annoyed her as much as this discussion of a future husband. She felt that there was no hurry about getting married—she was twenty-one; besides, she was waiting until "Mr. Right," as she put it, came along. "Can't you find anything else to talk about?" she exclaimed indignantly.

"Get awready engaged and I'll stop talking," Ma said.

"Don't worry," replied Bella, placing the bowl and its yellow contents in the center of the table, "you'll get rid of me soon enough."

"Sure! To a *schlemiel* like Mexie Fine, a collitch boy he can't even make a living yet!"

Bella turned toward her mother and, assuming a very haughty air, said, "I'll have you unnastann, Ma, that Max Fine and I are not keeping company."

This subject was too familiar to Pa to be of any interest. He gathered his newspaper and wandered out toward the bathroom.

"Max and I," Bella added, "we just happen to be platonic friends."

"Tonic-shmonic! Believe me, all I say is when I see my dutter married, I'll be happy like anything. When—" The doorbell interrupted Mrs. Gross.

Bella admitted Kitty Shapiro and Dr. Rappaport.

"Hello, Kitty." Mrs. Gross's greeting was very warm. "How's the Mamma filling? She's filling good?"

"She's O. K., thank you. Oh, this here is my intended, Dr. Rappaport." She turned to her intended and took his hand. "Come here, Butchkie," she said. "Dr. Rappaport, this here is Mrs. Gross, Billie's mother."

"Pleasta meetchoo, Mrs. Gross." He extended a hand. This surprised Ma Gross, who quickly wiped her hand on her apron before shaking his.

"Likewise," she said. Suddenly her eye was caught by the engagement ring Kitty was wearing. "Say, that's some beyoodyful stone!" Kitty extended her hand so that Mrs. Gross could make a closer examination. "A stone like that must cust heavy money, believe me."

"Dr. Rappaport got it wholesale fomm a patient of his, a jewlerer," Kitty explained. "Dincha, Butchkie?" She gave her fiancé a smile which expressed profound admiration and affection.

Pa Gross came out of the bathroom, his suspenders dangling from his trousers, his newspaper in his hand. "Oh, hello, Kitty," he said, becoming aware of his guests.

"Hello, Mr. Gross. Come here, Butchkie." Again Kitty took her fiancé's hand. "This here is Mr. Gross, Billie's father. Mr. Gross, this here is my intended, Dr. Rappaport."

"Hoddeya do, Mr. Gross?"

"I can't complain, thenks," replied Mr. Gross.

"Pa! Look at you!" Bella's eyes flashed as she pointed to his trailing suspenders.

"Excuse me, Docteh," Pa apologized. "Bella don't like to see by me the pents falling donn. It ain't stylish by her."

"And by you it's stylish?" Mrs. Gross jumped to the defense of her daughter. "Listen to him awready!"

"Gee, Billie." Kitty was now examining Bella's dress. "That's some nifty outfit you got on. Turn arounn." Bella did so. "Very chick, Billie. Very! Is it new?"

"I just got it last week. Max Fine gave me a card to the wholesaler's. Really like it?"

"I should say. It's very chick, Billie. Wear it in good health."

"Thank you."

Pa had sidled up to Dr. Rappaport. He tapped him on the shoulder and said, "Listen, Docteh. If you don't mind, I'd like to esk you something."

"Sure, go ahead."

"I got by me here in mouth a britch—" Pa opened his mouth and pulled his lip up with his finger. Bella turned and looked at her father in dismay.

"Pa!" she cried. "Waddeya doing?"

"Look at him! This is nice! This is refined!" It was Ma who was now indignant.

"What'sa metta?" Pa asked, closing his mouth. "What I done so terrible?"

"The Docteh is here a guest in house," Ma explained. "He didn't come here fa no visits fa two and a half dolless."

"Oh, that's awright," said Dr. Rappaport, generously. "I don't mind."

"Give him one of your cards, Butchkie." Kitty turned to the others. "I better start getting my future hubby some business now."

"What pickcha we seeing?" asked Bella, looking into the bureau mirror as she got into her coat.

"Oh, there's one down the street where Herbert Moshill takes off a doctor. I thought it would be good fa Dr. Rappaport to see it. You know," Kitty explained, "because they got things in common. Well, goodnight."

Goodnights were exchanged. Ma waited until Bella and her friends had gone before she expressed herself.

"You seen the stone Kitty got on?" she asked her husband.

"No," he said.

"Such a stone!" She shrugged her shoulders. "Such stones I don't even wish my worst enemies. In five-and-ten cent stores you get such stones. Believe me, before our Bella wears such a ring, betta she stick single."

"A nice boy, the Docteh," Pa said abstractedly, turning the pages of the newspaper.

"What's so nice? A shrimp! A skinny boy! Comes a good wind and blows him right away. Nice! Before our Bella marries such a shrimp, betta she stick single."

Pa looked up from his newspaper in surprise. "You want Bella to stay single?"

"God fabbid!" Ma quickly replied. "Oney such boggains like that denttist, Kitty Shapiro can kipp!"

Heywood Broun

MRS. HEYWOOD COX BROUN *

Maybe my mother won't like this column, but at least it seemed to me that she suggested it herself. Every once and so often there appears in the letter department of my home town paper a very violent communication about me signed Mrs. Heywood Cox Broun. Mrs. Heywood Cox Broun is my mother, and, unlike her younger son, she never pulls her punches or sneaks up on an adversary.

Although her economic point of view is highly conservative, she expresses it with all the flaming ardor of a revolutionist. I know some radicals who, by dint of hard practice, can actually hiss the words "Wall Street." My mother can do that with "labor union."

If she actually met a labor union face to face I believe her hostility would evaporate. You see, most of her contacts have been made through the editorial page of the New York *Herald Tribune*. I have lent her a few copies of the *New Masses,* but they only served to madden her. I imagine it would have been shrewder tactics to have started with the *New Republic.*

In the beginning Mrs. Heywood Cox Broun did not take "my views" very seriously, but I am happy to say that she no longer tries to dispose of me as a posing pink. Only the other day she admitted in all seriousness that she regarded me as a menace, and I was very proud.

"The trouble with you, Heywood," she told me, "is that you have never been an employer."

To be sure, that is not entirely accurate. For one year I was a minor newspaper executive, and theoretically I had the power to hire and fire. I never fired anybody, but the one writer whom I engaged turned out to be top man in his division. Not only did I pick and choose Bill McGeehan for the sport page of the *Tribune* but I exploited him.

* *This portrait first appeared in Broun's daily column, "It Seems to Me," in* The World-Telegram.

92

The bargaining base on which I was empowered to operate was very slim. The managing editor said I could have him if he would come for $50 a week, and if he wouldn't take that I could go as high as $55. Bill was a very shy man all the days of his life, and I was pretty shy myself back in 1916. Besides, I never had hired anybody before. The conference was carried on with each of us looking out the opposite window.

"Mr. McGeehan," I said, "I am empowered to offer you either $50 or $55 a week to come to work. Which would you rather have?"

Bill chose $55, and in a few months he was the best-known sports writer in New York. There is, then, no blot on my escutcheon as an employer. Still, it is probably true that my talents do not lie in that direction, and I have no ambition to try again. The strain of waiting to see which salary he would accept taught me my lesson.

My mother thinks I am a "phony," although I am pretty certain she did not use that word, in the matter of parading and picketing. "It might teach you a good lesson and you would get to bed earlier if somebody did send you to jail for a couple of months," is her dictum.

However, if anything of the martyr complex lurks in me I have a right to assert that it is hereditary. For one afternoon there was no elevator service in the apartment building in which my mother lives, and now it has been restored, which makes my mother pretty indignant. The service came back because the landlord signed up with the union. My mother is considering walking up and down the five flights of stairs as a protest.

Individually the elevator boys are all right by her. She furnishes ice cream on Sundays and takes up the Christmas collection from the tenants. I forgot to say that my mother is very executive. She would make an excellent agitator herself, but she doesn't like to see anybody else agitate. I can easily imagine a situation in which she would picket for Eddie and George and Caleb. But they mustn't do it themselves. In some way that isn't fair to Mr. Pease and Mr. Elliman.

I am using them as symbols. She has another landlord. Mrs. Heywood Cox Broun has been in the same building for twenty-five years, and to my certain knowledge she has called that landlord every conceivable name, short of profanity and obscenity, which my mother does not employ, that a gentlewoman can lay her tongue to. But when it's a union fight my mother switches sides. She does not think that anybody else should employ violence.

When the revolution comes it's going to be a tough problem what to do with her. We will either have to shoot her or make her a commissar. In the meantime we still dine together.

Mark Twain

HIS GRANDFATHER'S OLD RAM*

Every now and then, in these days, the boys used to tell me I ought to get one Jim Blaine to tell me the stirring story of his grandfather's old ram—but they always added that I must not mention the matter unless Jim was drunk at the time—just comfortably and sociably drunk. They kept this up until my curiosity was on the rack to hear the story. I got to haunting Blaine; but it was of no use, the boys always found fault with his condition; he was often moderately but never satisfactorily drunk. I never watched a man's condition with such absorbing interest, such anxious solicitude; I never so pined to see a man uncompromisingly drunk before. At last, one evening I hurried to his cabin, for I learned that this time his situation was such that even the most fastidious could find no fault with it—he was tranquilly, serenely, symmetrically drunk—not a hiccup to mar his voice, not a cloud upon his brain thick enough to obscure his memory. As I entered, he was sitting upon an empty powder-keg, with a clay pipe in one hand and the other raised to command silence. His face was round, red, and very serious; his throat was bare and his hair tumbled; in general appearance and costume he was a stalwart miner of the period. On the pine table stood a candle, and its dim light revealed "the boys" sitting here and there on bunks, candle-boxes, powder-kegs, etc. They said:

"Sh—! Don't speak—he's going to commence."

THE STORY OF THE OLD RAM

I found a seat at once, and Blaine said:

"I don't reckon them times will ever come again. There never was a more bullier old ram than what he was. Grandfather fetched him from Illinois—got him of a man by the name of Yates—Bill Yates—maybe

* *From "Roughing It."*

95

you might have heard of him; his father was a deacon—Baptist—and he was a rustler, too; a man had to get up ruther early to get the start of old Thankful Yates; it was him that put the Greens up to j'ining teams with my grandfather when he moved west. Seth Green was prob'ly the pick of the flock; he married a Wilkerson—Sarah Wilkerson—good cretur, she was—one of the likeliest heifers that was ever raised in old Stoddard, everybody said that knowed her. She could heft a bar'l of flour as easy as I can flirt a flapjack. And spin? Don't mention it! Independent? Humph! When Sile Hawkins come a-browsing around her, she let him know that for all his tin he couldn't trot in harness alongside of *her*. You see, Sile Hawkins was—no, it warn't Sile Hawkins, after all—it was a galoot by the name of Filkins —I disremember his first name; but he *was* a stump—come into pra'r-meeting drunk, one night, hooraying for Nixon, becuz he thought it was a primary; and old Deacon Ferguson up and scooted him through the window and he lit on old Miss Jefferson's head, poor old filly. She was a good soul—had a glass eye and used to lend it to old Miss Wagner, that hadn't any, to receive company in; it warn't big enough, and when Miss Wagner warn't noticing, it would get twisted around in the socket, and look up, maybe, or out to one side, and every which way, while t'other one was looking as straight ahead as a spy-glass. Grown people didn't mind it, but it 'most always made the children cry, it was so sort of scary. She tried packing it in raw cotton, but it wouldn't work, somehow—the cotton would get loose and stick out and look so kind of awful that the children couldn't stand it no way. She was always dropping it out, and turning up her old deadlight on the company empty, and making them oncomfortable, becuz *she* never could tell when it hopped out, being blind on that side, you see. So somebody would have to hunch her and say, 'Your game eye has fetched loose, Miss Wagner, dear'—and then all of them would have to sit and wait till she jammed it in again—wrong side before, as a general thing, and green as a bird's egg, being a bashful cretur and easy sot back before company. But being wrong side before warn't much difference, anyway, becuz her own eye was sky-blue and the glass one was yaller on the front side, so whichever way she turned it it didn't match nohow. Old Miss Wagner was considerable on the borrow, she was. When she had a quilting, or Dorcas S'iety at her house she gen'ally borrowed Miss Higgins's wooden leg to stump around on; it was considerable shorter than her other pin, but much *she* minded that. She said she couldn't abide crutches when she had company, becuz they were so slow; said when she had company and things had to be done, she wanted to get up and hump herself. She was as bald as a jug, and so she used to borrow Miss Jacops's wig— Miss Jacops was the coffin-peddler's wife—a ratty old buzzard, he was, that used to go roosting around where people was sick, waiting for 'em; and there that old rip would sit all day, in the shade, on a coffin that he judged would fit the can'idate; and if it was a slow customer and kind of uncertain, he'd fetch his rations and a blanket along and sleep in the coffin nights. He was anchored out that way, in frosty weather, for about three weeks, once, before old Robbins's place, waiting for him; and after that, for as much as two years, Jacops was not on speaking terms with the old man, on account of his disapp'inting him. He got one of his feet froze, and lost money, too, becuz old Robbins took a favorable turn and got well. The next time Robbins got sick, Jacops tried to make up with him, and varnished up the same old coffin and fetched it along; but old Robbins was too many for him; he had him in, and 'peared to be powerful weak; he bought the coffin for ten dollars and Jacops was to pay it back and twenty-five more besides if Robbins didn't like the coffin after he'd tried it. And then Robbins died, and at the funeral he bursted off the lid and riz up in his shroud and told the parson to let up on the performances, becuz he could *not* stand such a coffin as that. You see he had been in a trance once before, when he was young, and he took the chances on another, cal'lating that if he made the trip it was money in his pocket, and if he missed fire he couldn't lose a cent. And, by George, he sued Jacops for the rhino and got judgment; and he set up the coffin in his back parlor and said he 'lowed to take his time, now. It was always an aggravation to Jacops, the way that miserable old thing acted. He moved back to Indiany pretty soon—went to Wellsville—Wellsville was the place the Hogadorns was from. Mighty fine family. Old Maryland stock. Old Squire Hogadorn could carry around more mixed licker, and cuss better than 'most any man I ever see. His second wife was the Widder Billings—she that was Becky Martin; her dam was Deacon Dunlap's first wife. Her oldest child, Maria, married a missionary and died in grace—et up by the savages. They et *him,* too, poor feller—biled him. It warn't the custom, so they say, but they explained to friends of his'n that went down there to bring away his things, that they'd tried missionaries every other way and never could get any good out of 'em

—and so it annoyed all his relations to find out that that man's life was fooled away just out of a dern'd experiment, so to speak. But mind you, there ain't anything ever reely lost; everything that people can't understand and don't see the reason of does good if you only hold on and give it a fair shake; Prov'dence don't fire no blank ca'tridges, boys. That there missionary's substance, unbeknowns to himself, actu'ly converted every last one of them heathens that took a chance at the barbecue. Nothing ever fetched them but that. Don't tell *me* it was an accident that he was biled. There ain't no such a thing as an accident. When my Uncle Lem was leaning up agin a scaffolding once, sick, or drunk, or suthin, an Irishman with a hod full of bricks fell on him out of the third story and broke the old man's back in two places. People said it was an accident. Much accident there was about that. He didn't know what he was there for, but he was there for a good object. If he hadn't been there the Irishman would have been killed. Nobody can ever make me believe anything different from that. Uncle Lem's dog was there. Why didn't the Irishman fall on the dog? Becuz the dog would 'a' seen him a-coming and stood from under. That's the reason the dog warn't app'inted. A dog can't be depended on to carry out a special prov'dence. Mark my words, it was a put-up thing. Accidents don't happen, boys. Uncle Lem's dog—I wish you could 'a' seen that dog. He was a reg'lar shepherd—or ruther he was part bull and part shepherd—splendid animal; belonged to Parson Hagar before Uncle Lem got him. Parson Hagar belonged to the Western Reserve Hagars; prime family; his mother was a Watson; one of his sisters married a Wheeler; they settled in Morgan County, and he got nipped by the machinery in a carpet factory and went through in less than a quarter of a minute; his widder bought the piece of carpet that had his remains wove in, and people come a hundred mile to 'tend the funeral. There was fourteen yards in the piece. She wouldn't let them roll him up, but planted him just so—full length. The church was middling small where they preached the funeral, and they had to let one end of the coffin stick out of the window. They didn't bury him—they planted one end, and let him stand up, same as a monument. And they nailed a sign on it and put— put on—put on it—sacred to—the m-e-m-o-r-y—of fourteen y-a-r-d-s— of three-ply—car – – – pet—containing all that was—m-o-r-t-a-l—of—of —W-i-l-l-i-a-m—W-h-e—"

Jim Blaine had been growing gradually drowsy and drowsier—his head nodded, once, twice, three times—dropped peacefully upon his breast, and he fell tranquilly asleep. The tears were running down the boys' cheeks—they were suffocating with suppressed laughter—and had been from the start, though I had never noticed it. I perceived that I was "sold." I learned then that Jim Blaine's peculiarity was that whenever he reached a certain stage of intoxication, no human power could keep him from setting out, with impressive unction, to tell about a wonderful adventure which he had once had with his grandfather's old ram—and the mention of the ram in the first sentence was as far as any man had ever heard him get, concerning it. He always maundered off, interminably, from one thing to another, till his whisky got the best of him, and he fell asleep. What the thing was that happened to him and his grandfather's old ram is a dark mystery to this day, for nobody has ever yet found out.

Ring Lardner

ALIBI IKE

His right name was Frank X. Farrell, and I guess the X stood for "Excuse me." Because he never pulled a play, good or bad, on or off the field, without apologizin' for it.

"Alibi Ike" was the name Carey wished on him the first day he reported down South. O' course we all cut out the "Alibi" part of it right away for the fear he would overhear it and bust somebody. But we called him "Ike" right to his face and the rest of it was understood by everybody on the club except Ike himself.

He ast me one time, he says:

"What do you all call me Ike for? I ain't no Yid."

"Carey give you the name," I says. "It's his nickname for everybody he takes a likin' to."

"He mustn't have only a few friends then," says Ike. "I never heard him say 'Ike' to nobody else."

But I was goin' to tell you about Carey namin' him. We'd been workin' out two weeks and the pitchers was showin' somethin' when this bird joined us. His first day out he stood up there so good and took such a reef at the old pill that he had everyone lookin'. Then him and Carey was together in left field, catchin' fungoes, and it was after we was through for the day that Carey told me about him.

"What do you think of Alibi Ike?" ast Carey.

"Who's that?" I says.

"This here Farrell in the outfield," says Carey.

"He looks like he could hit," I says.

"Yes," says Carey, "but he can't hit near as good as he can apologize."

Then Carey went on to tell me what Ike had been pullin' out there. He'd dropped the first fly ball that was hit to him and told Carey his glove wasn't broke in good yet, and Carey says the glove could easy of been Kid Gleason's gran'father. He made a whale of a catch out o' the next one and Carey says "Nice work!" or somethin' like that, but

Ike says he could of caught the ball with his back turned only he slipped when he started after it and, besides that, the air currents fooled him.

"I thought you done well to get to the ball," says Carey.

"I ought to been settin' under it," says Ike.

"What did you hit last year?" Carey ast him.

"I had malaria most o' the season," says Ike. "I wound up with .356."

"Where would I have to go to get malaria?" says Carey, but Ike didn't wise up.

I and Carey and him set at the same table together for supper. It took him half an hour longer'n us to eat because he had to excuse himself every time he lifted his fork.

"Doctor told me I needed starch," he'd say, and then toss a shovelful o' potatoes into him. Or, "They ain't much meat on one o' these chops," he'd tell us, and grab another one. Or he'd say: "Nothin' like onions for a cold," and then he'd dip into the perfumery.

"Better try that apple sauce," says Carey. "It'll help your malaria."

"Whose malaria?" says Ike. He'd forgot already why he didn't only hit .356 last year.

I and Carey begin to lead him on.

"Whereabouts did you say your home was?" I ast him.

"I live with my folks," he says. "We live in Kansas City—not right down in the business part—outside a ways."

"How's that come?" says Carey. "I should think you'd get rooms in the post office."

But Ike was too busy curin' his cold to get that one.

"Are you married?" I ast him.

"No," he says. "I never run round much with girls, except to shows onct in a wile and parties and dances and roller skatin'."

"Never take 'em to the prize fights, eh?" says Carey.

"We don't have no real good bouts," says Ike. "Just bush stuff. And I never figured a boxin' match was a place for the ladies."

Well, after supper he pulled a cigar out and lit it. I was just goin' to ask him what he done it for, but he beat me to it.

"Kind o' rests a man to smoke after a good work-out," he says. "Kind o' settles a man's supper, too."

"Looks like a pretty good cigar," says Carey.

"Yes," says Ike. "A friend o' mine give it to me—a fella in Kansas City that runs a billiard room."

"Do you play billiards?" I ast him.

"I used to play a fair game," he says. "I'm all out o' practice now—can't hardly make a shot."

We coaxed him into a four-handed battle, him and Carey against Jack Mack and I. Say, he couldn't play billiards as good as Willie Hoppe; not quite. But to hear him tell it, he didn't make a good shot all evenin'. I'd leave him an awful-lookin' layout and he'd gather 'em up in one try and then run a couple o' hundred, and between every carom he'd say he'd put too much stuff on the ball, or the English didn't take, or the table wasn't true, or his stick was crooked, or somethin'. And all the time he had the balls actin' like they was Dutch soldiers and him Kaiser William. We started out to play fifty points, but we had to make it a thousand so as I and Jack and Carey could try the table.

The four of us set round the lobby a wile after we was through playin', and when it got along toward bedtime Carey whispered to me and says:

"Ike'd like to go to bed, but he can't think up no excuse."

Carey hadn't hardly finished whisperin' when Ike got up and pulled it:

"Well, good night, boys," he says. "I ain't sleepy, but I got some gravel in my shoes and it's killin' my feet."

We knowed he hadn't never left the hotel since we'd came in from the grounds and changed our clo'es. So Carey says:

"I should think they'd take them gravel pits out o' the billiard room."

But Ike was already on his way to the elevator, limpin'.

"He's got the world beat," says Carey to Jack and I. "I've knew lots o' guys that had an alibi for every mistake they made; I've heard pitchers say that the ball slipped when somebody cracked one off'n 'em; I've heard infielders complain of a sore arm after heavin' one into the stand, and I've saw outfielders tooken sick with a dizzy spell when they've misjudged a fly ball. But this baby can't even go to bed without apologizin', and I bet he excuses himself to the razor when he gets ready to shave."

"And at that," says Jack, "he's goin' to make us a good man."

"Yes," says Carey, "unless rheumatism keeps his battin' average down to .400."

Well, sir, Ike kept whalin' away at the ball all through the trip till everybody knowed he'd won a job. Cap had him in there regular the last few exhibition games and told the newspaper boys a week before the season opened that he was goin' to start him in Kane's place.

"You're there, kid," says Carey to Ike, the night Cap made the 'nnouncement. "They ain't many boys that wins a big league berth their third year out."

"I'd of been up here a year ago," says Ike, "only I was bent over all season with lumbago."

It rained down in Cincinnati one day and somebody organized a little game o' cards. They was shy two men to make six and ast I and Carey to play.

"I'm with you if you get Ike and make it seven-handed," says Carey. So they got a hold of Ike and we went up to Smitty's room.

"I pretty near forgot how many you deal," says Ike. "It's been a long wile since I played."

I and Carey give each other the wink, and sure enough, he was just as ig'orant about poker as billiards. About the second hand, the pot was opened two or three ahead of him, and they was three in when it come his turn. It cost a buck, and he throwed in two.

"It's raised, boys," somebody says.

"Gosh, that's right, I did raise it," says Ike.

"Take out a buck if you didn't mean to tilt her," says Carey.

"No," says Ike, "I'll leave it go."

Well, it was raised back at him and then he made another mistake and raised again. They was only three left in when the draw come. Smitty'd opened with a pair o' kings and he didn't help 'em. Ike stood pat. The guy that'd raised him back was flushin' and he didn't fill. So Smitty checked and Ike bet and didn't get no call. He tossed his hand away, but I grabbed it and give it a look. He had king, queen, jack and two tens. Alibi Ike he must have seen me peekin', for he leaned over and whispered to me.

"I overlooked my hand," he says. "I thought all the wile it was a straight."

"Yes," I says, "that's why you raised twice by mistake."

They was another pot that he come into with tens and fours. It was tilted a couple o' times and two o' the strong fellas drawed ahead of Ike. They each drawed one. So Ike throwed away his little pair and come out with four tens. And they was four treys against him. Carey'd looked at Ike's discards and then he says:

"This lucky bum busted two pair."

"No, no, I didn't," says Ike.

"Yes, yes, you did," says Carey, and showed us the two fours.

"What do you know about that?" says Ike. "I'd of swore one was a five spot."

Well, we hadn't had no pay day yet, and after a wile everybody except Ike was goin' shy. I could see him gettin' restless and I was wonderin' how he'd make the get-away. He tried two or three times. "I got to buy some collars before supper," he says.

"No hurry," says Smitty. "The stores here keeps open all night in April."

After a minute he opened up again.

"My uncle out in Nebraska ain't expected to live," he says. "I ought to send a telegram."

"Would that save him?" says Carey.

"No, it sure wouldn't," says Ike, "but I ought to leave my old man know where I'm at."

"When did you hear about your uncle?" says Carey.

"Just this mornin'," says Ike.

"Who told you?" ast Carey.

"I got a wire from my old man," says Ike.

"Well," says Carey, "your old man knows you're still here yet this afternoon if you was here this mornin'. Trains leavin' Cincinnati in the middle o' the day don't carry no ball clubs."

"Yes," says Ike, "that's true. But he don't know where I'm goin' to be next week."

"Ain't he got no schedule?" ast Carey.

"I sent him one openin' day," says Ike, "but it takes mail a long time to get to Idaho."

"I thought your old man lived in Kansas City," says Carey.

"He does when he's home," says Ike.

"But now," says Carey, "I s'pose he's went to Idaho so as he can be near your sick uncle in Nebraska."

"He's visitin' my other uncle in Idaho."

"Then how does he keep posted about your sick uncle?" ast Carey.

"He don't," says Ike. "He don't even know my other uncle's sick. That's why I ought to wire and tell him."

"Good night!" says Carey.

"What town in Idaho is your old man at?" I says.

Ike thought it over.

"No town at all," he says. "But he's near a town."

"Near what town?" I says.

"Yuma," says Ike.

Well, by this time he'd lost two or three pots and he was desperate. We was playin' just as fast as we could, because we seen we couldn't hold him much longer. But he was tryin' so hard to frame an escape that he couldn't pay no attention to the cards, and it looked like we'd get his whole pile away from him if we could make him stick.

The telephone saved him. The minute it begun to ring, five of us jumped for it. But Ike was there first.

"Yes," he says, answerin' it. "This is him. I'll come right down."

And he slammed up the receiver and beat it out o' the door without even sayin' good-by.

"Smitty'd ought to locked the door," says Carey.

"What did he win?" ast Carey.

We figured it up—sixty-odd bucks.

"And the next time we ask him to play," says Carey, "his fingers will be so stiff he can't hold the cards."

Well, we set round a wile talkin' it over, and pretty soon the telephone rung again. Smitty answered it. It was a friend of his'n from Hamilton and he wanted to know why Smitty didn't hurry down. He was the one that had called before and Ike had told him he was Smitty.

"Ike'd ought to split with Smitty's friend," says Carey.

"No," I says, "he'll need all he won. It costs money to buy collars and to send telegrams from Cincinnati to your old man in Texas and keep him posted on the health o' your uncle in Cedar Rapids, D. C."

And you ought to heard him out there on that field! They wasn't a day when he didn't pull six or seven, and it didn't make no difference whether he was goin' good or bad. If he popped up in the pinch he should of made a base hit and the reason he didn't was so-and-so. And if he cracked one for three bases he ought to had a home run, only the ball wasn't lively, or the wind brought it back, or he tripped on a lump o' dirt, roundin' first base.

They was one afternoon in New York when he beat all records. Big Marquard was workin' against us and he was good.

In the first innin' Ike hit one clear over that right field stand, but it was a few feet foul. Then he got another foul and then the count come to two and two. Then Rube slipped one acrost on him and he was called out.

"What do you know about that!" he says afterward on the bench. "I lost count. I thought it was three and one, and I took a strike."

"You took a strike all right," says Carey. "Even the umps knowed it was a strike."

"Yes," says Ike, "but you can bet I wouldn't of took it if I'd knew it was the third one. The score board had it wrong."

"That score board ain't for you to look at," says Cap. "It's for you to hit that old pill against."

"Well," says Ike, "I could of hit that one over the score board if I'd knew it was the third."

"Was it a good ball?" I says.

"Well, no, it wasn't," says Ike. "It was inside."

"How far inside?" says Carey.

"Oh, two or three inches or half a foot," says Ike.

"I guess you wouldn't of threatened the score board with it then," says Cap.

"I'd of pulled it down the right foul line if I hadn't thought he'd call it a ball," says Ike.

Well, in New York's part o' the innin' Doyle cracked one and Ike run back a mile and a half and caught it with one hand. We was all sayin' what a whale of a play it was, but he had to apologize just the same as for gettin' struck out.

"That stand's so high," he says, "that a man don't never see a ball till it's right on top o' you."

"Didn't you see that one?" ast Cap.

"Not at first," says Ike; "not till it raised up above the roof o' the stand."

"Then why did you start back as soon as the ball was hit?" says Cap.

"I knowed by the sound that he'd got a good hold of it," says Ike.

"Yes," says Cap, "but how'd you know what direction to run in?"

"Doyle usually hits 'em that way, the way I run," says Ike.

"Why don't you play blindfolded?" says Carey.

"Might as well, with that big high stand to bother a man," says

Ike. "If I could of saw the ball all the time I'd of got it in my hip pocket."

Along in the fifth we was one run to the bad and Ike got on with one out. On the first ball throwed to Smitty, Ike went down. The ball was outside and Meyers throwed Ike out by ten feet.

You could see Ike's lips movin' all the way to the bench and when he got there he had his piece learned.

"Why didn't he swing?" he says.

"Why didn't you wait for his sign?" says Cap.

"He give me his sign," says Ike.

"What is his sign with you?" says Cap.

"Pickin' up some dirt with his right hand," says Ike.

"Well, I didn't see him do it," Cap says.

"He done it all right," says Ike.

Well, Smitty went out and they wasn't no more argument till they come in for the next innin'. Then Cap opened it up.

"You fellas better get your signs straight," he says.

"Do you mean me?" says Smitty.

"Yes," Cap says. "What's your sign with Ike?"

"Slidin' my left hand up to the end o' the bat and back," says Smitty.

"Do you hear that, Ike?" ast Cap.

"What of it?" says Ike.

"You says his sign was pickin' up dirt and he says it's slidin' his hand. Which is right?"

"I'm right," says Smitty. "But if you're arguin' about him goin' last innin', I didn't give him no sign."

"You pulled your cap down with your right hand, didn't you?" ast Ike.

"Well, s'pose I did," says Smitty. "That don't mean nothin'. I never told you to take that for a sign, did I?"

"I thought maybe you meant to tell me and forgot," says Ike.

They couldn't none of us answer that and they wouldn't of been no more said if Ike had of shut up. But wile we was settin' there Carey got on with two out and stole second clean.

"There!" says Ike. "That's what I was tryin' to do and I'd of got away with it if Smitty'd swang and bothered the Indian."

"Oh!" says Smitty. "You was tryin' to steal then, was you? I thought you claimed I give you the hit and run."

"I didn't claim no such a thing," says Ike. "I thought maybe you might of gave me a sign, but I was goin' anyway because I thought I had a good start."

Cap prob'ly would of hit him with a bat, only just about that time Doyle booted one on Hayes and Carey come acrost with the run that tied.

Well, we go into the ninth finally, one and one, and Marquard walks McDonald with nobody out.

"Lay it down," says Cap to Ike.

And Ike goes up there with orders to bunt and cracks the first ball into that right-field stand! It was fair this time, and we're two ahead, but I didn't think about that at the time. I was too busy watchin' Cap's face. First he turned pale and then he got red as fire and then he got blue and purple, and finally he just laid back and busted out laughin'. So we wasn't afraid to laugh ourselfs when we seen him doin' it, and when Ike come in everybody on the bench was in hysterics.

But instead o' takin' advantage, Ike had to try and excuse himself. His play was to shut up and he didn't know how to make it.

"Well," he says, "if I hadn't hit quite so quick at that one I bet it'd of cleared the center-field fence."

Cap stopped laughin'.

"It'll cost you plain fifty," he says.

"What for?" says Ike.

"When I say 'bunt' I mean 'bunt,'" says Cap.

"You didn't say 'bunt,'" says Ike.

"I says 'Lay it down,'" says Cap. "If that don't mean 'bunt,' what does it mean?"

"'Lay it down' means 'bunt' all right," says Ike, "but I understood you to say 'Lay on it.'"

"All right," says Cap, "and the little misunderstandin' will cost you fifty."

Ike didn't say nothin' for a few minutes. Then he had another bright idear.

"I was just kiddin' about misunderstandin' you," he says. "I knowed you wanted me to bunt."

"Well, then, why didn't you bunt?" ast Cap.

"I was goin' to on the next ball," says Ike. "But I thought if I took a good wallop I'd have 'em all fooled. So I walloped at the first one to fool 'em, and I didn't have no intention o' hittin' it."

"You tried to miss it, did you?" says Cap.

"Yes," says Ike.

"How'd you happen to hit it?" ast Cap.

"Well," Ike says, "I was lookin' for him to throw me a fast one and I was goin' to swing under it. But he come with a hook and I met it right square where I was swingin' to go under the fast one."

"Great!" says Cap. "Boys," he says, "Ike's learned how to hit Marquard's curve. Pretend a fast one's comin' and then try to miss it. It's a good thing to know and Ike'd ought to be willin' to pay for the lesson. So I'm goin' to make it a hundred instead o' fifty."

The game wound up 3 to 1. The fine didn't go, because Ike hit like a wild man all through that trip and we made pretty near a clean-up. The night we went to Philly I got him cornered in the car and I says to him:

"Forget them alibis for a wile and tell me somethin'. What'd you do that for, swing that time against Marquard when you was told to bunt?"

"I'll tell you," he says. "That ball he throwed me looked just like the one I struck out on in the first innin' and I wanted to show Cap what I could of done to that other one if I'd knew it was the third strike."

"But," I says, "the one you struck out on in the first innin' was a fast ball."

"So was the one I cracked in the ninth," says Ike.

You've saw Cap's wife, o' course. Well, her sister's about twict as good-lookin' as her, and that's goin' some.

Cap took his missus down to St. Louis the second trip and the other one come down from St. Joe to visit her. Her name is Dolly, and some doll is right.

Well, Cap was goin' to take the two sisters to a show and he wanted a beau for Dolly. He left it to her and she picked Ike. He'd hit three on the nose that afternoon—off'n Sallee, too.

They fell for each other that first evenin'. Cap told us how it come off. She begin flatterin' Ike for the star game he'd played and o' course he begin excusin' himself for not doin' better. So she thought he was modest and it went strong with her. And she believed everything he said and that made her solid with him—that and her make-up. They was together every mornin' and evenin' for the five days we was

there. In the afternoons Ike played the grandest ball you ever see, hittin'
and runnin' the bases like a fool and catchin' everything that stayed
in the park.

I told Cap, I says: "You'd ought to keep the doll with us and he'd
make Cobb's figures look sick."

But Dolly had to go back to St. Joe and we come home for a long
serious.

Well, for the next three weeks Ike had a letter to read every day
and he'd set in the clubhouse readin' it till mornin' practice was half
over. Cap didn't say nothin' to him, because he was goin' so good.
But I and Carey wasted a lot of our time tryin' to get him to own up
who the letters was from. Fine chanct!

"What are you readin'?" Carey'd say. "A bill?"

"No," Ike'd say, "not exactly a bill. It's a letter from a fella I used
to go to school with."

"High school or college?" I'd ask him.

"College," he'd say.

"What college?" I'd say.

Then he'd stall a wile and then he'd say:

"I didn't go to the college myself, but my friend went there."

"How did it happen you didn't go?" Carey'd ask him.

"Well," he'd say, "they wasn't no colleges near where I lived."

"Didn't you live in Kansas City?" I'd say to him.

One time he'd say he did and another time he didn't. One time he
says he lived in Michigan.

"Where at?" says Carey.

"Near Detroit," he says.

"Well," I says, "Detroit's near Ann Arbor and that's where they
got the university."

"Yes," says Ike, "they got it there now, but they didn't have it there
then."

"I come pretty near goin' to Syracuse," I says, "only they wasn't no
railroads runnin' through there in them days."

"Where'd this friend o' yours go to college?" says Carey.

"I forget now," says Ike.

"Was it Carlisle?" ast Carey.

"No," says Ike, "his folks wasn't very well off."

"That's what barred me from Smith," I says.

"I was goin' to tackle Cornell's," says Carey, "but the doctor told me I'd have hay fever if I didn't stay up North."

"Your friend writes long letters," I says.

"Yes," says Ike; "he's tellin' me about a ball player."

"Where does he play?" ast Carey.

"Down in the Texas League—Fort Wayne," says Ike.

"It looks like a girl's writin'," Carey says.

"A girl wrote it," says Ike. "That's my friend's sister, writin' for him."

"Didn't they teach writin' at this here college where he went?" says Carey.

"Sure," Ike says, "they taught writin', but he got his hand cut off in a railroad wreck."

"How long ago?" I says.

"Right after he got out o' college," says Ike.

"Well," I says, "I should think he'd of learned to write with his left hand by this time."

"It's his left hand that was cut off," says Ike; "and he was left-handed."

"You get a letter every day," says Carey. "They're all the same writin'. Is he tellin' you about a different ball player every time he writes?"

"No," Ike says. "It's the same ball player. He just tells me what he does every day."

"From the size o' the letters, they don't play nothin' but double-headers down there," says Carey.

We figured that Ike spent most of his evenin's answerin' the letters from his "friend's sister," so we kept tryin' to date him up for shows and parties to see how he'd duck out of 'em. He was bugs over spaghetti, so we told him one day that they was goin' to be a big feed of it over to Joe's that night and he was invited.

"How long'll it last?" he says.

"Well," we says, "we're goin' right over there after the game and stay till they close up."

"I can't go," he says, "unless they leave me come home at eight bells."

"Nothin' doin'," says Carey. "Joe'd get sore."

"I can't go then," says Ike.

"Why not?" I ast him.

"Well," he says, "my landlady locks up the house at eight and I left my key home."

"You can come and stay with me," says Carey.

"No," he says, "I can't sleep in a strange bed."

"How do you get along when we're on the road?" says I.

"I don't never sleep the first night anywheres," he says. "After that I'm all right."

"You'll have time to chase home and get your key right after the game," I told him.

"The key ain't home," says Ike. "I lent it to one o' the other fellas and he's went out o' town and took it with him."

"Couldn't you borry another key off'n the landlady?" Carey ast him.

"No," he says, "that's the only one they is."

Well, the day before we started East again, Ike come into the club-house all smiles.

"Your birthday?" I ast him.

"No," he says.

"What do you feel so good about?" I says.

"Got a letter from my old man," he says. "My uncle's goin' to get well."

"Is that the one in Nebraska?" says I.

"Not right in Nebraska," says Ike. "Near there."

But afterwards we got the right dope from Cap. Dolly'd blew in from Missouri and was goin' to make the trip with her sister.

Well, I want to alibi Carey and I for what come off in Boston. If we'd of had any idear what we was doin', we'd never did it. They wasn't nobody outside o' maybe Ike and the dame that felt worse over it than I and Carey.

The first two days we didn't see nothin' of Ike and her except out to the park. The rest o' the time they was sight-seein' over to Cambridge and down to Revere and out to Brook-a-line and all the other places where the rubes go.

But when we come into the beanery after the third game Cap's wife called us over.

"If you want to see somethin' pretty," she says, "look at the third finger on Sis's left hand."

Well, o' course we knew before we looked that it wasn't goin' to be no hangnail. Nobody was su'prised when Dolly blew into the dinin' room with it—a rock that Ike'd bought off'n Diamond Joe the first trip to New York. Only o' course it'd been set into a lady's-size ring instead o' the automobile tire he'd been wearin'.

Cap and his missus and Ike and Dolly ett supper together, only Ike didn't eat nothin', but just set there blushin' and spillin' things on the table-cloth. I heard him excusin' himself for not havin' no appetite. He says he couldn't never eat when he was clost to the ocean. He'd forgot about them sixty-five oysters he destroyed the first night o' the trip before.

He was goin' to take her to a show, so after supper he went upstairs to change his collar. She had to doll up, too, and o' course Ike was through long before her.

If you remember the hotel in Boston, they's a little parlor where the piano's at and then they's another little parlor openin' off o' that. Well, when Ike come down Smitty was playin' a few chords and I and Carey was harmonizin'. We seen Ike go up to the desk to leave his key and we called him in. He tried to duck away, but we wouldn't stand for it.

We ast him what he was all duded up for and he says he was goin' to the theayter.

"Goin' alone?" says Carey.

"No," he says, "a friend o' mine's goin' with me."

"What do you say if we go along?" says Carey.

"I ain't only got two tickets," he says.

"Well," says Carey, "we can go down there with you and buy our own seats; maybe we can all get together."

"No," says Ike. "They ain't no more seats. They're all sold out."

"We can buy some off'n the scalpers," says Carey.

"I wouldn't if I was you," says Ike. "They say the show's rotten."

"What are you goin' for, then?" I ast.

"I didn't hear about it bein' rotten till I got the tickets," he says.

"Well," I says, "if you don't want to go I'll buy the tickets from you."

"No," says Ike, "I wouldn't want to cheat you. I'm stung and I'll just have to stand for it."

"What are you goin' to do with the girl, leave her here at the hotel?" I says.

"What girl?" says Ike.

"The girl you ett supper with," I says.

"Oh," he says, "we just happened to go into the dinin' room together, that's all. Cap wanted I should set down with 'em."

"I noticed," says Carey, "that she happened to be wearin' that rock you bought off'n Diamond Joe."

"Yes," says Ike. "I lent it to her for a wile."

"Did you lend her the new ring that goes with it?" I says.

"She had that already," says Ike. "She lost the set out of it."

"I wouldn't trust no strange girl with a rock o' mine," says Carey.

"Oh, I guess she's all right," Ike says. "Besides, I was tired o' the stone. When a girl asks you for somethin', what are you goin' to do?"

He started out toward the desk, but we flagged him.

"Wait a minute!" Carey says. "I got a bet with Sam here, and it's up to you to settle it."

"Well," says Ike, "make it snappy. My friend'll be here any minute."

"I bet," says Carey, "that you and that girl was engaged to be married."

"Nothin' to it," says Ike.

"Now look here," says Carey, "this is goin' to cost me real money if I lose. Cut out the alibi stuff and give it to us straight. Cap's wife just as good as told us you was roped."

Ike blushed like a kid.

"Well, boys," he says, "I may as well own up. You win, Carey."

"Yatta boy!" says Carey. "Congratulations!"

"You got a swell girl, Ike," I says.

"She's a peach," says Smitty.

"Well, I guess she's O. K.," says Ike. "I don't know much about girls."

"Didn't you never run round with 'em?" I says.

"Oh, yes, plenty of 'em," says Ike. "But I never seen none I'd fall for."

"That is, till you seen this one," says Carey.

"Well," says Ike, "this one's O. K., but I wasn't thinkin' about gettin' married yet a wile."

"Who done the askin'—her?" says Carey.

"Oh, no," says Ike, "but sometimes a man don't know what he's gettin' into. Take a good-lookin' girl, and a man gen'ally almost always does about what she wants him to."

"They couldn't no girl lasso me unless I wanted to be lassoed," says Smitty.

"Oh, I don't know," says Ike. "When a fella gets to feelin' sorry for one of 'em it's all off."

Well, we left him go after shakin' hands all round. But he didn't take Dolly to no show that night. Some time wile we was talkin' she'd came into that other parlor and she'd stood there and heard us. I don't know how much she heard. But it was enough. Dolly and Cap's missus took the midnight train for New York. And from there Cap's wife sent her on her way back to Missouri.

She'd left the ring and a note for Ike with the clerk. But we didn't ask Ike if the note was from his friend in Fort Wayne, Texas.

When we'd came to Boston Ike was hittin' plain .397. When we got back home he'd fell off to pretty near nothin'. He hadn't drove one out o' the infield in any o' them other Eastern parks, and he didn't even give no excuse for it.

To show you how bad he was, he struck out three times in Brooklyn one day and never opened his trap when Cap ast him what was the matter. Before, if he'd whiffed oncet in a game he'd of wrote a book tellin' why.

Well, we dropped from first place to fifth in four weeks and we was still goin' down. I and Carey was about the only ones in the club that spoke to each other, and all as we did was remind ourself o' what a boner we'd pulled.

"It's goin' to beat us out o' the big money," says Carey.

"Yes," I says. "I don't want to knock my own ball club, but it looks like a one-man team, and when that one man's dauber's down we couldn't trim our whiskers."

"We ought to knew better," says Carey.

"Yes," I says, "but why should a man pull an alibi for bein' engaged to such a bearcat as she was?"

"He shouldn't," says Carey. "But I and you knowed he would or we'd never started talkin' to him about it. He wasn't no more ashamed o' the girl than I am of a regular base hit. But he just can't come clean on no subjec'."

Cap had the whole story, and I and Carey was as pop'lar with him as an umpire.

"What do you want me to do, Cap?" Carey'd say to him before goin' up to hit.

"Use your own judgment," Cap'd tell him. "We want to lose another game."

But finally, one night in Pittsburgh, Cap had a letter from his missus and he come to us with it.

"You fellas," he says, "is the ones that put us on the bum, and if you're sorry I think they's a chancet for you to make good. The old lady's out to St. Joe and she's been tryin' her hardest to fix things up. She's explained that Ike don't mean nothin' with his talk; I've wrote and explained that to Dolly, too. But the old lady says that Dolly says that she can't believe it. But Dolly's still stuck on this baby, and she's pinin' away just the same as Ike. And the old lady says she thinks if you two fellas would write to the girl and explain how you was always kiddin' with Ike and leadin' him on, and how the ball club was all shot to pieces since Ike quit hittin', and how he acted like he was goin' to kill himself, and this and that, she'd fall for it and maybe soften down. Dolly, the old lady says, would believe you before she'd believe I and the old lady, because she thinks it's her we're sorry for, and not him."

Well, I and Carey was only too glad to try and see what we could do. But it wasn't no snap. We wrote about eight letters before we got one that looked good. Then we give it to the stenographer and had it wrote out on a typewriter and both of us signed it.

It was Carey's idear that made the letter good. He stuck in somethin' about the world's serious money that our wives wasn't goin' to spend unless she took pity on a "boy who was so shy and modest that he was afraid to come right out and say that he had asked such a beautiful and handsome girl to become his bride."

That's prob'ly what got her, or maybe she couldn't of held out much longer anyway. It was four days after we sent the letter that Cap heard from his missus again. We was in Cincinnati.

"We've won," he says to us. "The old lady says that Dolly says she'll give him another chance. But the old lady says it won't do no good for Ike to write a letter. He'll have to go out there."

"Send him to-night," says Carey.

"I'll pay half his fare," I says.

"I'll pay the other half," says Carey.

"No," says Cap, "the club'll pay his expenses. I'll send him scoutin'."

"Are you goin' to send him to-night?"

"Sure," says Cap. "But I'm goin' to break the news to him right now. It's time we win a ball game."

So in the clubhouse, just before the game, Cap told him. And I certainly felt sorry for Rube Benton and Red Ames that afternoon! I and Carey was standin' in front o' the hotel that night when Ike come out with his suitcase.

"Sent home?" I says to him.

"No," he says, "I'm goin' scoutin'."

"Where to?" I says. "Fort Wayne?"

"No, not exactly," he says.

"Well," says Carey, "have a good time."

"I ain't lookin' for no good time," says Ike. "I says I was goin' scoutin'."

"Well, then," says Carey, "I hope you see somebody you like."

"And you better have a drink before you go," I says.

"Well," says Ike, "they claim it helps a cold."

FABLES AND OTHER MORAL TALES

Fables teach a little lesson. This section of our book should prove useful to those who wish to improve their ways, or minds.

Among the moralists missing here is Kin Hubbard, a good teacher and a funny one. We fully intended putting him in, but backed down when we found, after collecting a bagful of Abe Martin's sayings, that we didn't enjoy reading them when they were strung together like sausages: they should be taken, as originally published, one after breakfast in the morning. It was hard to abandon Kin Hubbard after reading what he said about a garden. (He said in order to live off a garden, you practically had to live in it.)

James Thurber

FABLES FOR OUR TIME

THE OWL WHO WAS GOD

Once upon a starless midnight there was an owl who sat on the branch of an oak tree. Two ground moles tried to slip quietly by, unnoticed. "You!" said the owl. "Who?" they quavered, in fear and astonishment, for they could not believe it was possible for anyone to see them in that thick darkness. "You two!" said the owl. The moles hurried away and told the other creatures of the field and forest that the owl was the greatest and wisest of all animals because he could see in the dark and because he could answer any question. "I'll see about that," said a secretary bird, and he called on the owl one night when it was again very dark. "How many claws am I holding up?" said the secretary bird. "Two," said the owl, and that was right. "Can you give me another expression for 'that is to say' or 'namely'?" asked the secretary bird. "To wit," said the owl. "Why does a lover call on his love?" asked the secretary bird. "To woo," said the owl.

The secretary bird hastened back to the other creatures and reported that the owl was indeed the greatest and wisest animal in the world because he could see in the dark and because he could answer any question. "Can he see in the daytime, too?" asked a red fox. "Yes," echoed a dormouse and a French poodle. "Can he see in the daytime, too?" All the other creatures laughed loudly at this silly question, and they set upon the red fox and his friends and drove them out of the region. Then they sent a messenger to the owl and asked him to be their leader.

When the owl appeared among the animals it was high noon and the sun was shining brightly. He walked very slowly, which gave him an appearance of great dignity, and he peered about him with large, staring eyes, which gave him an air of tremendous importance. "He's God!" screamed a Plymouth Rock hen. And the others took up the cry "He's God!" So they followed him wherever he went and when he began to bump into things they began to bump into things, too. Finally he came to a concrete highway and he started up the middle of it and all the other creatures followed him. Presently a hawk, who was acting as outrider, observed a truck coming toward them at fifty miles an hour, and he reported to the secretary bird and the secretary bird reported to the owl. "There's danger ahead," said the secretary bird. "To wit?" said the owl. The secretary bird told him. "Aren't you afraid?" he asked. "Who?" said the owl calmly, for he could not see the truck. "He's God!" cried all the creatures again, and they were still crying "He's God!" when the truck hit them and ran them down. Some of the animals were merely injured, but most of them, including the owl, were killed.

Moral: You can fool too many of the people too much of the time.

THE SHRIKE AND THE CHIPMUNKS

Once upon a time there were two chipmunks, a male and a female. The male chipmunk thought that arranging nuts in artistic patterns was more fun than just piling them up to see how many you could pile up. The female was all for piling up as many as you could. She told her husband that if he gave up making designs with the nuts there would be room in their large cave for a great many more and he would soon become the wealthiest chipmunk in the woods. But he would not let her interfere with his designs, so she flew into a rage and left him. "The shrike will get you," she said, "because you are helpless and cannot look after yourself." To be sure, the female chipmunk had not been gone three nights before the male had to dress for a banquet and could not find his studs or shirt or suspenders. So

he couldn't go to the banquet, but that was just as well, because all the chipmunks who did go were attacked and killed by a weasel.

The next day the shrike began hanging around outside the chipmunk's cave, waiting to catch him. The shrike couldn't get in because the doorway was clogged up with soiled laundry and dirty dishes. "He will come out for a walk after breakfast and I will get him then," thought the shrike. But the chipmunk slept all day and did not get up and have breakfast until after dark. Then he came out for a breath of air before beginning work on a new design. The shrike swooped down to snatch up the chipmunk, but could not see very well on account of the dark, so he batted his head against an alder branch and was killed.

A few days later the female chipmunk returned and saw the awful mess the house was in. She went to the bed and shook her husband. "What would you do without me?" she demanded. "Just go on living, I guess," he said. "You wouldn't last five days," she told him. She swept the house and did the dishes and sent out the laundry, and then she made the chipmunk get up and wash and dress. "You can't be healthy if you lie in bed all day and never get any exercise," she told him. So she took him for a walk in the bright sunlight and they were both caught and killed by the shrike's brother, a shrike named Stoop.

Moral: Early to rise and early to bed makes a male healthy and wealthy and dead.

THE MOTH AND THE STAR

A young and impressionable moth once set his heart on a certain star. He told his mother about this and she counselled him to set his heart on a bridge lamp instead. "Stars aren't the thing to hang around," she said; "lamps are the thing to hang around." "You get somewhere that way," said the moth's father. "You don't get anywhere chasing stars." But the moth would not heed the words of either parent. Every evening at dusk when the star came out he would start flying toward it and every morning at dawn he would crawl back home worn out with his vain endeavor. One day his father said to him, "You haven't burned a wing in months, boy, and it looks to me as if you were never going to. All your brothers have been badly burned flying around street lamps and all your sisters have been terribly singed flying around house lamps. Come on, now, get out of here and get yourself scorched! A big strapping moth like you without a mark on him!"

The moth left his father's house, but he would not fly around street lamps and he would not fly around house lamps. He went right on trying to reach the star, which was four and one-third light years, or twenty-five trillion miles, away. The moth thought it was just caught in the top branches of an elm. He never did reach the star, but he went right on trying, night after night, and when he was a very, very old moth he began to think that he really had reached the star and he went around saying so. This gave him a deep and lasting pleasure, and he lived to a great old age. His parents and his brothers and his sisters had all been burned to death when they were quite young.

Moral: Who flies afar from the sphere of our sorrow is here today and here tomorrow.

THE UNICORN IN THE GARDEN

Once upon a sunny morning a man who sat in a breakfast nook looked up from his scrambled eggs to see a white unicorn with a golden horn quietly cropping roses in the garden. The man went up to the bedroom where his wife was still asleep and woke her. "There's a unicorn in the garden," he said. "Eating roses." She opened one unfriendly eye and looked at him. "The unicorn is a mythical beast," she said, and turned her back on him. The man walked slowly downstairs and out into the garden. The unicorn was still there; he was now browsing among the tulips. "Here, unicorn," said the man, and he pulled up a lily and gave it to him. The unicorn ate it gravely. With a high heart, because there was a unicorn in his garden, the man went upstairs and roused his wife again. "The unicorn ate a lily," he said. His wife sat up in bed and looked at him coldly. "You are a booby," she said, "and I am going to have you put in the booby hatch." The man, who had never liked the words "booby" and "booby hatch," and who liked them even less on a shining morning when there was a unicorn in the garden, thought for a moment. "We'll see about that," he said. He walked over to the door. "He has a golden horn in the middle of his forehead," he told her. Then he went back to the garden to watch the unicorn, but the unicorn had gone away. The man sat down among the roses and went to sleep.

As soon as the husband had gone out of the house, the wife got up and dressed as fast as she could. She was very excited and there was a gloat in her eye. She telephoned the police and she telephoned a psychiatrist; she told them to hurry to her house and bring a strait jacket. When the police and the psychiatrist arrived, they sat down in chairs and looked at her with great interest. "My husband," she said, "saw a unicorn this morning." The police looked at the psychiatrist and the psychiatrist looked at the police. "He told me it ate a lily," she said. The psychiatrist looked at the police and the police looked at the psychiatrist. "He told me it had a golden horn in the middle of its forehead," she said. At a solemn signal from the psychiatrist, the police leaped from their chairs and seized the wife. They had a hard time subduing her, for she put up a terrific struggle, but they finally subdued her. Just as they got her into the strait jacket, her husband came back into the house. "Did you tell your wife you saw a unicorn?" asked the psychiatrist. "Of course not," said the husband. "The unicorn is a mythical beast." "That's all I wanted to know," said the psychiatrist. "Take her away. I'm sorry, sir, but your wife is as crazy as a jay bird." So they took her away, cursing and screaming, and shut her up in an institution. The husband lived happily ever after.

   Moral: Don't count your boobies until they are hatched.

George Ade

FABLES IN SLANG

THE PROFESSOR WHO WANTED TO BE ALONE

Now it happens that in America a man who goes up hanging to a Balloon is a Professor.

One day a Professor, preparing to make a Grand Ascension, was sorely pestered by Spectators of the Yellow-Hammer Variety, who fell over the Stay-Ropes or crowded up close to the Balloon to ask Fool Questions. They wanted to know how fur up he Calkilated to go and was he Afeerd and how often had he did it. The Professor answered them in the Surly Manner peculiar to Showmen accustomed to meet a Web-Foot Population. On the Q. T. the Prof. had Troubles of his own. He was expected to drop in at a Bank on the following Day and take up a Note for 100 Plunks. The Ascension meant 50 to him, but how to Corral the other 50? That was the Hard One.

This question was in his Mind as he took hold of the Trapeze Bar and signaled the Farm Hands to let go. As he trailed Skyward beneath the buoyant silken Bag he hung by his Knees and waved a glad Adieu to the Mob of Inquisitive Yeomen. A Sense of Relief came to him as he saw the Crowd sink away in the Distance.

Hanging by one Toe, and with his right Palm pressed to his Eyes, he said: "Now that I am Alone, let me Think, let me Think."

There in the Vast Silence He Thought.

Presently he gave a sigh of Relief.

"I will go to my Wife's Brother and make a Quick Touch," he said. "If he refuses to Unbelt I will threaten to tell his Wife of the bracelet he bought in Louisville."

Having reached this Happy Conclusion, he loosened the Parachute and quickly descended to the Earth.

Moral: Avoid Crowds.

THE WAIST-BAND THAT WAS TAUT UP TO THE MOMENT IT GAVE WAY

Once there was a Family consisting of Mr. and Mrs. Stuffer and three little Stuffers.

Mrs. Stuffer had belonged to the Bolt Family back in Fodderville, where she put on Weight before being shipped up to the City.

Her Mother was a Gullep, and Lineal Descendant of a New England Pilgrim named Grubb.

Mr. Stuffer also was well connected, never fear.

His Mother had been one of the Gobbels and his Grandsire on the other Branch of the Tree was often referred to, for he was none other than Phillip Gormann-Deizer, with a Colonial Home near the Gorge at Eatonville.

Their Folks, as far back as Records carried, had regarded America as the Land of Plenty and Then Some.

Also one of the Traditions coming from the grand old Pioneer Stock seemed to be that the Main Tract of the Alimentary System is the Home of the Soul.

The Stuffers could say truly that not one of their previous Relatives ever permitted a Guest to go away Hungry.

Sometimes he was taking Bi-Carb when he departed, but, Thank Edna, he never was craving Nourishment.

So the Family Honour stood safe and intact.

Back in the Country, where the Stuffers received their early Schooling as two-handed Scoopers, no Man could hold up his Head unless he was a bountiful Provider, and no Woman was respected unless she had Apple Butter and two kinds of Pie on the Table.

Those were the Blissful Days when the Deacon with the Throat-Warmers would close his Eyes and ask that this Food be Blessed and Sanctified to our Uses.

And take it from Hortense, when the Deacon made that reasonable Request, there was something piled in front of him waiting to be Sanctified.

No one ever heard of Luxuries during that oleaginous Period.

Anything that could be Et was a Necessity.

The family that wanted a Sunday Dinner away back Yonder did not have to hock the Morris Chairs.

The Barn Lot was swarming with Springers; the Garden had many rows of Sass; Berries could be had for the Picking.

Anything you might think of was Ten Cents.

For one measly Dime, the genial Grocer would let you have a Pound of Butter or a Dozen Eggs or a Peck of Murphys or a hunk of Bacon or an armful of Roasting Ears.

Beans were about as costly as Gravel.

Off in the Pantry, the solid loaves of Salt-Rising Bread were stacked, careless-like, the same as Cord-Wood.

The Humble Toiler who stowed away 14 to 16 Spare-Ribs smothered with Kraut, four or five helpings of Fresh Vegetables, a few light Biscuits inlaid with golden Butter, and possibly a quarter of a mile of Noodles, would trick out his Modest Snack with Spiced Peaches, frosty Doughnuts, and a little quart Bowl of preserved Cherries, to say nothing of Coffee Curdled with heavy Cream, and never suspect that he was living somewhat Snooky.

He was simply getting regular every-day Chow of the Farm-Hand variety.

It was on Sunday, when the Minister and his Wife or Cousin Elam's Family came over, that Mother extended herself and showed Class.

The Family never had Flowers on the Table, because the Space was taken up with Jams and Jells.

At that time, Dinner did not open with *Canapé Scabouche* followed by *Potage à la Bohonque*.

It opened with a Breast and a Second Joint and a couple of Drumsticks and much Gravy, with here and there a Giblet, and enough Mashed Potatoes to plaster a Small Room, and a Million Green Peas that never had been to Market, and an awful mix-up of String Beans, while the Odd Corners were chinked in with Cottage Cheese and Pickled Watermelon Rind and Sweet Peppers.

Butter was not rolled into Marbles during the Seventies.

Well, we should say Not!

It was lifted in half-pound Gobs, and those who smeared it never felt Improvident.

What is now called Service consisted of cleaning up the Trough and going back for another Load.

The Conversation was wholly made up of:

(1) Urgent Appeals for every one to Pack in a little bit more;

(2) Weak Protests from the Packees;

(3) Contrite Apologies from the Cook as to the Quality and Amount of Eatables in sight;

(4) Stereotyped Assurances to perturbed Hostess that everything was Swell, Elegant, and Hunky.

If the Fig Cake was a Triumph and the Jelly Cake held its Shape but the Hickory-Nut Cake went Blah, that called for a lot of Explaining.

There was a Time when every Woman thought that a soggy Cake was a Reflection on her Character. Then, if the Visitors moved slowly from the Dining Room with their Eyes protruding slightly, the Meal was voted a Success.

Not every Parlour sported an upright Piano, and the Citizen who guided a team of Bays from the front Pad of a two-seated Carriage was some Rajah, but the humblest Family waded knee-deep in Vittles.

When Winter came on, each Cellar in the Township was loaded to the Guards with Turnips, Punkins, Bell-Flower Apples, Pop-Corn, Vinegar, Walnuts, Cabbage, Potatoes, Lye Hominy, Side-Meat, Canned Stuff, Hard Cider, Sorghum Molasses, Lard, Honey in the Comb, Rutabagas, Fruit-Jars in Platoons, Jelly-Glasses in Brigades, Sage, Carrots, Navy Beans, Corn Meal, Buckwheat Flour, Onions, and other Medicinal Herbs, with possibly a few chilled Geese and Rabbits for immediate Consumption.

A barbed-wire Entanglement could have been strung around any Domicile in the Autumn, and the imprisoned Family would have come out on May 1st wearing Double Chins.

After the Stuffers landed in Town and had to use pleading Language to get a couple of fibrous Chops, they would become sentimental over Memories of Hog-Killing.

Oh, Elmer!

The Steaming Kettles of Water and the sound of scraping Knives.

Pallid Carcasses suspended in the frosty Air and the gleeful Eviscerators singing "Molly Darling" as they Rummaged.

If a close-figuring Landlady, who tries to set a Table for Seven Per, could have seen the Cans of Lard, the Platters of Tenderloin, the Hams Waiting to be Cured, and the Sausage Meat ready to glide into the Links, she would have declared it was all a Mirage.

It is hard for some People to realize, along in this Stretch of Tribulation, that not long ago, out where Things are Grown, everyone who sat down to a Repast was urged to make a Grand Drive and go as far as he liked.

The mere Thought of any one going light on new-laid Eggs, or laying off on Butter, or messing around with Bran, Excelsior, Sawdust, Husks, Chop-Feed, and other Substitutes for Something to Eat would have been too Silly for Utterance.

The Practice of Economy was well-nigh Universal, but it did not involve playing a Joke on the Œsophagus.

The Woman of the House was Thrifty, for she fed her Cook-Stove a Splinter at a Time.

When Pa's red Unmentionables with the Glass Buttons became too Intimate and Itchy, they were chopped down for Ulysses or Grover.

Patches were made into Quilts and Rags worked over into Carpets.

A Peach-Basket, treated with a Nickel's Worth of Gold Paint and decked out with Bows of Ribbon, became a Hanging Basket for the Pet Geranium.

All the spare Coppers went into the little Tin Bank.

Only a favoured Few were permitted to walk on the Brussels Carpet.

Any good Citizen of Jasper Township would have assured you that Frugality was his Middle Name.

But Frugality did not mean getting up from the Table unsatiated.

For any one to back away before he felt himself Distended would have been regarded as Evidence of a cowardly Nature.

As soon as a Member of the Family began to fly at the Menu with a lack of wolfish Enthusiasm, he was subject to treatment as an Invalid.

The real Local Gazimbat was the Lad who held the Flapjack Record and was ready to meet all Comers during the Sweet-Corn Season.

A never-failing Appetite for anything that could be carried in and planked on the Table was classed as one of the Christian Virtues.

The Owner was held in Regard· as one who had acquired Moral Grandeur and lifted himself above the Weaklings.

He went around blowing that he could Eat Anything, and all the Light Feeders slunk into the Background when he lifted his Bazoo.

Now that you have a Steer on the Pre-Natal Influences and Environment of the Stuffer Family, can you see the Bunch dropped down in a Residence Thoroughfare of a congested Metropolis, three miles from a Cow and six miles from a Hen that could be relied upon to come across every Day?

Although badly separated from the Base of Supplies, they were still true to the honoured Customs of the Grubbs and the Gobbels and the Gulleps.

Mrs. Stuffer often said that she would rather cut off her Right Hand than have an Acquaintance drop in and find one Section of the Dining-Room Table unoccupied by tempting Viands.

She remarked time and again that, Come what Might, she never would Stint her Loved Ones or deny them such simple Essentials as Fresh Eggs, Sure-Enough Butter, Steak cut thick, Leg of Lamb, and submerged Short-Cake.

And there were a Hundred Thousand More like her.

If one is accustomed to the Best—and no real Daughter of a generous Mother ever compromised on Seconds or Culls—one must not Pike when telephoning the Orders.

This elaborate Overture will give you a Rough Idea of what Mr. Stuffer was up against.

He came to the City on a Guarantee.

His Salary looked like the Income of J. P. Morgan until he began to check up the Outgo.

Back in Fodderville, a neat frame Dwelling with a scroll-saw Veranda, a bed of Peonies, and Exposure on four Sides would set you back about $15 per Moon.

Up in the City, you couldn't get a Hat-Rack for any such Money.

It seemed to the Stuffers that everything in Town was sold by the Minute or the Ounce.

It was a grievous Shock to the Missus when they began to weigh the Vegetables on her.

She had got used to having them thrown at her with a Shovel.

The Neighbors no longer brought in Produce at Special inside Prices—Eggs figured by the wear and tear on the Fowl and no Overhead Charge on Honey except the Time put in by the Bees.

The Stuffers suddenly discovered that when you go out to spend a Dollar in the City, you don't have to take a Wheelbarrow along.

But Mr. Stuffer and Mrs. Stuffer and each of the miniature Stuffers had it firmly fixed in the Coke that the Minute you begin letting down on That to which you have been Accustomed you lose Self-Respect and indirectly confess to being in Straitened Circumstances.

It was all right for those living in Huts and Hovels to cheapen the Standards of Living, but the Stuffers could not endure the Thought of giving up any of the old Stand-by Dishes.

Some Persons of a Poetical Turn mark the changing Seasons by the Trailing Arbutus, which precedes the bold Iris; then old-fashioned

Roses, followed by a riotous show of Dahlias; Autumn Leaves tinged Red and Yellow, harbingers of snowy Fields and icy Boughs.

Every Sign of the Zodiac meant a new Item in the Bill of Fare for the practical Stuffers.

With the first warm days of Spring, did they go looking for Wood-Violets?

Not one Look.

They began to sit up and demand Green Onions, Asparagus, Head Lettuce, and Strawberries.

June is the Month of Roses. Also of Fried Chicken and a pleasant gateway to Corn on the Cob.

Autumn Days need not be Melancholy if one is surrounded by Turkey and Mincemeat.

Even Winter has a Charm of its own, if Sausage and Buckwheat Cakes are ever smiling in the Background.

When Prices began to Sizz-Boom-Ah, the old Pay Envelope failed to stand up under the Strain, but can you expect one reared on the Fat of the Land to accept Macaroni as a Compromise?

The Producer would let out a Howl every time the Meat Bill came in, but he would have howled in a higher Key if the Good Woman had failed to throw him his Roast Beef and Mutton Chops.

He wielded a very consistent Knife and Fork and his daily Demand was for something that Sticks to the Ribs.

Of course, both of them saw the Article in the Paper, entitled "How to feed a Family of Five on 80 Cents a Day."

Once, just after the 1st of the Month, while Mr. Stuffer was still Bleeding, his Companion tried out a Sample Menu recommended by Hazel McGinnis Updyke, a famous Tipster weighing between 80 and 90 pounds.

He stirred the watery Soup as if moved by a dull Curiosity as to the grains of Barley hiding at the Bottom, and then he gave Friend Wife a Look—but, Ooey, such a Look!

It seemed to say, "And this is the Woman who promised to Love, Honour, and be of some Help!"

Then came Rice Croquettes, one of the most startling Specimens of Near-Food ever touted by a Lady writing Syndicate Come-Ons and boarding at an Italian Table d'Hôte.

You eat it, but after you get through you are not sure that anything has Happened.

After which, Bread Pudding, said to have broken up more Homes than High White Shoes.

As Mr. Stuffer left the House, his well-meaning Partner felt in her Heart of Hearts that he was going out to a Restaurant to get some Ham and Eggs.

She resolved that never again would she ask him to be Untrue to his Nobler Self.

So, at the next Meal, she jollied him up with Lamb Steak and Kidneys, Mushrooms in Cream, Succotash, Waffles and Maple Syrup, Endive Salad and Sharp Cheese, with a Finale of Blueberry Pie à la Mode.

Experts tell us that Blueberry Pie, showing its bold Colour between the slopes of Vanilla Ice Cream, is practically the Last Word with those who want something to hit the Spot.

It is the *Pièce de Résistance,* the *Dénouement,* the Dramatic Climax, the Grand Transformation, Little Eva ascending to Paradise.

Nothing comes after it except the Pepsin Tablet and the Hot-Water Bag.

Mrs. Stuffer watched her Husband as he lighted his Sublima.

He had a Sleepy Look, which is always a Good Sign.

Then he Groaned, and she knew that she had won back his Love.

Any time you get them to Groaning, you are a Jewel of a Housekeeper.

Having set out to defy the Increased Cost and indulge themselves within Reason, the little Family soon found itself riding a troublous Sea with the Breakers just ahead. Man's Chief Enemies, they had been told long ago, are Pride, Lust, Avarice, etc.

Now they learned Different. They came to know that the two principal Destroyers of Happiness are the Middleman and the Cold-Storage Warehouse.

Hemmed in by extortionate Retailers, Food Pirates, and Commission Sharks, they stood Resolute and vowed they would never Surrender.

As they were riding over the Hills to the Poor-House, Mr. Stuffer made the dismal Observation that it was a Blue Finish for a Life of Honest Endeavour.

"That may be true," said Mrs. Stuffer, "but I have this Satisfaction," as she lifted her Head proudly: "I set a scrumptious Table to the very last."

Moral: Cling to your Ideals, such as they are.

THE NINNY WHO SWAM AWAY FROM THE LIFE PRESERVER

Once there was a Citizen who put in most of his Time acting as Custodian of a Thirst.

He could inhale through a Straw, bury his Nose in it or leave it flow from the Original Package.

After he had bombarded the Innards with Aqua Fortis for a matter of 20 years, he awoke one Morning suffering from a combination of Pin-Wheels, Moving-Pictures and a General Alarm of Fire.

Doc came in answer to a Hurry-Up and found that he was on the Job about 8 years too late.

The Patient had something like 15 Things the matter with him, ranging from Cirrhosis of the Liver to Water on the Brain, although the latter did not sound Reasonable.

He had six Weeks in which to settle up his Affairs before receiving the Wreaths and Pillows.

During that time he chopped on the Fire-Water because he somewhat blamed the Old Stuff for sending him away at 42 when he might have stuck around to be 87.

His Pals came to see him just before he winked out.

They found him very white and drawn and sort of Aghast at the Record he had established.

After the funeral the Pall-Bearers took off many Dark Gloves and flew at the High Balls.

One of them expressed the Opinion that what killed Jim was cutting out the Stimulants. The Shock was too much for him.

All the other Diagnosticians nodded their heads gravely.

And the Host went to the Cellar for another Load.

Moral: It is absolutely Harmless unless Discontinued.

Don Marquis

FABLE OF THE IRON DOGS

Once there were two iron dogs on the front lawn of a Pennsylvania millionaire.

One of them said, "I do not believe in a future for iron dogs. When I lose another leg, I will go to the scrap heap, and that will be the end of me."

The other one said, "I have the utmost faith in some noble destiny for iron dogs; though I should be broken to bits, yet will I live again somehow, somewhere, somewhen, to some excellent purpose."

The millionaire just then came along and directed a workman to remove the iron dogs, for his daughter had come home from a select school and told him they were a Mistake.

The first iron dog was thrown upon the junk heap as he had predicted, and became rust, doing no one any good.

But the second one, who had believed in his own destiny, was melted down and made into munitions with which to kill Germans.

* * *

MORAL

You don't have to have a soul unless you want one.

Milt Gross

FERRY-TAIL FROM KEENG MITAS FOR NIZE BABY

Oohoo, nize baby, itt opp all de Cheeken Zoop so mamma'll gonna tell you a Ferry-Tail from Keeng Mitas. Wance oppon a time was a werry, werry reech Keeng from de name from Keeng Mitas. Sotch a welt wot he hed!—wot it would make J. P. Morgan witt Hanry Fudd witt John D. Rockefeller dey should look like puppers. (Nize baby, take anodder spoon cheeken zoop—)

So instat from bing setisfite witt contempted—he becrutched yat averybody helse wot dey possassed, und he was only trying how he could incriss yat wot he had (mmmm-dot griddy ting). So a whole time he was hudding opp de moneh witt glutting yat from it like a miser. So wan day he was wukking opp witt don in de godden so he was tinking so, "Hm—wot could I do, dot I should hev it ivvin more yat from wot I got?" (mmm-dot salfish critchure). So he was interropted by a leedle Ferry wot it was stending in de front from him witt a Megic Want.

So de Ferry sad, "You Keeng Mitas? ? ?"

So de Keeng sad, "So wot is? ?"

So de Ferry sad, "I'm a Ferry wot I could grent you wot annyting wot you'll weesh so'll be foolfeeled de weesh! ! !" So de Keeng sad, "Wot kind bunco-steerage game you call dees, ha? You got maybe some goot-for-notting Hoil Stocks wot you want to sell it, ha, maybe? Odder a petent carpet-swipper, odder maybe a phuny Gold mine yat, ha! ! Try batter by Old Keeng Cole, not by me—Goot hefternoon! !"

So de Ferry sad, "Hm—you a werry septical poison, ha? Soppose wot you geeve me a hopportunity I should conweence you?"

So de Keeng sad, "Ho K, I weesh wot averyting wot I toch it, it should toin into gold."

So he was holding in de hand a spectre, so de Ferry gave him a tree times a tep witt de megic want—so he gave a look—so it was by him a solit gold spectre in de hend! !—Noo, noo!—So don't esk! ! !

So de Keeng was dencing witt jomping witt lipping witt bonding witt prencing from joy. You should see wot he was deshing hitter witt titter—opp witt don, high witt low—beck witt futt, to witt frau,—wot he was touching averyting on wheech he put on de hends. So his Wessel sad, "Is goot now?" So de Keeng sad, "Yeh, is good bot look a hincome-tax I'll gonna have und'll be mine lock yat wot I'll gat maybe to-morrow roomateezum in de hends." (MMMmmm—dot apparitious ting.)

So it came gredually deener-time so de Keeng was werry hongry so he set don he should itt opp a hoyster. So so soon wot he toched de hoyster it became solit gold! ! So he said, "Hm—Wott's dees? ?" So he tried he should ketch in queek a potato in de mout no one should see, so so soon wot he stodded he should chew it, it became solit gold wot it broke him two teet witt a cron witt a heff from de breedge—woik yat besites wot it was werry hot so it made him yat a bleesters on de tong! !

So he sad—"Hm!—Is a seerous preposition. It simms wot I'll have to employ stragedy." So he sad to de Wessel, "I'll gonna stend witt de mout open—So you'll put in a binn-shooter a hepple, wot you'll shoot it, it should go in mine mout wot I'll swallow it queeck it shouldn't toch me." So de Wessel compiled gredually witt de requast, bot he was a werry poor mox-man, so instat from de Keeng's mout it went in de had wot it became immiditly gold wot it gave him sotch a knock wot he had almost conclusion from de brain.

So was a werry cricketal situation—wot de Keeng sad, "Hm, so it rimmains wot I'll gonna hev to leeve maybe a whole life on gold-feesh, Ha! !" So it was gredually all kind from trobbles! ! It came de night so he stodded in he should ondrass so it was dere by him a pair from 18 carrot Bivvy Dizz wot de wessels had to ondrass him yat witt a can-uppener. So one day he was wukking opp witt don so it came ronning over to heem his leedle dudder—Hm, deed she was a switt child! ! So he was so epsom minded, dot dope, wot he put on her head de hend he should toch her so she became solit gold. Yi yi yi yi—So you should see a griff from a remuss wot it was by de Keeng—mmm! ! ! Deed he was sowry! ! ! witt meeserable witt don-hotted—witt rependant—wot he was wipping beeterly.

So it gredually appeared in de front from him de Ferry witt de

Megic Want so he sad, "Goot Monnink, Keeng, How is by you de Gold Rosh? ? ?" So de Keeng gave sotch a grun from meesery wot it toched de Ferry's hott—so he sad, "You'll gonna be steengy witt griddy witt salfish anny more?"

So de Keeng sad, "NO."

"You'll gonna dunnate maybe itch year someting to de Meelk Fond?"

"Yeh."

"Wid de Selwation Ommy?"

"Yeh."

"Widd de Uffan's Home?"

"Yeh."

"So you'll gonna refumm, ha?"

"Yeh."

"In odder woids you'll gonna be from now on a deeference indiwijial halltogadder?"

"Cruss mine hott!"

So de Ferry gave him tree times a tep witt de Megic Want so dere it was stending in de front from him de leedle dudder jost like new, wot dey leeved heppily hever hefter.

(Hm—Sotch a dollink baby—ate opp all de cheeken Zoop!)

Ambrose Bierce

FANTASTIC FABLES

THE DISINTERESTED ARBITER

Two Dogs who had been fighting for a bone, without advantage to either, referred their dispute to a Sheep. The Sheep patiently heard their statements, then flung the bone into a pond.

"Why did you do that?" said the Dogs.

"Because," replied the Sheep, "I am a vegetarian."

THE PARTY OVER THERE

A Man in a Hurry, whose watch was at his lawyer's, asked a Grave Person the time of day.

"I heard you ask that Party Over There the same question," said the Grave Person. "What answer did he give you?"

"He said it was about three o'clock," replied the Man in a Hurry; "but he did not look at his watch, and as the sun is nearly down I think it is later."

"The fact that the sun is nearly down," the Grave Person said, "is immaterial, but the fact that he did not consult his timepiece and make answer after due deliberation and consideration is fatal. The answer given," continued the Grave Person, consulting his own timepiece, "is of no effect, invalid, and void."

"What, then," said the Man in a Hurry, eagerly, "is the time of day?"

"The question is remanded to the Party Over There for a new answer," replied the Grave Person, returning his watch to his pocket and moving away with great dignity.

He was a Judge of an Appellate Court.

CAT AND KING

A Cat was looking at a King, as permitted by the proverb.

"Well," said the monarch, observing her inspection of the royal person, "how do you like me?"

"I can imagine a King," said the Cat, "whom I should like better."

"For example?"

"The King of Mice."

The sovereign was so pleased with the wit of the reply that he gave her permission to scratch his Prime Minister's eyes out.

REVENGE

An Insurance Agent was trying to induce a Hard Man to Deal With to take out a policy on his house. After listening to him for an hour, while he painted in vivid colors the extreme danger of fire consuming the house, the Hard Man to Deal With said:

"Do you really think it likely that my house will burn down inside the time that my policy will run?"

"Certainly," replied the Insurance Agent; "have I not been trying all this time to convince you that I do?"

"Then," said the Hard Man to Deal With, "why are you so eager to have your Company bet me money that it will not?"

The Agent was silent and thoughtful for a moment; then he drew the other apart into an infrequented place and whispered in his ear:

"My friend, I will impart to you a dark secret. Years ago the Company betrayed my sweetheart by promise of marriage. Under an assumed name I have wormed myself into its service for revenge; and as there is a heaven above us, I will have its heart's blood."

OFFICER AND THUG

A Chief of Police who had seen an Officer beating a Thug was very indignant, and said he must not do so any more on pain of dismissal.

"Don't be too hard on me," said the Officer, smiling; "I was beating him with a stuffed club."

"Nevertheless," persisted the Chief of Police, "it was a liberty that must have been very disagreeable, though it may not have hurt. Please do not repeat it."

"But," said the Officer, still smiling, "it was a stuffed Thug."

In attempting to express his gratification the Chief of Police thrust out his right hand with such violence that his skin was ruptured at the arm-pit and a stream of sawdust poured from the wound. He was a stuffed Chief of Police.

SAINT AND SOUL

St. Peter was sitting at the gate of Heaven when a Soul approached, and, bowing civilly, handed him its card.

"I am very sorry, sir," said St. Peter, after reading the card, "but I really cannot admit you. You will have to go to the Other Place. Sorry, sir, very sorry."

"Don't mention it," said the Soul; "I have been all the month at a watering place, and it will be an agreeable change. I called only to ask if my friend Elihu Root is here."

"No, sir," the Saint replied; "Mr. Root is not dead."

"O, I know that," said the Soul, "I thought he might be visiting God."

E. B. White

THE PARABLE OF THE FAMILY WHICH
DWELT APART

On a small, remote island in the lower reaches of Barnetuck Bay there lived a family of fisherfolk by the name of Pruitt. There were seven of them, and they were the sole inhabitants of the place. They subsisted on canned corn, canned tomatoes, pressed duck, whole-wheat bread, terrapin, Rice Krispies, crabs, cheese, queen olives, and home-made wild-grape preserve. Once in a while Pa Pruitt made some whiskey and they all had a drink.

They liked the island and lived there from choice. In winter, when there wasn't much doing, they slept the clock around, like so many bears. In summer they dug clams and set off a few pinwheels and salutes on July 4th. No case of acute appendicitis had ever been known in the Pruitt household, and when a Pruitt had a pain in his side he never even noticed whether it was the right side or the left side, but just hoped it would go away, and it did.

One very severe winter Barnetuck Bay froze over and the Pruitt family was marooned. They couldn't get to the mainland by boat because the ice was too thick, and they couldn't walk ashore because the ice was too treacherous. But inasmuch as no Pruitt had anything to go ashore for, except mail (which was entirely second class), the freeze-up didn't make any difference. They stayed indoors, kept warm, and ate well, and when there was nothing better to do, they played crokinole. The winter would have passed quietly enough had not someone on the mainland remembered that the Pruitts were out there in the frozen bay. The word got passed around the county and finally reached the Superintendent of State Police, who immediately notified Pathé News and the United States Army. The Army got there first, with three bombing planes from Langley Field, which flew low over the island and dropped packages of dried apricots and bouillon cubes,

143

which the Pruitts didn't like much. The newsreel plane, smaller than
the bombers and equipped with skis, arrived next and landed on a
snow-covered field on the north end of the island. Meanwhile, Major
Bulk, head of the state troopers, acting on a tip that one of the Pruitt
children had appendicitis, arranged for a dog team to be sent by plane
from Laconia, New Hampshire, and also dispatched a squad of troopers to attempt a crossing of the bay. Snow began falling at sundown, and during the night three of the rescuers lost their lives
about half a mile from shore, trying to jump from one ice cake to
another.

The plane carrying the sled dogs was over southern New England
when ice began forming on its wings. As the pilot circled for a forced
landing, a large meat bone which one of the dogs had brought along
got wedged in the socket of the main control stick, and the plane went
into a steep dive and crashed against the side of a powerhouse, instantly killing the pilot and all the dogs, and fatally injuring Walter
Ringstead, 7, of 3452 Garden View Avenue, Stamford, Conn.

Shortly before midnight, the news of the appendicitis reached the
Pruitt house itself, when a chartered autogiro from Hearst's International News Service made a landing in the storm and reporters informed Mr. Pruitt that his oldest boy, Charles, was ill and would have
to be taken to Baltimore for an emergency operation. Mrs. Pruitt
remonstrated, but Charles said his side did hurt a little, and it ended
by his leaving in the giro. Twenty minutes later another plane came in,
bearing a surgeon, two trained nurses, and a man from the National
Broadcasting Company, and the second Pruitt boy, Chester, underwent an exclusive appendectomy in the kitchen of the Pruitt home,
over the Blue Network. This lad died, later, from eating dried apricots
too soon after his illness, but Charles, the other boy, recovered after a
long convalescence and returned to the island in the first warm days of
spring.

He found things much changed. The house was gone, having caught
fire on the third and last night of the rescue when a flare dropped by
one of the departing planes lodged in a bucket of trash on the piazza.
After the fire, Mr. Pruitt had apparently moved his family into the
emergency shed which the radio announcers had thrown up, and
there they had dwelt under rather difficult conditions until the night
the entire family was wiped out by drinking a ten-per-cent solution of

carbolic acid which the surgeon had left behind and which Pa Pruitt had mistaken for grain alcohol.

Barnetuck Bay seemed a different place to Charles. After giving his kin decent burial, he left the island of his nativity and went to dwell on the mainland.

ALL SORTS OF DILEMMAS

Humorists fatten on trouble. They have always made trouble pay. They struggle along with a good will and endure pain cheerfully, knowing how well it will serve them in the sweet by and by. Here in this department you see them wrestling with foreign languages, fighting folding ironing boards and swollen drainpipes, suffering the terrible discomfort of tight boots (or as Josh Billings wittily called them, "tite" boots). They pour out their sorrows profitably, in a form which is not quite fiction nor quite fact either.

The New Yorker *has lately been a handy repository for these literary exaggerations and has even given them a name, for convenience in handling. It calls them "casuals." We need hardly assure the reader, as he dips into the coming section, that beneath the sparkling surface of these comical dilemmas flows the strong tide of human woe.*

Frank Moore Colby

CONFESSIONS OF A GALLOMANIAC

Down to the outbreak of the war I had no more desire to converse
with a Frenchman in his own language than with a modern Greek.
I thought I understood French well enough for my own purposes,
because I had read it off and on for twenty years, but when the war
aroused sympathies and sharpened curiosities that I had not felt
before, I realized the width of the chasm that cut me off from what
I wished to feel. Nor could it be bridged by any of the academic,
natural, or commercial methods that I knew of. They were either too
slow or they led in directions that I did not wish to go. I tried a
phonograph, and after many bouts with it I acquired part of a
sermon by Bossuet and real fluency in discussing a quinsy sore throat
with a Paris physician, in case I ever went there and had one. I then
took fourteen conversation lessons from a Mme. Carnet, and being
rather well on in years at the start, I should, if I had kept on dili-
gently, have been able at the age of eighty-five to inquire faultlessly
my way to the post-office. I could already ask for butter and sing a
song written by Henry IV—when my teacher went to France to take
care of her half-brother's children. I will say this for Mme. Carnet.
I came to understand perfectly the French for all her personal and
family affairs. No human being has ever confided in me so abundantly
as she did. No human being has ever so sternly repressed any answering confidences of my own. Her method of instruction, if it was one,
was that of jealous, relentless, unbridled soliloquy.

Thrown on the world with no power of sustaining a conversation
on any other subject than the members of the Carnet family, I nevertheless resolved to take no more lessons but to hunt down French
people and make them talk. What I really needed was a governess to
take me to and from my office and into the park at noon, but at my
age that was out of the question. Then began a career of hypocritical
benevolence. I scraped acquaintance with every Frenchman whom I

heard talking English very badly, and I became immensely interested in his welfare. I formed the habit of introducing visiting Frenchmen to French-speaking Americans, and sitting, with open mouth, in the flow of their conversation. Then I fell in with M. Bernou, the commissioner who was over here buying guns, and whose English and my French were so much alike that we agreed to interchange them. We met daily for two weeks and walked for an hour in the park, each tearing at the other's language. Our conversations, as I look back on them, must have run about like this:

> "It calls to walk," said he, smiling brilliantly.
> "It is good morning," said I, "better than I had extended."
> "I was at you yestairday ze morning, but I deed not find."
> "I was obliged to leap early," said I, "and I was busy standing up straight all around the forenoon."
> "The book I prayed you send, he came, and I thank, but positively are you not deranged?"
> "Don't talk," said I. "Never talk again. It was really nothing anywhere. I had been very happy, I reassure."
> "Pardon, I glide, I glode. There was the hide of a banane. Did I crash you?"
> "I noticed no insults," I replied. "You merely gnawed my arm."
> Gestures and smiles of perfect understanding.

I do not know whether Bernou, who like myself was middle-aged, felt as I did on these occasions, but by the suppression of every thought that I could not express in my childish vocabulary, I came to feel exactly like a child. They said I ought to think in French and I tried to do so, but thinking in French when there is so little French to think with, divests the mind of its acquisitions of forty years. Experience slips away for there are not words enough to lay hold of it. Knowledge of good and evil does not exist; the sins have no names; and the mind under its linguistic limitations is like a rather defective toy Noah's ark. From the point of view of Bernou's and my vocabulary, Central Park was as the Garden of Eden after six months—new and unnamed things everywhere. A dog, a tree, a statue taxed all our powers of description, and on a complex matter like a policeman our minds could not meet at all. We could only totter together a few steps in any mental direction. Yet there was a real pleasure in this earnest interchange of insipidities and they were highly valued on each side. For my part I shall always like Bernou, and feel toward him as my childhood's friend. I wonder if he noticed that I was an old, battered man, bothered with a tiresome profession. I certainly never suspected that he was. His language utterly failed to give me that impression.

After I lost Bernou I fastened upon an unfrocked priest who had come over here and gone into the shoe trade—a small, foxy man, who regarded me, I think, in the light of an aggressor. He wanted to become completely American and forget France, and as I was trying to reverse the process, I rather got in his way. He could talk of mediæval liturgies and his present occupation, but nothing in between, and as he spoke English very well, his practical mind revolted at the use of a medium of communication in which one of us almost strangled when there was another available in which we were both at ease. I could not pump much French out of him. He would burst into English rather resentfully. Then I took to the streets at lunch-time and tried newsdealers, book-shops, restaurants, invented imaginary errands, bought things that I did not want, and exchanged them for objects even less desirable. That kept a little conversation going day by day, but on the whole it was a dry season. It is a strange thing. There are more than thirty thousand of them in the city of New York, and I had always heard that the French are a clannish folk and hate to learn another language, but most of my overtures in French brought only English upon me. The more pains I took the more desirable it seemed to them that I should be spared the trouble of continuing. I was always diving into French and they were always pulling me out again. They thought they were humane.

French people hate broken French worse than most of us hate broken English. But when dragged out into the light of English I tried to talk just as foolishly in order that they might think it was not really my French that was the matter with me. Sometimes that worked quite well. Finding me just as idiotic in my own language they went back to theirs. It certainly worked well with my friend M. Bartet, a paralytic tobacconist in the West Thirties near the river, to whom my relation was for several months that of a grandchild, though, I believe we were of the same age. He tried to form my character by bringing me up on such praiseworthy episodes of his early life as he thought I was able to grasp.

Now at the end of a long year of these persistent puerilities I am able to report two definite results: In the first place a sense of my incapacity and ignorance infinitely vaster than when I began, and in the second a profound distrust, possibly vindictive in its origin, of all Americans in the city of New York who profess an acquaintance with French culture, including teachers, critics, theater audiences, lecture audiences, and patronesses of visiting Frenchmen.

It was perhaps true, as people said at the time, that a certain French theatrical experiment in New York could not continue for the simple reason that it was too good a thing for the theater-going public to support. It may be that the precise equivalent of the enterprise, even if not hampered by a foreign language, could not have permanently endured. Yet from what I saw of its audiences, critics, enthusiasts, and from what I know of the American Gallophile generally, including myself, I believe the linguistic obstacle to have been more serious than they would have us suppose—serious enough to account for the situation without dragging in our æsthetic incapacity. It was certainly an obstacle that less than one-half of any audience ever succeeded in surmounting.

I do not mean that the rest of the audience got nothing out of it, for so expressive were the players by other means than words, that they often sketched the play out in pantomime. The physical activities of the troupe did not arise, as some of the critics declared, from the vivacity of the Gallic temperament; nor were they assumed, as others believed, because in the seventeenth century French actors had been acrobats. These somewhat exaggerated gestures were occasioned by the perception that the majority of the spectators were beginners in French. They were supplied by these ever-tactful people as a running translation for a large body of self-improving Americans.

I do not blame other Americans for dabbling in French, since I myself am the worst of dabblers, but I see no reason why any of us should pretend that it is anything more than dabbling. The usual way of reading French does not lead even to an acquaintance with French literature. Everybody knows that words in a living language in order to be understood have to be lived with. They are not felt as a part of living literature when you see them pressed out and labeled in a glossary, but only when you hear them fly about. A word is not a definite thing susceptible of dictionary explanation. It is a cluster of associations, reminiscent of the sort of men that used it, suggestive of social class, occupation, mood, dignity or the lack of it, primness, violences, pedantries, or platitudes. It hardly seems necessary to say that words in a living literature ought to ring in the ear with the sounds that really belong to them, or that poetry without an echo cannot be felt.

It may be that there is no way out of it. Perhaps it is inevitable that the colleges which had so long taught the dead languages as if they were buried should now teach the living ones as if they were dead. But there is no need of pretending that this formal acquaintance with books results in an appreciation of literature. No sense of the intimate quality of a writer can be founded on a verbal vacuum. His plots, his place in literature, his central motives, and the opinion of his critics could all be just as adequately conveyed, if his books were studied in the language of the deaf and dumb. Of course, one may be drawn to an author by that process but it would hardly be the artistic attraction of literature; it is as if one felt drawn to a woman by an interest exclusively in her bones.

Elementary as these remarks may seem I offer them to Gallophiles without apology. On the contrary I rather fear that I am writing over their heads.

St. Clair McKelway

AN AFFIX FOR BIRDS

When I was in Tokio a few years ago, I decided to study the Japanese language. My Japanese teacher, whose name was Watanabe-san, used to ride out to my house every morning on his motorcycle. He wore a gray felt hat turned up at the front, a wing collar with a striped bow tie, a vest with white piping, a short black coat, and long flannel underdrawers. The trousers to his suit he carried rolled and strapped on the parcel rack of his motorcycle in order to keep them from getting muddy when the motorcycle was churning through Tokio's unpaved streets. Promptly at eight o'clock each morning I would hear in front of the house the putt-putting and then the expiring gasps of Watanabe-san's motorcycle, and I would go down and let him in. He would enter the vestibule bowing, and inhaling noisily through his teeth. Then he would put on his pants and we would sit down at the breakfast table. For him to come at this hour was my own idea. I had to get to work at nine, and I thought this plan would save me some time. When I first told him that I would take my breakfast while he gave me the lesson, I had no idea that he would breakfast with me. I thought he would eat his meal at his own home, before he mounted his motorcycle, and since I never had anything but orange juice and coffee, I thought it would be all right for me to sit there and have them while he taught me the language of the country. This was perfectly all right with Watanabe-san, but after the first two mornings he brought his own breakfast with him in a red lacquer box, which he strapped on his parcel-carrier along with his trousers. It was a Japanese breakfast. There were black lacquer dishes and bowls, all intricately fitted into the red lacquer box. On the plates and in the bowls were daubs and pools. The little pieces of pickled fish, the preserved turnip, the bean custard, the chips of cold fried beef, the tepid mauve soup, and the stewed rice would be laid out on my breakfast table, and Watanabe-san would go at them with his chopsticks, which he carried in an upper vest pocket. "This," he would say, holding up a cube of preserved radish, "is *daikon*. We say in Japanese *daikon*. You say after me, *daikon*." "Daikon," I would say.

Watanabe-san was a teacher of English in one of the city high schools, an ambitious man, small, round, and full of energy. He had protuberant teeth, like Willie Stevens. Watanabe-san's teeth were so long and so disparate that you felt he ought to be able to cross them, like fingers, if he tried. When he talked animatedly, it was as if he were waving a hand at you. His grin was circular on account of these teeth and was, for the same reason, incessant. Most Japanese I have met have had a nervous laugh, but Watanabe-san's grin was purely physical. He would have had to use force to bring his lips together. He was as patient a man as I have ever seen and he tried hard to teach me how to say Japanese words. He never talked about anything that did not directly concern the lesson I was laboring over. I never heard him express an opinion of any kind. He was affable but detached. His excellent references showed that he had tried to teach many young foreigners the Japanese language.

As the lessons progressed, Watanabe-san's most frequent remark to me got to be, "Wrong affix, I am very sorry. That is the affix for birds." He would start his lips crawling toward one another when he said this, to show me that he was not laughing at me, but I never saw them meet. What was happening to my Japanese lessons was that Watanabe-san had tried to teach me twelve simple affixes for each verb we took up, and the only affixes I ever seemed to remember were the affixes one was supposed to use when speaking of, or to, birds. Perhaps I had better go into this a little way at this point. The idea is something like this: In Japanese, when you say "go" to, or of, a servant, you use one affix, and when you say "go" to, or of, your father, you use another; moreover, you use an entirely different affix when you say "go" to, or of, your mother, and you use still another affix when you say "go" to, or of, birds. There are separate affixes, as well, for horses, soldiers, fish, policemen, dogs, alligators, automobile-drivers, and so on—twelve simple, as they say, affixes and dozens of complex ones for every verb in the language. My parents were not in Japan, and this made it simpler, but for the first two weeks or so, and for some obscure reason that I never want to know the truth about, I would seem to forget all the affixes of all the verbs I learned, except the ones for birds, so that whenever I said anything in Japanese, I would find myself talking to, or of, birds. For instance, I learned, or thought I learned, how to say to a taxi-driver, "Please turn at the next corner and stop at the little stone house on the right." What I said, when I thought I was saying that, was, according to subsequent lessons from Watanabe-san, "Birds, please turn at the next corner and stop flying at the little stone aviary on the right." I used to try it on taxi-drivers, and they always turned around and laughed nervously. Then I would point to the corner at which we were to turn, and when we reached my house, I would lean over and clutch the driver's shoulder, crying "Stoppo! Stoppo!" Most drivers knew this hybrid, but sometimes it was necessary to pretend I was about to jump from the car as it passed the little stone house on the right, or else reach up front and pull back the emergency brake.

I would have fought this tendency to talk only to, or of, birds, and I might have conquered it, but I found out in succeeding weeks that there was a great deal more to the Japanese language than verb affixes. Take the mere arrangement of words, admitting for the sake of the explanation that the things I was studying *were* words. I found that if I got one word in the wrong place, the sentence would change itself materially and the whole paragraph would, in all likelihood, never mean the same thing again. What happens when you do that is a lot worse than the collapse of a house of cards. The sentence doesn't go to pieces, exactly. It takes on new life, all the words revise themselves, the nouns, as likely as not, become verbs, the verbs adjectives, and here and there a word shudders so that it becomes a different thing. I have seen cases in which a word has disappeared altogether. I found that a mere twitch of the lip on my part would fix my sentence about stopping at the little stone house so that I, a dog, would be instructing the policeman in the front seat to throw me under the wheels of the taxicab and let the birds stone me. Almost any foreign language is apt to throw a student off for a while, but Japanese has peculiarities not quite like any other I have ever heard of. When a sentence goes striding away on its own hook this way, not even the Japanese have any sure method of telling what it was you meant to say. A student of English might say something like "stone house stop right," and alert people familiar with the language would know what he was getting at. But when you tell Japanese policemen to let the birds stone you, they think that is what you mean, and from the way you have arranged the words and affixes, there is absolutely no reason for them to think otherwise.

The sensation that comes from starting out to say one thing and then finding that you have said something entirely different is a fascinating one, once you get used to it. One morning, I remember, I tried to say, "The cherry blossoms in Hibiya Park are very beautiful this spring," and Watanabe-san told me afterward that what I had really said was "We cherry-colored birds always fly in Hibiya Park in the spring." This was a good instance of word-disappearance. The word "blossom" had vanished.

"What became of 'blossom'?" I said to Watanabe-san that morning.

"The word 'blossom,'" he said, "became the word 'colored' and, combined with the word 'cherry,' became a descriptive phrase. You see," he added, "you used the affix for birds." Watanabe-san would tell me these things, grinning cheerfully, and I would grin back at him a little across the breakfast table.

I bought, at his suggestion, a large and comprehensive English-Japanese dictionary, and this served to get me even deeper into the thing when Watanabe-san was nowhere around. I would say something to myself in Japanese intended to be fairly simple and direct, and then, by means of the dictionary and its phonetic symbols, I would be able, a few minutes later, to find out what I had said to myself. Once anybody starts something of this kind, he can never know where he will end up. At first I would just find out what I had said and then let it go. For instance, having found that instead of saying, "What an ancient temple bell you are ringing there beside the pond," I had said, "Dogs, keep barking until we have put our mother under water," I would think about it for a while and then try something else. The thing never did get to me, as it well might have, because when I began replying to what I found I had said and then looking up my replies, I carried the dictionary down the street to a bookstore and sold it.

Watanabe-san was as polite and tractable about it all as anybody could possibly have been. I had the feeling that he had been through this sort of thing before, and would go through it again and again in the future. I settled the bill for the lessons the morning after I had disposed of the dictionary, and Watanabe-san said goodbye very gracefully, took off his pants, and departed.

Frederic S. Cozzens

AN INVITATION TO A PARTY*

"We have an invitation to a party," said Mrs. Sparrowgrass, "on Friday next, and I think a party is a very pleasant thing in the country. There is more sociability, more hospitality, warmer welcomes, less dress, and less style than there is in the city." Here Mrs. Sparrowgrass handed me an engraved card of rather formidable dimensions, which I must confess looked anything but *rural*. I took the missive with some misgivings, for I have a natural horror of parties. "I wonder," said I, in the most playful kind of bitter irony, "whether we will meet out here that young lady that never sings herself, but is always so passionately fond of music?" Mrs. Sparrowgrass said she thought not; she said she heard she was married.

"And that gentleman," I continued, "who was a stranger to me, that always wanted to be presented to some young lady that I didn't know?"

Mrs. Sparrowgrass said she believed he had gone to California.

"And that lady who prized confectionery above good-breeding, and went home with her pockets well stuffed with mottoes, in defiance of the eighth commandment, and the laws of propriety?"

Mrs. Sparrowgrass said she knew the lady to whom I alluded, but she assured me she was yet in New York, and had not been seen about our village.

"Then," said I, "Mrs. Sparrowgrass, we will go to the party. Put my best shirt, and the white waistcoat in Monday's wash. Never mind expense. Get me a crumb of bread, and bring me my old white gloves. I am going to be gay."

"I think," said Mrs. Sparrowgrass, "that a party in town is nothing but an embarrassment." "True," said I. "Don't you remember," said she, "what a fuss I used to make about getting my hair fixed, and how put out I was that night when you forgot the japonica?" "Certainly."

* From "The Sparrowgrass Papers," 1856.

"And then, when we were all dressed and ready, how we used to wait for fear of getting there too early, and after we did reach the house, how we always got in a corner, and made happy wall-flowers of ourselves, and some old friends." "Of course I do." "Where nobody took any notice of us." "Exactly." "Then what difference did it make how I was dressed—whether I wore Honiton lace or cotton edging?" "I am afraid," said I, "Mrs. Sparrowgrass, if you had made a point of wearing cotton lace, you would not have been invited." At this palpable *double entendre* I felt that secret satisfaction which every man must feel when he has said a good thing. It was lost upon Mrs. Sparrowgrass. "Here," she continued, "we expect a simple, old-fashioned entertainment." Then I chimed in—"No gas-lights to make your eyes ache—no patent-leather to make your feet ache—no fashionable follies to make your heart ache—and no overheated, ill-ventilated rooms, boned-turkies, game, ice-cream, Charlotte Russe, pâtés, champagne, and chicken-salad, to make your head ache next morning." "There will be oysters and ice-cream," said Mrs. Sparrowgrass, dubiously. "I wish," said I, "there was a prospect of apples and cider instead. The moment I get inside the doors, and breathe the mingled odors of oysters and geraniums, it will carry me back to town, and for one evening, at least, I shall forget that we are living in the country.

> ——'I could be content
> To see no other *verdure* than its own;
> To feel no other breezes than are blown
> Through its tall woods;'

but we must succumb; we will go like plain, sensible people, won't we?"

"If you were me, what would you wear?" said Mrs. Sparrowgrass. "Something very plain, my dear."

"Then," said Mrs. Sparrowgrass, "I have nothing very plain, suitable for a party, and to-morrow I must go to town and do a little shopping."

"I am afraid," said I (after the second day's hard shopping in town) "your dress is going to be too plain, my dear. Every hour brings a fresh boy, with a fresh bundle, and a fresh bill, to my office." Mrs. Sparrowgrass said, "that if I thought so, perhaps she had better get something expensive when she went to buy the trimmings." I told her I thought her dress would do without trimming. She said, "it would be ridiculous without gimp or gallon; but perhaps I would prefer velvet ribbon, on account of the flounces?" I told her she had better get the velvet ribbon, and omit the gimp and galloon. Mrs. Sparrowgrass said, "very well," and the next day another boy brought another bundle, and another bill, which convinced me that extras form an important item in rural architecture. Then we had a dressmaker for several days, and the stitching went on by sun-light and lamp-light, and on the last day Mrs. S. discovered that she had nothing for her head, and the new bonnet was taken to pieces to get at the feathers for a coiffure. Then when the night fell, there fell, too, a soaking rain; and I had forgotten the carriage, so I was obliged to go a mile in the mud to order one from the village livery stable. Then I had to walk back, as the man said "it was out;" but he promised to send it for us right straight off. Then I had to get dressed over again. Then Mrs. Sparrowgrass could not find her best handkerchief, and I dropped five spermacetti blotches on the new silk dress looking for it. Then she found the handkerchief. Then our girl said that the new dog had run off with one of my boots. Then I had to go out in the mud in my slippers after the dog. Then I got the boot and put it on so as to make that sure. Then we waited for the carriage. We were all dressed and ready, but no carriage. We exercised all the patience we could muster, on account of the carriage, and listened at the windows to see if we could hear it. Two months have elapsed, and it hasn't come yet. Next day we heard that the party had been an elegant affair. That everybody was there, so we concluded the carriage had not been able to come for us on account of business.

I have bought me another dog. I bought him on account of his fine, long ears, and beautiful silky tail. He is a pup, and much caressed by the young ones. One day he went off to the butcher's and came back with no more tail than a toad. The whole bunch of young Sparrowgrasses began to bawl when he reached the cottage, on account of his tail. I did not know him when I came home, and he could not recognize me—he had lost his organ of recognition. He reminded me of a dog I once heard of, that looked as if he had been where they wanted a tail merely, and had taken his, and thrown the dog away. Of course I took my stick, and went to see the butcher. Butcher said "he supposed I was something of a dog fancier, and would like to see my dog look stylish." I said on the contrary, that I had bought him on account of his handsome silky tail, and that I would give ten dollars to have it replaced. Then the idea of having it replaced seemed so ludicrous that I could not restrain a smile, and then the butcher caught the joke, and said there was no way to do it except with fresh putty. I do love a man who can enjoy a joke, so I took a fancy to that butcher. When I got home and saw the dog, I thought less of the butcher, but put a piece of black court-plaster on the dog, and it improved his appearance at once. So I forgave the butcher, and went to bed at peace with all mankind.

———

Our neighbor has been making an improvement in his house. He has had a drain made in the kitchen, with a long earthen pipe ending in a cess-pool at the end of his garden. The object of it is to carry off the superfluous water from the house. It was a great convenience, he said, "on wash days." One objection might be urged, and that was, after every heavy rain he found a gully in his garden path, and several cart loads of gravel in his cess-pool. Besides, the pipe was of an equal width, and one obstruction led to another; sometimes it was a silver spoon and a child's frock; sometimes it was a scrubbing-brush, a piece of soap, and a handkerchief. I said that if he had made a square wooden trough, gradually widening from end to end, it would have cleared itself, and then I thought it would be a good thing for me to have such a one myself. Then I had a cess-pool built at the bottom of the wall, under the bank, which is about one hundred and fifty feet from the kitchen, and told my carpenter to make a trough of that length. Carpenter asked me "how big I wanted it?" I told him about eight inches in diameter at the end nearest to the house, and then gradually widening all the way for the whole length. As I said this, my carpenter smiled, and said he never heard of such a thing. I told him no, that the idea was an original one of my own. He asked me how much I would like to have it widened. I thought for a moment, and said, "about half an inch to the foot." He said very well, and the next week he came with two horses, and an edifice in his cart that looked like a truncated shot-tower. I asked him what that was? He said it was the big end of my pipe. When he laid it on the ground on its side I walked through it, and could not touch the upper side with my hand. Then I asked the carpenter what he meant by it, and he said it was made according to directions. I said not at all, that I told him to increase the diameter at the rate of half an inch to the foot, and he had made it about a foot to the foot, as near as I could judge. "Sparrowgrass," said he, a little nettled, "jest take your pencil and put down eight inches." "Well, that's the diameter of the small end, I believe?" I told the carpenter he was right so far. "Now, for every foot there is an increase of half an inch in the width; that's according to directions, too, ain't it?" Yes. "Well, then, put down one hundred and fifty half inches, how much does that make, altogether, in feet?" Six feet eleven inches. "Now," said he, "jest you take my rule, and measure the big end of that 're pipe." "Carpenter," said I, "I see it all; but the next time I build an aqueduct I will be a little more careful in the figures." "Sparrowgrass," said he, pointing to the pipe, "didn't you tell me that that was an original idea of your own?" I answered that I believed I did make a remark of that kind. "Well," said he, with a sort of muffled laugh, "that is the first time that I see an original idea come out at the big end."

Max Adeler

A VERY DANGEROUS INVENTION

A step-ladder is an almost indispensable article to persons who are moving into a new house. Not only do the domestics find it extremely convenient when they undertake to wash the windows, to remove the dust from the door and window-frames, and to perform sundry other household duties, but the lord of the castle will require it when he hangs his pictures, when he fixes the curtains and when he yields to his wife's entreaty for a hanging shelf or two in the cellar. I would, however, warn my fellow-countrymen against the contrivance which is offered to them under the name of the "Patent Combination Step-ladder." I purchased one in the city just before we moved, because the dealer showed me how, by the simple operation of a set of springs, the ladder could be transformed into an ironing-table, and from that into a comfortable settee for the kitchen, and finally back again into a step-ladder, just as the owner desired. It seemed like getting the full worth of the money expended to obtain a trio of such useful articles for a single price, and the temptation to purchase was simply irresistible. But the knowledge gained by a practical experience of the operation of the machine enables me to affirm that there is no genuine economical advantage in the use of this ingenious article.

Upon the day of its arrival, the servant-girl mounted the ladder for the purpose of removing the globes from the chandelier in the parlor, and while she was engaged in the work the weight of her body unexpectedly put the springs in motion, and the machine was suddenly converted into an ironing-table, while the maid-servant was prostrated upon the floor with a sprained ankle and amid the fragments of two shattered globes.

Then we decided that the apparatus should be used exclusively as an ironing-table, and to this purpose it would probably have been devoted permanently if it had suited. On the following Tuesday, however, while half a dozen shirts were lying upon it ready to be ironed, some one knocked against it accidentally. It gave two or three ominous preliminary jerks, ground two shirts into rags, hurled the flat-iron out into the yard, and after a few convulsive movements of the springs, settled into repose in the shape of a step-ladder.

It became evident then that it could be used with greatest safety as a settee, and it was placed in the kitchen in that shape. For a few days it gave much satisfaction. But one night when the servant had company the bench was perhaps overloaded, for it had another and most alarming paroxysm; there was a trembling of the legs, a violent agitation of the back, then a tremendous jump, and one of the visitors was hurled against the range, while the machine turned several somersaults, jammed itself halfway through the window-sash, and appeared once more in the similitude of an ironing-table.

It has now attained to such a degree of sensitiveness that it goes through the entire drill promptly and with celerity if any one comes near it or coughs or sneezes close at hand. We have it stored away in the garret, and sometimes in the middle of the night a rat will jar it, or a current of air will pass through the room, and we can hear it dancing over the floor and getting into service as a ladder, a bench and a table fifteen or twenty times in quick succession.

The machine will be disposed of for a small fraction of the original cost. It might be a valuable addition to the collection of some good museum. I am convinced that it will shine with greater lustre as a curiosity than as a household utensil.

Francis Steegmuller

A RIDE WITH RALPH

At Raton, late one afternoon, we transcontinental passengers were waiting in our places, wondering whether we would approve of the new driver who was to take us on to Santa Fe and Albuquerque, when we suddenly heard the group of drivers lounging outside the bus station burst into a cheer. "Yeah, Ralph!" they cried, and we saw a blond and very boyish giant coming toward us, wearing the company's uniform and a dazzling pair of new cowhide boots. "So long, boys!" he called, looking very handsome and serious, and after climbing on board and examining our tickets, he at once made himself as popular within the bus as he seemed to be without.

"Well, folks," he said earnestly, facing us all, "I'll be with you as far as Albuquerque, and I hope you'll like me as much as I know I'll like you all. I'll do my best to be satisfactory, and I'll do everything in my power to give you a fine ride. It's mighty dandy country through these parts, and I hope you enjoy it. If you have any suggestions or complaints, I'll be glad to have 'em. Let's go!" He swung into his seat, there was an appreciative murmur, and we were off.

Since I rode just beside Ralph in the front seat, we soon fell to talking, and long before we made our first comfort stop—the bus halts considerably every two hours from New York to Los Angeles— he had revealed that a certain subject was very much on his mind. "A pair of boots is quite an investment," he stated. "Have you any idea of what a good pair of boots costs?" I confessed ignorance. "If I was to buy them retail, in a regular swell shoestore in Denver," he informed me, "they'd cost me plenty, and I'd go without. But anybody's foolish to go to those swell stores; what you do is to write to a firm in K.C., give 'em your measurements, and you get a fine pair of boots by mail. It's a sort of wholesale proposition, see, and it certainly is worth while. But would you believe it, even buyin' 'em that way,

165

these boots set me back sixteen bucks; you can see they're quite an investment."

I pointed out that so handsome a pair was worth investing in, but admitted that I was disappointed to hear that they weren't real New Mexican boots, and that they came from Kansas City. "You can buy two kinds of boots in New Mexico," Ralph told me. "You can buy common ordinary boots that ain't worth half what you pay for 'em, and you can buy the best boots in the world—made of imported kangaroo hide—but you've got to be richer than you and me to get *them*. They'll set you back anywhere from fifty to a hundred bucks. But oh, man, they're soft as velvet and sure worth it if you got the dough. Now, these boots are O.K., but you know they're—they're —uh, beginnin' to pinch a little. As a matter of fact, they're—they're beginnin' to hurt me quite a good deal. Isn't that funny?"

I said I thought it was anything but funny, and Ralph agreed. "It ain't funny a heck of a bit," he revealed. "They sure feel pretty bad, and I've got to do something about it pretty quick. I've got a friend up here in Wagon Mound; he'll fix me up. We stop there ten minutes anyway."

"Well, you'd better get to Wagon Mound as fast as you can," I suggested. "You don't want to be in misery."

"That's right," said Ralph. "I don't know whether it's the cowhide beginnin' to bind, or my feet beginnin' to swell, but it's gettin' worse every minute." He took my advice with thrilling literalness, and we rushed over the road at a rate that permitted him to talk no more. I watched the speedometer go from the usual 50 to 55, to 60 and a little over. It was dark by now, and after a breathless half-hour a cluster of lights appeared and we drew up in front of a ramshackle chili joint. "Folks," said Ralph, switching on the lights and turning around to us, "this is Wagon Mound. It ain't much of a place, but you'll find some good chili inside the café and the comfort stations are around to the left. We'll be here ten minutes." He gave me an intent glance. "I'm in torture," he confided in a low voice, and disappeared.

The passengers followed him, but the chili joint struck me as uninviting, and I remained in the bus. After a while they began to drift back, very garrulous and interested. "The driver's certainly having a hell of a time with those new boots," one of them announced. "He's got a Mexican in there trying to pull them off and they won't budge; whenever the Mexican pulls, the driver yells and says he's taking his skin off, and they don't seem to be getting any place. He's afraid he's gonna have to cut 'em off, and he hates to do that. They're brand-new." As the bus filled, everyone talked of Ralph and his boots; we remained in Wagon Mound a good deal longer than ten minutes, but finally Ralph limped in, still wearing his cowhides, and in a bad mood. He made no reply to our sympathetic inquiries, informed us crossly that the next stop would be Las Vegas, switched off the lights, and drove on. "The next stop'll be Las Vegas if I live to get the hell there," I heard him mutter mirthlessly in the darkness, but as I was not sure whether he was addressing me or not, I judged it wiser not to reply.

The ride to Las Vegas, accomplished in considerably less than the scheduled time, made the spurt to Wagon Mound seem stodgy, and after telling us that we had something over half an hour for our supper, Ralph limped away out of sight. Speculation was vociferous as we ate at a long counter, and bets were made as to whether he would reappear with or without his boots. Nobody got into the bus, but all waited near it, to get a good view, and the silence of pity fell over us when Ralph emerged limping, still booted, from the gloom of some nearby buildings. "All aboard," he called, in a voice in which despair had taken the place of surliness. "All aboard, folks. We make no stop between here and Santa Fe." We filed sombrely aboard. I was the last, and could not resist murmuring that it was too bad. "Get in, buddy," said the boy, dully. "If I go nuts, you grab the wheel."

For the sake of all of us, I hoped Ralph wouldn't go nuts, for evidently Santa Fe contained further possibility of aid, and we tore through the darkness like a shell, Ralph's hands now and again straying alarmingly and futilely from the wheel to his boots. After a long stretch of silence he looked around, evidently to see if I was there, and after clearing his throat a few times he asked, in a private, piteous, small voice, "*You* don't happen to know anything about pullin' off boots, do you, buddy?" I replied just as privately that while I had never done it, I should be glad to try, but at this he merely shook his head, and drove on. Unspoken sympathy filled the speeding bus. Ralph's misery seemed to permeate us all, the ride began to seem endless. Then, suddenly, all was changed. Dramatically, far ahead in the darkness on the road we saw a waving light; Ralph shoved on his brakes, which hissed alarmingly, and as we all stared he opened the door to a Mexican, who blew out his lantern, climbed in, and asked for a ticket to Santa Fe. This transaction took a little time, and though I couldn't understand the Spanish, I realized that Ralph and the Mexican were conversing about something other than the ticket. Finally, after the Mexican had uttered several emphatic statements, Ralph abruptly killed the motor and turned to us. "Folks," he announced thrillingly, "I can't go on like this! If you'll have the kindness to put up with a few minutes' delay, I'll sure appreciate it. This friend of mine is going to perform some first aid, and then we'll shoot right along. Is that O.K. with everybody?" We all called out our assent, and preparations began. Ralph left the wheel, sat on the step of the bus, and stretched out one leg; the Mexican turned his back, straddled Ralph's leg, grasped the enormous boot tightly, found a footing, and bent forward; Ralph, holding onto the bus, placed his other foot firmly against the Mexican's posterior, and while one pulled, the other pushed, and both grunted. Everyone crowded to watch. The Mexican manipulated the toe and heel, and Ralph shoved with all the strength of his gigantic self. It appeared hopeless at first; the leather was so tight about Ralph's great calf and foot that it seemed to be almost part of him. That was evidently the way it felt to him, too; he whispered and cursed. Finally, the boot began wonderfully to move, and after a few particularly Herculean efforts, it actually slipped forward and the Mexican fell flat on his face, the boot clutched triumphantly in his hands. The crowd exclaimed with delight; Ralph whispered to himself some more, and stretched out his other leg, the Mexican manipulated as deftly as before, and was rewarded by falling flat on his face once again.

We were all much impressed by the way Ralph sat with his head in his hands for a few moments. "Does that relieve you?" I asked him, when he finally breathed deeply and looked around at us.

"Relieve me!" he cried. "Take it from me, folks, there's one boy that knows what heaven is now!"

Obviously, Ralph couldn't drive us to Santa Fe with only stockings on his feet, so I offered him my slippers, which were in the suitcase on the rack above me; he gingerly slipped his sore toes into them, and after a little experimenting decided he could make them do by wearing them as mules. "All right, folks!" he called, when he had thanked us. "Everything's O.K. now. Let's go to Santa Fe!" Cheers arose, he switched out the lights, and we were off. The Mexican hero grinned himself into a snoring sleep, and for the next hour and a half we tore over the mountains, making up for lost time.

"This is Santa Fe, folks; we'll be here ten minutes!" Ralph called out when we had rolled through the dark streets to the station. "The comfort stations are at the rear of the waiting-room!" I was going to stop over in Santa Fe for the night, so when the passengers dismounted, Ralph handed me my suitcase and bade me farewell, standing beside the bus in my slippers. "It's sure nice of you to let me wear these to Albuquerque," he said earnestly. "I just don't know what I'd do without 'em. Because those boots"—he almost smiled— "those boots, well, I sure couldn't wear *them* to Albuquerque!"

"No," I said. "You'd better send them back to K.C., don't you think?"

He ignored this. "The slippers will be waitin' for you here when you take your bus tomorrow night," he replied. "I sure hope you have a good trip all the way to L.A., and I'm sorry I won't be drivin' you."

I was sorry, too. The drivers between Santa Fe and L.A. were all good fellows, but none of them was quite the boy Ralph was, and his absence was hardly compensated for even by the note which I had found with my slippers in the bus station the next night. "Dear Friend," it said, "I am deeply grateful to you for letting me use your slippers. They came in very handy. On inspection I note they are in rather poor condition and as I know my feet are large if I am responsible for the damage I would be glad to have them sewed if you would leave them together with your address. Yours truly, Ralph L."

James T. Fields

A WATCH THAT "WANTED CLEANING"

I think I never saw a person who needed renewal of garments in a more pronounced degree than the gaunt individual I encountered a few weeks ago in Omaha. We met casually on the upland overlooking Council Bluffs, whither I had gone for a morning walk in that city of newness and hospitality. The man was sitting on the stump of a recently beheaded tree, regarding a watch, which he now and then held up in a kind of hopeless manner, and listened to for a sign of life from its inner apartments. When he saw me approaching he rose up and asked for "the time o' day." As I had only "Boston time," and that was of no use so far "out West," he sighed, again shook the unresponsive article in his hand, and spoke as follows: —"This 'ere watch, stranger, 's a puzzler. Some thing's the matter with 'er. I've seen a good-dle of trouble in my day, but nothin' at all like *this* afore. In my younger days I once had a personal difficulty with a bear, but that was fun compared to this affliction."

Noticing a settled grief on the poor fellow's soiled and sunken countenance, I sat down beside him on the ample resting-place he had chosen, and made inquiry as to the cause of his *untimely* sorrow. After a brief pause he thus unburdened himself:—"Stranger, if you was in the watch line, we'd have nothing to do with one another; but as you ain't, I don't mind givin' you 'er history, which you'll allow is somewhat discouragin'. I bought 'er two months ago in *She*-cargo for sixteen dollars down and five dollars in poultry. I had 'er of a fine-lookin' man who keeps jewillry on the sidewalk down by the Palmer House. He was a perfect gentleman in appearance, wore studs himself, and his conversation was high-toned. He said he was a member in reg'lar standin' of more'n fifty churches in various parts of the United States where he traded. He said he set his life by the watch, but *would* part with 'er if he was shore the man he sold 'er to was a moral man, and would take good care of 'er. He said she was wunst the property of a particular friend o' hisn, one o the craowned heads o' Ure-up, but the king was obleeged to sell 'er on accoaunt of a change in his circumstarnces. He said there was more'n two hundred jewills in 'er which was invisible to the naked eye. Waal, to make a long story short, I negoshated for 'er on the spot, and I 'member just as well as if't was yisterday, he said she wouldn't warnt cleanin' ef I car'd 'er in mur pocket, keerful, for twenty year.

"So, ye see, I took 'er 'long to Rock Island on the Mississippi, where I live, but she seemed to go on the jump all the way daown. Waal, I carried 'er into Jason's one day, and asked *him* to give a look into 'er insides, and tell me, ef he could, what made 'er act so. He screwed *his* old glass into the right eye, and arter a while he laid 'er down on the coaunter, and says he, 'She's a powerful good watch, but she *warnts cleanin'!"* When I heerd that, I was dumbfounded. Says I, 'She was cleaned all over last week.' Says he, 'That may be, but she's full o' dirt naow. It's dusty this fall,' says he, 'and some on it's got into *'er.'* Waal, I thought it all over, and said he might go to work on 'er next day; and he charged me tew dollars and fifty cents for cleanin' on 'er aout. Pooty soon I had to go off to Aurory, and she begun to act quair agin. So I took 'er into a watchmaker's there, and asked him to fling *his* eye round, and see what ailed 'er. Waal, he did, for ez much as five minits, and then says he, 'She's a fust-rate watch, but she warnts cleanin'!' Says I (and I couldn't help gittin' riled then), 'She's bin cleaned aout twice lately, and that's a fact.' 'Waal,' says he, 'I never seed a dirtier, and if she ain't 'tended to, double quick, in twenty-four hours she'll bust of 'er own accord, and fly all to pieces, and never go agin.' This illarmed me, nat'rally, and so I told him to strip 'er and go to work with his toothbrush and things, and I'd pay him what was right. So he did, and he sot down on me for one seventy-five, and one fifty for what he called *inside-entle* expenses. Waal, she went ellygant all the way on to Milwaukee, but the fust night I got thar she begun to hitch and sputter to that extent I run over to a watchmaker, early in the mornin', for assistance. Waal, he turned 'er over three or four times, and kind o' smiled at the rumblin' inside on 'er. Then he looked thoughtful and pried 'er open. Says I, *'Enny thing serious?'* Says he,—and his reply run through me like a fawk,—says he, 'She's a *remarkable* good timepiece, but she warnts *cleanin'!'* Waal, to make an end to mur story, I had 'er put through *his* mill, and some o' *his* ile slung into 'er. He said 't was such a ugly job (I told him when he took 'er in hand to be careful o' the invisible jewills), that his bill would be four dollars and ten cents, the ten cents bein' for fingerin' careful round the reubies and things. Waal, Sir, she cut up agin last night, and I stept in to Cross & Jones's, and asked their young man to ixamine 'er parts, and pronoaunce upon 'er. Waal, he rubbed in *his* magnifying-glass, and screwtenized 'er, and says he, 'That's the most valuble watch I ever seed inside o' Omaha, but she warnts *cleanin'* most ——y!' When I heerd that, I expressed myself like a *dis*gusted night-hawk, and snatched 'er aout o' *his* hands, and brought 'er raound here to ponder over. What I wish to inquire is, Stranger (and I ask for information), how many times a watch thet's full o' invisible jewills has to be cleaned aout in the course o' two months? I never owned one afore, but if the jewills *nee-sessiates* that expense, as I'm a pore man, hadn't I better have 'em punched aout, don't you think?"

   And I advised him to have the "jewills" removed immediately, and sold in Europe for the most they would bring.

Cornelia Otis Skinner

IT'S A WISE PARENT

To one born west of the Alleghenies and reared in a suburban community, the social life of the New York child seems nothing short of amazing. In that remote and happy time known (unless Mrs. Roosevelt has a copyright on the title) as "my day," children met and played together for the simple reason that their mothers were "such good friends." This convention seems to have gone the way of family prayers and afternoon calls, and every year I become increasingly aware that I do not move in those charmed circles in which my son apparently whirls. However, no other New York parent appears to share my antiquated sense of etiquette. Once I ventured to send a shy message to a nebulous mother to the effect that since our offspring were such good buddies it might be nice if she'd come to tea some afternoon—an overture that caused as much bewilderment as if I'd asked her to dinner because we patronized the same osteopath.

Recently, while walking in the Park, my seven-year-old son and I encountered a little girl who was out with her father. The children exchanged a greeting that implied close acquaintanceship. I asked my son who she was and was casually informed she was his "girl friend." Concealing the stab to a mother's heart, I smiled generously and ventured to beam understandingly at the father. He gave me the kind of look Robert Taylor might give an autograph seeker, tipped his hat, and strolled on, the while his child rushed over to whisper into my son's ear that she'd be seeing him Thursday.

Hers, it turned out, had been one of those whimsical "won't-you-come-to-my-party" cards that arrive by post or are brought home, somewhat mangled, from school. My child receives a good many of these. Not that he is especially in demand; it's just that he knows a large number of children who have birthdays and, presumably, parents. Children's parties in New York are fast becoming something that isn't far behind the débutante racket, and it wouldn't surprise me if those society impresarios who arrange the coming-out parties have up their enterprising sleeves a list, purchasable for a consideration, of eligible little boys between the ages of six and ten. These festivities are expensive not only to the parents of the hosts but also to the parents of the gift-bearing guests, and I consider my monthly bill from Schwarz's one more social outrage that should be righteously ignored.

Once, thinking it might be my maternal duty to catch an inside glimpse of the houses to which my son has entrée, I committed the error of calling for him at a residence whose marble exterior and wrought-iron garage door should have forewarned me of the elaborate juvenile goings-on in there. A butler answered the bell. Butlers have an over-refining effect on me and in their presence I hear myself using the broad "a" on words like "hat." I murmured my son's name and the fact that I had come to fetch him. After I had made it plain that I was my child's mother and not his governess, the butler reluctantly led me up a carved stone stairway, opened a period door, and thrust me into a completely dark room. I was greeted by the whoops and catcalls of fifteen small boys and it was some moments before I realized that a moving picture was being shown and that I was standing between the screen and the projection machine. There was nothing to do but drop to a crouching position. My eyes were by now getting focussed—the way they do in the Blue Grotto—and in the dusk I could distinguish, over on a couch across the room, a pair of adults whom I presumed to be the parents of the child host. Fearing to cut off any more breathless moments of "Our Gang," I approached their presence in a crouching shuffle that must have seemed like a definite throwback to the Neanderthal Man. This startled them a good deal, but what startled them much more was my announcement that I was the mother of such-and-such a boy. Even in the gloom I could see their shocked astonishment. It was all very well for the nursemaids, waiting below, to crash the gate, but for a parent! They did manage, though, to utter a few polite phrases and we all three simulated an animated interest in the film, which was blessedly nearing its custard-pie finale. The lights flashed on and the party was pronounced over. My son and I thanked our hosts and departed, I sheepishly, he triumphantly with a considerable quantity of loot in the way of candy, favors, and, I later found out, a few of the birthday gifts of the unsuspecting host.

Only once have I attempted giving a child's party in New York.

Five little boys were invited and, as a refining influence, three little girls. My son supplied the list of names. Knowing practically none of the parents, I felt that along with the invitations I should at least send a few references. But New York parents are a trusting lot. As long as their children attend the same school or their nanas gossip together in the Park, they ask no questions. The invitations were unanimously accepted, and on the day and hour specified the children arrived all at once. I hovered nervously about the front door. Remembering my own recent experience, I wanted to prove, in case some child arrived accompanied by a mother, that here was one New York parent with neighborly instincts. This resulted in my shaking hands, effusively, with a number of nursery governesses who clearly thought me demented but who nonetheless left their charges in my dubious custody.

With the forethought of the Georgia women who buried their silver before the advent of Sherman, I had put away most of my bric-a-brac and sent the plants and the goldfish to spend a quiet day with a friend on another floor of my apartment house. The dog, I figured, could defend himself. Altogether there was little damage done— nothing more serious than a lollipop rammed into the piano strings and a spot on the carpet caused by a displaced butter ball. The entertainment was simple—one or two games and supper. There was no movie and no magician and no one even pinned a tail on a donkey. There was complete bedlam during the games and an equally complete silence during supper, which I understand is proof that the party was a hit. At the end several children said "Aw, do we have to go now?" though one young bounder informed me that at *his* party they had had Charlie McCarthy and a couple of trained seals. The governesses arrived at precisely six-thirty and the unknown children marched off to unknown homes to tell unknown parents that they'd had ice cream. My son retired to bed in a vile humor—another proof the party was a success—and I poured myself a drink fit for a lumberjack. I had hardly taken a sip when the telephone rang and the maid informed me that the mother of one of the children wished to speak with me. I felt sure she was calling to thank me for my kindness to her child and said "Hello" in a voice of honey. Someone with ill-concealed irritation announced she was Cynthia's mother. I remembered Cynthia, and none too pleasantly. I had seen her surreptitiously pouring her soup into the centrepiece and I suspected her of being the vandal who stuck the lollipop in the piano strings. The voice went on to say that Cynthia had returned home without her band.

"Her band?" I asked incredulously.

"Yes," came the voice. "She takes it out when she eats. It must be in your house somewhere. Would you mind looking for it?"

With a shudder I said no, and added that I'd bring it by on my way out to dinner. I'm not good at finding things and Cynthia's band was no exception. I searched with avidity and dread. When my husband came home, he too joined the search. It was the cook who found it, carefully wrapped in a paper napkin and deposited in an empty glass. It was a repellent contraption of wire and silver, vaguely surrealist in aspect. I wrapped it tenderly in cotton and placed it in a box from Cartier's. Cynthia lives on Park Avenue in a penthouse I am never likely to enter, although my child informs me he has been there. I left the box with the doorman, requesting him to see that Cynthia's mother got it immediately. I had it well timed and it seemed probable that she would be at the dinner table when she opened it. At least I hoped so.

Ring Lardner

LARGE COFFEE

Note: Readers of the daily papers will recall a paragraph printed earlier this week to the effect that the body of a Mr. Lardner was found in a New York hotel room by a house officer who had broken in after the chambermaids had reported that they had rapped on the door every day for over a fortnight and had received no response, and were disposed to believe that the occupant of the room would need a clean towel if living, and perhaps two of them if dead. The occupant was in the last-named condition or worse. Dressed as usual in pajamas, he was sprawled out on the floor, his head crushed in by a blow from some blunt instrument, probably another hotel. At the time the item appeared, there was mention of the discovery of a diary. It now develops that one really was unearthed and turned over to the police, who used parts of it as curl papers for Grover Whalen. We have acquired the mechanical rights to the balance and herewith publish extracts from it as a human document of particular interest to men and women who, like the writer thereof, have been battered and broken by an insensate world.

Friday, May 31

Today I registered and was assigned this room, 657, which is to be my home through most of the summer. At a conference of my wife and children, it was decided that I ought to contribute something to their support and they recommended that I do a little writing for the magazines or newspapers. I told them this would be impossible in our hut on Long Island unless they and the neighbors agreed to become hermits so that my mind would not be constantly distracted by the knowledge that other people were having fun. It is my plan to visit the family one day in the middle of each week, not at the week-end when there seems to be a tendency to drink cocktails and expect you to sit by, look on and like it. The hotel is giving me a rate of $4.00 a day, really a bargain because the room has a window.

You can look right into other people's rooms on the courtyard if they don't keep their shades down. O diary, I hope it's a hot summer. (Editors' Note: Did he get his hope?)

Sunday, June 2

I spent so much thought yesterday and this morning on what I would have sent up for breakfast that when I sat down at the typewriter, my mind was too tired to work. I spoke of this over the telephone (my only means of communication with the outside world) to a friend and he advised me to make a selection of a few nourishing and inoffensive victuals, commit them to memory and order them every morning. I then asked him what to do about the coffee problem, which is something of a problem to me. You see, when you drink lots of coffee you can kind of kid yourself into believing it's something else, so for breakfast I always want four cups. What I mean is enough coffee to fill one cup four times. Yesterday morning I said to the order clerk, "Two orders of coffee," and the result was two small pots of coffee, each containing enough for two cups. But the set-up, as I believe they call it, was for two people; there were two cereal dishes, two plates for my bacon and eggs and two cups for my coffee. This lay-out congested the table, leaving no space for my shoe tree. So this morning I said, "Two orders of coffee, but served for one person." The result was a small pot of coffee, containing enough for two cups. Well, my friend said I would have to work this out for myself; the only advice he could give me was ridiculous—that I give up coffee. This evening I will try to think of a solution and also select a permanent breakfast so there will be no more brain fag or waste of time.

Friday, June 7

The breakfast I have picked out for the summer consists of orange juice, corn flakes, medium hard boiled eggs and buttered toast. Boiled eggs are preferable to other kinds because they don't bring you two plates for them even if your coffee order makes them believe you are two people. I selected toast instead of plain rolls or sweet rolls because the sweet ones are too filling and messy, and the plain ones are made in Bethlehem, Pa. The toast is also immune, but you have to say something when the order clerk insists. The coffee situation is just as baffling as a week ago. One morning I said, "I am living alone, but I drink four cups of coffee." I got a large pot of coffee and four cups. Another morning I said, "Double coffee, served for one." I got a large pot of coffee, two cups and two orders of tooth-proof toast. Yesterday I asked the waiter how much a large pot of coffee cost. He said it was sixty cents. So this morning I said to the order clerk, "One orange juice, one corn flakes, one medium hard boiled egg, one buttered toast and sixty cents worth of coffee." "Coffee," she replied, "is only thirty cents a pot." "But I want twice as much as that." "Oh, all right. You want two orders." "Yes, but I'm not two people." I got one small pot of coffee.

Monday, July 8

It is the hottest summer in history. Everybody on our court is free and easy. Formality and modesty have been thrown to the winds, if there are any. A business woman who looks like Tom Heeney and has a red splotch under her left shoulder blade is occupying the room just opposite. She is out all day and goes to bed at eight and reads the Brooklyn telephone directory. The electric light in my bathroom wouldn't work today and I wanted to shave on account of the waiters. I told the floor clerk to send me the electrician. Pretty soon a plumber came and turned on everything but the light. "I don't see anything wrong," he said. "The light won't turn on," I said. "Oh," said he. "You want the electrician." The electrician came. I said, "The light won't turn on in the bathroom and I know the bulb isn't burned out because I tried another bulb and it wouldn't work." So the electrician tried another bulb and found it wouldn't work. "It must be something else," he said. He found the trouble and fixed it. This may have no bearing on the case, but I want to tell all.

I have been getting my large pot of coffee every morning, but never with less than two cups and nearly always with two egg cups, two dishes for cereal and two orders of toast.

Friday, July 12

Double coffee, large coffee, enough coffee for four cups, sixty cents worth of coffee, enough coffee for two people served for one person. I have thought I might ask Percy Hammond to come and room with me, but that would only mean six or eight cups on the same-sized table. An assistant manager called me up at twenty minutes to three this morning and said somebody had just complained that I was using a typewriter. What the hell does Mrs. Heeney think I moved in here for, to be near Gimbel Brothers?

Thursday, August 22

Yesterday morning I got what I wanted and I called right back and asked for the order clerk. "Are you the only order clerk?" "Oh, no." "Well, are you the one that just took the order for 657?" "Yes. Was it wrong?" "No. It was right. Now listen, I'm not trying to start a flirtation, but what is your name?" "If there's any complaint, I'll connect you with the superintendent." "There's no complaint, but I want your name so I can give you my order every morning." "Well, my name is Foley." "Thanks, Miss Foley. And when I call you to-morrow and other mornings, please do as you just did—send me a large pot of coffee and only one cup."

Every day the paper says cooler tomorrow. They ought to put that with the rest of the comics. A mystifying combination of tenants has taken the room across the court. There are two young women and a man. They can't be going to stay in town very long because the women apparently haven't brought anything but nightgowns and when the man isn't in B.V.D.'s he's out of them. I feel as if some time I would almost have to shout at them, "Don't you want a fourth for bridge?"

Monday, September 2

The worst has happened. Miss Foley "isn't here any more." My house was built on sand. I've got to start all over again and work up from the bottom.

And I'm pretty sure that late tonight I will lean out the window and holler, "Hey! Don't you want a fourth for strip bridge?"

Donald Moffat

"DOUCEMENT, DOUCEMENT!"

Those who expect the French to take up any of the idealistic policies which have been offered to the world as insurance against future catastrophes without, so to speak, first carefully reading through all the fine print would spare themselves disillusionment by hearkening to Mr. Mott's experience in buying an automobile.

The actual purchase of the car was simple. He bought it sight unseen before ever he set sail for France, from an American acquaintance named Walters, who had left it in a garage at Nice before coming home for good. The car was of the type known as a touring *camionette,* a word which sounded to Mr. Mott like the name of an affectionate, pretty, and frolicsome girl. He gained further comfort by learning that this pleasant fancy lost nothing in translation, as the equivalent for *camionette,* in the United States, is a small truck with a "pick-up body."

So Mr. Mott gladly paid the agreed price, and received, besides the keys and a walletful of licenses, a receipted bill of sale and a copy of a letter from Mr. Walters to the garage at Nice, containing an account of the sale and a description of Mr. Mott, for identification.

Mr. Mott therefore sailed for France feeling well confirmed in his title to the car, and thought no more about it until a week before he left Paris to take possession, when he wrote to M. Roux, proprietor of the Garage d'Angleterre et de la Méditerranée, saying that he would be in Nice the following Saturday, and hoped to find the car ready. He got no answer until Thursday, on which day M. Roux replied that the *camionette* was well, but that before Mr. Mott could have it he must get authority from the *patron,* M. Meyer, who conducted a transport agency at a certain address in Paris. Mr. Mott was slightly annoyed, because time was short; but he reflected that a day and a half ought to be ample to conclude a mere formality like this.

The next morning he set out in search of M. Meyer, and, after spending an hour marvelling at the taste of small Parisian businessmen for hiding their offices behind dark courtyards and misleading stairways, he eventually found him. M. Meyer greeted him with smiling politeness, led him to a dim inner office, sat him in a comfortable chair, and faced him across the flat-topped desk—a gracious, round, and ruddy little man with a head completely bald, and a dense, curved mustache, black as a derby hat. M. Meyer leaned forward in his chair, smiled sympathetically, and waited.

Mr. Mott said: "My name is Mott, Monsieur. I am the American who bought Mr. Walters' *camionette,* which is now in the garage at Nice. I have come to ask you for a letter authorizing the *garagiste* to let me have the car. I go to Nice tomorrow."

"Ah," said M. Meyer, "of course. A charming fellow, M. Walters. So you have bought his little car, Monsieur?"

"Yes, before I sailed. Permit me to offer my passport, for identification."

M. Meyer examined every page of the passport with interest and care. Then he turned to the photograph, held it out at arm's length, and compared it with the original, feature by feature. "Well," he said at length, pleasure and surprise in his voice. "A good likeness. I compliment you. And now?"

"A letter to M. Roux, if you will be so kind." Mr. Mott was congratulating himself on M. Meyer's amiability, and the simplicity of the little transaction, when M. Meyer hesitated and fell to drumming on the desk, plunged in profound thought. After a full minute of this, "Monsieur," he said, apologetically, "pardon me; but in an affair of this kind it is not well to move too quickly. For both our sakes, care must be exercised. I shall therefore be so ungracious as to beg of you some further identification—identification, that is to say, as the actual purchaser of the little car. That you are indeed M. Mott is established. But that M. Mott has bought the car of M. Walters?" He stopped, and smiled agreeably.

"Certainly, M. Meyer," replied Mr. Mott. He took out the wallet given him by Mr. Walters, and spread on the desk the keys and the four licenses, besides his own *certificate de domicile* and *carte d'identité* for good measure, acquired since reaching Paris. M. Meyer examined them earnestly, then conceded, with a polite bow, that the defence had scored one point at least.

"Perfect," he said. "Everything in perfect order; *mais*" (Oh! that French *mais*, thought Mr. Mott) "you will forgive me, Monsieur? Papers like these, as you know, may be easily lost and as easily picked up by another, not the true owner. You will also agree that they may easily be stolen, and while I do not, of course, suggest for an instant that such is here the case—a thousand pardons—you will appreciate that it is my unfortunate duty not to neglect such a possibility. Also, Monsieur—"

"I understand perfectly, Monsieur," Mr. Mott interrupted, digging once more into his pocketbook. "As a man of business you could pursue no other course. But here is the copy of a letter Mr. Walters wrote to the *garagiste* telling of the sale. If you will send for the original, which is doubtless in your files, you may compare them and so satisfy your praiseworthy scruples."

M. Meyer rang for a clerk and sent him for the letter. And to Mr. Mott's surprise he was back with it before M. Meyer had finished Chapter I of his recitation on the subject of Paris Weather—Past, Present, and Future. M. Meyer compared the copy with the original word for word, then fitted them together, held them up to the light over his head, and gazed through them for signs of forgery.

Finally he lowered his arms. "The letters," he pronounced, "are identical. I congratulate you, Monsieur.... Yet," he added, after a thoughtful pause, "how easy it would be for a clever man to make up such a letter, and having dispatched it, to keep a copy to produce at the required moment. Of course," he went on, with a jolly laugh, "I know perfectly well that *you* have not been guilty of such villainy; but you see my difficulty: I am compelled to act on that very supposition. You pretend to be M. Mott; your passport confirms the assertion. You pretend to have bought an automobile from M. Walters, and in support of this contention you show me these licenses. But"—here M. Meyer spread his arms wide, as if beseeching Mr. Mott's co-operation and charity—"nothing to show that you have paid for the car except"—shaking his head regretfully, and letting his arms fall—"this letter, which, as I have demonstrated, is technically open to suspicion."

Mr. Mott watched him, fascinated. Then suddenly, cursing himself for his stupidity, he remembered the receipted bill of sale, his trump card. Once more he reached into his pocket, bulging with the accumulation of papers that always seemed mysteriously to fill his clothes after a few days in Paris. He found the bill of sale, unfolded it. "Here, Monsieur," he said, handing it over, "here is Mr. Walters' own receipt for the money, signed by his own hand. Examine it carefully, I beg."

M. Meyer took him at his word; then mournfully shook his head. "It is obviously correct," he said, "but, alas, worthless. *Tenez,* I believe you to be M. Mott; I believe that you actually bought the little car from M. Walters, and paid for it. It is my great desire to help you, to serve you. But this!" Again he shook his head. "As the world knows, Monsieur, a receipted bill is valueless in the eyes of the law unless payment of the sales tax is attested by the affixation of the government stamps, and countersigned by the vendor. On this paper, as you see, there are no stamps whatever. Therefore, alas, the sale is not yet complete. It is unfortunate.... I regret, Monsieur, infinitely."

"But, Monsieur," Mr. Mott protested, "the sale occurred in the United States, where the custom of taxing receipted bills has not yet been introduced. How could there be stamps?"

"You argue well, Monsieur. But! We are not now in the United States. That, you will agree, is evident." On this point M. Meyer was polite, but quite firm. "We are in France. The little *camion,* the subject of the transaction, is also in France. Thus you see, Monsieur, there must be stamps. I am sure that you understand the friendliness of my attitude, and that I take these precautions not from any doubt of you, but because such affairs must be concluded in an orderly fashion. Indeed, the fact that the principals in the transaction are both foreigners, Americans, makes my position all the more delicate. Consider the international complications that might arise if I did not take my responsibilities, as intermediary, at the foot of the letter." He paused.

Mr. Mott said slowly: "Yes, I see, Monsieur.... But these stamps? Where may they be procured?"

"I do not know. It is not, strictly speaking, my affair. But if I may offer the suggestion, your American consul might be able to help you."

Mr. Mott got up and held out his hand. "Thank you, Monsieur, I will go there directly." He congratulated himself, as M. Meyer showed him to the door, on having kept firm hold of his sense of reality—as well as his temper.

At the consulate, when Mr. Mott looked into the waiting-room, he found it so full of troubled-looking compatriots that he left at once, and went to a café to brood. His brooding brought him an idea, the idea that comes eventually to most Americans who get up against it in France. He went to the office of a lawyer he knew, an American lawyer named Emily. "Emily," he said, "I'm up against it. What shall I do?" and he explained the situation. Emily told him. "What you need," she said, "is seals. Give me that paper." She took the receipted bill and disappeared, and presently came back with a gorgeous seal, fixed to the paper with masses of wax and red ribbon. "What's that?" Mr. Mott asked. "That's a seal," said Emily. "Take it to the consul, tell him I sent you, and have him put on stamps." "What kind?" asked Mr. Mott. "Don't be so fussy," Emily replied. "Goodbye."

The consul was young, bored, and, as soon as Mr. Mott mentioned Emily's name, obliging. He stuck on stamps—what stamps Mr. Mott did not inquire—cancelled them with a flourishing signature, and also gave Mr. Mott a letter to the consul at Nice, in case. It was then too late to go back to M. Meyer.

The next morning he packed and took his baggage to the Gare de Lyon, to be sure of having plenty of time to catch his afternoon train in case M. Meyer had any further ideas. But he had none. His eyes lit up with pleasure when he saw the glorified document. He barely glanced at it. "Perfect," he said. "I am truly delighted. Now I will compose the letter to M. Roux." He wrote. "There, Monsieur, and forgive my precautions; they have been a trouble to you, I know, but a necessary one. I wish you many happy days of touring under our sunny, smiling skies." They parted on the best of terms, with many gallant expressions of mutual admiration and esteem; but as Mr. Mott turned on the stairs to bow a last farewell, he caught M. Meyer gazing inscrutably after him, in his eye still glowing the living embers of doubt—not, Mr. Mott knew, of his personal honesty, but of the completeness and authenticity of his chain of evidence.

At Nice, Mr. Mott went straight to the garage, where M. Roux, huge, greasy, and jolly, greeted him with warmth, and thus dispelled his secret fear that M. Meyer, in the last throes of suspicion, had cancelled the letter by wire.

M. Roux led him to the *camionette*. "*Voilà,* Monsieur, all ready for the *tourisme: essence,* oil, water—everything. A fine little bus."

Mr. Mott thanked him and offered M. Meyer's letter, explaining what it was.

"Oh, that," M. Roux laughed. "Keep it. *I* don't want it. Any friend of M. Walters is a friend of mine, and unquestionably an honest man."

"But you wrote me," Mr. Mott protested, "that you couldn't let me have the car without it. Would you have?"

"But, of course. Those were just the orders of the *patron*; I had to write to you. He's careful, that one. However"—he shrugged—"one must remember that he is not only a man of affairs, but from the North as well. What would you?" M. Roux took the letter and, without reading it, folded it small (the worldwide sign of the peasant), put it in his pocket, and proceeded to think of other things.

HISTORY, POLITICS, AND
AFFAIRS OF STATE

The following is the only section in the book arranged chronologically. We thought it would be easier for our readers to understand history if they took events up in proper sequence.

One of the supposedly humorous American historians was Bill Nye. A chapter from his "History of the United States" might logically have found a place in here if it had been funny (to us), and we wish it had, because Opper's illustrations are so good.

The editors wish to point out to military experts the timeliness of Orpheus C. Kerr's observations on. Civil War artillery. We also refer you, for the history of the Whisky Rebellion, to the parody section.

Washington Irving

THE MOST HORRIBLE BATTLE EVER
RECORDED IN POETRY OR PROSE *

Now had the Dutchmen snatched a huge repast, and finding themselves wonderfully encouraged and animated thereby, prepared to
take the field. Expectation, says the writer of the Stuyvesant manuscript,—Expectation now stood on stilts. The world forgot to turn
around, or rather stood still, that it might witness the affray,—like
a round-bellied alderman, watching the combat of two chivalrous
flies upon his jerkin. The eyes of all mankind, as usual in such cases,
were turned upon Fort Christina. The sun, like a little man in a
crowd at a puppet-show, scampered about the heavens, popping his
head here and there, and endeavoring to get a peep between the
unmannerly clouds that obtruded themselves in his way. The historians
filled their inkhorns; the poets went without their dinners, either
that they might buy paper and goose-quills, or because they could not
get anything to eat. Antiquity scowled sulkily out of its grave, to see
itself outdone,—while even Posterity stood mute, gazing in gaping
ecstasy of retrospection on the eventful field.

The immortal deities, who whilom had seen service at the "affair"
of Troy, now mounted their feather-bed clouds, and sailed over the
plain, or mingled among the combatants in different disguises, all
itching to have a finger in the pie. Jupiter sent off his thunderbolt
to a noted coppersmith, to have it furbished up for the direful occasion. Venus vowed by her chastity to patronize the Swedes, and in
semblance of a blear-eyed trull paraded the battlements of Fort Christina, accompanied by Diana, as a sergeant's widow, of cracked reputation. The noted bully, Mars, stuck two horse-pistols into his belt,
shouldered a rusty firelock, and gallantly swaggered at their elbow,
as a drunken corporal,—while Apollo trudged in their rear, as a
bandy-legged fifer, playing most villanously out of tune.

* A chapter from "Knickerbocker's History of New York."

On the other side, the ox-eyed Juno, who had gained a pair of black eyes overnight, in one of her curtain-lectures with old Jupiter, displayed her haughty beauties on a baggage-wagon; Minerva, as a brawny gin-suttler, tucked up her skirts, brandished her fists, and swore most heroically, in exceeding bad Dutch (having but lately studied the language), by way of keeping up the spirits of the soldiers; while Vulcan halted as a club-footed blacksmith, lately promoted to be a captain of militia. All was silent awe, or bustling preparation; war reared his horrid front, gnashed loud his iron fangs, and shook his direful crest of bristling bayonets.

And now the mighty chieftains marshalled out their hosts. Here stood stout Risingh, firm as a thousand rocks,—incrusted with stockades, and intrenched to the chin in mud batteries. His valiant soldiery lined the breastwork in grim array, each having his mustachios fiercely greased, and his hair pomatumed back, and queued so stiffly, that he grinned above the ramparts like a grisly death's-head.

There came on the intrepid Peter,—his brows knit, his teeth set, his fists clenched, almost breathing forth volumes of smoke, so fierce was the fire that raged within his bosom. His faithful squire Van Corlear trudged valiantly at his heels, with his trumpet gorgeously bedecked with red and yellow ribbons, the remembrances of his fair mistresses at the Manhattoes. Then came waddling on the sturdy chivalry of the Hudson. There were the Van Wycks, and the Van Dycks, and the Ten Eycks; the Van Nesses, the Van Tassels, the Van Grolls; the Van Hoesens, the Van Giesons, and the Van Blarcoms; the Van Warts, the Van Winkles, the Van Dams; the Van Pelts, the Van Rippers, and the Van Brunts. There were the Van Hornes, the Van Hooks, the Van Bunschotens; the Van Gelders, the Van Arsdales, and the Van Bummels; the Vander Belts, the Vander Hoofs, the Vander Voorts, the Vander Lyns, the Vander Pools, and the Vander Spiegels;—then came the Hoffmans, the Hooghlands, the Hoppers, the Cloppers, the Ryckmans, the Dyckmans, the Hogebooms, the Rosebooms, the Ooothouts, the Quackenbosses, the Roerbacks, the Garrebrantzes, the Bensons, the Brouwers, the Waldrons, the Onderdonks, the Varra Vangers, the Schermerhorns, the Stoutenburghs, the Brinkerhoffs, the Bontecous, the Knickerbockers, the Hockstrassers, the Ten Breecheses and the Tough Breecheses, with a host more of worthies, whose names are too crabbed to be written, or if they could be written, it would be impossible for man to utter,—

all fortified with a mighty dinner, and, to use the words of a great
Dutch poet,

"Brimful of wrath and cabbage."

For an instant the mighty Peter paused in the midst of his career,
and mounting on a stump, addressed his troops in eloquent Low
Dutch, exhorting them to fight like *duyvels,* and assuring them that if
they conquered, they should get plenty of booty,—if they fell, they
should be allowed the satisfaction, while dying, of reflecting that it
was in the service of their country, and after they were dead, of seeing
their names inscribed in the temple of renown, and handed down, in
company with all the other great men of the year, for the admiration
of posterity. Finally, he swore to them, on the word of a governor
(and they knew him too well to doubt it for a moment), that if he
caught any mother's son of them looking pale, or playing craven, he
would curry his hide till he made him run out of it like a snake in
spring-time. Then lugging out his trusty sabre, he brandished it three
times over his head, ordered Van Corlear to sound a charge, and
shouting the words "St. Nicholas and the Manhattoes!" courageously
dashed forwards. His warlike followers, who had employed the interval in lighting their pipes, instantly stuck them into their mouths, gave
a furious puff, and charged gallantly under cover of the smoke.

The Swedish garrison, ordered by the cunning Risingh not to fire
until they could distinguish the whites of their assailants' eyes, stood
in horrid silence on the covert-way, until the eager Dutchmen had
ascended the glacis. Then did they pour into them such a tremendous
volley, that the very hills quaked around, and were terrified even unto
an incontinence of water, insomuch that certain springs burst forth
from their sides, which continue to run unto the present day. Not a
Dutchman but would have bitten the dust beneath that dreadful fire,
had not the protecting Minerva kindly taken care that the Swedes
should, one and all, observe their usual custom of shutting their eyes
and turning away their heads at the moment of discharge.

The Swedes followed up their fire by leaping the counterscarp,
and falling tooth and nail upon the foe with furious outcries. And now
might be seen prodigies of valor, unmatched in history or song. Here
was the sturdy Stoffel Brinkerhoff brandishing his quarter-staff, like
the giant Blanderon his oak-tree (for he scorned to carry any other
weapon), and drumming a horrific tune upon the hard heads of the

Swedish soldiery. There were the Van Kortlandts, posted at a distance, like the Locrian archers of yore, and plying it most potently with the long-bow, for which they were so justly renowned. On a rising knoll were gathered the valiant men of Sing-Sing, assisting marvellously in the fight, by chanting the great song of St. Nicholas; but as to the Gardeniers of Hudson, they were absent on a marauding party, laying waste the neighboring water-melon patches.

In a different part of the field were the Van Grolls of Antony's Nose, struggling to get to the thickest of the fight, but horribly perplexed in a defile between two hills, by reason of the length of their noses. So also the Van Bunschotens of Nyack and Kakiat, so renowned for kicking with the left foot, were brought to a stand for want of wind, in consequence of the hearty dinner they had eaten, and would have been put to utter rout but for the arrival of a gallant corps of voltigeurs, composed of the Hoppers, who advanced nimbly to their assistance on one foot. Nor must I omit to mention the valiant achievements of Antony Van Corlear, who, for a good quarter of an hour, waged stubborn fight with a little pursy Swedish drummer, whose hide he drummed most magnificently, and whom he would infallibly have annihilated on the spot, but that he had come into the battle with no other weapon but his trumpet.

But now the combat thickened. On came the mighty Jacobus Varra Vanger and the fighting-men of the Wallabout; after them thundered the Van Pelts of Esopus, together with the Van Rippers and the Van Brunts, bearing down all before them; then the Suy Dams, and the Van Dams, pressing forward with many a blustering oath, at the head of the warriors of Hell-gate, clad in their thunder-and-lightning gaberdines; and lastly, the standard-bearers and body-guard of Peter Stuyvesant, bearing the great beaver of the Manhattoes.

And now commenced the horrid din, the desperate struggle, the maddening ferocity, the frantic desperation, the confusion and self-abandonment of war. Dutchman and Swede commingled, tugged, panted, and blowed. The heavens were darkened with a tempest of missiles. Bang! went the guns; whack!·went the broad-swords; thump! went the cudgels; crash! went the musket-stocks; blows, kicks, cuffs, scratches, black eyes and bloody noses swelling the horrors of the scene! Thick thwack, cut and hack, helter-skelter, higgledy-piggledy, hurly-burly, head-over-heels, rough-and-tumble! Dunder and blixum! swore the Dutchmen; splitter and splutter! cried the Swedes. Storm

the works! shouted Hardkoppig Peter. Fire the mine! roared stout
Risingh. Tanta-rar-ra-ra! twanged the trumpet of Antony Van Corlear;—until all voice and sound became unintelligible,—grunts of pain,
yells of fury, and shouts of triumph mingling in one hideous clamor.
The earth shook as if struck with a paralytic stroke; trees shrunk
aghast, and withered at the sight; rocks burrowed in the ground like
rabbits; and even Christina creek turned from its course, and ran up
a hill in breathless terror!

Long hung the contest doubtful; for though a heavy shower of rain,
sent by the "cloud-compelling Jove," in some measure cooled their
ardor, as doth a bucket of water thrown on a group of fighting mastiffs,
yet did they but pause for a moment, to return with tenfold fury to
the charge. Just at this juncture a vast and dense column of smoke
was seen slowly rolling toward the scene of battle. The combatants
paused for a moment, gazing in mute astonishment, until the wind,
dispelling the murky cloud, revealed the flaunting banner of Michael
Paw, the Patroon of Communipaw. That valiant chieftain came fearlessly on at the head of a phalanx of oyster-fed Pavonians and a *corps
de reserve* of the Van Arsdales and Van Bummels, who had remained
behind to digest the enormous dinner they had eaten. These now
trudged manfully forward, smoking their pipes with outrageous vigor,
so as to raise the awful cloud that has been mentioned, but marching
exceedingly slow, being short of leg, and of great rotundity in the
belt.

And now the deities who watched over the fortunes of the Neder-
landers having unthinkingly left the field, and stepped into a neighboring tavern to refresh themselves with a pot of beer, a direful catas-
trophe had wellnigh ensued. Scarce had the myrmidons of Michael
Paw attained the front of battle, when the Swedes, instructed by the
cunning Risingh, levelled a shower of blows full at their tobacco-
pipes. Astounded at this assault, and dismayed at the havoc of their
pipes, these ponderous warriors gave way, and like a drove of frightened elephants broke through the ranks of their own army. The little
Hoppers were borne down in the surge; the sacred banner emblazoned
with the gigantic oyster of Communipaw was trampled in the dirt;
on blundered and thundered the heavy-sterned fugitives, the Swedes
pressing on their rear and applying their feet *a parte poste* of the Van
Arsdales and the Van Bummels with a vigor that prodigiously accel-
erated their movements; nor did the renowned Michael Paw himself

fail to receive divers grievous and dishonorable visitations of shoe-leather.

But what, oh Muse! was the rage of Peter Stuyvesant, when from afar he saw his army giving way! In the transports of his wrath he sent forth a roar, enough to shake the very hills. The men of the Manhattoes plucked up new courage at the sound, or, rather, they rallied at the voice of their leader, of whom they stood more in awe than of all the Swedes in Christendom. Without waiting for their aid, the daring Peter dashed, sword in hand, into the thickest of the foe. Then might be seen achievements worthy of the days of the giants. Wherever he went, the enemy shrank before him; the Swedes fled to right and left, or were driven, like dogs, into their own ditch; but as he pushed forward singly with headlong courage, the foe closed behind and hung upon his rear. One aimed a blow full at his heart; but the protecting power which watches over the great and good turned aside the hostile blade and directed it to a side-pocket, where reposed an enormous iron tobacco-box, endowed, like the shield of Achilles, with supernatural powers, doubtless from bearing the portrait of the blessed St. Nicholas. Peter Stuyvesant turned like an angry bear upon the foe, and seizing him, as he fled, by an immeasureable queue, "Ah, whoreson caterpillar," roared he, "here's what shall make worms' meat of thee!" So saying, he whirled his sword, and dealt a blow that would have decapitated the varlet, but that the pitying steel struck short and shaved the queue forever from his crown. At this moment an arquebusier levelled his piece from a neighboring mound, with deadly aim; but the watchful Minerva, who had just stopped to tie up her garter, seeing the peril of her favorite hero, sent old Boreas with his bellows, who, as the match descended to the pan, gave a blast that blew the priming from the touch-hole.

Thus waged the fight, when the stout Risingh, surveying the field from the top of a little ravelin, perceived his troops banged, beaten, and kicked by the invincible Peter. Drawing his falchion and uttering a thousand anathemas, he strode down to the scene of combat with some such thundering strides as Jupiter is said by Hesiod to have taken when he strode down the spheres to hurl his thunder-bolts at the Titans.

When the rival heroes came face to face, each made a prodigious start in the style of a veteran stage-champion. Then did they regard each other for a moment with the bitter aspect of two furious ram-

cats on the point of a clapper-clawing. Then did they throw themselves
into one attitude, then into another, striking their swords on the
ground, first on the right side, then on the left; at last at it they went,
with incredible ferocity. Words cannot tell the prodigies of strength
and valor displayed in this direful encounter,—an encounter compared to which the far-famed battles of Ajax with Hector, of Aeneas
with Turnus, Orlando with Rodomont, Guy of Warwick with Col-
brand the Dane, or of that renowned Welsh knight, Sir Owen of the
Mountains, with the giant Guylon, were all gentle sports and holiday
recreations. At length the valiant Peter, watching his opportunity,
aimed a blow, enough to cleave his adversary to the very chine; but
Risingh, nimbly raising his sword, warded it off so narrowly, that,
glancing on one side, it shaved away a huge canteen in which he carried his liquor,—thence pursuing its trenchant course, it severed off a
deep coat-pocket, stored with bread and cheese,—which provant rolling among the armies, occasioned a fearful scrambling between the
Swedes and Dutchmen, and made the general battle to wax more furious than ever.

Enraged to see his military stores laid waste, the stout Risingh,
collecting all his forces, aimed a mighty blow full at the hero's crest.
In vain did his fierce little cocked hat oppose its course. The biting
steel clove through the stubborn ram beaver, and would have cracked
the crown of any one not endowed with supernatural hardness of
head; but the brittle weapon shivered in pieces on the skull of Hardkoppig Piet, shedding a thousand sparks, like beams of glory, round
his grizzly visage.

The good Peter reeled with the blow, and turning up his eyes
beheld a thousand suns, besides moons and stars, dancing about the
firmament; at length, missing his footing, by reason of his wooden
leg, down he came on his seat of honor with a crash which shook the
surrounding hills, and might have wrecked his frame, had he not been
received into a cushion softer than velvet, which Providence, or
Minerva, or St. Nicholas, or some cow, had benevolently prepared for
his reception.

The furious Risingh, in despite of the maxim, cherished by all true
knights, that "fair play is a jewel," hastened to take advantage of the
hero's fall; but, as he stooped to give a fatal blow, Peter Stuyvesant
dealt him a thwack over the sconce with his wooden leg, which set
a chime of bells ringing triple bob-majors in his cerebellum. The

bewildered Swede staggered with the blow, and the wary Peter seizing a pocket-pistol, which lay hard by, discharged it full at the head of the reeling Risingh. Let not my reader mistake; it was not a murderous weapon loaded with powder and ball, but a little sturdy stone pottle charged to the muzzle with a double dram of true Dutch courage, which the knowing Antony Van Corlear carried about him by way of replenishing his valor, and which had dropped from his wallet during his furious encounter with the drummer. The hideous weapon sang through the air, and true to its course as was the fragment of a rock discharged at Hector by bully Ajax, encountered the head of the gigantic Swede with matchless violence.

This heaven-directed blow decided the battle. The ponderous pericranium of General Jan Risingh sank upon his breast; his knees tottered under him; a deathlike torpor seized upon his frame, and he tumbled to the earth with such violence, that old Pluto started with affright, lest he should have broken through the roof of his infernal palace.

His fall was the signal of defeat and victory: the Swedes gave way, the Dutch pressed forward; the former took to their heels, the latter hotly pursued. Some entered with them, pell-mell, through the sallyport; others stormed the bastion, and others scrambled over the curtain. Thus in a little while the fortress of Fort Christina, which, like another Troy, had stood a siege of full ten hours, was carried by assault, without the loss of a single man on either side. Victory, in the likeness of a gigantic ox-fly, sat perched upon the cocked hat of the gallant Stuyvesant; and it was declared, by all the writers whom he hired to write the history of his expedition, that on this memorable day he gained a sufficient quantity of glory to immortalize a dozen of the greatest heroes in Christendom!

Orpheus C. Kerr

THE LATEST IMPROVEMENTS IN ARTILLERY

Washington, D. C., August —, 1861.
By invitation of a well-known official, I visited the Navy-Yard yesterday, and witnessed the trial of some newly-invented rifled cannon. The trial was of short duration, and the jury brought in a verdict of "innocent of any intent to kill."

The first gun tried was similar to those used in the Revolution, except that it had a larger touch-hole, and the carriage was painted green, instead of blue. This novel and ingenious weapon was pointed at a target about sixty yards distant. It didn't hit it, and as nobody saw any ball, there was much perplexity expressed. A midshipman did say that he thought the ball must have run out of the touch-hole when they loaded up—for which he was instantly expelled from the service. After a long search without finding the ball, there was some thought of summoning the Naval Retiring Board to decide on the matter, when somebody happened to look into the mouth of the cannon, and discovered that the ball hadn't gone out at all. The inventor said this would happen sometimes, especially if you didn't put a brick over the touch-hole when you fired the gun. The Government was so pleased with this explanation, that it ordered forty of the guns on the spot, at two hundred thousand dollars apiece. The guns to be furnished as soon as the war is over.

The next weapon tried was Jink's double back-action revolving cannon for ferry-boats. It consists of a heavy bronze tube, revolving on a pivot, with both ends open, and a touch-hole in the middle. While one gunner puts a load in at one end, another puts in a load at the other end, and one touch-hole serves for both. Upon applying the match, the gun is whirled swiftly round on a pivot, and both balls fly out in circles, causing great slaughter on both sides. This terrible engine was aimed at the target with great accuracy; but as the gunner has a large family dependent on him for support, he refused to apply the match. The Government was satisfied without firing, and ordered six of the guns at a million dollars apiece. The guns to be furnished in time for our next war.

The last weapon subjected to trial was a mountain howitzer of a new pattern. The inventor explained that its great advantage was, that it required no powder. In battle it is placed on the top of a high mountain, and a ball slipped loosely into it. As the enemy passes the foot of the mountain, the gunner in charge tips over the howitzer, and the ball rolls down the side of the mountain into the midst of the doomed foe. The range of this terrible weapon depends greatly on the height of the mountain and the distance to its base. The Government ordered forty of these mountain howitzers at a hundred thousand dollars apiece, to be planted on the first mountains discovered in the enemy's country.

These are great times for gunsmiths, my boy; and if you find any old cannon around the junk-shops, just send them along.

There is much sensation in nautical circles arising from the immoral conduct of the rebel privateers; but public feeling has been somewhat easier since the invention of a craft for capturing the pirates, by an ingenious Connecticut chap. Yesterday he exhibited a small model of it at a cabinet meeting, and explained it thus:

"You will perceive," says he to the President, "that the machine itself will only be four times the size of the Great Eastern, and need not cost over a few millions of dollars. I have only got to discover one thing before I can make it perfect. You will observe that it has a steam-engine on board. This engine works a pair of immense iron clamps, which are let down into the water from the extreme end of a very lengthy horizontal spar. Upon approaching the pirate, the captain orders the engineer to put on steam. Instantly the clamps descend from the end of the spar and clutch the privateer athwartships. Then the engine is reversed, the privateer is lifted bodily out of the water, the spar swings around over the deck, and the pirate ship is let down into the hold by the run. Then shut your hatches, and you have ship and pirates safe and sound."

The President's gothic features lighted up beautifully at the words of the great inventor; but in a moment they assumed an expression of doubt, and says he:

"But how are you going to manage, if the privateer fires upon you while you are doing this?"

"My dear sir," says the inventor, "I told you I had only one thing to discover before I could make the machine perfect, and that's it."

So you see, my boy, there's a prospect of our doing something on the ocean next century, and there's only one thing in the way of our taking in pirates by the cargo.

Last evening a new brigadier-general, aged ninety-four years, made a speech to Regiment Five, Mackerel Brigade, and then furnished each man with a lead-pencil. He said that, as the Government was disappointed about receiving some provisions it had ordered for the troops, those pencils were intended to enable them to draw their rations as usual. I got a very big pencil, my boy, and have lived on a sheet of paper ever since.

Yours, pensively,

ORPHEUS C. KERR.

James Russell Lowell

SUNTHIN' IN THE PASTORAL LINE *

Jaalam, 17th May, 1862

To the Editors of The Atlantic Monthly

GENTLEMEN,—At the special request of Mr. Biglow, I intended to inclose, together with his own contribution, (into which, at my suggestion, he has thrown a little more of pastoral sentiment than usual,) some passages from my sermon on the day of the National Fast, from the text, "Remember them that are in bonds, as bound with them," Heb. xiii. 3. But I have not leisure sufficient at present for the copying of them, even were I altogether satisfied with the production as it stands. I should prefer, I confess, to contribute the entire discourse to the pages of your respectable miscellany, if it should be found acceptable upon perusal, especially as I find the difficulty in selection of greater magnitude than I had anticipated. What passes without challenge in the fervour of oral delivery, cannot always stand the colder criticism of the closet. I am not so great an enemy of Eloquence as my friend Mr. Biglow would appear to be from some passages in his contribution for the current month. I would not, indeed, hastily suspect him of covertly glancing at myself in his somewhat caustick animadversions, albeit some of the phrases he girds at are not entire strangers to my lips. I am a more hearty admirer of the Puritans than seems now to be the fashion, and believe, that, if they Hebraized a little too much in their speech, they showed remarkable practical sagacity as statesmen and founders. But such phenomena as Puritanism are the results rather of great religious than of merely social convulsions, and do not long survive them. So soon as an earnest conviction has cooled into a phrase, its work is over, and the best that can be done with it is to bury it. *Ite, missa est.* I am inclined to agree with Mr. Biglow that we cannot settle the great political questions which are now presenting themselves to the nation by the opinions of Jere-

---

* *From "The Biglow Papers—Second Series."*

miah or Ezekiel as to the wants and duties of the Jews in their time, nor do I believe that an entire community with their feelings and views would be practicable or even agreeable at the present day. At the same time I could wish that their habit of subordinating the actual to the moral, the flesh to the spirit, and this world to the other, were more common. They had found out, at least, the great military secret that soul weighs more than body.—But I am suddenly called to a sick-bed in the household of a valued parishioner.

With esteem and respect,

Your obedient servant,

HOMER WILBUR.

Once git a smell o' musk into a draw,
An' it clings hold like precerdents in law:
Your gra'ma'am put it there,—when, goodness knows,—
To jes' this-worldify her Sunday-clo'es;
But the old chist wun't sarve her gran'son's wife,
(For, 'thout new funnitoor, wut good in life?)
An' so ole clawfoot, from the precinks dread
O' the spare chamber, slinks into the shed,
Where, dim with dust, it fust or last subsides
To holdin' seeds an' fifty things besides;
But better days stick fast in heart an' husk,
An' all you keep in 't gits a scent o' musk.

Jes' so with poets: wut they 've airly read
Gits kind o' worked into their heart an' head,
So 's 't they can't seem to write but jest on sheers
With furrin countries or played-out ideers,
Nor hev a feelin', ef it doos n't smack
O' wut some critter chose to feel 'way back:
This makes 'em talk o' daisies, larks, an' things,
Ez though we'd nothin' here that blows an' sings,—
(Why, I'd give more for one live bobolink
Than a square mile o' larks in printer's ink,)—
This makes 'em think our fust o' May is May,
Which 't ain't, for all the almanicks can say.

O little city-gals, don't never go it
Blind on the word o' noospaper or poet!

They 're apt to puff, an' May-day seldom looks
Up in the country ez it doos in books;
They 're no more like than hornets'-nests an' hives,
Or printed sarmons be to holy lives.
I, with my trouses perched on cowhide boots,
Tuggin' my foundered feet out by the roots,
Hev seen ye come to fling on April's hearse
Your muslin nosegays from the milliner's,
Puzzlin' to find dry ground your queen to choose,
An' dance your throats sore in morocker shoes:
I've seen ye an' felt proud, thet, come wut would,
Our Pilgrim stock wuz pethed with hardihood.
Pleasure doos make us Yankees kind o' winch,
Ez though 't wuz sunthin' paid for by the inch;
But yit we du contrive to worry thru,
Ef Dooty tells us thet the thing 's to du,
An' kerry a hollerday, ef we set out,
Ez stiddily ez though 't wuz a redoubt.

I, country-born an' bred, know where to find
Some blooms thet make the season suit the mind,
An' seem to metch the doubtin' bluebird's notes,—
Half-vent'rin' liverworts in furry coats,
Bloodroots, whose rolled-up leaves ef you oncurl,
Each on 'em 's cradle to a baby-pearl,—
But these are jes' Spring's pickets; sure ez sin,
The rebble frosts 'll try to drive 'em in;
For half our May's so awfully like May n't,
't would rile a Shaker or an evrige saint;
Though I own up I like our back'ard springs
Thet kind o' haggle with their greens an' things,
An' when you 'most give up, 'uthout more words
Toss the fields full o' blossoms, leaves, an' birds;
Thet's Northun natur', slow an' apt to doubt,
But when it *doos* git stirred, ther' 's no gin-out!

Fust come the blackbirds clatt'rin' in tall trees,
An' settlin' things in windy Congresses,—
Queer politicians, though, for I'll be skinned
Ef all on 'em don't head aginst the wind.

'fore long the trees begin to show belief,—
The maple crimsons to a coral-reef,
Then saffern swarms swing off from all the willers
So plump they look like yaller caterpillars,
Then gray hossches'nuts leetle hands unfold
Softer 'n a baby's be at three days old:
Thet 's robin-redbreast's almanick; he knows
Thet arter this ther' 's only blossom-snows;
So, choosin' out a handy crotch an' spouse,
He goes to plast'rin' his adobe house.

Then seems to come a hitch,—things lag behind,
Till some fine mornin' Spring makes up her mind,
An' ez, when snow-swelled rivers cresh their dams
Heaped-up with ice thet dovetails in an' jams,
A leak comes spirtin' thru some pin-hole cleft,
Grows stronger, fercer, tears out right an' left,
Then all the waters bow themselves an' come,
Suddin' in one gret slope o' shedderin' foam,
Jes' so our Spring gits everythin' in tune
An' gives one leap from Aperl into June:
Then all comes crowdin' in; afore you think,
Young oak-leaves mist the side-hill woods with pink;
The catbird in the laylock-bush is loud;
The orchards turn to heaps o' rosy cloud;
Red-cedars blossom tu, though few folks know it,
An' look all dipt in sunshine like a poet;
The lime-trees pile their solid stacks o' shade
An' drows'ly simmer with the bees' sweet trade;
In ellum-shrouds the flashin' hangbird clings
An' for the summer vy'ge his hammock slings;
All down the loose-walled lanes in archin' bowers
The barb'ry droops its strings o' golden flowers,
Whose shrinkin' hearts the school-gals love to try
With pins,—they'll worry yourn so, boys, bimeby!
But I don't love your cat'logue style,—do you?—
Ez ef to sell off Natur' by vendoo;
One word with blood in 't 's twice ez good ez two:

'nuff sed, June's bridesman, poet o' the year,
Gladness on wings, the bobolink, is here;
Half-hid in tip-top apple-blooms he swings,
Or climbs aginst the breeze with quiverin' wings,
Or, givin' way to 't in a mock despair,
Runs down, a brook o' laughter, thru the air.

I ollus feel the sap start in my veins
In Spring, with curus heats an' prickly pains,
Thet drive me, when I git a chance, to walk
Off by myself to hev a privit talk
With a queer critter thet can't seem to 'gree
Along o' me like most folks,—Mister Me.
Ther' 's times when I'm unsoshle ez a stone,
An' sort o' suffercate to be alone,—
I'm crowded jes' to think thet folks are nigh,
An' can't bear nothin' closer than the sky;
Now the wind's full ez shifty in the mind
Ez wut it is ou'-doors, ef I ain't blind,
An' sometimes, in the fairest sou'west weather,
My innard vane pints east for weeks together,
My natur' gits all goose-flesh, an' my sins
Come drizzlin' on my conscience sharp ez pins:
Wal, et sech times I jes' slip out o' sight
An' take it out in a fair stan'-up fight
With the one cuss I can't lay on the shelf,
The crook'dest stick in all the heap,—Myself.

'T wuz so las' Sabbath arter meetin'-time:
Findin' my feelin's would n't noways rhyme
With nobody's, but off the hendle flew
An' took things from an east-wind pint o' view,
I started off to lose me in the hills
Where the pines be, up back o' 'Siah's Mills:
Pines, ef you 're blue, are the best friends I know,
They mope an' sigh an' sheer your feelin's so,—
They hesh the ground beneath so, tu, I swan,
You half-forgit you've gut a body on.

Ther' 's a small school'us' there where four roads meet,
The door-steps hollered out by little feet,
An' side-posts carved with names whose owners grew
To gret men, some on 'em, an' deacons, tu;
't ain't used no longer, coz the town hez gut
A high-school, where they teach the Lord knows wut:
Three-story larnin' 's pop'lar now; I guess
We thriv' ez wal on jes' two stories less,
For it strikes me ther' 's sech a thing ez sinnin'
By overloadin' children's underpinnin':
Wal, here it wuz I larned my A B C,
An' it 's a kind o' favorite spot with me.

We're curus critters: Now ain't jes' the minute
Thet ever fits us easy while we're in it;
Long ez 't wuz futur', 't would be perfect bliss,—
Soon ez it's past, *thet* time's wuth ten o' this;
An' yit there ain't a man thet need be told
Thet Now's the only bird lays eggs o' gold.
A knee-high lad, I used to plot an' plan
An' think 't wuz life's cap-sheaf to be a man;
Now, gittin' gray, there's nothin' I enjoy
Like dreamin' back along into a boy:
So the ole school'us' is a place I choose
Afore all others, ef I want to muse;
I set down where I used to set, an' git
My boyhood back, an' better things with it,—
Faith, Hope, an' sunthin', ef it is n't Cherry,
It's want o' guile, an' thet's ez gret a rerrity,—
While Fancy's cushin', free to Prince and Clown,
Makes the hard bench ez soft ez milk-weed-down.

Now, 'fore I knowed, thet Sabbath arternoon
When I sot out to tramp myself in tune,
I found me in the school'us' on my seat,
Drummin' the march to No-wheres with my feet.
Thinkin' o' nothin', I've heerd ole folks say,
Is a hard kind o' dooty in its way:

It's thinkin' everythin' you ever knew,
Or ever hearn, to make your feelin's blue.
I sot there tryin' thet on for a spell:
I thought o' the Rebellion, then o' Hell,
Which some folks tell ye now is jest a metterfor
(A the'ry, p'raps, it wun't *feel* none the better for);
I thought o' Reconstruction, wut we'd win
Patchin' our patent self-blow-up agin:
I thought ef this 'ere milkin' o' the wits,
So much a month, warn't givin' Natur' fits,—
Ef folks warn't druv, findin' their own milk fail,
To work the cow thet hez an iron tail,
An' ef idees 'thout ripenin' in the pan
Would send up cream to humor ary man:
From this to thet I let my worryin' creep,
Till finally I must ha' fell asleep.

Our lives in sleep are some like streams thet glide
'twixt flesh an' sperrit boundin' on each side,
Where both shores' shadders kind o' mix an' mingle
In sunthin' thet ain't jes' like either single;
An' when you cast off moorin's from To-day,
An' down towards To-morrer drift away,
The imiges thet tengle on the stream
Make a new upside-down'ard world o' dream:
Sometimes they seem like sunrise-streaks an' warnin's
O' wut 'll be in Heaven on Sabbath-mornin's,
An', mixed right in ez ef jest out o' spite,
Sunthin' thet says your supper ain't gone right.
I'm gret on dreams, an' often when I wake,
I've lived so much it makes my mem'ry ache,
An' can't skurce take a cat-nap in my cheer
'thout hevin' 'em, some good, some bad, all queer.

Now I wuz settin' where I'd ben, it seemed,
An' ain't sure yit whether I r'ally dreamed,
Nor, ef I did, how long I might ha' slep',
When I hearn some un stompin' up the step,

An' lookin' round, ef two an' two make four,
I see a Pilgrim Father in the door.
He wore a steeple-hat, tall boots, an' spurs
With rowels to 'em big ez ches'nut-burrs,
An' his gret sword behind him sloped away
Long 'z a man's speech thet dunno wut to say.—
"Ef your name 's Biglow, an' your given-name
Hosee," sez he, "it's arter you I came;
I 'm your gret-gran'ther multiplied by three."—
"My *wut?*" sez I.—"Your gret-gret-gret," sez he:
"You would n't ha' never ben here but for me.
Two hundred an' three year ago this May
The ship I come in sailed up Boston Bay;
I 'd been a cunnle in our Civil War,—
But wut on airth hev *you* gut up one for?
Coz we du things in England, 't ain't for you
To git a notion you can du 'em tu:
I 'm told you write in public prints: ef true,
It 's nateral you should know a thing or two."—
"Thet air 's an argymunt I can't endorse,—
't would prove, coz you wear spurs, you kep' a horse:
For brains," sez I, "wutever you may think,
Ain't boun' to cash the drafs o' pen-an'-ink,—
Though mos' folks write ez ef they hoped jes' quickenin'
The churn would argoo skim-milk into thickenin';
But skim-milk ain't a thing to change its view
O' wut it's meant for more 'n a smoky flue.
But du pray tell me, 'fore we furder go,
How in all Natur' did you come to know
'bout our affairs," sez I, "in Kingdom-Come?"—
"Wal, I worked round at sperrit-rappin' some,
An' danced the tables till their legs wuz gone,
In hopes o' larnin' wut wuz goin' on,"
Sez he, "but mejums lie so like all-split
Thet I concluded it wuz best to quit.
But, come now, ef you wun't confess to knowin',
You 've some conjectures how the thing 's a-goin'."—
"Gran'ther," sez I, "a vane warn't never known
Nor asked to hev a jedgment of its own;

An' yit, ef 't ain't gut rusty in the jints,
It's safe to trust its say on certin pints:
It knows the wind's opinions to a T,
An' the wind settles wut the weather'll be."
"I never thought a scion of our stock
Could grow the wood to make a weather-cock;
When I wuz younger 'n you, skurce more 'n a shaver,
No airthly wind," sez he, "could make me waver!"
(Ez he said this, he clinched his jaw an' forehead,
Hitchin' his belt to bring his sword-hilt forrard.)—
"Jes' so it wuz with me," sez I, "I swow,
When *I* wuz younger 'n wut you see me now,—
Nothin' from Adam's fall to Huldy's bonnet,
Thet I warn't full-cocked with my jedgment on it;
But now I'm gittin' on in life, I find
It 's a sight harder to make up my mind,—
Nor I don't often try tu, when events
Will du it for me free of all expense.
The moral question 's ollus plain enough,—
It's jes' the human-natur' side thet's tough;
Wut's best to think may n't puzzle me nor you,—
The pinch comes in decidin' wut to *du;*
Ef you *read* History, all runs smooth ez grease,
Coz there the men ain't nothin' more 'n idees,—
But come to *make* it, ez we must to-day,
Th' idees hev arms an' legs an' stop the way:
It's easy fixin' things in facts an' figgers,—
They can't resist, nor warn't brought up with niggers;
But come to try your the'ry on,—why, then
Your facts an' figgers change to ign'ant men
Actin' ez ugly—" —"Smite 'em hip an' thigh!"
Sez gran'ther, "and let every man-child die!
Oh for three weeks o' Cromwle an' the Lord!
Up, Isr'el, to your tents an' grind the sword!"—
"Thet kind o' thing worked wal in ole Judee,
But you forgit how long it's ben A.D.;
You think thet 's ellerkence,—I call it shoddy,
A thing," sez I, "wun't cover soul nor body;

I like the plain all-wool o' common-sense,
Thet warms ye now, an' will a twelvemonth hence.
You took to follerin' where the Prophets beckoned,
An', fust you knowed on, back come Charles the Second;
Now wut I want 's to hev all *we* gain stick,
An' not to start Millennium too quick;
We hain't to punish only, but to keep,
An' the cure 's gut to go a cent'ry deep."
"Wall, milk-an'-water ain't the best o' glue,"
Sez he, "an' so you'll find afore you're thru;
Ef reshness venters sunthin'," shilly-shally
Loses ez often wut 's ten times the vally.
Thet exe of ourn, when Charles's neck gut split,
Opened a gap thet ain't bridged over yit:
Slav'ry 's your Charles, the Lord hez gin the exe"—
"Our Charles," sez I, "hez gut eight million necks.
The hardest question ain't the black man's right,
The trouble is to 'mancipate the white;
One 's chained in body an' can be sot free,
But t' other's chained in soul to an idee:
It's a long job, but we shall worry thru it;
Ef bagnets fail, the spellin'-book must du it."
"Hosee," sez he, "I think you're goin' to fail:
The rettlesnake ain't dangerous in the tail;
This 'ere rebellion 's nothin' but the rettle,—
You 'll stomp on thet an' think you've won the bettle;
It's Slavery thet's the fangs an' thinkin' head,
An' ef you want selvation, cresh it dead,—
An' cresh it suddin, or you'll larn by waitin'
Thet Chance wun't stop to listen to debatin'!"—
"God's truth!" sez I,—"an' ef *I* held the club,
An' knowed jes' where to strike,—but there's the rub!"—
"Strike soon," sez he, "or you'll be deadly ailin',—
Folks thet's afeared to fail are sure o' failin';
God hates your sneakin' creturs thet believe
He'll settle things they run away an' leave!"
He brought his foot down fercely, ez he spoke,
An' give me sech a startle thet I woke.

Petroleum V. Nasby

THE GREAT PRESIDENTIAL EXCURSION

The Great Presidential Excursion to the Tomb of Douglas.—An Account of the Ride of the Modern John Gilpin, who went a Pleasuring and came Home with nothing but the Necks of His Bottles: by His Chaplain.—From Washington to Detroit.

AT THE BIDDLE HOUSE
(wich is in Detroit, Michigan),
September the 4th, 1866.

Step by step I am assendin the ladder uv fame; step by step I am climbin to a proud eminence. Three weeks ago I wuz summoned to Washinton by that eminently grate and good man, Androo Johnson, to attend a consultation ez to the proposed Western tour, wich wuz to be undertaken for the purpose uv arousin the masses uv the West to a sence uv the danger wich wuz threatnin uv em in case they persisted in centralizin the power uv the Government into the hands uv a Congress, instid uv diffusin it throughout the hands uv one man, wich is Johnson. I got there too late to take part in the first uv the discussion. When I arrove they hed everything settled cepting the appintment uv a Chaplain for the excursion. The President insisted upon my fillin that position, but Seward objected. He wanted Beecher, but Johnson wuz inflexibly agin him. "I am determined," sez he, "to carry out my policy, but I hev some bowels left. Beecher hez done enuff already, considerin the pay he got. No, no! he shel be spared this trip; indeed he shel."

"Very good," said Seward; "but at least find some clergyman who endorses us without hevin P. M. to his honored name. It wood look better."

"I know it wood," replied Johnson; "but where kin we find sich a one? I hev swung around the entire circle, and hevn't ez yet seen him. Nasby it must be."

There wuz then a lively discussion ez to the propriety, before the

procession started, of removin all the Federal offis-holders on the proposed route, and appintin men who beleeved in us (Johnson, Beecher,
and Me), that we might be shoor uv a sootable recepshun at each
pint at wich we wuz to stop. The Annointed wuz in favor uv it. Sez
he, "Them ez won't support my polisy shan't eat my bread and butter."
Randall and Doolittle chimed in, for it's got to be a part of their
religion to assent to whatever the President sez, but I mildly protested. I owe a duty to the party, and I am determined to do it.

"Most High," sez I, "a settin hen wich is lazy makes no fuss; cut
its head off, and it flops about, for a while, lively. Lincoln's offis-
holders are settin hens. They don't like yoo nor yoor policy, but while
they are on their nests, they will keep moderitly quiet. Cut off their
heads, and they will spurt their blood in your face. Ez to bein en-
shoord of a reception at each point, you need fear nothin. Calkerlatin
moderately, there are at least twenty-five or thirty patriots who feel a
call for every offis in your disposal. So long, Yoor Highnis, ez them
offisis is held just where they kin see em, and they don't know wich
is to git em, yoo may depend upon the entire enthoosiasm uv each,
individyooally and collectively. In short, ef there's 4 offises in a town,
and yoo make the appointments, yoo hev sekoored 4 supporters;
till yoo make the appointments yoo hev the hundred who expect to
get em."

The President agreed with me that until after the trip the gullotine
shood stop.

Secretary Seward sejested that a clean shirt wood improve my personal appearance, and akkordingly a cirkular wuz sent to the clerks
in the Departments, assessin em for that purpose. Sich uv em ez re-
foosed to contribute their quota wuz instantly dismissed for disloyalty.

At last we started, and I must say we wuz got up in a highly con-
ciliatory style. Every wun of the civilians uv the party wore buzzum
pins, et settry, wich wuz presented to em by the Southern delegates to
the Philadelphia convention, wich wuz made uv the bones uv Federal soldiers wich hed fallen at various battles. Sum uv em were par-
tiklerly valuable ez anteeks, hevin bin made from the bones uv the
fust soldiers who fell at Bull Run.

The Noo York recepshun wuz a gay affair. I never saw His Imperial Highness in better spirits, and he delivered his speech to better
advantage than I ever heard him do it before, and I bleeve I've heard
it a hundred times. We left Noo York sadly. Even now, ez I write,

the remembrance uv that perceshun, the recollection uv that banquet, lingers around me, and the taste uv them wines is still in my mouth. But we hed to go. We hed a mishn to perform, and we put ourselves on a steamboat and started.

ALBANY.—There wuz a immense crowd, but the Czar uv all the Amerikas didn't get orf his speech here. The Governor welcomed him, but he welcomed him ez the Cheef Magistrate uv the nashen, and happened to drop in Lincoln's name. That struck a chill over the party, and the President got out uv it ez soon ez possible. Bein reseeved ez Cheef Magistrate, and not ez the great Pacificator, ain't His Eggslency's best holt. It wuz unkind uv Governor Fenton to do it. If he takes the papers, he must know that His Mightiness ain't got but one speech, and he ought to hev made sich a reception ez wood hev enabled him to hev got it off. We shook the dust off uv our feet, and left Albany in disgust.

SKENACTADY.—The people uv this delightfull little village wuz awake when the Imperial train arrived. The changes hadn't bin made in the offises here, and consekently there wuz a splendid recepshun. I didn't suppose there wuz so many patriots along the Mohawk. I wuz pinted out by sum one ez the President's private adviser—a sort uv private Secretary uv State; and after the train started, I found jest 211 petitions for the Post Offis in Skenactedy in my side coat pocket, wich the patriots who hed hurrahed so vociferously hed dexterously deposited there. The incident wuz a movin one. "Thank God!" thought I. "So long ez we hev the post offises to give, we kin alluz hev a party." The Sultan swung around the cirkle wunst here, and leavin the Constooshun in their hands, the train moved off.

UTICA.—The President spoke here with greater warmth, and jerked more originality than I hed before observed. He introdoost here the remark that he didn't come to make a speech; that he wuz goin to shed a tear over the tomb uv Douglas; that, in swingin around the cirkle, he hed fought traitors on all sides uv it, but that he felt safe. He shood leave the Constooshun in their hands, and ef a martyr wuz wanted, he wuz ready to die with neetnees and dispatch.

ROME.—Here we hed a splendid recepshun, and I never heard His Majesty speek more felicitously. He menshuned to the audience that he had swung around the Southern side uv the cirkle, and wuz now swingin around the Northern side uv it, and that he wuz fightin traitors on all sides. He left the Constitooshun in their hands, and bid em good bye. I reseeved at this pint only 130 petitions for the post offis, wich I took ez a bad omen for the comin election.

LOCKPORT.—The President is improvin wonderfully. He rises with the occasion. At this pint he mentioned that he wuz sot on savin the country wich hed honored him. Ez for himself, his ambishn wuz more than satisfied. He hed bin Alderman, Member uv the Legislacher, Congressman, Senator, Military Governor, Vice President, and President. He hed swung around the entire cirkle uv offises, and all he wanted now wuz to heal the wounds uv the nashen. He felt safe in leavin the Constooshn in their hands. Ez he swung around the cirkle—

At this pint I interrupted him. I told him that he hed swung around the cirkle wunst in this town, and ez useful ez the phrase wuz, it might spile by too much yoose.

At Cleveland we begun to get into hot water. Here is the post to which the devil uv Ablishnism is chained, and his chain is long enough to let him rage over neerly the whole state. I am pained to state that the President wuzn't treated here with the respeck due his station. He commenst deliverin his speech, but wuz made the subjeck uv ribald laffture. Skasely hed he got to the pint uv swingin around the cirkle, when a foul-mouthed nigger-lover yelled "Veto!" and another vociferated "Noo Orleans!" and another remarked "Memphis!" and one after another interruption occurred until His Highness wuz completely turned off the track, and got wild. He forgot his speech, and struck out crazy, but the starch wuz out uv him, and he wuz worsted. Grant, wich we hed taken along to draw the crowds, played dirt on us here, and stepped onto a boat for Detroit, leavin us only Farragut ez a attraction, who tried twice to git away ditto, but wuz timely prevented. The President recovered his ekanimity, and swung around the cirkle wunst, and leavin the Constooshun in their hands, retired.

At the next pint we wuz astounded at seein but one man at the station. He wuz dressed with a sash over his shoulder, and wuz wavin a flag with wun hand, firin a saloot with a revolver with the other, and playin "Hail to the Chief!" on a mouth organ, all to wunst.

"Who are you, my gentle friend?" sez I.

"I'm the newly-appinted Postmaster, sir," sez he. "I'm a perceshun a waitin here to do honor to our Cheef Magistrate, all alone, sir. There wuz twenty Johnsonians in this hamlet, sir; but when the commishn came for me, the other nineteen wuz soured, and sed they didn't care a d—n for him nor his policy, sir. Where is the President?"

Androo wuz a goin to swing around the cirkle for this one man, and leave the Constooshn in his hands, but Seward checked him.

At Fremont we hed a handsome recepshun, for the offises hevn't bin changed there, but Toledo didn't do so well. The crowd didn't cheer Androo much, but when Farragut was trotted out they gave him a rouser, wich wuz anything but pleasin to the Cheef Magistrate uv this nashen, who bleeves in bein respected.

Finally we reeched Detroit. This bein a Democratic city, the President wuz hisself agin. His speech here wuz wun uv rare merit. He gathered together in one quiver all the sparklin arrows he had used from Washington to this point, and shot em one by one. He swung around the cirkle; he didn't come to make a speech; he hed bin Alderman uv his native town; he might hev been Dicktater, but woodent; and ended with a poetickal cotashun wich I coodent ketch, but wich, ez neer ez I cood understand, wuz,

"Kum wun, kum all; this rock shel fly
From its firm base—in a pig's eye."

Here we repose for the nite. To-morrow we start onward, and shel continue swingin around the cirkle till we reach Chicago.

PETROLEUM V. NASBY, P. M.

(wich is Postmaster),

and likewise Chaplin to the expedishn.

Mark Twain

THE HUNTING OF THE COW*

(*October 18, 1907*). Two colossal historical incidents took place yesterday, incidents which must go echoing down the corridors of time for ages, incidents which can never be forgotten while histories shall continue to be written. Yesterday, for the first time, business was opened to commerce by the Marconi Company and wireless messages sent entirely across the Atlantic, straight from shore to shore; and on that same day the President of the United States for the fourteenth time came within three miles of flushing a bear. As usual he was far away, nobody knew where, when the bear burst upon the multitude of dogs and hunters and equerries and chamberlains in waiting, and sutlers and cooks and scullions, and Rough Riders and infantry and artillery, and had his customary swim to the other side of a pond and disappeared in the woods. While half the multitude watched the place where he vanished, the other half galloped off, with horns blowing, to scour the State of Louisiana in search of the great hunter. Why don't they stop hunting the bear altogether and hunt the President? He is the only one of the pair that can't be found when he is wanted.

By and by the President was found and laid upon the track and he and the dogs followed it several miles through the woods, then gave it up, because Rev. Dr. Long, the "nature fakir," came along and explained that it was a cow track. This is a sorrowful ending to a mighty enterprise. His Excellency leaves for Washington today, to interest himself further in his scheme of provoking a war with Japan with his battleships. . . .

(*October 21, 1907*). Alas, the President has got that cow after all! If it was a cow. Some say it was a bear—a real bear. These were eyewitnesses, but they were all White House domestics; they are all under wages to the great hunter, and when a witness is in that condition it makes his testimony doubtful. The fact that the President himself

*From *Mark Twain's Memoirs*. The entry for October 18 has been cut.*

215

thinks it was a bear does not diminish the doubt but enlarges it. He was once a reasonably modest man, but his judgment has been out of focus so long now that he imagines that everything he does, little or big, is colossal.

I am sure he honestly thinks it was a bear, but the circumstantial evidence that it was a cow is overwhelming. It acted just as a cow would act; in every detail from the beginning to the end it acted precisely as a cow would act when in trouble; it even left a cow track behind, which is what a cow would do when in distress, or indeed at any other time if it knew a President of the United States was after it —hoping to move his pity, you see; thinking maybe he would spare her life on account of her sex, her helpless situation, and her notorious harmlessness. In her flight she acted just as a cow would have done when in a frenzy of fright, with a President of the United States and a squadron of bellowing dogs chasing after her; when her strength was exhausted, and she could drag herself no further, she did as any other despairing cow would have done—she stopped in an open spot, fifty feet wide, and humbly faced the President of the United States with the tears running down her cheeks, and said to him with the mute eloquence of surrender: "Have pity, sir, and spare me. I am alone, you are many; I have no weapon but my helplessness, you are a walking arsenal; I am in awful peril, you are as safe as you would be in a Sunday school; have pity, sir—there is no heroism in killing an exhausted cow."

Here are the scareheads that introduce the wonderful dime-novel performance:

ROOSEVELT TELLS OF HUNTING TRIP

Ate All the Game, Except a Wildcat, and That
Had a Narrow Escape.

Swam Despite Alligators.

Charged Into the Canebrake After Bear and
Hugged the Guides After the Kill.

There it is—he hugged the guides after the kill. It is the President all over; he is still only fourteen years old after living half a century; he takes a boy's delight in showing off; he is always hugging something or somebody—when there is a crowd around to see the hugging and envy the hugged. A grown person would have milked the cow and let her go; but no, nothing would do this lad but he must kill her and be a hero. The account says: "The bear slain by the President was killed Thursday, and the killing was witnessed by one of the McKenzies and by Alex Ennolds."

These names will go down in history forever, in the company of an exploit which will take a good deal of the shine out of the twelve labors of Hercules. Testimony of the witnesses: "They say that the President's bearing was extremely sportsmanlike."

Very likely. Everybody knows what mere sportsmanlike bearing is, unqualified by an adverb, but none of us knows quite what it is when it is extremely sportsmanlike, because we have never encountered that inflamed form of the thing before. The probabilities are that the sportsmanlike bearing was not any more extremely sportsmanlike than was that of Hercules; it is quite likely that the adverb is merely emotional and has the hope of a raise of wages back of it. The chase of the frightened creature lasted three hours and reads like a hectic chapter in a dime novel—and this time it is a chapter of pathetically humble heroics.

In the outcome the credit is all with the cow, none of it is with the President. When the poor hunted thing could go no further it turned, in fine and picturesque defiance, and gallantly faced its enemies and its assassin. From a safe distance Hercules sent a bullet to the sources of its life; then, dying, it made fight—so there *was* a hero present after all. Another bullet closed the tragedy, and Hercules was so carried away with admiration of himself that he hugged his domestics and bought a compliment from one of them for twenty dollars. But this résumé of mine is pale; let us send it down to history with the colors all in it:

The bear slain by the President was killed Thursday, and the killing was witnessed by one of the McKenzies and by Alex Ennolds. They say that the President's bearing was extremely sportsmanlike. The animal had been chased by the dogs for three hours, the President following all the time. When at last they came within hearing distance the President dismounted, threw off his coat and dashed into the canebrake, going to within twenty paces of the beast. The dogs were coming up rapidly, with the President's favorite, Rowdy, in the lead.

The bear had stopped to bid defiance to the canines when the President sent a fatal bullet from his rifle through the animal's vitals. With the little life left in it the bear turned on the dogs. The President then lodged a second bullet between the bear's shoulders, breaking the creature's neck.

Other members of the party soon came up, and the President was so rejoiced over his success that he embraced each of his companions. Ennolds said: "Mr. President, you are no tenderfoot."

Mr. Roosevelt responded by giving Ennolds a $20 note.

There was little hunting yesterday, because the dogs encountered a drove of wild hogs, more ferocious than bears. One of the best dogs was killed by a boar.

There were daily swims in the lake by members of the party, including the President.

"The water was fine," he said, "and I did not have the fear of alligators that some seem to have."

Whatever Hercules does is to him remarkable; when other people are neglectful and fail to notice a detail, here and there, proper for admiration and comment, he supplies the omission himself. Mr. Ennolds lost a chance; if he had been judiciously on watch he could have done the alligator compliment himself, and got another twenty for it.

Finley Peter Dunne

MR. DOOLEY ON THE POWER OF MUSIC

"I always told ye," said Mr. Dooley, "that 'twas as a vocal entertainer that I preferred me frind Willum Jennings Bryan, an' glad I am we're goin' to hear his meelojous voice on th' concert platform again. Whin th' good Lord has give a man th' power iv speech in a volyum on-known in ancyent or modhren times, it's a shame f'r him to hide th' gift in a speechless job. To go an' make this gr-reat barytone Sicrety iv State was like turnin' a nightingale into a hod carrier. It was conthry to nature. All a Sicrety iv State has to do is to think. It's a kind iv a menial job, beneath a man that has a harp in his throat with a hurri-cane behind it, so that whin he aven breathes a faint melody purrs fr'm his lips an' whin he utthers so much as a how-d'ye-do, 'tis as though a mighty hand had slammed th' sthrings iv a joynt guitar. There ar-re plenty iv thinkers in th' world, poor fellows, with squeaky voices. They have to do something to arne a livin'. So they think, an' a hard livin' it is. But there's niver enough music to go around, an' why shud a gr-reat orkesthry iv sthring an' wind an' wood an' brass be asked to pondher? Is th' slide thrombone, is th' organ at th' audjiotoroom, is th' harp that wanst through Tara's halls, expicted to think? Does Adeliny Patti cook, or Melba sew, or Caruso dhrive a dhray? Ye bet they don't.

"Those who see Willum Jennings in those tur-rble days whin he was discussin' th' thrivyal dee-tails iv foolish threaties with th' bunco steerers that have been sintinced be their governments to come over here as ambassadures, were shocked at th' appearance iv th' popylar favrite. His pictures looked thoughtful. Gazin' fearlessly into th' cam-era, with a quill pen in his hand an' his brow knitted, he was th' livin' image iv a gr-reat mind in th' midst iv a large an' gloomy think an' caught off his guard be a shameless phottygrafter who had come upon him onobsarved. But those who knew him well saw a faraway look in his dhreamy eyes that seemed to say: 'Oh, that I were out iv this prison

219

again an' tastin' th' glad, free life iv th' concert platform, with a sea
iv upturned faces lookin' at me through their spectacles, an' th' little
handkerchiefs iv th' ladies flutterin' th' Chat-talky salute at me, an'
me voice flyin' out an' meltin' th' hearts iv th' aujience an' returnin'
to nestle in th' pouches iv me own happy ears.'

"He was well-threated. Th' vouchers f'r his pay were cashed without
a kick be Bill McAdoo. He was inthrojooced to sivral prom'nent ambassadures be th' lawyer iv th' departmint. An' as often as wanst a
week th' good, kind, onselfish ol' gintleman in th' White House ast
him over an' pointed out where he was to sign a docymint that had
been thoughtfully prepared f'r him. Still he was not happy. Nobody
iver ast him to oblige with a melody. Th' people around him bumped
him in th' hall. Ivrybody he met seemed indiff'rent to music. Week
afther week he set alone hummin' snatches iv old orations till wan day
he cud stand it no longer. He up an' quit.

"Th' partin' between th' two ol' frinds was pathetic. 'Must ye be
goin' so soon?' says the Prisidint. 'Why, ye've on'y been here three
years, an' I've har'ly seen annything iv ye,' he says, openin' a letter. 'I
must,' says th' Sicrety iv State. 'Well, Gawd bless ye, Willum. Tumulty,
tell th' gintleman that's waitin' I won't keep him a minyit. Well, Gawd
bless ye, Willum.' 'Gawd bless ye, Dock.' Th' two great men seized
each other be both hands, but prompt interference be th' polis pre-
vinted anny actual vilence.

"So our hero bust th' bars iv his gilded cage, flew out into th' air,
lit on th' bough iv a three, an' poored forth his bursting heart to th'
stars. An' there he is now, like th' lark that Hogan writes about whin
he has too much. Though singin' he's always sore an' while sore is
iver singin'. Day afther day he serenades his former boss an' pupil with
a melody that sounds like 'Come into th' garden, Dock, an' I'll dhrop a
brick on ye.'

"What does he sing about? He's set th' Bible to music. He's arrangin'
th' articles iv war f'r th' piccolo. But his principal songs ar-re songs iv
love. I r-read a head line in th' pa-aper an' it says: 'Misther Bryan dis-
cusses internaytional complications.' 'Well,' says I, 'I guess I can affoord
to miss this wan. But no,' thinks I, 'I will read it if on'y to see to what
extint this heer bricklayin' job has damaged a gr-reat artist.' Well, sir,
wud ye believe it, he's come out absolutely oninjured. There ain't a
crack in his voice or a blot on his beautiful ideels. There was niver a
word in this ballad about threaties, or agreements, th' Hague confer-

ence, or torpedoes, or Bilgium. It was just a sweet song. It was all about love. 'Ye wish to hear me on th' subjick iv war an' our foreign situations,' he says. 'Very well, Profissor, th' key iv G, if ye plaze. Are ye ready? Let her go! Love, love, love. All th' wurruld is love. Soft an' sweet an' sticky it covers th' globe. It is heerd fr'm th' throats iv th' little sparrows in th' sthreets, in th' flight iv th' wind through th' pines, in th' swash iv th' waves that break on th' shores iv Lake Chattalky (where I appear week endin' July fifteen), in th' cry iv th' shrapnel whirlin' over th' threnches, in th' cooin' iv th' pnoomatic guns squirtin' their wealth iv green an' goolden gas. I love ivry-body. I love th' Kaiser, th' Mikado iv Japan, th' Sultan iv Turkey, Tom Ryan, Champ Clark, th' reptile press, an' th' infamious conspiracy iv Wall Sthreet criminals that has skinned me out iv th' prisidincy three times runnin'.'

"Well, sir, whin I heard this magnificint an' statesmanlike appeal to th' American people, who had just took off their coats an' were squarin' away, th' tears came to me eyes an' I felt like grabbin' Gin'ral von Hindenburg around th' waist an' waltzin' out into th' consarvatory with him. Th' effect iv this pow'rful utthrance was instantanyous. Lord Kitchener tilly-grafted to Charlie Schwab: 'I've been so affected be th' wurruds iv ye'er peerless leader Thomas J. O'Brien (if our papers gets th' name right) that I've made up me mind this hijous war must be ended at wanst. So plaze cancel th' order f'r two millyon sixteen-inch shells. Make it five millyon eighteen-inch an' be sure ye fill them full iv th' juice.' Th' German Impror announced that th' message iv Willum Jennings Bryan had melted his heart. He was sorry he hadn't been more neighborly iv late with his English cousins an' he'd ordhered a fleet iv Zeppelins to call on thim an' pay his respicts. An' all th' other nations iv Europe that hadn't got into th' riot, now saw that their attichood might be mistook an' voted to make th' war unanimous. Such is th' effect iv th' human voice on th' human heart.

"Mind ye, I don't want ye to go away with th' idee that I don't think Willum Jennings Bryan is a thoughtful man. Haven't I voted f'r him more times thin I've voted f'r annywan but Carther Haitch? I voted f'r him whin votin' f'r him was wan way iv proclaimin' to th' wurruld that I cudden't pay me room rint. I voted f'r him whin 'twas th' same as tellin' th' groceryman that he gave me credit at his peril. There is plenty iv room f'r all th' thoughts in th' wurruld under that splendid dome. If he doesn't care to exercise thim it's his own business.

He entertains thim an' sings thim to sleep. Wanst in a while he lets wan out f'r a romp. Th' little crather comes thrippin' into th' wurruld where rough people knock it down an' stamp on it an' thin he calls it back an' it creeps into its little cot in th' organ loft an' is niver seen or heerd again. He let loose a thought on silver that had an excitin' time while it was out, but long ago he hauled it in an' tucked it away. Thin I remimber he released a thought about th' govermint ownin' th' railroads. It was chased back to th' consarvatory iv music be th' Ku Klux an' hasn't aven showed its face at th' window since. Th' other day he let out a pretty little idee. I hope no harm will come to it. 'Tis nawthin' less thin startin' a polis foorce to prevint war. Yes, sir, an internaytional organization iv coppers to keep th' peace in th' rowdy neighborhood iv th' wurruld. How'll they be ar-rmed? What a foolish question. They'll be ar-rmed with love, iv coorse. Who'll pay thim? That's a financyal deetail that can be arranged later on. What'll happen if wan iv th' roughnecks reaches f'r a gun? Don't bother me with thrifles.

"Th' gin'ral idee as him an' me see it is this: All is quiet at th' headquarters iv th' internaytional peace polis at Chat-talky. Th' chief iv polis is settin' in a bower iv roses playin' a mandolin whin a snow-white pigeon flutthers through th' window. There is a pink ribbon around its neck. Th' chief onties it an' finds a message that reads: 'Pancho Villa is on th' loose agin. He has filled himself up with paint an' is out with a Winchester shootin' up th' bordher.' Th' chief calls th' resarves. Th' peace bulls in unyforms iv crame-colored pongee silk an' carryin' bunches iv f'rget-me-nots, turn out an' throt to th' scene iv th' disturbance at a double-quick. They find Pancho, but instead iv slammin' the desprit patriot over th' head with a walnut log an' dhraggin' him be wan ankle to th' wagon, which is th' custom iv some peace agents I know, they shower him with petals fr'm their bokays. Th' sergeant disarms him with a melting look, whispers something soothing in his ear, smooths his hair, fixes his tie, an' maybe kisses him on th' forehead. An' that's th' end iv th' throuble.

"It sounds all right to me. It ain't th' way I've seen polis business thransacted, but a little more tinderness in dealin' with th' rough an' petulant might not be out iv place. Th' worst that cud happen wud be more polismen wud be kilt.

"An' there ye ar-re. I don't know whether 'twill succeed or not. I hope so. But there's wan thing I am afraid iv, Hinnissy. Ye see, me boy, th' wurruld is a pretty old hunk of mud an' wickedness, an' I've been here a long time an' I've obsarved this sad thruth. Ye don't have to lend a man money. Ye don't have to amuse him; ye don't have to take care iv him if he's sick; ye don't have to do annything f'r him but wan thing."

"An' what's that?" asked Mr. Hennessy.

"If he wants to fight ye, ye've got to accommodate him," said Mr. Dooley.

James M. Cain

THE GOVERNOR

THE GOVERNOR's *office, about two o'clock in the afternoon. Ranged about the table, talking in whispers, are a petitioner for a pardon, dressed in ordinary clothes, but having a pasty pallor, a singularly close haircut, and a habit of starting nervously whenever he is addressed; two guards, carrying guns on their hips in holsters; a witness, a prosecutor, and counsel for the petitioner.* THE GOVERNOR *enters, accompanied by a woman secretary, and they all stand up until he has sat down and donned his glasses. In a moment a lovely aroma begins to perfume the air. It is such an aroma as pervades a bonded distillery, and unmistakably it comes from the head of the table, where* THE GOVERNOR *has taken his place.*

THE GOVERNOR. Gen'lemen, y' may p'ceed.

COUNSEL FOR THE PETITIONER. Yes, Yexcellency.

THE GOVERNOR. 'N I'll ashk y' t' be's brief's y' can, c'se busy af'noon w' me. Gi' me th' facksh, that's all I w'nt know. 'M plain, blunt man, got no time f' detailsh. Gi' me facksh, 'n 'y won't have t' worry 'bout fair trea'm'nt f'm me.

COUNSEL. I think I speak for everybody here, Yexcellency, when I say we're all anxious to save Yexcellency's time, and—

THE GOVERNOR. 'Preciate 'at.

COUNSEL. And so I imagine the best way would be for me to sketch in for Yexcellency, briefly of course, the history of this case, I may say this very unusual case—

THE PROSECUTOR. So unusual, Yexcellency, that the Parole Board threw up its hands and refused to have anything to do with it whatsoever, and that is why Yexcellency's valuable time—

THE GOVERNOR. Nev' min' Parole Board. Is 't mer'tor's case, tha's all want know.

224

THE PROSECUTOR. I understand that, Yexcellency. I only wanted to say that the prawscution regards this case as abslutely prepawstrous.

THE GOVERNOR. A' right. Y' said it.

COUNSEL. Now, Yexcellency, this young man Greenfield Farms, this young man you see here—

THE GOVERNOR. One mom'nt. When's ex'cution take plashe?

COUNSEL. I'm glad Yexcellency reminded me of that, because praps I ought to have explained it sooner. Fact of the matter, Yexcellency, this is not a capital case—

THE GOVERNOR. Gi' me facksh, gi' me facksh! I got no time f' detailsh. When's ex'cution take plashe, I said.

COUNSEL. Yes, Yexcellency. I was only telling Yexcellency that there won't be any execution, because—

THE GOVERNOR. Wha's 'at?

COUNSEL. Because this young man Farms wasn't sentenced to death; he was sentenced to the penitentiary.

THE GOVERNOR. Oh!

COUNSEL. On a ten-year term, ten years in prison, for participation in the armed march we had some years ago, when the miners made all that trouble. Or, as it's never been clear in my mind that Farms had any idea what he was doing at that time—

THE PETITIONER. Never did. I hope my die I just went out there to see what was going on—

A GUARD. Hey! Sh!

COUNSEL. Praps I should have said alleged participation.

THE PROSECUTOR. And another thing praps you should have said was that of his ten years in prison he has already served three and he'll get two more off for good behavior and that leaves five and five is a little different from ten.

THE GOVERNOR. C'me on, c'me on!

THE PROSECUTOR. I'm only—

THE GOVERNOR. Y' only pett'fogg'n. Shu' up.

COUNSEL. Now, Yexcellency will recall that as a result of that uprising, six defendants, of which Farms was one, were convicted of treason to the State and the rest were allowed to plead guilty of unlawful assemblage—

THE GOVERNOR. Don't was' m' time talk'n 'bout 'at upris'n. I know all 'bout it. I's right there 'n saw fi' thous'n of 'm march by m' own front ya'd. Get on 'th facksh.

COUNSEL. Then if Yexcellency is familiar with that, we're ready now for this witness, and after he has told his story I can outline briefly to Yexcellency the peculiar bearing it has on this case, and—

THE GOVERNOR. Is 'at witness?

THE WITNESS. Yes, sir.

THE GOVERNOR. Sit over here where I c'n see y' better. 'N don't shtan' 'n awe 'f me. Washa name?

THE WITNESS. Ote Bailey, sir.

THE GOVERNOR. Shpeak right out, Bailey. 'M plain, blunt man 'n y' needn't shtan' 'n awe 'f me.

COUNSEL. Now, Bailey, if you'll tell the Governor in your own words what you told the Parole Board—

THE WITNESS. Well, it was like this. I was coming down the street on the milk-wagon early in the morning, right down Center Street in Coal City, and it was cold and there was a thin skim of ice on the street. And the mare was a-slipping and sliding pretty near every step, because she was old and the cheap dairy company hadn't shoed her right for cold weather. And—

THE GOVERNOR. Wha's 'at? Milk-wagon?

COUNSEL. Just a moment, Yexcellency. Now, Bailey, you forgot to tell the Governor when this was.

THE WITNESS. This here was twenty-three year ago come next January.

COUNSEL. All right, now go ahead and—

THE GOVERNOR. Hol' on, Bailey, hol' on. (*To* COUNSEL) Young man, I got worl' o' patience. 'M plain, blunt man, al's will'n t' help people 'n distress, p'ticularly when—p'ticularly—p'ticularly—h'm—p'ticularly. But wha's twen'-three yea's 'go got t' do 'th 'is ex'cution? Tell me that.

COUNSEL. Well, Yexcellency, I thought it would save time if we let Bailey tell his story first, and then I can outline the bearing it has on this case. But if Yexcellency prefers, I'll be glad to—

THE GOVERNOR. Young man, 're you trifl'n 'th me?

COUNSEL. Not at all, Yexcellency, I—

THE GOVERNOR. I warn y' ri' now I won't shtan' f' trifl'n. Facksh, facksh, tha's what I want!

COUNSEL. Yes, Yexcellency.

THE GOVERNOR. A' right, Bailey, g' on 'th it. I'll see 'f I c'n get facksh m'self.

THE WITNESS. So pretty soon, the mare went down. She went right down in the shafts, and I seen I would have to unhook her to get her up.

THE GOVERNOR. Y' right, y' qui' right. Y' can't get 'm up 'thout y' unhook 'm. No use try'n. G' on.

THE WITNESS. So then I got down offen the wagon and commence unhooking her. And I just got one breeching unwrapped, 'cause they didn't have snap breechings then, when I hearded something.

THE GOVERNOR. Whasha hear?

THE WITNESS. I hearded a mewling.

THE GOVERNOR. Mewl'n?

THE WITNESS. That's right. First off, sound like a cat, but then it didn't sound like no cat. Sound funny.

THE GOVERNOR. What sound like?

THE WITNESS. Sound like a child.

THE GOVERNOR. Y' sure?

THE WITNESS. Yes, sir.

THE GOVERNOR. Sound' like child. Thank God, now 'm gett'n some facksh. G' on. What 'en?

THE WITNESS. So I left the mare, left her laying right where she was, and commence looking around to see where it was coming from.

THE GOVERNOR. Where *what* was com'n f'm?

THE WITNESS. This here mewling.

THE GOVERNOR. Oh, yes. Mewl'n. F'got f' mom'nt. G' on, Bailey. Shpeak right out. Don't shtan' 'n awe 'f me. What 'en?

THE WITNESS. So pretty soon I figured it must be coming from the sewer, what run right down under Center Street, and I went over to the manhole and listened and sure enough that was where it was coming from.

THE GOVERNOR. Shew'r?

THE WITNESS. Yes, sir.

THE GOVERNOR. Keep right on, Bailey. Y' g' me more facksh 'n fi' minutes 'n whole pack' lawyersh g' me 'n week.

COUNSEL. I assure Yexcellency—

THE GOVERNOR. Keep out o' this, young man. Y' tried m' patience 'nough already. 'M after facksh 'n 'm gett'n 'm. G' on, Bailey.

THE WITNESS. So I tried to get the cover offen the manhole, but I couldn't lift it. I tried hard as I could, but I couldn't budge it.

THE GOVERNOR. Busha tried?

THE WITNESS. Yes, sir.

THE GOVERNOR. Thasha shtuff! G' on.

THE WITNESS. So then I figured the best thing was to get some help and I run all the way up and down the street looking for a cop. And pretty soon I found a couple of them. And first off they didn't believe it, but then when they come to the manhole and heared this here mewling, they tried to lift the cover with me, and all three of us couldn't move it, and why we couldn't move it was it was froze to the rim.

THE GOVERNOR. F'oze?

THE WITNESS. Yes, sir.

THE GOVERNOR. F'oze. G'on.

THE WITNESS. So then we figured the best thing to do would be to put in a alarm. We figured if we got the fire company down there, maybe they would have something to move it with.

THE GOVERNOR. G'on. Keep right on till I tell y' to shtop, Bailey.

THE WITNESS. So we went to the box and put in a alarm. And pretty soon here come the hook-and-ladder galloping down the street. And five fellows what was members of the Coal City Volunteer Fire Department was on it, because they was still setting in the fire-house playing a poker game what they had started the night before after supper.

THE GOVERNOR. The Coal City Vol'teer Fi' D'pa'ment?

THE WITNESS. Yes, sir. So then—

THE GOVERNOR. Wait minute. Wait minute, Bailey. Y' touch m' heart now. The ol' Coal City Vol'teer Fi' D'pa'ment, wha' y' know 'bout 'at? I was mem' that m'self. I was mem' that—le's see, mus' been thirty yea's 'go.

COUNSEL. I hear it was a wonderful company in those days, Yexcellency.

THE GOVERNOR. Won'ful 'n 'en some. We won State ca'nival three times runn'n. C'n y' 'magine 'at?

COUNSEL. You don't mean it, Yexcellency!

THE GOVERNOR. Well, well! Y' touch m' heart now, Bailey, y' cert'ny have. 'S goin' be ha'd f' me t' send y' t' chair 'f y' was mem' old Coal City Vol'teer Fi' D'pa'ment. G' on. What en?

THE WITNESS. —?

COUNSEL. Don't sit there with your mouth hanging open like that, Bailey. The Governor was thinking of something else, of course.

THE WITNESS. Oh! So then them fellows pulled in their horses and got down offen the hook-and-ladder and commence hollering where was the fire. So we told them it wasn't no fire, but a child down the sewer, and then they got sore, because they claim we broke up their poker game and it was roodles.

THE GOVERNOR. What 'en?

THE WITNESS. So we ast them to help us get the cover off, and they wasn't going to do it. But just then this here mewling come again, just a little bit. It had kind of died off, but now it started up again, and them fellows, soon as they heard it, they got busy. 'Cause this here mewling, it give you the shivers right up and down your back.

THE GOVERNOR. What 'en?

THE WITNESS. So then we put the blade of one of them axes next to the cover, between it and the rim, and beat on it with another ax. And that broke it loose and we got it off.

THE GOVERNOR. What 'en?

THE WITNESS. So then them fireman put a belt on me, what they use to hook on the hose when they shove it up on them ladders, and let me down in the sewer. And I struck a match and sure enough there was the child, all wrapped up in a bunch of rags, laying out on the sewer water. And why it hadn't sunk was that the sewer water was froze and a good thing we didn't shove no ladder down there because if we had the ice would of got broke and the child would of fell in.

THE GOVERNOR. What 'en?

THE WITNESS. So I grabbed the child, and them fellows pulled me up, and then we all got on the hook-and-ladder and whipped up them horses for the Coal City Hospital, 'cause it looked like to me that child was half froze to death, but when we give it in to the hospital we found out that being in the sewer hadn't hurt it none and it was all right.

THE GOVERNOR. So y' saved child?

THE WITNESS. Yes, sir.

THE GOVERNOR. Tha's good! ... Well, Bailey, y' made good case f' y'self. I don't min' say'n, 'm 'pressed.

COUNSEL. But this witness isn't quite finished with his testimony, Yexcellency.

THE GOVERNOR. Wha's 'at? He saved child, didn' he? 'A's all wan' know. Facksh, facksh, tha's what I go on!

COUNSEL. But Yexcellency—

THE GOVERNOR. A' right, a'right. G' on, Bailey, what 'en?

THE WITNESS. So then, when I got back to the milk-wagon and unwrapped the other breeching and unslipped the traces, the old mare couldn't get up nohow. She was stiff from cold, and I had to get them cops again and shoot her. So the dairy company was pretty sore. The old mare, she weren't worth more'n twenty-five dollars, but them company men let on I was hired to take care of the company property and not pull no babies outen the sewer.

THE GOVERNOR. What 'en?

THE WITNESS. So we had it pretty hot for a while, and then later on that day I went down to the hospital for to look at the baby and got them nurses there to name him Greenfield Farms, what was the name of the dairy company, so when they put it in the Coal City *News* about the baby being found, the company would get a free ad outen it, anyway twenty-five dollars' worth, what was the worth of the mare, and they did and we was square.

THE GOVERNOR. What 'en?

THE WITNESS. Well, I reckon that's all. 'Cepting I picked up the paper about six months ago, and I seen where a fellow name of Greenfield Farms had spoke a piece at a entertainment what they had in the penitentiary, and I got to wondering if it was the same one, and I asked one or two people about it, and they sent me to this gentleman here, and come to find out it was.

COUNSEL. So Yexcellency can see that this young man here, this young man Greenfield Farms, is one and the same with the child this witness pulled out of the sewer twenty-three years ago.

THE GOVERNOR. 'N 'a's all?

THE WITNESS. Yes, sir.

THE GOVERNOR. Well Bailey, don' min' say'n y' touch m' heart. The ol' Coal City Vol'teer Fi' D'pa'ment, wha' y' know 'bout 'at?

COUNSEL. Now, Yexcellency, you've heard the story of this witness, I may say the truly remarkable story of this witness, which I think Yexcellency will agree had the stamp of truth all over it—

THE GOVERNOR. The ol' Coal City Vol'teer Fi' D'pa'ment . . . !

COUNSEL. A story, praps I should add, that we are prepared to substantiate in every particular from the hospital records, which we will leave with Yexcellency, and I may call Yexcellency's attention to this certificate in particular, which states that the child was at least a month old when it was admitted, and—

THE GOVERNOR. Now wha's all 'is got t' do 'th pa'don f' Bailey?

COUNSEL. Farms, Yexcellency.

THE GOVERNOR. Farmsh, 'en?

COUNSEL. I'm coming to that, Yexcellency. Now the salient point about this evidence, Yexcellency, is that it establishes beyond any reasonable doubt in my mind that there is nowhere in existing records any proof of Farms's citizenship. He was, I remind Yexcellency, a month old when admitted to the Coal City Hospital. And what does that prove? It proves, Yexcellency, that he *might* have been born almost anywhere on the whole face of the earth. He *might* have been born anywhere from Greenland's icy mountains to India's coral strand. He is, so far as documentary proof to the contrary goes, Yexcellency that *most* unfortunate being, I may say that *pitiable* being, who can claim *no* land as his own, being *nothing* more or less, Yexcellency, as the fellow says, a man without a country!

THE GOVERNOR. Well, well, well, I ashk y' f' facksh, 'n now y' begin shpout'n poetry at me. Man 'thout country, hunh? Tha's in'st'n.

COUNSEL. Now I remind Yexcellency once more that the crime of which Farms stands convicted is treason. And treason is unique among crimes, Yexcellency, in that before any man can be *convicted* of it, his *citizenship* must be established, beyond all *shadow* of doubt, because TREASON, Yexcellency, as all the AUTHORITIES agree—

THE GOVERNOR. Shtop yell'n!

COUNSEL. Yes, Yexcellency—implies a ALLEGIANCE—a allegiance to the State against which it is alleged to have been committed. And under the law—

THE GOVERNOR. Law? Law? Y' talk'n t' me 'bout law?

COUNSEL. Yes, Yexcellency, and—

THE GOVERNOR. Washa com'n t' me 'bout law for? Why 'nsha go t' court 'bout law?

COUNSEL. We've been to court, Yexcellency. We applied to the Supreme Court two months ago for a new trial, on the basis of the evidence which Yexcellency has just listened to, and which, praps I should have explained sooner, was not presented at the original trial because Farms had no idea at that time of the importance of his citizenship and neglected to inform me of the peculiar circumstances attending his birth. And the court denied the application, on the ground that while this evidence, if it *had* been presented at the trial, *might* have resulted in the granting of a motion to dismiss, it could not properly be regarded as *new* evidence, as it is essentially evidence of *lack* of evidence on the part of the State, rather than *direct* evidence of innocence.

THE PROSECUTOR. In other words, Yexcellency is being asked to certify that if the dog hadn't stopped to scratch fleas he would have caught the rabbit.

COUNSEL. Not in the least, Yexcellency—

THE GOVERNOR. Y' know what? Y' both pair pett-fogg'n lawyersh. Y' 'sgrace t' bar. Farmsh! C'me here. I'll do this m'self. Sit there, where c'n see y'.

THE PETITIONER. Yes, sir. Thank you, sir, Governor.

THE GOVERNOR. A' right, Farmsh, shpeak right up now. Y' needn't shtan' 'n awe 'f me. 'M plain, blunt man 'n got heart 's big 's all outdoorsh. Washa got say f' y'self?

THE PETITIONER. Governor, all I got to say is I went out there when them miners was gathering by the creek forks just to see what was going on—

THE GOVERNOR. Thasha shtuff! Facksh! Motivesh! Tha's wha' want. G' on, Farmsh. What 'en?

THE PETITIONER. And then when they marched down the road, I went along with them just for fun, and then two months afterwards, when they come and arrested me, I didn't have no more idea what they meant than the man in the moon, and—

THE GOVERNOR. Now we com'n. G'on.

THE PETITIONER. And then they sent me up. And—and . . .

THE GOVERNOR. Farmsh, now I ask y' some'n. If I was t' set y' free, what would y' do 'th y' lib'ty?

THE PETITIONER. If you was to set me free, Governor, the first thing I would do would be to go to the judge and get my citizenship fixed up—

THE PROSECUTOR. That's great! I'll say that's great! There you are, Yexcellency, right out of their own mouths! First this man isn't guilty because maybe the prawscution couldn't have proved his citizenship. And the first thing he's going to do if he gets a pardon is to get his citizenship fixed up! If that doesn't—

COUNSEL. Not at all, Yexcellency. In fact, I resent the imputation of—

THE GOVERNOR. Shtop! F' God's sake shtop! (*To the Secretary*) C'mute 'sen'ce 'mpris'nment f' life!

THE PETITIONER. What? Oh my God!

THE PROSECUTOR. Hunh?

COUNSEL. But, Yexcellency—

THE GOVERNOR. No more! 'M not g'n lis'n 'nother word! 'S comp'mise. 'S comp'mise, I know it's comp'mise. But 's bes' c'n do. Who y' think y' are, tak'n up my time way y' have? Don' min' f' m'self. 'M plain, blunt man 'n give y' shirt off m' back 'f y' need it. But my time b'longsh t' people. Y' und'shtan' 'at? My time b'longsh t' people, 'n wha' y' do with it? I ashk y' f' facksh 'n y' come in here 'th noth'n but tech'calitiesh! Tech'calitiesh I said! Pett'fogg'n! Trifl'n detailsh! Dog! Fleash! Rabbit! Poetry! 'M done with it! 'M not g'n lis'n 'nother word!

COUNSEL. But really, Yexcellency—

THE PETITIONER. Yeah, a fine lawyer you was. First you git me sent up for ten year and now you git me sent up for life—

THE WITNESS. Yeah, and a fine thing the Coal City Volunteer Fire Department done for the country when they pulled you out of the sewer—

THE GOVERNOR. Wha's 'at? Wha's 'at?

COUNSEL. I'm just trying to tell Yexcellency—

THE GOVERNOR. Jus' minute, jus' minute! ... The ol' Coal City Vol'teer Fi' D'pa'ment! Wha' y' know 'bout 'at? So Farmsh, y' were memb' ol' Coal City Vol'teer Fi' D'pa'ment?

THE PETITIONER. Well ... I reckon I was, in a way, Governor. I reckon I was, ha ha! I reckon I was kind of born to it, ha ha ha! I reckon I must be pretty near the only person in the world that was ever born to a fire department, ha ha, ha ha!

THE GOVERNOR. Farmsh, 'm g'n ask y' some'n. Look m' 'n eye, Farmsh. Farmsh, y' guilty 'r y' not guilty?

THE PETITIONER. Governor, I hope my die I ain't no more guilty than you are.

THE GOVERNOR. Farmsh, I believe y' tell'n' me truth. Farmsh, y' free man.

THE PETITIONER. Oh my Gawd, Governor, thank you sir, thank—!
THE GOVERNOR. The o' Coal City Vol'teer Fi' D'pa'ment. Wha' y' know
    'bout 'at? Wha' y' know 'bout 'at? . . .
    (*While the Secretary makes out a pardon and the* GOVERNOR *signs
    it, the group breaks up in a round of hand-shaking, the lawyers to go
    out and have a drink together, the petitioner to go back to the peni-
    tentiary for the last formalities. When they have all gone, the* GOVERNOR
    still sits nodding to himself, and presently falls amiably asleep.)

Frank Sullivan

A WEEKEND AT LADY ASTOR'S *

For years I had been saying to myself, "Now I must go down to Cliveden and spend a weekend with Lady Astor," but you know how those things are. Weekends are such a bore. I kept putting it off and putting it off and—well—putting it *off* until I read in the newspapers that Nancy and the Cliveden Set were running the Chamberlain Government, and I decided that was something definitely not to be missed. So the following Saturday I threw a few things into a bag, caught the 4:45 tram from Piccadilly Circus, and arrived at Cliveden just as the cuckoos were beginning their evening serenade.

Naturally, my heart beat a little faster as I neared Cliveden. Somewhere in that castle, I thought, is the little woman who rose from a humble beginning as a member of one of the First Families of Virginia to a place in the front rank of the British peerage. I should have counted myself a poor sort of American had I not felt some pride in this doughty little fellow-countrywoman who held the destiny of the British Empire in her small hands; who, by a discreet whisper behind a potted palm or a fan, could probably cause Australia to be abolished or a law passed forbidding Englishmen to dress for dinner.

I thought of the many times my heart had swelled with pride as I sat in the visitors' gallery of the House of Commons and heard the House roar an affectionate greeting to Nancy Astor, rising to a man as she entered and hollering "Shut up!," "Sit down!," or "Go on back to Ameddica, where you came from," even before she had opened her trap.

Cliveden was lovely. The yews were in full bloom and cast blue-black shadows on the silver perukes of the liveried footmen. Scores of beautiful women strolled on the terrace, influencing the decisions of monocled British statesmen by their charm and wit.

"Is the Lady of the House in?" I asked the butler who took my bag.

* It was in the spring of 1938.

"Lady Astor is upstairs at the moment, rewriting the *Court Circular* for Monday's *Times*," said the butler. "Are you expected, sir?"

"Well, not exactly. I'm just a fellow-countryman of Lady Astor. I can't really say I know her."

"Ah, you'll like her," smiled the butler. "She's a holy terror. Always on the go. And a mind like a steel trap. Click!" The butler imitated a mind like a steel trap.

"She'll be delighted to see you, sir. Now you'd better run upstairs and police yourself up. Dinner's at nine. White tie."

I was agog at the prospect of being present at one of those famous dinners of the British ruling class I had always read about so much, at which from time immemorial clever girls like Lily Langtry, Margot Asquith, Boadicea, and Nancy Astor have influenced the course of empire by their brilliance and charm. And the Cliveden Set particularly! The Cliveden Set rules the British ruling class at the moment. When you rule the ruling class of England, boy, I'm telling you, you're *ruling!*

It was indeed a brilliant assemblage that gathered in the dining room at nine. There were no cocktails, as Lady Astor is a teetotaller, but fortunately the second assistant gamekeeper ran a speakeasy in one of the haunted rooms of the castle and those of us who had been tipped off, or whose noses had been rendered sufficiently keen by thirst, fortified ourselves there prior to dinner.

We were a company of a hundred and forty-six, twenty-nine being absent. The Honourable Ursula Godolphin-Potts was forced to remain in her room with a headache, the result of overinfluencing a British statesman on the terrace that afternoon. The German Ambassador was also upstairs nursing an injury. While giving Lord Halifax the Nazi salute that afternoon, he had struck his hand a rather nasty bang on a low-hanging branch of an oak, lacerating it severely. Twenty-seven of the guests had left for home just before dinner on receipt of telegrams announcing the serious illnesses of their grandmothers.

The women wore two ostrich plumes, as Lady Astor is only a viscountess. She is ten thousand four hundred and twentieth in direct line of succession to the British Crown, or four thousand two hundred and thirty-eight behind Lady Peel (Beatrice Lillie) and eight hundred and sixty-five and sixty-six, respectively, ahead of Dame May Whitty and Sir Cedric Hardwicke—Noel Coward, of course, being still a commoner.

All the men wore knee breeches and silk stockings except me. As a virile, patriotic Yankee I refused to kowtow to British flummery in this respect, but as a concession to international good will I did roll my trousers up to my knees. The men wore their decorations. Mine consisted of my Junior Order of Birdmen jewel, my gold badge as former honorary police commissioner of Long Beach, Long Island, my insignia of the St. Aloysius Sodality of St. Peter's Church, Saratoga Springs, and my blue ribbon as healthiest American boy in the national 4-H Contest of 1932. We were a brilliant throng and Lady Astor never looked lovelier as she sat on the woolsack at the head of the table, with Neville Chamberlain on her right and Lord Lothian on her left. Of course there was "one vacant chair," as the saying goes. Good old Joe Ribbentrop was missing from his usual place, having been transferred to his home office.

After a deal of good-natured roughhouse over who should precede whom, during which some of the older duchesses got banged about quite a bit, we all reached our correct seats and Lady Astor motioned for silence.

"Welcome to Cliveden, ladies and gentlemen," she said.

"Oh, shut your mouth," said one of the guests.

Nancy Astor was on her feet in an instant.

"If the honourable gentleman from Upper Tooting," she snapped, "thinks that telling me to shut my mouth is any solution of the vital problem which confronts this assemblage at this momentous and solemn hour—I refer to the problem of getting the soup served before it gets cold—then all I can say to the honourable . . ."

"Oh, go sit on a tack!" shouted the honourable gentleman from Upper Tooting.

Would Nancy Astor stand for that? Would the famed mistress of Parliamentary repartee parry this clever thrust or would she allow it to floor her? The dinner table held its breath. Then she let him have it.

"Go sit on one yourself and see how you like it," she snapped.

A murmur of admiration swept the dining room.

"Gad, I wish I'd said that," said Geoffrey Dawson, editor of the *Times,* an Astor paper.

"Isn't she in ripping form tonight, though?" said J. L. Garvin, editor of the *Observer,* another Astor paper.

"I thought she gave him Hail Columbia—if you'll pardon the Americanism," said Lord Lothian.

The Archbishop of Canterbury also seemed pleased.

"Who is the lad who asked our hostess to sit on the tack?" I said to my dinner partner, Lady Feather Barksdale-Wotton.

"Oh, he's a spy from His Majesty's Opposition," said Lady Feather. "He's here every weekend. Rather nice chap."

The dinner proceeded smoothly. Lady Astor, skilled hostess that she is, had assembled a truly stimulating group, representing every shade of political thought, from conservatives who felt that Hitler should be given only Czechoslovakia, Memel, the Ukraine, the Polish Corridor, and Denmark, to extreme radicals who felt he should also be given France and England.

The conversation sparkled. I heard a chap up the table a piece from me say, "Now don't misunderstand me. Some of my best friends are Jews."

"Gad, I wish I'd said that," I exclaimed to Lady Gwydd Stensitty-Wowdle, who sat on my left. "Who's he?"

"That's Lord Londonderry," said Lady Gwydd. "You know—he wrote that amusing book in praise of Hitler."

"Oh, is *he* the one?"

I leaned over and called to him.

"Lord Londonderry."

"Yes, my good man."

"How's tricks? Everything according to *Heil?*"

But he muffed it. The British are so slow at getting a joke.

I caught another fragment of conversation.

"You know," I heard a peer named Lord Featherstonehaugh (pronounced Fuff) say, "sometimes I think Nancy Astor has got herself slightly confused with the British Empire."

Instantly every guest produced a notebook and started writing.

"What are they doing?" I asked the Honourable Hebe Quart, who sat next Lord Fuff.

"Jotting down notes for their memoirs," said Lady Hebe, who was hard at it herself. "We'll all claim we said that instead of Fuff."

I must say that it seemed to me, from what discreet peeking I could do, that not all of them were good reporters. Some of the older peers who were hard of hearing had not quite caught Fuff's mot and other peers who were hard of artery had caught it all right but could not remember it long enough to record it, so that many inaccurate versions got jotted down, such as "Sometimes I think Nancy Astor has got the British Empire slightly confused" or "Sometimes I think Nancy Astor has got herself slightly confused."

This was all very well, but I wanted to see some action.

"When is Lady Astor going to start influencing the British Government?" I asked Lady Feather. "It's four minutes past ten now and I haven't seen anything."

"Silly," admonished Lady Feather. "You have, too. You are seeing the entire Cliveden Set in action. Scarcely a remark has been passed at this table tonight—except by you, of course—that has not been fraught with significance."

"You mean?"

"I mean that we are not so gauche as to come right out and influence the British Empire directly. It's not so much what we say, it's the way we say it. With us, the most commonplace remark, uttered with just the right flicker of an eye, takes on a significance that can cause repercussions in the farthest-flung outposts of the Empire."

Well, that put a different light on things. Here I had been kicking because I thought the dinner conversation was lagging and apparently hell had been popping right in front of me all the time, and I never knew it.

After that I had a grand time. It was fun to hear somebody like Lord Halifax say something about foxhunting and then try to figure out whether that remark meant that Britain would or would not go to the aid of France if France went to the aid of Czechoslovakia when Hitler started his *Putsch* there.

Then Lady Astor asked Neville Chamberlain if he would have another helping of asparagus. It sounded innocent enough, but everybody at the table knew that it really meant: Would Neville get a place in the Cabinet for General Franco? It was done so neatly that even the old seasoned diplomats at the table could not repress enthusiastic gurgles of admiration.

"By gad," said Lord Lothian, "I wouldn't be a bit surprised if sooner or later Nancy Astor succeeded in changing the map of Europe."

"Or vice-versa," heckled the spy from His Majesty's Opposition.

That crack at our gallant little hostess seemed scarcely cricket to me and I rather burned.

"See here," I drawled, "I'm jest a plain, red-blooded American and

I s'pose I ain't up to the ways of you Bridish, but by gum, I'm durned ef I'm a-goin' to set here and listen to y'all cast aspersions on a little woman from Virginia, the Mother of Presidents, that ain't done y'all a mite o' harm. Now get this, you ornery passel o' furriners. George III got England away from the United States but by jiminy, Nancy Astor has got it back. Yip-e-e-e-e!"

"Yip-e-e-e-e! Hear! Hear!" shouted the gentleman from His Majesty's Opposition.

Lady Astor gave me a smile of gratitude.

"Why don't you play that on your bazooka?" sneered Lady Feather.

"You want to make something of it?" I ra'red.

"Sure do, pardner," said Lady Feather, rising.

"Keep your shirt on, honey," I advised. "I never hit a woman with a tiara on yet, and now ain't no time to start."

"I'll take it off," said Lady Feather, taking it off. "Now you take your glasses off."

For a minute it looked as though Lady Feather and I might mix it, but Neville Chamberlain stepped between us and fixed things up. He conceded his watch and chain to me and gave Lady Feather a half-interest in Spain.

After that the ladies retired and when we fellows were left alone over the port and nuts, Bernard Shaw talked most interestingly for an hour or two on why it was all right for Hitler to burke Austria. Then we fellows joined the ladies in the drawing room—all except Bernard, who stayed on alone in the dining room because he still had an hour or so talking to do.

The dinner conversations were resumed in the drawing room, but you couldn't fool me now. I knew that when Nancy Astor asked Neville if he took sugar in his demitasse it could mean anything from the transfer of a British diplomat in Hong Kong to a new alliance with Mussolini.

It set me up no end to be in the know like this, for a while anyhow. Then the idea struck me that if I hung around Cliveden much longer *I* might start saying things fraught with significance. My common sense told me it was unlikely, but you can't be too careful. What would the folks back home think if they heard I was helping the Cliveden Set influence the course of empire? I got pretty uneasy.

I wanted to leave but didn't have any good excuse, because I hadn't thought to arrange to have one of those telegrams sent about my grandmother being sick.

Then something happened that spurred me to action. I saw Lord Londonderry approaching with a copy of his book on Hitler. He was heading straight for me.

I felt like some wild thing about to be trapped.

Londonderry came on ... on ... on.

I had to act quickly. There wasn't a second to lose. Already he was saying, "Now don't misunderstand me ..."

A footman happened to pass with a tray heaped with telegrams.

With a wit born of desperation I seized one and ripped it open. It was for Neville Chamberlain. It read, "Return home immediately. Grandmother ill. Urgent."

Darting between Lord Londonderry's legs, I escaped to Lady Astor, pretended the telegram was for me, made my apologies, expressed my thanks for her hospitality, caught the 1:20 goods train back to Waterloo, and was on my old bench on the Embankment in an hour. And never did home seem so sweet.

PARODIES AND BURLESQUES

Good parody should be funny in itself, whether or not one has read the book or author parodied. Nevertheless, we have tried to choose only parodies or burlesques in which the literary —or unliterary—source will still be reasonably familiar to present-day readers.

Parody is an easy form of humorous writing, in its lesser manifestations; but a really good parody is rare, and is only performed by a person with high intelligence and a good ear. Some of the items which follow are not true parody but are burlesque, a literary form in which the author takes a healthy swipe at a manner of writing or a habit of mind.

We have made little effort to collect parody verse, because there have been anthologies of such material. What few verse parodies appear in this book will be found in the verse section.

Eugene Field

THE TRIBUNE PRIMER *

THE EDITOR'S HOME

Here is a Castle. It is the Home of an Editor. It has stained Glass windows and Mahogany stairways. In front of the Castle is a Park. Is it not Sweet? The lady in the Park is the editor's wife. She wears a Costly robe of Velvet trimmed with Gold Lace, and there are Pearls and Rubies in her Hair. The editor sits on the front Stoop smoking an Havana Cigar. His little Children are playing with diamond Marbles on the Tesselated Floor. The editor can afford to Live in Style. He gets Seventy-Five Dollars a month Wages.

THE BAD MAN

Here is a Man who has just Stopped his Paper. What a Miserable looking Creature he is. He looks as if he had been stealing Sheep. How will he Know what is going on, now that he has Stopped his Paper? He will Borrow his Neighbor's Paper. One of these Days he will Break his leg, or be a Candidate for Office, and then the Paper will Say Nothing about it. That will be treating him just Right, will it not, little Children?

THE OYSTER

Here we have an Oyster. It is going to a Church Fair. When it Gets to the Fair, it will Swim around in a big Kettle of Warm Water. A Lady will Stir it with a Spoon, and sell the Warm Water for Forty Cents a pint. Then the Oyster will move on to the next Fair. In this Way, the Oyster will visit all the Church Fairs in Town, and Bring a great many Dollars into the Church Treasury. The Oyster goes a great Way in a Good Cause.

* *Excerpts from a parody primer, which appeared first in* the Denver Tribune *(1882) and were later published in book form. This was Field's first book.*

THE UNFORTUNATE MOUSIE

Poor little Mouse! He got into the Flour Barrel and Made Himself Dead. The Cook baked him in a Loaf of Bread, and here he lies on the Table cut in two by the Sharp bread Knife. But we will not Eat poor Mouse. We will eat the Bread, but we will Take the Mousie and Put him in the Cistern.

THE COAL HOD

Oh, how nice and Black the Coal-Hod is! Run, children, Run quick and put your Little Fat hands in it. Mercy me, your Hands are as Black as the Coal-Hod now! Hark! Mamma is Coming. She will spank you when she Finds your Hands so Dirty. Better go and Rub the Black Dirt off on the Wall Paper before she Comes.

MAMMA'S SCISSORS

These are Mamma's Scissors. They do not Seem to be in good Health. Well, they are a little Aged. They have considerable Work to Do. Mamma uses them to Chop Kindling, cut Stove Pipe, pull Tacks, drive Nails, cut the children's Hair, punch new Holes in the Calendar, slice Bar soap, pound beef Steak, open tomatoe Cans, Shear the New Foundland dog and cut out her New silk Dress. Why doesn't Papa get Mamma a new Pair of Scissors? You should not Ask such a Naughty question. Papa cannot Afford to Play Billiards and Indulge his Extravagant Family in the Luxuries of Life.

THE BOTTLE

This is a Bottle. What is in the Bottle? Very bad Whiskey. It has been Sent to the Local Editor. He did not Buy it. If he had Bought it the Whiskey would have been Poorer than it is. Little children, you Must never Drink Bad Whiskey.

THE HASH

Is this a Chignon? No, it is a Plate of Hash. But where are the Brush and Comb. We cannot serve the Hash unless we have a Brush and Comb. The Comb is in the Butter, and the Baby has put the Brush in the Coffee-Pot. Don't cry, Children, we will Give you some nice Molasses with Pretty, green Flies in it.

THE MUD

The Mud is in the Street. The Lady has on a pair of Red Stockings. She is Trying to Cross the Street. Let us all give Three cheers for the Mud.

THE WASP

See the Wasp. He has pretty yellow Stripes around his Body, and a Darning Needle in his Tail. If you Will Pat the Wasp upon the Tail, we will Give You a Nice Picture Book.

THE BUSINESS MANAGER

Here we Have a Business Manager. He is Blowing about the Circulation of the Paper. He is Saying the Paper has Entered upon an Era of Unprecedented Prosperity. In a Minute he will Go up Stairs and Chide the Editor for leaving his Gas Burning while he Went out for a Drink of Water, and he will dock a Reporter Four Dollars because a Subscriber has Licked him and he cannot Work. Little Children, if we Believed Business Managers went to Heaven, we would Give up our Pew in Church.

THE CONCENTRATED LYE

What a Pretty Can it is. What do you Suppose is in the Can? Open it and see. Goodness me, it is Concentrated Lye! How Nice! Are you not Glad? Let us eat it. Taste it and See how Warm it is. If you will Eat it you will not Want anything More to Eat For a Long Time.

Robert C. Benchley

CHRISTMAS AFTERNOON

(Done in the Manner, if Not the Spirit, of Dickens)

What an afternoon! Mr. Gummidge said that, in his estimation, there never had *been* such an afternoon since the world began, a sentiment which was heartily endorsed by Mrs. Gummidge and all the little Gummidges, not to mention the relatives who had come over from Jersey for the day.

In the first place, there was the *ennui*. And such *ennui* as it was! A heavy, overpowering *ennui*, such as results from a participation in eight courses of steaming, gravied food, topping off with salted nuts which the little old spinster Gummidge from Oak Hill said she never knew when to stop eating—and true enough she didn't—a dragging, devitalizing *ennui*, which left its victims strewn about the living-room in various attitudes of prostration suggestive of those of the petrified occupants in a newly unearthed Pompeiian dwelling; an *ennui* which carried with it a retinue of yawns, snarls and thinly veiled insults, and which ended in ruptures in the clan spirit serious enough to last throughout the glad new year.

Then there were the toys! Three and a quarter dozen toys to be divided among seven children. Surely enough, you or I might say, to satisfy the little tots. But that would be because we didn't know the tots. In came Baby Lester Gummidge, Lillian's boy, dragging an electric grain-elevator which happened to be the only toy in the entire collection which appealed to little Norman, five-year-old son of Luther, who lived in Rahway. In came curly-headed Effie in frantic and throaty disputation with Arthur, Jr., over the possession of an articulated zebra. In came Everett, bearing a mechanical negro which would no longer dance, owing to a previous forcible feeding by the baby of a marshmallow into its only available aperture. In came Fonlansbee, teeth buried in the hand of little Ormond, which bore a popular but battered remnant of what had once been the proud false-bosom of a hussar's uniform. In they all came, one after another, some crying,

248

some snapping, some pulling, some pushing—all appealing to their respective parents for aid in their intra-mural warfare.

And the cigar smoke! Mrs. Gummidge said that she didn't mind the smoke from a good cigarette, but would they mind if she opened the windows for just a minute in order to clear the room of the heavy aroma of used cigars? Mr. Gummidge stoutly maintained that they were good cigars. His brother, George Gummidge, said that he, likewise, would say that they were. At which colloquial sally both the Gummidge brothers laughed testily, thereby breaking the laughter record for the afternoon.

Aunt Libbie, who lived with George, remarked from the dark corner of the room that it seemed just like Sunday to her. An amendment was offered to this statement by the cousin, who was in the insurance business, stating that it was worse than Sunday. Murmurings indicative of as hearty agreement with this sentiment as their lethargy would allow came from the other members of the family circle, causing Mr. Gummidge to suggest a walk in the air to settle their dinner.

And then arose such a chorus of protestations as has seldom been heard. It was too cloudy to walk. It was too raw. It looked like snow. It looked like rain. Luther Gummidge said that he must be starting along home soon, anyway, bringing forth the acid query from Mrs. Gummidge as to whether or not he was bored. Lillian said that she felt a cold coming on, and added that something they had had for dinner must have been undercooked. And so it went, back and forth, forth and back, up and down, and in and out, until Mr. Gummidge's suggestion of a walk in the air was reduced to a tattered impossibility and the entire company glowed with ill-feeling.

In the meantime, we must not forget the children. No one else could. Aunt Libbie said that she didn't think there was anything like children to make a Christmas; to which Uncle Ray, the one with the Masonic fob, said, "No, thank God!" Although Christmas is supposed to be the season of good cheer, you (or I, for that matter) couldn't have told, from listening to the little ones, but what it was the children's Armageddon season, when Nature had decreed that only the fittest should survive, in order that the race might be carried on by the strongest, the most predatory and those possessing the best protective coloring. Although there were constant admonitions to Fonlansbee to "Let Ormond have that now; it's his," and to Arthur, Jr., not to be selfish, but to "give the kiddie-car to Effie; she's smaller than you are,"

the net result was always that Fonlansbee kept the whistle and Arthur
Jr., rode in permanent, albeit disputed, possession of the kiddie-car
Oh, that we mortals should set ourselves up against the inscrutable
workings of Nature!

Hallo! A great deal of commotion! That was Uncle George stum
bling over the electric train, which had early in the afternoon ceased
to function and which had been left directly across the threshold. A
great deal of crying! That was Arthur, Jr., bewailing the destruction
of his already useless train, about which he had forgotten until the
present moment. A great deal of recrimination! That was Arthur, Sr.
and George fixing it up. And finally a great crashing! That was Baby
Lester pulling over the tree on top of himself, necessitating the bring
ing to bear of all of Uncle Ray's knowledge of forestry to extricate him
from the wreckage.

And finally Mrs. Gummidge passed the Christmas candy around
Mr. Gummidge afterward admitted that this was a tactical error on
the part of his spouse. I no more believe that Mrs. Gummidge thought
they wanted that Christmas candy than I believe that she thought they
wanted the cold turkey which she later suggested. My opinion is that
she wanted to drive them home. At any rate, that is what she succeeded in doing. Such cries as there were of "Ugh! Don't let me see
another thing to eat!" and "Take it away!" Then came hurried scram-
blings in the coat-closet for overshoes. There were the rasping sounds
made by cross parents when putting wraps on children. There were
insincere exhortations to "come and see us soon" and to "get together
for lunch some time." And, finally, there were slammings of doors
and the silence of utter exhaustion, while Mrs. Gummidge went about
picking up stray sheets of wrapping paper.

And, as Tiny Tim might say in speaking of Christmas afternoon as
an institution, "God help us, every one."

HAPPY CHILDHOOD TALES

We have had so many stories lately dealing with the sordid facts of
life, about kitchen sinks and lynchings and young girls thrown out
into the streets by mean old farmers who live in horsehair trunks, to
say nothing of incidental subjects, such as gin and cold oatmeal and
unfortunate people who have only one glove apiece, that a reaction is

taking place in the mind of the reading public and a demand is going up for some of the fanciful happy tales of our youth.

"Enough of these stories of crime and unhappiness!" the people are crying. "Tell us again some of the ancient myths of an older day, the gay little legends on which we were brought up before the world grew grim and sordid."

And so, my little readers, I am going to try to recall to you some of the charming fairy tales, or, at any rate, to make up some like them, and I hope that after this little trip back into the Never-Never Land of our youth, those little cheeks of yours will be blooming again and that you will shut your traps. For, after all, there must be *some* good in the world, else why were erasers put on the ends of lead pencils?

ENDREMIA AND LIASON

(From the Greek Mythology)

Endremia was the daughter of Polygaminous, the God of Ensilage, and Reba, the Goddess of Licorice. She was the child of a most unhappy union, it later turned out, for when she was a tiny child her father struck her mother with an anvil and turned himself into a lily pad to avoid the vengeance of Jove. But Jove was too sly for Polygaminous and struck him with a bolt of lightning the size of the Merchants Bank Building which threw him completely off his balance so that he toppled over into a chasm and was dashed to death.

In the meantime, Little Endremia found herself alone in the world with nobody but Endrocine, the Goddess of Lettuce, and her son Bilax, the God of Gum Arabic, to look after her. But, as Polygaminous (her father; have you forgotten so soon, you dope?) had turned Endremia into a mushroom before he turned himself into a lily pad, neither of her guardians knew who she was, so their protection did her no good.

But Jove had not so soon forgotten the daughter of his favorite (Reba), and appeared to her one night in the shape of a mushroom gatherer. He asked her how she would like to get off that tree (she was one of those mushrooms which grow on trees) and get into his basket. Endremia, not knowing that it was Jove who was asking her, said not much. Whereupon Jove unloosed his mighty wrath and struck down the whole tree with a bolt of lightning which he had brought with him in case Endremia wouldn't listen to reason.

This is why it is never safe to eat the mushrooms which grow on trees, or to refuse to get into Jove's basket.

MILGRIG AND THE TREE WILFS
(Something like Hans Christian Andersen)

Once upon a time there was a little girl named Milgrig, believe it or not. She lived in the middle of a deep dark forest with her three ugly sisters and their husbands, who were charcoal burners. Every night the three ugly sisters used to take little Milgrig and pull out a strand of her golden hair, so that by the time she was thirteen years old she looked something awful. And after the three sisters had pulled out her hair, their three husbands (I forgot to tell you that the three husbands were even uglier than the three sisters and much nastier) would stick pins into little Milgrig until she looked like a war map.

One night, when little Milgrig was so full of pins that she couldn't see straight, a fairy prince came riding up to the door of the charcoal burners' hut and asked if he had lost his way.

"How should I know?" replied the oldest sister, who was uglier than all the rest. "What was your way?"

"My way was to the king's castle," replied the prince, "and I must get there before midnight, for my father is torturing my mother with red-hot irons."

"Your father sounds like a good egg," replied the oldest husband, who was uglier than all the rest. "We must ask him down some night."

The prince, however, did not think that this was very funny and asked if little Milgrig might not be allowed to show him the way to the castle.

The ugly husbands and sisters, thinking that Milgrig would not know the way and would get the prince lost in the forest, agreed heartily to this suggestion, and the pins were pulled out of Milgrig to make it possible for her to walk.

"Good luck and a happy landing!" they all called out after the two young people as they set forth on their perilous journey.

But the prince was no fool, and knew his way through the forest as well as you or I do (better, I'll wager), and he took little Milgrig to the palace just as fast as his palfrey would carry him.

She wasn't particularly crazy about going, but a prince is a prince, and she knew enough to keep her mouth shut.

When they reached the palace and the prince found that his father had already killed his mother, he turned to little Milgrig and said: "Now you are the queen."

At this, little Milgrig was very pleased and immediately dispatched messengers to the charcoal burners' hut, where the three ugly sisters and three still uglier brothers-in-law were burned alive in a slow fire. Little Milgrig and the prince, happy in this termination to their little affair, lived happily ever after.

And so now, my readers, you must toddle off to bed, for we have had an evening with the happy, happy story-tellers of an earlier day and have had a vacation, for one night at least, from the drab, unpleasant sordidness of present-day writing.

THE BLUE SLEEVE GARTER

(Sex and Political Economy as blended by Mr. Galsworthy)

I

PROSCENIUM

In the rich gloom of the Board Room, surrounded by charts showing the Unemployment Situation and the old Corn Laws, Lister Hoag, seventeenth baronet, reviewed in his well dressed mind the situation which confronted his heart. There was, of course, Melisse. Tomorrow! Seventh anniversary of their wedding day! Seven years of what? He broke a lead pencil. Seven years of Melisse. Poor Melisse! And yet—in a way—poor Trevor! Sentiment was tip. Unquestionably sentiment was tip. Still, Lister felt a strange ache when he thought of it all. What good in thinking? What good in tying one's tie? No—by Gad!

Old Breamley was speaking. To sell these ships now would mean a clear profit of thirty thousand pounds. Thirty thousand Melisses! Fifteen minutes—half an hour—what difference did it make? He would soon be with Melisse. He would take her in his arms and tell her that everything was tup. And that would be no lie. Everything *was* tup. Silly old guff! Would Rodney Granish mind? And if he did, would Maxton Sixby blorrow? Jolly—if young Sixby blorrowed! What a mess! And now about these ships. The Germans wanted them. And England needed them. Reconstruction. Well, perhaps. But Melisse's neck was whiter than Reconstruction. And her eyes deeper. What a jolly old mup it all was! Everything! Or—perhaps—nothing! Lister shut his eyes and marked "Three hundred pounds" on his pad. No use to have a heart. Or a liver either, for that matter.

II

CODA

It was warm in bed. Heavy brocade shut out the smart breeze which blew in the long windows from the Free Trade Club across Cavendish Square. Lister Hoag ran his bare arm along the soft mountain ranges of the coverlet. Nice.

Melisse was asleep beside him. At any rate, Melisse was beside him. The curve from her chin to her shoulder reminded Lister of the curve on the chart showing the Unemployment Situation. It was a long, gentle curve and yet to him it cried out that the Government was wrong, all wrong. What right had one man to have a job when another hadn't? What right had they to tax wheat when Bleeker and Tony Napin and Thornlip and all those other poor devils were eating ha'penny rolls? Political principles—he mused—were tip. Absolutely tip. And yet if one had no political principles one was likely to have no principles at all. If, as a member of the community, as an Englishman—and he certainly was an Englishman—he accepted the challenge, what was left but revolution? No, by George! England was there, and since England was there, there she must stay.

Melisse stirred softly at his side. She wanted to speak. She said: "What time is it, dear?"

Automatically, Lister looked at his wrist watch. It was the watch that had been given him by the governors of the Liberal Union. A rum crowd, the Union. No spines. No convictions. Like the Board. Seven per cent preference—nine per cent ordinary. What whip! And, since it *was* whip, why bother? But somehow the War had changed all that. The War had changed everything. Nobody was sure now. A chap didn't know in the morning what the Prime would be by night, and the Prime didn't know at night what a chap would be in the morning. England was twill. But she was England, nevertheless.

"It's a quarter to eight, dear."

But Melisse was asleep again, with a faint curl of disgust on her fifteenth century lips.

III

TEATIME AT BLEEMS

Nine hours later Trevor Ramsty stood facing the tea table across which Melisse Hoag was stretching a white arm. England was still England.

"Draw up. Cream, Trevor? Go away, Whang! You've had your tea. Don't tell me, Trevor, that you are going out for the Socialists? That's sugar you're taking, you know, ducky, not opium."

"Not so much going out for Socialists as going in for talking, empress."

Melisse looked at him. Very nicely put! Trevor *would* be nice to have with one on a canal boat.

"'Ware shoals, Melisse!" said Ramsty.

"Budney, my dear, sheer budney!"

Trevor bit his lip thoughtfully.

"You stweem a bit—for you."

"That will do, Cherry! And please someone take Whang downstairs. He has become intolerable since the Free Trade Club gave him that new leash."

Whang placed his paws on Lister's spats and said:

"Put me out if you will, but remember, I can vote at the next General Election."

Lister was incalculable—did such odd things! To be sure, he was nice. Very nice. But incalculable.

"I'm sorry, Melisse, if I have made a gaff."

"Not a bit; jolly good tib. The thing about England today is that we are too English. Whang here knows better. He eats anything."

Trevor smiled queerly.

"Are you quite, quite sure?" asked Melisse.

"Rather! And, by the way, is it full fig tonight?"

"Just as you like. Meemie will be there."

"Full fig, then."

"I thought so."

"I thought you would think so."

"It *was* good of you to get me Rennie Cleenist, though. I do hope he'll behave and not be full of Debt Refunding. I'm putting him between Lillie Omster and Neyla Brann. Seven. You know them all.

Oh, and you mustn't mind if Old Wadney talks Merchant Marine. He loves it so. Did you read Willie's story about him? Oh, too frightfully amusing—clearly meant for H. K. V. Whang, put that hat down! Whose hat is it?"

"Mine," said Lister, as he entered the room, "but never mind. We sold those ships."

IV

NAPIN REFULGENT

The Board Room was no brighter than it had ever been. In fact, as Lister sat and poked holes in the map of Solvent Europe, the room seemed full of four per cents. Napin had been caught. Why quibble about that? Caught red handed, stealing the rudders off the ships which the company had sold to the Germans. But as Lister looked at the pale face of the young man, he saw on beyond Tony Napin and into the system which engulfed him. Capital. Labour. Tripe! It was man against man. Bug against bug. Oxford against Cambridge. And Napin had stolen rudders.

"See here, Napin! Come home with me and have a drink. You'll jolly well need one."

Tony said nothing but put on someone's hat and coat which were hanging on the wall and waited for Lister to lead the way.

"Napin, old bean," said Lister, "you're about done in. How can a man funk it when the world is as it is today? Look at the Liberals. Fed up on Liability Insurance. Look at the Labour Party. Eating Enfranchisement pap. Look at the Hangnail Prevention League. Nothing but—"

"I beg pardon, Mr. Hoag," said Napin. "You were saying something about a drink. I haven't all night, you know, sir. I'm due at jail at seven sharp."

V

MELISSE

Tony Napin had been in the room with Melisse just fifteen minutes when he asked her to run away with him. The afternoon sun was slanting in through the stained glass windows on which old Manton Hoag, sixteenth baronet, had had lettered in old English the complete text of the Reform Act. To speak perfectly frankly, Melisse was quite impressed with the twelfth century directness of Napin's proposition. Her brown eye rested on the silver tea service, her blue eye following suit.

Of course, there was Lister. Poor, dear Lister. He would be cut up no end. But really, Lister was frightfully civic. For seven years Lister had made love to her by explaining the principles of Public Ownership of Metropolitan Utilities. Their baby had been conceived in Single Tax and had run away from home at the age of four rather than hear more about Redistribution of Unearned Capital. It was harsh to think, but dear Lister was suffering from hardening of the Trade Arteries.

Then there was Trevor. Trevor was a sweet lover. Melisse could not deny that. But he *did* talk of Socialism when he should have been talking ways and means. Funny! That Trevor had—and here Melisse upset the sugar bowl—oh, well! Trevor *had,* that was all. Thinking was tosh. Tosh—and rather dreadful.

And now Napin. He had walked into the room, said how-do-you-do, and had asked her to run away with him. Nothing about Germany's debt. Nothing about the Merchant Marine. Nothing about taxation. Simply, "Pack your things!" It was stupendous. And terribly exciting. Why not? Or perhaps rather—why?

The telephone was over there. Melisse took her hand out of the hot tea and went to it.

"Can I speak to Mr. Hoag, please? ... In the Board Room ... Mrs. Hoag speaking ... Lister, dear ... How is the Bill of Rights coming on? ... Bully! ... And the Swedish Disenfranchisement? ... Sweet! ... And do you still feel the same way about taxing indeterminate inheritances? ... Ducky! ... Well, then, Lister dear, please do something for me.... Take them all, the Bill of Rights, the Swedish Disenfranchisement, and the Inheritance Tax and roll them up in one big bundle.... Have you done that? ... Righto ... What are you to do with them now? ... You know very well, my dear.... I'm off for Innsbruck with young Napin.... Yes. N-a-p-i-n. Care of General Delivery, Innsbruck ... Cheerio ...."

Whang climbed up on the tea table and pushed his nose into the sugar bowl. At last he was alone.

MORE SONGS FOR MELLER

As Señorita Raquel Meller sings entirely in Spanish, it is again explained, the management prints little synopses of the songs on the program, telling what each is all about and why she is behaving the way she is. They make delightful reading during those periods when Señorita Meller is changing mantillas, and, in case she should run out of songs before she runs out of mantillas, we offer a few new synopses for her repertoire.

(1) ¿ VOY BIEN?
(Am I Going in the Right Direction?)

When the acorns begin dropping in Spain there is an old legend that for every acorn which drops there is a baby born in Valencia. This is so silly that no one pays any attention to it now, not even the gamekeeper's daughter, who would pay attention to anything. She goes from house to house, ringing doorbells and then running away. She hopes that some day she will ring the right doorbell and will trip and fall, so that Prince Charming will catch her. So far, no one has even come to the door. Poor Pepita! if that is her name.

(2) CAMISETAS DE FLANELA
(Flannel Vests)

Princess Rosamonda goes nightly to the Puerta del Sol to see if the early morning edition of the papers is out yet. If it isn't she hangs around humming to herself. If it is, she hangs around humming just the same. One night she encounters a young matador who is returning from dancing school. The finches are singing and there is Love in the air. Princess Rosamonda ends up in the Police Station.

(3) LA GUIA
(The Time-Table)

It is the day of the bull fight in Madrid. Everyone is cock-eyed. The bull has slipped out by the back entrance to the arena and has gone home, disgusted. Nobody notices that the bull has gone except Nina, a peasant girl who has come to town that day to sell her father. She looks with horror at the place in the Royal Box where the bull ought to be sitting and sees there instead her algebra teacher whom she had told that she was staying at home on account of a sick headache. You can imagine her feelings!

(4) NO PUEDO COMER ESO
(I Can Not Eat That!)

A merry song of the Alhambra—of the Alhambra in the moonlight —of a girl who danced over the wall and sprained her ankle. Lititia is the ward of grouchy old Pampino, President of the First National Banco. She has never been allowed further away than the edge of the piazza because she teases people so. Her lover has come to see her and finds that she is fast asleep. He considers that for once he has the breaks, and tiptoes away without waking her up. Along about eleven o'clock she awakes, and is sore as all get-out.

(5) LA LAVANDERA
(The Laundryman)

A coquette, pretending to be very angry, bites off the hand of her lover up to the wrist. Ah, naughty Cirinda! Such antics! However does she think she can do her lessons if she gives up all her time to love-making? But Cirinda does not care. Heedless, heedless Cirinda!

(6) ABRA VD. ESA VENTANA
(Open That Window)

The lament of a mother whose oldest son is too young to vote. She walks the streets singing: "My son can not vote! My son is not old enough!" There seems to be nothing that can be done about it.

Ring Lardner

ODD'S BODKINS

AUTHOR'S NOTE:
Each morn when the neighbors are through with our papers
And stealthily slide them beneath our front door,
I grab the *American*, knowing that there I can
Find O. O. McIntyre's column of lore.
You ask what it's like? I've no copy right here,
But p'rhaps I can give you some sort of idear.

Diary of a Modern New Yorker: Up and out five hours before dawn, and by scooter to the Hermitage Hotel, where the big Seminole Indian chef, Gwladys, cooked me a flagon of my favorite breakfast dish, beet root and wrestlers' knees. Hallooed to Lily Langtry and we fell to arguing over the origin of the word "breakfast," she contending that it was a combination of "break" and "fast," derived from a horse's instructions to a starter in a six-furlong race, and I maintaining that it was five furlongs. We decided to leave it to Percy Hammond, the philatelist, but his nurse told us he was out shoplifting.

Home for a moment to slit my mail and found invitations from Mussolini, Joan Blondell, Joan Crawford, Joan of Arc, President Buchanan, Joe Walcott, and Louisa M. Alcott. Then answered a pleasant long-distance call from Gwladys, the little French chef in the Café des Trois Outfielders in Sydney, her voice as plain as if she were in Melbourne. She had heard I had a cold, she said, and was worried. It was gratifying to hear her whimpers of relief when I assured her the crisis was past.

Breaking bread in the evening at the office of J. P. Morgan & Company and sat between Bernie Shaw, H. J. Wells, Charlie Dickens, Lizzie Barrett, Will Thackeray, Lottie Brontë, Paul Whiteman, and Bill Klem. Chatted for a moment after dinner with *Who's Who* and, finding a heavy rainstorm outside, dismissed my driver, Gwladys, and pirouetted to the lower West Side, where I sat on the New York

Central tracks till dawn, watching the operations of a switch engine. I have always been a sucker for a New York Central switch engine in a heavy rainstorm.

Thingumabobs: I once motored around Vienna for two weeks thinking it was Vienna. When I chided the native jehu, Gwladys, he chirped: "Why, Massa, Ah done thought you knowed it was Vienna all de time." . . . If they did not wear identical hats, Jack Dempsey and Connie Bennett could easily pass for sisters. . . . Ellsworth Vines, the golf pro, is a dead ringer for Frank Crowninshield. . . . One-word description of Franklin Delano Roosevelt—President. . . . Otto Kahn always wears a union suit at first nights. . . . There is something about the name Babe Ruth that suggests rare old Dresden filigree work. . . . Mayor O'Brien is the image of Joan Crawford. . . . One of my favorite people—Senator Long. . . . Tallulah Bankhead and Jimmy Durante have profiles exactly alike. . . . Few ladies with as little money can act as grampous as Bernie Baruch. . . . Two of my favorite people—Senator Long.

Thoughts While Strolling: Damon Runyon's feet. Kate Smith, a small-town girl who became nation-wide in a big city. Rosamond Pinchot and Theodore Dreiser could pass for twins. How did I get to thinking about "The Song of the Shirt"? Oh, yes; it started at tea when Fannie Hurst brought up Arthur Brisbane's quaint method of writing. His syndicated column averages close to 130,000 words a day, yet he writes it all in longhand on his shirt bosom, then forgets it and sends his shirt to the laundry. Damon Runyon's feet.

Mention of the name Rex Cole invariably reminds me of the Mother Goose rhyme, "Old King Cole," etc., and I never can figure out why. The surnames of two successful *Saturday Evening Post* writers, Samuel Blythe and Charles Francis Coe, begin with the second and third letters of the alphabet. Damon Runyon's feet. Personal nomination for the most thrilling of the summer's detective yarns—"Dracula." If you saw only the left side of Theodore Dreiser's face, you would swear it was the right side of Ruth Etting's. Rube Goldberg, cover-designer for *Spalding's Base Ball Guide,* never wears a hat to bed. Damon Runyon's feet. One-word description of the Vice-President—Garner.

Insomniacs: While writing a novel "Red" (Socker) Lewis never eats anything but alphabet soup. . . . Irvin S. Cobb cannot eat before, during, or after 5 A.M. .... Theodore Dreiser always dresses according to the time of day he happens to be writing about. Thus, if an incident in one of his novels takes place in the morning, he puts on a morning coat; if at noon, a noon coat, etc. .... There is a striking resemblance between Damon Runyon's feet and Ethel Merman. ... Theodore Dreiser often arises at 2 A.M. and walks for two hours steadily. I once knew a fellow in Gallipolis who often arose at 6 P.M., and at 2 A.M. walked for two hours unsteadily. No dog as cunning as the Cubanola Glide.

Frank Sullivan

A GARLAND OF IBIDS

I have just finished reading a book [1] which struck me as being one of the finest books I have read since I read "The Flowering of New England," by the same author. [2] But there is a fly in the ointment. I have been rendered cockeyed by the footnotes. There seem to be too many of them, even for a book largely about Boston. [3] I do not know why the author had to have so many footnotes. Maybe he had a reason for each one, but I suspect the footnote habit has crept up on him, for I got out his book on Emerson, [4] published in 1932, and he used practically no footnotes in it.

You read along in "New England: Indian Summer," interested to the hilt in what Van Wyck Brooks is telling you about Longfellow, [5]

---

[1] "New England: Indian Summer."

[2] Van Wyck Brooks, author of "New England: Indian Summer," "The Flowering of New England," "The Life of Emerson," "The Ordeal of Mark Twain," and other books.

[3] Sometimes referred to as The Hub. Capital and chief city of Massachusetts. Scene of the Boston Tea Party and the arrest of Henry L. Mencken. Bostonians are traditionally noted for their civic pride, or, as an envious New York critic once termed it, their parochial outlook. It is related that on an occasion when Saltonstall Boylston learned that his friend L. Cabot Lowell was leaving for a trip around the world, he inquired of Lowell, "Which route shall you take, L.C.?" "Oh, I shall go by way of Dedham, of course," replied Mr. Lowell. On another occasion, the old Back Bay aristocrat Ralph Waldo Mulcahy said to Oliver Wendell Rooney, "By the way, Rooney, did your ancestors come over on the Mayflower?" "Oh, no," replied Mr. Rooney. "They arrived on the next boat. They sent the servants over on the Mayflower."

[4] Ralph Waldo Emerson, Sage of Concord and famous transcendentalist philosopher, not to be confused with Ralph McAllister Ingersoll, editor of PM.

[5] Henry Wadsworth Longfellow, Good Gray Poet. Longfellow was no footnote addict. He preferred foot*prints*. Cf. his "Psalm of Life":

> And, departing, leave behind us
> Footprints on the sands of time.

Thoreau,[6] Phillips,[7] James,[8] Alcott,[9] Lowell,[10] Adams,[11] and other great figures of the Periclean Age of The Hub,[12] when suddenly there is a footnote.

[6] Henry David Thoreau, philosopher who lived at Walden Pond for two years on carrots, twigs, nuts, minnows, creek water, and, as Margaret Fuller suspected (booming it out at Brook Farm in that full, rich voice of hers, to the dismay of William Ellery Channing, Henry Wadsworth Longfellow, Edward Everett Hale, John Lothrop Motley, Charles Eliot Norton, and William Lloyd Garrison), sirloin steaks and creamery butter smuggled to him by Emerson. Suffering as he did from a vitamin deficiency, the result of too much moss in his diet, Thoreau became somewhat of a misanthrope and would often creep up behind members of the Saturday Club and shout "Boo!," or, as some authorities maintain, "Pooh!" The matter is not clarified very much, one must admit, by a letter Mrs. Harriet Beecher Stowe wrote to her son, Harriet Beecher Stowe, Jr. (not to be confused with Herbert Bayard Swope), on June 7, 1854, in which she states: "Not much to write home about, as the saying goes. Dave Thoreau here for supper last nite [sic.] He got into an argument with John Greenleaf Whittier, the Good Gray Poet, as to whether snow is really ermine too dear for an earl, and Greenleaf called him a Communist. Dave then crept up behind Greenleaf and shouted either 'Boo!' [sic] or 'Pooh!' [sic], I couldn't make out wich [sic]. All well here except F. Marion Crawford, Sarah Orne Jewett, Charles Dudley Warner, Thomas Wentworth Higginson, and William Dean Howells, who complain of feeling sic [sic]. Your aff. mother, H. B. Stowe, Sr."

[7] Wendell Phillips. He was about the only Bostonian of his time who wore no middle name and he was therefore considered half naked. Even Mark Twain, when he went to visit Howells in Boston, registered as Samuel Langhorne Clemens.

[8] Probably not Jesse James. Probably is either William James, deviser of Pragmatic Sanctions, or his brother Henry, the novelist. It was about this time that Henry James was going through his transition period, and could not make up his mind whether he was in England living in America or in America living in England.

[9] Amos Bronson Alcott, educator and bad provider. The Mr. Micawber of his day. Not to be confused with Novelist Bus Bronson of Yale or Mrs. Chauncey Olcott.

[10] James Russell Lowell, poet, essayist, and kinfolk of late rotund, cigar-smoking Back Bay Poetess Amy Lowell, no rhymester she.

[11] Henry Adams, author of "The Education of Henry Adams," by Henry Adams. Not to be confused with Henry Adams, Samuel Adams, John Adams, John Quincy Adams, Abigail Adams, Charles Edward Adams (not to be confused with Charles Francis Adams, Charles Henry Adams, or Henry Adams), Maude Adams, Franklin Pierce Adams, Samuel Hopkins Adams, Bristow Adams, George Matthew Adams, James Truslow Adams, Adams Express, Adams & Flanagan, Horace Flanagan, or Louis Adamic.

[12] Sometimes referred to as Boston. One is reminded of the famous quatrain:

Here's to the City of Boston,
The home of Filene and the Card.,
Where the Rileys speak only to Cabots
And the Cabots speak only to God!

The text is in fine, clear type. The footnotes are in small type. So it is quite a chore to keep focussing up and down the page, especially if you have old eyes or a touch of astigmatism.[13] By and by you say to yourself, "I be damn if I look down at any more footnotes!," but you do, because the book is so interesting you don't want to miss even the footnotes.[14]

When you get to the footnote at the bottom of the page, like as not all you find is *ibid*. *Ibid* is a great favorite of footnote-mad authors.[15] It was a great favorite with Gibbon.[16] How come writers of fiction do not need footnotes? Take Edna Ferber.[17] She doesn't use footnotes. Suppose Edna Herford [18] took to writing her novels in this manner:

[13] In this connection, it is interesting to note that Louisa May Alcott had a touch of astigmatism, if we are to accept the word of Charles Eliot Norton. Edward Everett Hale states in his Letters, Vol. XV, Ch. 8, pp. 297 *et seq.*, that William Cullen Bryant told Oliver Wendell Holmes that on one occasion when the fun was running high at Thomas Wentworth Higginson's home and all barriers were down, Thomas Bailey Aldrich had put the question bluntly to Charles Eliot Norton, saying, "Now listen, has Louisa May Alcott got astigmatism or hasn't she?" Charles Eliot Norton answered, perhaps unwisely, "Yes." Cf. the famous dictum of General William Tecumseh Sherman, sometimes erroneously ascribed to General Ulysses Simpson Grant: "Never bring up a lady's name in the mess."

[14] Ah there, Van Wyck!

[15] So is cf.

[16] Edward Gibbon, English historian, not to be confused with Cedric Gibbons, Hollywood art director. Edward Gibbon was a great hand for footnotes, especially if they gave him a chance to show off his Latin. He would come sniffing up to a nice, spicy morsel of scandal about the Romans and then, just as the reader expected him to dish the dirt, he'd go into his Latin routine, somewhat as follows: "In those days vice reached depths not plumbed since the reign of Caligula and it was an open secret that the notorious Empress Theodoro *in tres partes divisa erat* and that she was also addicted to the *argumentum ad hominem!*" Gibbon, prissy little fat man that he was, did that just to tease readers who had flunked Caesar.

[17] Edna Cabot Ferber, contemporary New England novelist. It is related of Edna Ferber that she once met Oliver Herford in Gramercy Park and recoiled at the sight of an extremely loud necktie he was wearing. "Heavens above, Oliver Herford!" exclaimed Miss Ferber, never one not to speak her mind. "That is a terrible cravat. Why do you wear it?" "Because it is my wife's whim that I wear it," explained Oliver Herford. "Well, land sakes alive, before I'd wear a tie like that just on account of a wife's whim!" jeered Miss Ferber. "You don't know my wife," said Oliver Herford. "She's got a whim of iron." Miss Ferber later made this incident the basis for the dramatic battle between the husband and wife in her novel "The Cravat."

[18] No, no, no, not Edna Herford! Edna *Ferber!* Edna Herford is the fellow who had the wife with the iron whim.

"Cicely Ticklepaw * sat at her dressing table in a brown study. She had 'a very strange feeling she'd ne'er felt before, a kind of a grind of depression.' † Could it be love? ‡ If so, why had she sent him § away? She sighed, and a soft cry of 'Aye me!' ‖ escaped her. Seizing a nail file desperately, she commenced hacking away at her fingernails, when a voice behind her said, 'O! that I were a glove upon that hand, that I might touch that cheek!' $ Cicely reddened, turned. It was Cleon Bel Murphy! Softly, she told him, 'What man art thou, that, thus bescreen'd in night, so stumblest on my counsel?' " &

What would Van Wyck Brooks say if Edna Ferber wrote like that? ¹⁹ Yes. Exactly. Now, where were we? ²⁰ No, I was not. I know what I was saying. You keep out of this. You're a footnote.²¹ Yeah? Well, just for that, no more footnotes. Out you go! ²² I am, that's who.²³ See what I mean, Van Wyck? Give a footnote an inch and it'll take a foot.²⁴ I give up. They got me. And they'll get you too in the end, Van Wyck. You may think you're strong enough to keep 'em under control; you may think you can take a footnote or leave it. All I say is, remember Dr. Jekyll! Lay off 'em, Van. I'm telling you for your own good.

—Uneasy Brooks Fan ²⁵

* Blonde, lovely, and twenty-one.
† See "I'm Falling in Love with Someone"—Victor Herbert.
‡ Sure.
§ Cleon Bel Murphy, the man she loves.
‖ "Romeo and Juliet," Act. II, Scene 2.
$ Ibid.
& Ibid.
¹⁹ And what would Edna Ferber say if Edna Ferber wrote like that?
²⁰ You were saying Louisa May Alcott had astigmatism.
²¹ Yeah? And how far would you have got in this article without footnotes?
²² Who's gonna put me out?
²³ Yeah? You and who else?
²⁴ Yoo-hoo! Footnote!
²⁵ Frank Saltonstall Sullivan.

Donald Ogden Stewart

THE WHISKY REBELLION

(*In the Bedtime Story Manner of Thornton W. Burgess*)

"Just the *day* for a Whisky Rebellion," said Aunt Polly and off she ran, lipperty-lipperty-lip, to get a few shooting rifles.

"Oh goody goody," cried little Emily. "Now we can all shoot at those horrid Revenue Officers," for the collectors of internal revenue were far from popular with these kindly Pennsylvania folk and Aunt Polly Pinkwood had often promised the children that if they were good some day they would be allowed to take a shot at a Revenue Officer.

Soon she returned, bearing in her arms a number of bright shiny new guns. The children crowded around in glee and soon all were supplied with weapons except little Frank who of course was too young to use a gun and was given a two-gallon jug of nice, old whisky to carry. Jed hitched up old Taylor, the faithful farm horse, and as quick as you could say Jack Robinson the little ones had piled into the old carryall. Round Mr. Sun was just peeping over the Purple Hills when the merry little party started on its way, singing and laughing at the prospect of the day's sport.

"I bet I kill five Revenue Officers," said little Edgar.

"Ha Ha Ha—you boaster, you," laughed Aunt Polly. "You will be lucky if you kill two, for I fear they will be hard to find today."

"Oh do you think so, Aunt Polly?" said little Elinor and she began to cry, for Elinor dearly loved to shoot.

"Hush dear," said Miss Pinkwood with a kindly pat, for she loved her little charges and it hurt her to see them unhappy. "I was only joking. And now children I will tell you a story."

"Oh goody goody," cried they all. "Tell us a true story."

"All right," said Aunt Polly. "I shall tell you a true story," and she began.

"Once there was a brave handsome man—"

"Mr. Welsbach," cried the children with one voice, for it was well known in the neighborhood that Aunt Polly had long been sweet on

267

Julius Welsbach, the popular superintendent of the Sabbath School and the best whisky maker for miles around.

"Hush children," said Aunt Polly blushing in vexation. "Of course not. And if you interrupt me I shall not tell my story at all." But she was not really angry.

"And one day this brave handsome man was out making whisky and he had just sampled some when he looked up and what do you suppose he saw?"

"Snakes," cried little Elmer whose father had often had delirium tremens, greatly to the delight of his children.

"No, Elmer," said Miss Pinkwood, "not snakes."

"Pink lizards," cried little Esther, Elmer's sister.

"No," said Aunt Polly, with a hearty laugh, "he saw a—stranger. And what do you suppose the stranger had?"

"A snoot full," chorused the Schultz twins. "He was pie-eyed."

"No," replied Miss Pinkwood laughing merrily. "It was before noon. Guess again children. What did the stranger have?"

"Blind staggers," suggested little Faith whose mother had recently been adjudged insane.

"Come children," replied Aunt Polly. "You are not very wide awake this morning. The stranger had a gun. And when the brave handsome man offered the stranger a drink what do you suppose the stranger said?"

"I know," cried little Prudence eagerly. "He said, 'Why yes I don't care if I do.' That's what they all say."

"No, Prudence," replied Miss Pinkwood. "The stranger refused a drink."

"Oh come now, Aunt Polly," chorused the boys and girls. "You said you were going to tell us a true story." And their little faces fell.

"Children," said Miss Polly, "the stranger refused the drink because he was a Revenue Officer. And he pointed his gun at the brave handsome man and said he would have to go to jail because he had not paid the tax on his whisky. And the brave handsome man would have had to have gone to jail, too; but fortunately his brother came up just at the right time and—"

"Shot the Revenuer dead," cried the children in glee.

"Yes children," said Miss Polly. "He shot the Revenue Officer dead."

"Oh goody goody," cried all. "Now tell us another story. Tell us about the time your father killed a Revenue Officer with an ax."

"Oh you don't want to hear that again, do you children?" said Aunt Polly.

"Oh yes—yes—please," they cried, and Aunt Polly was just going to begin when Jed the driver stopped his horses and said:

"This hilltop is as good a place to shoot from as I know of, Miss Pinkwood. You can see both roads, and nobody can see you."

"Thank you, Jed," said Aunt Polly giving him a kindly smile, and without more ado the children clambered out of the carryall and filled their guns with powder and bullets.

"I get first shot," proudly announced Robert, the oldest boy, and somewhat of a bully.

"Robert!" said Aunt Polly severely, and she looked almost ready to cry, for Aunt Polly had tried hard to teach the boys to be true knights of chivalry and it hurt her to have Robert wish to shoot a Revenue Officer before the girls had had a chance. Robert had not meant to hurt Aunt Polly's feelings but had only been thoughtless, and soon all was sunshine again as little Ellen the youngest made ready to fire the first shot.

The children waited patiently and soon they were rewarded by the sight of a Revenue Officer riding on horseback in the distant valley, as pretty a target as one could wish.

"Now do be careful, dear," whispered Miss Pinkwood, "for if you miss, he may take alarm and be off." But little Ellen did not miss. "Bang" went her gun and the little Merry Breezes echoed back and forth, "She got him. She got him," and old Mother West Wind smiled down at the happy sport. Sure enough, when old Mr. Smoke had cleared away there was a nice dead Revenue Officer lying in the road. "Well done, Ellen," said Miss Pinkwood, patting her little charge affectionately which caused the happy girl to coo with childish delight.

Mary had next shot and soon all were popping away in great glee. All the merry wood folk gathered near to watch the children at their sport. There was Johnny Chuck and Reddy Fox and Jimmy Skunk and Bobby Coon and oh everybody.

Soon round Mr. Sun was high in the Blue Sky and the children began to tire somewhat of their sport. "I'm as hungry as a bear," said little Dick. "I'm as hungry as two bears," said Emily. "Ha Ha

Ha," laughed Miss Pinkwood, "I know what will fix that," and soon she had spread out a delicious repast.

"Now children," said Miss Pinkwood when all had washed their faces and hands, "while you were busy washing I prepared a surprise for you," and from a large jug, before their delighted gaze, she poured out—what do you think? "Bronxes," cried little Harriet. "Oh goody goody." And sure enough Aunt Polly had prepared a jug of delicious Bronx cocktails which all pronounced excellent.

And after that there were sandwiches and olives and pie and good three year old whisky, too.

"That's awfully smooth rye, Aunt Polly," said little Prudence smacking her two red lips. "I think I'll have another shot."

"No dear," said Miss Pinkwood, pleased by the compliment, but firm withal. "Not now. Perhaps on the way home, if there is any left," for Aunt Polly knew that too much alcohol in the middle of the day is bad for growing children, and she had seen many a promising child spoiled by over-indulgent parents.

After lunch those children who could stand helped Aunt Polly to clear away the dishes and then all went sound asleep, as is the custom in Pennsylvania.

When they awoke round Mr. Sun was just sinking behind the Purple Hills and so, after taking a few more scattered shots at Revenue Officers, they piled once more into the carryall and drove back to town. And as they passed Mrs. Oliphant's house (Aunt Polly's sister) Aunt Flo Oliphant came out on the porch and waved her handkerchief at the merry party.

"Let's give her a cheer," said Fred.

"Agreed," cried they all, and so twelve little throats united in three lusty "huzzahs" which made Auntie Flo very happy you may be sure.

And as they drove up before the Pinkwoods' modest home twelve tired but happy children with one accord voted the Whisky Rebellion capital fun and Aunt Polly a brick.

E. B. White

DUSK IN FIERCE PAJAMAS

Ravaged by pink eye, I lay for a week scarce caring whether I lived or died. Only Wamba, my toothless old black nurse, bothered to bring me food and quinine. Then one day my strength began to return, and with it came Wamba to my bedside with a copy of *Harper's Bazaar* and a copy of *Vogue*. "Ah brought you couple magazines," she said proudly, her red gums clashing.

In the days that followed (happy days of renewed vigor and re-awakened interest), I studied the magazines and lived, in their pages, the gracious lives of the characters in the ever-moving drama of society and fashion. In them I found surcease from the world's ugliness, from disarray, from all unattractive things. Through them I escaped into a world in which there was no awkwardness of gesture, no unsuitability of line, no people of no importance. It was an enriching experience. I realize now that my own life is by contrast an unlovely thing, with its disease, its banalities, its uncertainties, its toil, its single-breasted suits, and its wine from lesser years. I am aware of a life all around me of graciousness and beauty, in which every moment is a tiny pearl of good taste, and in which every acquaintance has the common decency to possess a good background.

Lying here in these fierce pajamas, I dream of the *Harper's Bazaar* world, the *Vogue* life; dream of being a part of it. In fancy I am in Mrs. Cecil Baker's pine-panelled drawing-room. It is dusk. (It is almost always dusk in the fashion magazines.) I have on a Gantner & Mattern knit jersey bathing suit with a flat-striped bow and an all-white buck shoe with a floppy tongue. No, that's wrong. I am in chiffon, for it is the magic hour after bridge. Suddenly a Chippendale mahogany hors-d'œuvre table is brought in. In its original old blue-and-white Spode compartments there sparkle olives, celery, hard-boiled eggs, radishes—evidently put there by somebody in the employ of Mrs. Baker. Or perhaps my fancy wanders away from the

271

drawing-room: I am in Mrs. Baker's dining-room, mingling unostentatiously with the other guests, my elbows resting lightly on the dark polished oak of the Jacobean table, my fingers twiddling with the early Georgian silver. Or perhaps I am not at Mrs. Baker's oak table in chiffon at all—perhaps instead I am at Mrs. Jay Gould's teakwood table in a hand-knitted Anny Blatt ensemble in diluted tri-colors and an off-the-face hat.

It is dusk. I am dining with Rose Hobart at the Waldorf. We have lifted our champagne glasses. "To sentiment!" I say. And the haunting dusk is shattered by the clean glint of jewels by Cartier.

It is dusk. I am seated on a Bruce Buttfield pouf, for it is dusk.

Ah, magazine dreams! How dear to me now are the four evenings in the life of Mrs. Allan Ryan, Junior. I have studied them one by one, and I feel that I know them. They are perfect little crystals of being—static, precious. There is the evening when she stands, motionless, in a magnificent sable cape, her left arm hanging gracefully at her side. She is ready to go out to dinner. What will this, her first of four evenings, bring of romance, or even of food? Then there is the evening when she just sits on the edge of a settee from the Modernage Galleries, the hard bright gleam of gold lamé topping a slim, straight, almost Empire skirt. I see her there (the smoke from a cigarette rising), sitting, sitting, waiting. Or the third evening—the evening with books. Mrs. Ryan is in chiffon; the books are in morocco. Or the fourth evening, standing with her dachshund, herself in profile, the dog in full face.

So I live the lives of other people in my fancy: the life of the daughter of Lord Curzon of Kedleston, who has been visiting the Harold Talbotts on Long Island. All I know of her is that she appeared one night at dinner, her beauty set off by the lustre of artificial satin and the watery fire of aquamarine. It is all I know, yet it is enough; for it is her one perfect moment in time and space, and I know about it, and it is mine.

It is dusk. I am with Owen Johnson over his chafing dish. It is dusk. I am with Prince Matchabelli over his vodka. Or I am with the Countess de Forceville over her bridge tables. She and I have just pushed the tables against the wall and taken a big bite of gaspacho. Or I am with the Marquis de Polignac over his Pommery.

How barren my actual life seems, when fancy fails me, here with Wamba over my quinine. Why am I not to be found at dusk, slicing black bread very thin, as William Powell does, to toast it and sprinkle it with salt? Why does not twilight find me (as it finds Mrs. Chester Burden) covering a table with salmon-pink linens on which I place only white objects, even to a white salt shaker? Why don't I learn to simplify my entertaining, like the young pinch-penny in *Vogue,* who has all his friends in before the theatre and simply gives them champagne cocktails, caviar, and one hot dish, then takes them to the show? Why do I never give parties after the opera, as Mr. Paul Cravath does, at which I have the prettiest women in New York? Come to think of it, why don't the prettiest women in New York ever come down to my place, other than that pretty little Mrs. Fazaenzi, whom Wamba won't let in? Why haven't I a butler named Fish, who makes a cocktail of three parts gin to one part lime juice, honey, vermouth, and apricot brandy in equal portions—a cocktail so delicious that people like Mrs. Harrison Williams and Mrs. Goodhue Livingston seek him out to get the formula? And if I *did* have a butler named Fish, wouldn't I kid the pants off him?

All over the world it is dusk! It is dusk at Armando's on East Fifty-fifth Street. Armando has taken up his accordion; he is dreaming over the keys. A girl comes in, attracted by the accordion, which she mistakes for Cecil Beaton's camera. She is in stiff green satin, and over it she wears a silver fox cape which she can pull around her shoulders later in the evening if she gets feeling like pulling a cape around her shoulders. It is dusk on the Harold Castles' ranch in Hawaii. I have risen early to shoot a goat, which is the smart thing to do in Hawaii. And now I am walking silently through hedges of gardenias, past the flaming ginger flowers, for I have just shot a goat. I have on nothing but red sandals and a Martex bath towel. It is dusk in the Laurentians. I am in ski togs. I feel warm and safe, knowing that the most dangerous pitfall for skiers is *color,* knowing that although a touch of brilliance against the snow is effective, too much of it is the sure sign of the amateur. It is the magic hour before cocktails. I am in the modern penthouse of Monsieur Charles de Beistegui. The staircase is entirely of cement, spreading at the hemline and trimmed with padded satin tubing caught at the neck with a bar of milk chocolate. It is dusk in Chicago. I am standing beside Mrs. Howard Linn, formerly Consuelo Vanderbilt, formerly Sophie M. Gay, formerly Ellen Glendinning, formerly Saks-Fifth Avenue. It is dusk! A pheasant has Julian Street down and is pouring a

magnificent old red Burgundy down his neck. Dreams, I'm afraid.
It is really dusk in my own apartment. I am down on my knees in
front of an airbound radiator, trying to fix it by sticking pins in the
vent. Dusk in these fierce pajamas. Kneeling here, I can't help wondering where Nancy Yuille is, in her blue wool pants and reefer
and her bright red mittens. For it is dusk. I said *dusk*, Wamba!
Bring the quinine!

Franklin P. Adams

THE DIARY OF OUR OWN SAMUEL PEPYS *

Friday, November 30, 1923

Up, and by subway to my office, and I spied in the subway the most lovely lady ever I saw in my life, and she was carrying a rose, which I looked at, and just before I made to get off the car she gave it to me, and I wore it in my buttonhole, but at the office I took it off and put it into a drawer. And I deemed it as pleasant and warming a thing as ever had happened to me. So to do my stint, and thence to Gerald Brooks, for some frivolity.

Monday, December 31, 1923

So to see "The Song and Dance Man," and found most of it amusing, but nothing so much as the song and dance Mr. Cohan performed between acts, about My Maggie May, or some such trumpery. So home and had a bath and did on my black suit, and so to Ruth Hale's, where a great crowd was gathered, and Miss Edna Ferber said I looked as though I had just been confirmed. I am a confirmed admirer of you, quoth I, which was a quick and chivalrous thing to say, true though it was. So all the evening in songs and merrymaking, and as happy an eve of a New Year as ever I had. So ends the year, in which I have had the joyousest content of any year, and the lowest times, too. Cast up my accounts, and am the solventest ever I have been, all of which gives me the highest hope for the New Year ever I had. So end two years under my present employer, and so pleasant they were never would I work anywhere else, and so dreamed of a headline in 1974, World Man, Ninety-Two, Dies at Desk as Year Begins.

* *Selections from the weekly chronicles of New York City and of his own life which Franklin P. Adams has been writing for various newspapers since 1911.*

Monday, February 25, 1924

Early up and to my office, and read how M. Alonso beat Will Tilden yesterday at indoor tennis, and read some matters about the taxes, but I have the feeling that the taxes are built on such political foundations, and more destined to placate voters than to be equable. To Beatrice Kaufman's for dinner, and she asked me questions about H. Ross's tobogganing, the noise of it having been bruited about for a radius of thirty miles. And did he look funny tobogganing? she asked. Well, quoth I, you know how he looks *not* tobogganing, which seems to answer her.

Monday, May 5, 1924

To the office, and pretty hard at work all day, and thence to Neysa's, and met Mary Brandon, who told me how she had made Rob Sherwood laugh by telling him she thought the Riviera was a street in Paris, and he said You do not really think so, do you? And she said, No, I know it is a big store. Whereat Neysa laughed sympathetically, for it is not so long ago that she took ship for Antwerp and felt deeply aggrieved to learn on arrival that it was not in Italy. So to Kate Spaeth's for dinner and thence to see "Peg o' My Dreams," and save for a pair of gracile girl dancers, and one remark of Mr. Huntley's, when, upon somebody saying he had not visited the Aquarium, said, Well, what do you *do* all day?, I found it a *dull* piece.

Thursday, May 8, 1924

At my desk all the morning, merrily enough, and thence to A. Bachrach's, who gave me a fine yellow tye, and had me help him solve a cross-word puzzle, and so home by omnibuss, on the roof of one and in the rain, and there was a lady behind me who called "George!" to somebody on the Avenue, and he mounted the stage and sate beside her, and she said, "Of all things!" And when the conductor came for the fare, she said to him, "Think of meeting your husband like that," as who should say, "Don't get the idea that I am roguish." So home, and D. Taylor and Ethel Kelley to dinner, and she told me a limerick Brian Hooker told her:

> There was an old fellow named Sidney
> Who drank till he ruined a kidney.
> It shriveled and shrank
> As he sat there and drank
> But he had a good time of it, didney?

Sunday, March 22, 1925

So to catch up H. Harrison and Dorothy Parker, and we were for driving Miss Edna Ferber with us, but she ill in bed, but not so ill that she did not look lovely, with, quoth Dorothy, the pink maribou flowing like water. Thence to the country, and I and all to lunch at an inn, very gay and merry, and thence to the city again, and to Mistress Ruth Fleischmann's to dinner, and very late to bed.

Monday, March 23, 1925

Read this morning a highly amusing story by Anita Loos, in Harper's Bazaar, called "Gentlemen Prefer Blondes," and I had no notion Miss Loos had so much writing humour and insight, and I hope she will write other stories. And I read a fine story of R. Lardner's, too, in Liberty, called "Haircut." Mr. Ramsay MacDonald is concerned over the state of society, and asks whither it is going, but I doubt that things are in a bad way. Ignorance and bigotry and greed are with us, but they do grow a little less every few centuries. In the evening to see "The Little Minister," and I thought it a tenuous play and tedious, and Miss Chatterton acted with a charm that seemed to me unspontaneous and synthetick. But even in 1898, when I took my grandmother to see that play, I did not care for it, and the part I enjoyed the most was being let go to the theatre in the evening.

Saturday, March 28, 1925

Very betimes up, and read in a copy of Lord Byron's Poems, and was struck with how tedious the long ones were; and I wondered, if some of the long poems that Keats and Shelley and Tennyson and Byron used to write were printed to-day, would anybody read them? I doubt that anybody reads them to-day, for that matter. Read in the publick prints that the income taxes for the State are to be smaller, which pleased me, but I do find any taxpaying very irksome, having to work so hard for the money I earn. For when I am writing I feel that there is no sum of money great enough to pay me for the travail I go through, yet when I do get my weekly pay, I do feel that nobody, let alone myself, could write so well or so amusingly or so profoundly as to merit such a huge guerdon. I always have felt so, regardless of the worth of my writings or the size of the reward for them. News from Albany that the school teachers are to have an increase in their pay, which I am glad to hear, for teaching seemeth to me the hardest work there is, and the most thankless. So to see Mistress Neysa for a little, and played my piece on the pianoforte, "Sleep, Baby, Sleep," but R. Ives said I played it so loud that it would wake up the inmates of a maternity home a mile off, which was not true. So to Miss Ruth Hale's, and caught up H. Broun; and with him to a picture show, and he bought a picture of Arthur Dove's, with no title, and it seemed to me it might be called "Now is the Time to Paint That Barn: Order by Number," the picture being some samples of various colors of paint. But B. thought it had great beauty, but all the others could say was that it was very interesting, which is a great thing to say about any work of art or any persons nowadays. For there is no argument against that, for the describer, if pressed, will say that it is interesting because of its dulness, or its lack of interest. All of which is too complex for me.

Thursday, April 23, 1925

Very betimes up, and read of the fight that is raging between the Governor and the Mayor, and whether this means that Mr. Hylan will not be elected Mayor again I can not tell, but those who are deep in the city's politicks say so. A fine, warm day, but I at my stint all the day, and so uptown and met Nell Wylie the poet, and said, "Guess whose birthday this is," and she said "Yours?" and I said, "No, but you are getting warm." "Shakespeare's" she said. Which was the prettiest compliment I had had all day. So to Miss E. Root's, and she played me all the score of "Princess Ida," as melodick and full of sweetness as anything Sullivan ever wrote, and I vowed to hear the opera as soon as I might. So took Will Benét home with me, and early to bed.

Wolcott Gibbs

SHAKESPEARE, HERE'S YOUR HAT

(A New Play by Mr. William Saroyan, in Book Form, with the Customary Prefatory Notes by the Author)

I

This play is a masterpiece. It is young, gusty, comical, tragic, beautiful, heroic, and as real as a slaughterhouse or some dame fixing her hair. It could only have been written in America, by an Armenian boy who is an artist and a lover and a dreamer. All at once. All mixed up. It could only have been written by Saroyan.

Other people write plays, but they are no good. I go to them and I sit there and think, "My God, this is lousy! It was written by a man in an English suit of clothes who makes fifty thousand dollars a year, but it is not alive. It is dead. It stinks." A man making fifty thousand dollars a year doesn't write about Life; he writes about other people who make fifty thousand dollars a year; he writes about a bunch of rich corpses and, generally speaking, he is a rich corpse himself. Not me, though. Not Saroyan. This play is lyric and simple and alive. It says just exactly what it means. When the boy in this play dynamites his grandmother because he needs some money to get gin, that is something real. When he puts a nickel in the piano for music, that is real, too. When he meets the society girl and says "How's chances, sister?" and she answers "O.K., Mac," that is a real, lovely, and heartbreaking thing.

In the plays about the rich corpses, it takes three acts and about sixty thousand dollars' worth of scenery to get around to a beautiful and natural request like that, and half the time nothing comes of it, either.

II

I am a warm, rich, and passionate human being and very few things are too much for me. Not even dramatic criticism. When a man writes in a newspaper or a magazine that he doesn't understand this play

279

or is bored by it, that is all right with me. It is hard to imagine anybody not liking something that is as eloquent and native and true as a child running after a butterfly or a colored man scratching himself, but I do not get sore. I am just sorry for the crazy bastard.

III

The following are excerpts from some of the reviews published in the New York press:

RICHARD WATTS, JR., *Herald Tribune:* It is a darling play . . . but we must not ignore the Chinese.

BROOKS ATKINSON, *Times:* Lit with the same ineluctable fire that once informed the witches and the cauldron on the heath.

JOHN MASON BROWN, *Post:* Challenges the best of Aristophanes, Gogol, Pirandello, Racine, and the Song of Solomon.

SIDNEY B. WHIPPLE, *World-Telegram:* Either Saroyan is crazy . . . or I am. A child has done this horrid thing.

IV

This play was written in an hour and a half with a quill pen I generally keep in a little bowl of bird shot. For a man like me, an original, talented, profound, sensitive, and humorous Armenian, a typewriter is an artificial barrier standing between the living brain and the clean paper. It is not for me, as the airbrush was not for Michelangelo and the adding machine was not for Euclid.

At that time I was working in Hollywood, where all authors use typewriters. "The greatest play in the world is right there on those keys, if you can only figure out how to hit them in the right order," one of them said to me. He was a man who made forty, fifty, a hundred thousand dollars a year, and he went around with a falcon on his wrist. I would rather use the quill pen. Me, personally.

V

Generally speaking, the American theatre is the aspirin of the middle classes. People go to a play because they want to get in out of the rain. Or because they have a date with some rabbit in it later on. Or just because they happen to know the press agent and don't have to pay. It is not that way with me. I go because I love Life.

That is an important statement and I want to repeat it: *William
Saroyan loves Life.*

In the theatre today, except in this play of mine, what you see is
not Life. It is a drawing-room compromise with Life arrived at by
a man who has never had to sleep in a silo or eat birch bark or trap
mice to make himself a hat or any of the other brave, haunting,
and sometimes foolish things people do when they don't happen
to have been born on Park Avenue or in Newport, Rhode Island.

The cure for the American theatre is more plays like this one.
More plays by Saroyan.

THE TIME OF <u>WHOSE</u> LIFE?

(*A dormitory at Groton, just before vespers. Three of the boys—
Jones Minor, Ferris Major, and Tilden Elliott III—are changing from
their rugger togs into their vespers togs. They are breathless and
wondering, enchanted with a sweet world that also holds things like
ginger beer and scones and "Esquire" magazine. Ferguson Nicholson,
the housemaster, a tall, thin man, noble because of the pain in his
heart, is sitting in one corner, reading "Variety" and drinking a dry
Martini. In another corner an old graduate, mad and very dirty, is
throwing cards into a hat. A scrubwoman comes in. A lifetime of toil,
including six years with the Shuberts, has not quenched her brimming
and precious spirit.*)

SCRUBWOMAN (*compassionate, supernatural; the Earth Mother*):
How about sweeping up around here, gents? Get some of the fug
out of the joint.

JONES MINOR: Sweep. You won't sweep the torture and despair of
Life from the heart with a broom....

FERRIS MAJOR: Or the beauty of it either.

OLD GRADUATE (*lost in his eternal dream of the past*): Dissolute
and damned. Both the student body and the faculty.

HOUSEMASTER: Elliott.

ELLIOTT: Yes, sir?

HOUSEMASTER: Go down to the Greek's and get me two ham sandwiches and a billiard ball.

ELLIOTT (*uneasily*): What for?

HOUSEMASTER (*watching the scrubwoman; fascinated by the unique,
all-female, and mysterious experiences once enjoyed somewhere in*

the world by this scrubwoman): Ham on white. British mustard.

ELLIOTT (*still puzzled, but going out dutifully*): A cue ball?

HOUSEMASTER: No, the red one. (*To the scrubwoman; waving the cocktail-shaker*) Martini?

SCRUBWOMAN: No thanks, pal. The Head don't like us to drink on duty.

HOUSEMASTER: You're missing a lot. *I'm* always drunk. The days and nights are whittling me away, and—(*he breaks off as the Headmaster, a quiet, grave man, carrying a bridle, comes into the cubicle.*) Were you looking for something, sir?

HEADMASTER (*genially*): Ah, Nicholson. Fried again, I see. (*With a change of mood, sternly*) Ferris Major!

FERRIS MAJOR (*springing up, dynamic, translated*): Sir?

HEADMASTER: Is there a polo pony in this room?

FERRIS MAJOR: A what, sir?

HEADMASTER (*going to a closet, opening it, and discovering a polo pony*): As I thought. You know the rules, I believe, Ferris. No polo ponies or young women in dorm after four o'clock.

FERRIS MAJOR (*in a low voice, accepting his doom*): Yes, sir.

HEADMASTER: This means a birching, of course. (*He goes out, leading the polo pony; fatal, inexorable, the Scourge of God.*)

OLD GRADUATE (*throwing the ace of spades at the hat*): Dissolute and damned. Both the student body and the faculty.

HOUSEMASTER (*still preoccupied by the scrubwoman; the strange, illicit, bygone adventures of the scrubwoman*): I drink to your unconquerable spirit, Mrs. Le Bogan.

SCRUBWOMAN: My name ain't Mrs. Le Bogan.

HOUSEMASTER: Then Guinevere or Héloïse. In any case, I drink. To your ancient sins, Faustine.

SCRUBWOMAN: Listen, what the hell you talking about?

HOUSEMASTER (*wearily*): I don't know. What do any of us talk about? Love. Happiness. Towering injustice everywhere. The game with St. Paul's. (*Furiously, draining the Martini*) How the hell do I know? What do *you* talk about?

SCRUBWOMAN (*sly, roguish, Salome, old but not regenerate*): Jeez, I dunno, mister. Harry K. Thaw. The time we burned up the city of Chicago. Shooting Garfield. All like that.

HOUSEMASTER: Life! The terror and the wonder and the beauty of it. (*Gathering momentum*) Life! *Life!* LIFE!

(As he goes on, Elliott reënters with the sandwiches and the billiard ball; the scrubwoman wrings out her mop and starts to wipe up the floor; the old graduate opens another pack of cards and begins throwing them at the hat; Jones Minor and Ferris Major gather up their hymnals and prayer books; the polo pony trots in through the door and back into the closet. Life has come full circle.)

OLD GRADUATE *(sombre, triumphant; his opinion of everything borne out)*: Dissolute and damned. Both the student body and the faculty.

(From the courtyard the bell for vespers sounds, very wonderful and sad. The curtain falls.)

DEATH IN THE RUMBLE SEAT

(With the Usual Apologies to Ernest Hemingway)

Most people don't like the pedestrian part, and it is best not to look at that if you can help it. But if you can't help seeing them, long-legged and their faces white, and then the shock and the car lifting up a little on one side, then it is best to think of it as something very unimportant but beautiful and necessary artistically. It is unimportant because the people who are pedestrians are not very important, and if they were not being *cogido* by automobiles it would just be something else. And it is beautiful and necessary because, without the possibility of somebody getting *cogido*, driving a car would be just like anything else. It would be like reading "Thanatopsis," which is neither beautiful nor necessary, but hogwash. If you drive a car, and don't like the pedestrian part, then you are one of two kinds of people. Either you haven't very much vitality and you ought to do something about it, or else you are yellow and there is nothing to be done about it at all.

If you don't know anything about driving cars you are apt to think a driver is good just because he goes fast. This may be very exciting at first, but afterwards there is a bad taste in the mouth and the feeling of dishonesty. Ann Bender, the American, drove as fast on the Merrick Road as anybody I have ever seen, but when cars came the other way she always worked out of their terrain and over in the ditch so that you never had the hard, clean feeling of danger, but only bumping up and down in the ditch, and sometimes hitting your head on the top of the car. Good drivers go fast too, but it is always down the middle of the road, so that cars coming the other way are dominated, and have to go in the ditch themselves. There are a great many ways of getting the effect of danger, such as staying in the middle of the road till the last minute and then swerving out of the pure line, but they are all tricks, and afterwards you know they were tricks, and there is nothing left but disgust.

The cook: I am a little tired of cars, sir. Do you know any stories?

I know a great many stories, but I'm not sure that they're suitable.

The cook: The hell with that.

Then I will tell you the story about God and Adam and naming the animals. You see, God was very tired after he got through making the world. He felt good about it, but he was tired so he asked Adam if he'd mind making up names for the animals.

"What animals?" Adam said.

"Those," God said.

"Do they have to have names?" Adam said.

"You've got a name, haven't you?" God said.

I could see—

The cook: How do *you* get into this?

Some people always write in the first person, and if you do it's very hard to write any other way, even when it doesn't altogether fit into the context. If you want to hear this story, don't keep interrupting.

The cook: O.K.

I could see that Adam thought God was crazy, but he didn't say anything. He went over to where the animals were, and after a while he came back with the list of names.

"Here you are," he said.

God read the list, and nodded.

"They're pretty good," he said. "They're all pretty good except that last one."

"That's a good name," Adam said. "What's the matter with it?"

"What do you want to call it an elephant for?," God said.

Adam looked at God.

"It looks like an elephant to me," he said.

The cook: Well?

That's all.

The cook: It is a very strange story, sir.

It is a strange world, and if a man and a woman love each other, that is strange too, and what is more, it always turns out badly.

In the golden age of car-driving, which was about 1910, the sense of impending disaster, which is a very lovely thing and almost non-existent, was kept alive in a number of ways. For one thing, there was always real glass in the windshield so that if a driver hit anything, he was very definitely and beautifully *cogido*. The tires weren't much good either, and often they'd blow out before you'd gone ten miles. Really, the whole car was built that way. It was made not only so that it would precipitate accidents but so that when the accidents came it was honestly vulnerable, and it would fall apart, killing all the people with a passion that was very fine to watch. Then they began building the cars so that they would go much faster, but the glass and the tires were all made so that if anything happened it wasn't real danger, but only the false sense of it. You could do all kinds of things with the new cars, but it was no good because it was all planned in advance. Mickey Finn, the German, always worked very far into the other car's terrain so that the two cars always seemed to be one. Driving that way he often got the *faender,* or the clicking when two cars touch each other in passing, but because you knew that nothing was really at stake it was just an empty classicism, without any value because the insecurity was all gone and there was nothing left but a kind of mechanical agility. It is the same way when any art gets into its decadence. It is the same way about s-x—

The cook: I like it very much better when you talk about s-x, sir, and I wish you would do it more often.

I have talked a lot about s-x before, and now I thought I would talk about something else.

The cook: I think that is very unfortunate, sir, because you are at your best with s-x, but when you talk about automobiles you are just a nuisance.

Corey Ford

THE NORRIS PLAN *

Aroused by the frank discussion of Birth Control in Mr. Charles G. Norris's tract, entitled "Seed," as well as by the mention of the same subject in Mrs. Kathleen Norris's "Passion Flower" and other novels, the young and impressionable Mr. Riddell attempted in the following to try his own hand at the all-important theme of limiting our excess productivity in America. It is of added interest to note that the influence of the Norris style was so strong that young Riddell, perhaps unconsciously, framed his treatise in the respective manners of the Norrises themselves.

When this was written, Mrs. Kathleen Norris was already the author of thirty-three novels.†

It was early in the summer that Kathy told him that Edgar Wallace was going to have another novel.

It was a heavenly warm bright shiny clear happy Sunday morning, and the broad green velvety smooth flat rolling croquet field in the middle of Central Park was filled with gay yellow warm sunlight. She and Charles were moving idly among the wickets, swinging their mallets at the smooth fat shiny round balls. Charles had tried for the stake and missed it, and now he sat on his up-ended mallet, his smooth fat shiny round face puckered into a frown.

"Edgar thinks he's going to have another novel, Charlie."

"Gosh, that's tough!" Charlie commented absently. He was trying to remember whether he was dead on her.

"He's been typing his eyes out," Kathy continued in a rather faint voice. "He says the first ten novels aren't so bad, or even the first twenty," she pursued. "But when you get to write the fiftieth novel or so, it's terrible."

* This parody book review was first published in somewhat longer form over the signature John Riddell.

† Thirty-four at the time of going to press. J. R.

Charlie extended his toe, slyly moved his ball over an inch or two in front of the wicket, and faced her with a great wholesome happy cheerful laugh.

"What's terrible, honey?" he asked.

"The novel, of course!" she conceded honestly. "Charlie," she went on suddenly, deliberately, not looking at him as she knocked her ball into position for the center wicket, "I wonder how you'd feel if I were going to have another novel?"

"I know how I'd feel," Charlie said promptly; "I'd take it out into a vacant lot somewhere and burn it!"

"Oh, Charlie, why?" Kathy asked, widening her big dark round bright eyes reproachfully. "Everybody writes them." Her cheeks were suddenly red, and her eyes full of tears. "Look at Faith Baldwin, or Hugh Walpole, or Mary Roberts Rinehart, or Mazo de la Roche, or Margaret Ayer Barnes—they deliver one every year. Sometimes they even have twins."

"Well, if I was in Edgar's place," Charlie said, as he judged his distance and then rapped the stake smartly, "I'd go to my publishers and have them decide that the public couldn't stand another novel just now, that they'd have to save his reputation by—well, cutting it out."

"Oh, but Charlie! Isn't that a terribly wrong thing to do?"

"What's wrong with it?"

"Well—well—" She stopped, puzzled and a little sick. "It seems so unfair to the novel. It—it ought to have its little chance."

"Don't you think the public ought to have a chance, too?"

"But—but there seems to be something so *humiliating* about it," Kathy faltered, her cheeks burning. "To have a whole season go by without being on the best-seller lists! To have to give up the first-serial rights—and the second-serial rights—and the movie rights—and the foreign rights—"

"It isn't half as bad, I should think, as writing it," Charlie argued.

"Oh, no, Charlie, that's natural!"

"I don't know about that," Charlie began, laying his mallet down and pointing an argumentative forefinger at the woman before him. "I've been doing a lot of thinking about this whole subject of book-control. Of course, my publishers don't agree with me. They believe that the practice of Literary Contraception profanes the sacrament of Inspiration, and is a frustration of the creative instinct in Art. It is my opinion, however, that reckless breeding should be checked for the sake of the author's reputation. It unquestionably takes the lives of thousands of writers annually, ruins the careers of as many more, and in addition brings hundreds of thousands of diseased, crippled and deformed novels into the world that should never have been written. Some of them die, many linger on in dire poverty, shivering in their paper jackets, while others roam at large, doubtless interbreeding in the movies and producing a weak and imbecile line of sequels that threatens to lower the whole stock of American literature.

"Several authors that you and I know are—or were—examples of such reckless breeding. You may recall, Kathy, an author by the name of John Erskine?"

"Very well."

"His history came to my attention very forcibly the other day in a Liggett's window. He's confined now in the dollar reprints; but before he was put where he couldn't do any further harm, he had brought a weak and helpless novel into the world named *Unfinished Business*, which was totally unable to exist alone, and was forced to depend on its older sister Helen and its brother Galahad for its entire support. Thus the future happiness of two healthy novels was threatened by this imbecile brother; and the poor author—whose health had been none too good after having *Adam and Eve* and *Uncle Sam*—went into a serious decline."

He shook his head.

"The saddest case is that of Emil Ludwig. After writing the life of everyone else, the poor fellow has now produced a biography of himself!"

"Uncle Emil! *Himself?*"

"Pitiful case. A fine talent gone to pot-boiling. He had a publisher in New York, and he bore him one volume after another. After Emil had delivered six or seven books in rapid succession, however, the public grew tired of him, disappeared at intervals, rejected a couple. You wouldn't know him today; he's beaten in spirit, in substance, in artistic integrity. The biography-racket has crushed him body and soul. You can't deny it, legal book-control undoubtedly would have been a blessing to Uncle Emil."

Kathy leaned weakly on her mallet. The warm bright sunny cheerful Park swam before her, the croquet-wickets, stakes, balls, and idle spectators seemed blurred before her eyes.

"You look kind of white yourself, Kathy," interrupted Charles curiously.

"I don't know—I'm all right, I guess."

"You've been having too many novels in the last few years," he said solicitously. "Every three months or so. It weakens you, honey. *Passion Flower* was too much for you—let alone *Margaret Yorke.*"

The very title made waves of nausea sweep over her. She clutched her mallet and swung listlessly at the croquet-ball before her. It went short of the wicket.

"A lot of other American authors present interesting phases of this same problem," continued Charlie, hitting his ball deftly between two wickets, and rapping the stake. "Take the late James Branch Cabell, for instance. He was undoubtedly one of the outstanding figures of our era; but he did not know the meaning of book-control. Overproduction weakened him, and he died in giving birth to his last novel. If he had practiced literary contraception, he might have been alive today. Let me see—are you still for the middle wicket?"

Kathy shook her head vaguely. She was thinking again of her panic-stricken visit to her publisher this very morning and her face burned, and her hands were dry. A business-like man; it was nothing to him. No, there was no question about Mrs. Norris's condition; she was scheduled for his fall lists. He was sorry, but he did not know any way out of it now. It would be extremely expensive to remove it at this late. He never advised it.

It was like a nightmare. Her publisher had removed her last doubt. This was no longer fear: it was terrible certainty.

"I'm going to have a novel. In October."

No, she did not have the courage to tell Charlie. She dragged herself across the court, and swung dizzily again at the ball. Charlie smiled as it wired itself behind the wicket, and he took his turn, grasping the mallet firmly as he elaborated further on his favorite theme: "There is one thing more I'd like to bring up about this question, and I'm done. It requires approximately three novels a year to sustain our present-day novelists, if they depend on royalties alone. The average number of novels born of literate stock is 2.8; while those of men and women from the pulpwoods is 97.2. You can clearly see where book-control is being practiced. In order to save the decent novelists from bringing about a complete suicide of American literature, not only must they publish more, but the fecundity of the illiterate writers must be curtailed. It must be obvious to anyone who stops to consider the situation at all that our intellectual class of writers is dying out, and the cheaper novelists and less mentally fit are on the increase; it must necessarily follow that our standard of national literature will decline and continue to decline."

He paused and drew out a sheaf of notes from his hip pocket. Kathy saw the scene rapidly growing black before her eyes; she felt herself swaying guiltily as Charlie read the climax of his argument aloud.

"The crux of the whole situation is simply this: our intelligent writers are not producing, and our ignorant, inferior ones are. Unless book-control is stopped among the upper classes, and its use legalized among the lower classes, the best part of our literature will die off, and the country will be over-run by incompetents and morons—"

There was a little moan, and then a faint thud behind him. Kathy had fainted.

"Kathy! Kathy!"

She found herself stretched upon the wooden bench at the side of the croquet field. Her teeth chattered, and Charlie, who was fumbling about vaguely, pale with concern and sympathy, held her hands.

"You're freezing!"

"Don't look so scared, Charlie!"

She laughed frantically, her teeth still chattering. He stared at her sympathetically.

"Anything I could do for you, Kath?" He was not thinking of what he was saying. Her heart beat fast, and she regarded him steadily, not moving a muscle. Suddenly, in an odd tone, he began, "Kathy—"

She looked at him, turning over to lie on her back, her face flushed, her hands icy, and her head rocking.

"Kath," he said, clearing his throat. "Have you thought—you know, this might be—"

Kath swallowed with a dry throat and patted his hand.

"It is, Charlie," she whispered, with a little effort.

"How d'you know?" he asked quickly.

"I asked a publisher. Our publisher."

"And he said—?"

"—Said there was no mistake about it. It is due some time in October."

"He—What do you know about that?" Charlie stammered, his face lighted with bewilderment and surprise. "You poor kid," he added awkwardly.

Kathy's cold fingers continued to cling tightly to his hand; she watched him anxiously.

"Isn't there some way to—get out of it, Kath?" Charlie asked presently, a little doubtfully. "You've had thirty-three, you see. I just thought maybe—well, remember, you're not as strong as you were—you see, the last ten or twelve you've had have all died—"

Her pale face grew whiter, and gripping his hand, with sudden fear and entreaty in her voice, she said:

"Charlie, I won't. It means—no, I couldn't do that. Getting rid of your own novel! That's—that's *badder,* to me, than not writing a novel at all. Think of it, dear—not to have the name of Norris on the best-seller lists this fall—"

"Well, now, I don't know about that," said Charlie in a queer strained voice.

"Charlie!" She looked up at him in sudden comprehension. "You don't mean that *you*—"

Suddenly she was sitting up, her arm tightly about him, her wet cheek pressed against his. He spoke after a long pause, his eyes lowered guiltily.

"It's true, Kathy. My publisher told me today. *I'm going to have a novel in October myself.*"

She was laughing joyfully, exultantly.

"Then all this that you were saying about literary contraception, and book-control, and our country being over-run by incompetents and morons—you don't mean a word of it?"

"Of course I mean it," he affirmed stoutly. "I'm strongly in favor of book-control—"

She stared at him in bewilderment.

"—for everybody else," he concluded hastily.

The Norrises embraced together in perfect understanding.

James Thurber

IF GRANT HAD BEEN DRINKING AT APPOMATTOX

("Scribner's" magazine is publishing a series of three articles: "If Booth Had Missed Lincoln," "If Lee Had Not Won the Battle of Gettysburg," and "If Napoleon Had Escaped to America." This is the fourth.)

The morning of the ninth of April, 1865, dawned beautifully. General Meade was up with the first streaks of crimson in the eastern sky. General Hooker and General Burnside were up, and had breakfasted, by a quarter after eight. The day continued beautiful. It drew on toward eleven o'clock. General Ulysses S. Grant was still not up. He was asleep in his famous old navy hammock, swung high above the floor of his headquarters' bedroom. Headquarters was distressingly disarranged: papers were strewn on the floor; confidential notes from spies scurried here and there in the breeze from an open window; the dregs of an overturned bottle of wine flowed pinkly across an important military map.

Corporal Shultz, of the Sixty-fifth Ohio Volunteer Infantry, aide to General Grant, came into the outer room, looked around him, and sighed. He entered the bedroom and shook the General's hammock roughly. General Ulysses S. Grant opened one eye.

"Pardon, sir," said Corporal Shultz, "but this is the day of surrender. You ought to be up, sir."

"Don't swing me," said Grant, sharply, for his aide was making the hammock sway gently. "I feel terrible," he added, and he turned over and closed his eye again.

"General Lee will be here any minute now," said the Corporal firmly, swinging the hammock again.

"Will you cut that out?" roared Grant. "D'ya want to make me sick or what?" Shultz clicked his heels and saluted. "What's he coming here for?" asked the General.

"This is the day of surrender, sir," said Shultz. Grant grunted bitterly.

"Three hundred and fifty generals in the Northern armies," said Grant, "and he has to come to *me* about this. What time is it?"

"You're the Commander-in-Chief, that's why," said Corporal Shultz. "It's eleven twenty-five, sir."

"Don't be crazy," said Grant. "Lincoln is the Commander-in-Chief. Nobody in the history of the world ever surrendered before lunch. Doesn't he know that an army surrenders on its stomach?" He pulled a blanket up over his head and settled himself again.

"The generals of the Confederacy will be here any minute now," said the Corporal. "You really ought to be up, sir."

Grant stretched his arms above his head and yawned.

"All right, all right," he said. He rose to a sitting position and stared about the room. "This place looks awful," he growled.

"You must have had quite a time of it last night, sir," ventured Shultz.

"Yeh," said General Grant, looking around for his clothes. "I was wrassling some general. Some general with a beard."

Shultz helped the commander of the Northern armies in the field to find his clothes.

"Where's my other sock?" demanded Grant. Shultz began to look around for it. The General walked uncertainly to a table and poured a drink from a bottle.

"I don't think it wise to drink, sir," said Shultz.

"Nev' mind about me," said Grant, helping himself to a second, "I can take it or let it alone. Didn' ya ever hear the story about the fella went to Lincoln to complain about me drinking too much? 'So-and-So says Grant drinks too much,' this fella said. 'So-and-So is a fool,' said Lincoln. So this fella went to What's-His-Name and told him what Lincoln said and he came roarin' to Lincoln about it. 'Did you tell So-and-So I was a fool?' he said. 'No,' said Lincoln, 'I thought he knew it.'" The General smiled, reminiscently, and had another drink. "*That's* how I stand with Lincoln," he said, proudly.

The soft thudding sound of horses' hooves came through the open window. Shultz hurriedly walked over and looked out.

"Hoof steps," said Grant, with a curious chortle.

"It is General Lee and his staff," said Shultz.

"Show him in," said the General, taking another drink. "And see what the boys in the back room will have."

Shultz walked smartly over to the door, opened it, saluted, and stood aside. General Lee, dignified against the blue of the April sky, magnificent in his dress uniform, stood for a moment framed in the doorway. He walked in, followed by his staff. They bowed, and stood silent. General Grant stared at them. He only had one boot on and his jacket was unbuttoned.

"I know who you are," said Grant. "You're Robert Browning, the poet."

"This is General Robert E. Lee," said one of his staff, coldly.

"Oh," said Grant. "I thought he was Robert Browning. He certainly looks like Robert Browning. There was a poet for you, Lee: Browning. Did ja ever read 'How They Brought the Good News from Ghent to Aix'? 'Up Derek, to saddle, up Derek, away; up Dunder, up Blitzen, up Prancer, up Dancer, up Bouncer, up Vixen, up—'"

"Shall we proceed at once to the matter in hand?" asked General Lee, his eyes disdainfully taking in the disordered room.

"Some of the boys was wrassling here last night," explained Grant. "I threw Sherman, or some general a whole lot like Sherman. It was pretty dark." He handed a bottle of Scotch to the commanding officer of the Southern armies, who stood holding it, in amazement and discomfiture. "Get a glass, somebody," said Grant, looking straight at General Longstreet. "Didn't I meet you at Cold Harbor?" he asked. General Longstreet did not answer.

"I should like to have this over with as soon as possible," said Lee. Grant looked vaguely at Shultz, who walked up close to him, frowning.

"The surrender, sir, the surrender," said Corporal Shultz in a whisper.

"Oh sure, sure," said Grant. He took another drink. "All right," he said. "Here we go." Slowly, sadly, he unbuckled his sword. Then he handed it to the astonished Lee. "There you are, General," said Grant. "We dam' near licked you. If I'd been feeling better we *would* of licked you."

Nunnally Johnson

DR. C-DM-N'S DAILY

(Overset matter which failed to get into one of our local news-papers)

What is the broadest definition of religion?

Love is *all.*

I have eczema in the worst way. Is there any certain cure?

Live from day to day that love may grow in thy heart and may there be blessings on thy eczema.

What is Mussolini's first name?

Benito.

Where was he born?

A pure heart is richer by far than a pure heart. Honor thy father and thy mother.

Bound the Club Alabam.

Sin is fleeting but love stayeth in the heart and enriches him that giveth and him that receiveth.

What day of the week did July 3, 1887 fall on?

Blessed be he that standeth by love and charity for education will prevail and self control is the definition of birth control.

Where is the Metropolitan Museum of Art?

The Metropolitan Museum of Art is on Fifth Avenue at—well, love conquereth all and a heart full of sweetness and goodfellowship bring-eth fair days and long.

Where did you say the Metropolitan Museum of Art is?

Love is *all.*

I am about to be married. Now what do you think of that?

Huxley said, "Let love be in thy heart," while Aristotle said, "Let love be in thy heart," but Burton said, "Let love be in thy heart."

I wonder where my baby is tonight?

After the storm cometh calm and if love be in thy heart then love be in thy heart.

Bret Harte

JUNGLE FOLK *

BY R-DY-D K-PL-G

It was high noon of a warm summer's day when Moo Kow cam
down to the watering-place. Miaow, otherwise known as "Puskat"—
the warmth-loving one—was crouching on a limb that overhung th
pool, sunning herself. Brer Rabbit—but that is Another Story by An
other Person.

Three or four Gee Gees, already at the pool, moved away on th
approach of Moo Kow.

"Why do ye stand aside?" said the Moo Kow.

"Why do you say 'ye'?" said the Gee Gees together.

"Because it's more impressive than 'you.' Don't you know that al
animals talk that way in English?" said the Moo Kow.

"And they also say 'thou,' and don't you forget it!" interrupted
Miaow from the tree. "I learnt that from a Man Cub."

The animals were silent. They did not like Miaow's slang, and were
jealous of her occasionally sitting on a Man Cub's lap. Once Dun-kee
a poor relation of the Gee Gees, had tried it on, disastrously—but that
is also Another and a more Aged Story.

"We are ridden by The English—please to observe the Capital let
ters," said Pi Böl, the leader of the Gee Gees, proudly. "They are a
mighty race who ride anything and everybody. D'ye mind that—I
mean, look ye well to it!"

"What should they know of England who only England know?"
said Miaow.

"Is that a conundrum?" asked the Moo Kow.

"No; it's poetry," said the Miaow.

"I know England," said Pi Böl prancingly. "I used to go from th

* This is one of three sections of a Kipling parody called "Stories Three," from
Bret Harte's second book of "Condensed Novels."

Bank to Islington three times a day—I mean," he added hurriedly, "before I became a screw—I should say, a screw-gun horse."

"And I," said the Moo Kow, "am terrible. When the young women and children in the village see me approach they fly shriekingly. My presence alone has scattered their sacred festival—The Sundés Kool Piknik. I strike terror to their inmost souls, and am more feared by them than even Kreep-mows, the insidious! And yet, behold! I have taken the place of the mothers of men, and I have nourished the mighty ones of the earth! But that," said the Moo Kow, turning her head away bashfully, "that is Anudder Story."

A dead silence fell on the pool.

"And I," said Miaow, lifting up her voice, "I am the horror and haunter of the night season. When I pass like the night wind over the roofs of the houses men shudder in their beds and tremble. When they hear my voice as I creep stealthily along their balconies they cry to their gods for succor. They arise, and from their windows they offer me their priceless household treasures—the sacred vessels dedicated to their great god Shiv—which they call 'Shivin Mugs'—the Kloes Brösh, the Boo-jak, urging me to fly them! And yet," said Miaow mournfully, "it is but my love song! Think ye what they would do if I were on the war-path."

Another dead silence fell on the pool. Then arose that strange, mysterious, indefinable Thing, known as "The Scent." The animals sniffed.

"It heralds the approach of the Stalkies—the most famous of British Skool Boaz," said the Moo Kow. "They have just placed a decaying guinea-pig, two white mice in an advanced state of decomposition, and a single slice of Limburger cheese in the bed of their tutor. They had previously skillfully diverted the drains so that they emptied into the drawing-room of the head-master. They have just burned down his house in an access of noble zeal, and are fighting among themselves for the spoil. Hark! do ye hear them?"

A wild medley of shrieks and howls had arisen, and an irregular mob of strange creatures swept out of the distance toward the pool. Some were like pygmies, some had bloody noses. Their talk consisted of feverish, breathless ejaculations,—a gibberish in which the words "rot," "oach," and "giddy" were preëminent. Some were exciting themselves by chewing a kind of "bhang" made from the plant called pappahmint; others had their faces streaked with djam.

"But who is this they are ducking in the pool?" asked Pi Böl.

"It is one who has foolishly and wantonly conceived that his parents have sent him here to study," said the Moo Kow; "but that is against the rules of the Stalkies, who accept study only as a punishment."

"Then these be surely the 'Bander Log'—the monkey folk—of whom the good Rhuddyidd has told us," said a Gee Gee—"the ones who have no purpose—and forget everything."

"Fool!" said the Moo Kow. "Know ye not that the great Rhuddyidd has said that the Stalkies become Major-Generals, V.C.'s, and C.B.'s of the English? Truly, they are great. Look now; ye shall see one of the greatest traits of the English Stalky."

One of the pygmy Stalkies was offering a bun to a larger one, who hesitated, but took it coldly.

"Behold! it is one of the greatest traits of this mighty race not to show any emotion. He *would* take the bun—he *has* taken it! He is pleased—but he may not show it. Observe him eat."

The taller Stalky, after eating the bun, quietly kicked the giver, knocked off his hat, and turned away with a calm, immovable face.

"Good!" said the Moo Kow. "Ye would not dream that he was absolutely choking with grateful emotion?"

"We would not," said the animals.

"But why are they all running back the way they came?" asked Pi Böl.

"They are going back to punishment. Great is its power. Have ye not heard the gospel of Rhuddyidd the mighty? 'Force is everything! Gentleness won't wash, courtesy is deceitful. Politeness is foreign. Be ye beaten that ye may beat. Pass the kick on!'"

But here he was interrupted by the appearance of three soldiers who were approaching the watering-place.

"Ye are now," said the Moo Kow, "with the main guard. The first is Bleareyed, who carries a raven in a cage, which he has stolen from the wife of a deputy commissioner. He will paint the bird snow white and sell it as a dove to the same lady. The second is Otherwise, who is dragging a small garden engine, of which he has despoiled a native gardener, whom he has felled with a single blow. The third is Mulledwiney, swinging a cut-glass decanter of sherry which he has just snatched from the table of his colonel. Mulledwiney and Otherwise will play the engine upon Bleareyed, who is suffering from heat apoplexy and djim-djams."

The three soldiers seated themselves in the pool.

"They are going to tell awful war stories now," said the Moo Kow, "stories that are large and strong! Some people are shocked—others like 'em."

Then he that was called Mulledwiney told a story. In the middle of it Miaow got up from the limb of the tree, coughed slightly, and put her paw delicately over her mouth. "You must excuse me," she said faintly. "I am taken this way sometimes—and I have left my salts at home. Thanks! I can get down myself!" The next moment she had disappeared, but was heard coughing in the distance.

Mulledwiney winked at his companions and continued his story:—

"Wid that we wor in the thick av the foight. Whin I say 'thick' I mane it, sorr! We wor that jammed together, divil a bit cud we shoot or cut! At furrest, I had lashed two mushkits together wid the baynits out so, like a hay fork, and getting the haymaker's lift on thim, I just lifted two Paythians out—one an aych baynit—and passed 'em, aisy-like, over me head to the rear rank for them to finish. But what wid the blud gettin' into me ois, I was blinded, and the pressure kept in-craysin' until me arrums was thrussed like a fowl to me sides, and sorra a bit cud I move but me jaws!"

"And bloomin' well you knew how to use them," said Otherwise.

"Thrue for you—though ye don't mane it!" said Mulledwiney, play-fully tapping Otherwise on the head with a decanter till the cut glass slowly shivered. "So, begorra! there wor nothing left for me to do but to ate them! Wirra! but it was the crooel worruk."

"Excuse me, my lord," interrupted the gasping voice of Pi Böl as he began to back from the pool, "I am but a horse, I know, and being built in that way—naturally have the stomach of one—yet, really, my lord, this—er"— And his voice was gone.

The next moment he had disappeared. Mulledwiney looked around with affected concern.

"Save us! But we've cleaned out the Jungle! Sure, there's not a baste left but ourselves!"

It was true. The watering-place was empty. Moo Kow, Miaow, and the Gee Gees had disappeared. Presently there was a booming crash and a long, deep rumbling among the distant hills. Then they knew they were near the old Moulmein Pagoda, and the dawn had come up like thunder out of China 'cross the bay. It always came up that way there. The strain was too great, and day was actually breaking.

S. J. Perelman

WAITING FOR SANTY

A CHRISTMAS PLAYLET

(WITH A BOW TO MR. CLIFFORD ODETS)

Scene: The sweatshop of S. Claus, a manufacturer of children's toys, on North Pole Street. Time: The night before Christmas.

At rise, seven gnomes, Rankin, Panken, Rivkin, Riskin, Ruskin, Briskin, and Praskin, are discovered working furiously to fill orders piling up on stage right. The whir of lathes, the hum of motors, and the hiss of drying lacquer are so deafening that at times the dialogue cannot be heard, which is very vexing if you vex easily. (Note: The parts of Rankin, Panken, Rivkin, Riskin, Ruskin, Briskin, and Praskin are interchangeable, and may be secured directly from your dealer or the factory.)

RISKIN (*filing a Meccano girder, bitterly*). A parasite, a leech, a blood-sucker—altogether a five-star no goodnick! Starvation wages we get so he can ride around in a red team with reindeers!

RUSKIN (*jeering*). Hey, Karl Marx, whyn'tcha hire a hall?

RISKIN (*sneering*). Scab! Stool pigeon! Company spy! (*They tangle and rain blows on each other. While waiting for these to dry, each returns to his respective task.*)

BRISKIN (*sadly, to Panken*). All day long I'm painting "Snow Queen" on these Flexible Flyers and my little Irving lays in a cold tenement with the gout.

PANKEN. You said before it was the mumps.

BRISKIN (*with a fatalistic shrug*). The mumps—the gout—go argue with City Hall.

PANKEN (*kindly, passing him a bowl*). Here, take a piece fruit.

BRISKIN (*chewing*). It ain't bad, for wax fruit.

PANKEN (*with pride*). I painted it myself.

BRISKIN (*rejecting the fruit*). Ptoo! Slave psychology!

RIVKIN (*suddenly, half to himself, half to the Party*). I got a belly full of stars, baby. You make me feel like I swallowed a Roman candle.

300

PRASKIN (*curiously*). What's wrong with the kid?

RISKIN. What's wrong with all of us? The system! Two years he and Claus's daughter's been making goo-goo eyes behind the old man's back.

PRASKIN. So what?

RISKIN (*scornfully*). So what? Economic determinism! What do you think the kid's name is—J. Pierpont Rivkin? He ain't even got for a bottle Dr. Brown's Celery Tonic. I tell you, it's like gall in my mouth two young people shouldn't have a room where they could make great music.

RANKIN (*warningly*). Shhh! Here she comes now! (*Stella Claus enters, carrying a portable gramophone. She and Rivkin embrace, place a record on the turntable, and begin a very slow waltz, unmindful that the gramophone is playing "Cohen on the Telephone."*)

STELLA (*dreamily*). Love me, sugar?

RIVKIN. I can't sleep, I can't eat, that's how I love you. You're a double malted with two scoops of whipped cream; you're the moon rising over Mosholu Parkway; you're a two weeks' vacation at Camp Nitgedaiget! I'd pull down the Chrysler Building to make a bobbie pin for your hair!

STELLA. I've got a stomach full of anguish. Oh, Rivvy, what'll we do?

PANKEN (*sympathetically*). Here, try a piece fruit.

RIVKIN (*fiercely*). Wax fruit—that's been my whole life! Imitations! Substitutes! Well, I'm through! Stella, tonight I'm telling your old man. He can't play mumblety-peg with two human beings! (*The tinkle of sleigh bells is heard offstage, followed by a voice shouting, "Whoa, Dasher! Whoa, Dancer!" A moment later S. Claus enters in a gust of mock snow. He is a pompous bourgeois of sixty-five who affects a white beard and a false air of benevolence. But tonight the ruddy color is missing from his cheeks, his step falters, and he moves heavily. The gnomes hastily replace the marzipan they have been filching.*)

STELLA (*anxiously*). Papa! What did the specialist say?

CLAUS (*brokenly*). The biggest professor in the country...the best cardiac man that money could buy.... I tell you I was like a wild man.

STELLA. Pull yourself together, Sam!

CLAUS. It's no use. Adhesions, diabetes, sleeping sickness, decalcomania —oh, my God! I got to cut out climbing in chimneys, he says— me, Sanford Claus, the biggest toy concern in the world!

STELLA (*soothingly*). After all, it's only one man's opinion.

CLAUS. No, no, he cooked my goose. I'm like a broken uke after a Yosian picnic. Rivkin!

RIVKIN. Yes, Sam.

CLAUS. My boy, I had my eye on you for a long time. You and Stella thought you were too foxy for an old man, didn't you? Well, let bygones be bygones. Stella, do you love this gnome?

STELLA (*simply*). He's the whole stage show at the Music Hall, Papa; he's Toscanini conducting Beethoven's Fifth; he's—

CLAUS (*curtly*). Enough already. Take him. From now on he's a partner in the firm. (*As all exclaim, Claus holds up his hand for silence.*) And tonight he can take my route and make the deliveries. It's the least I could do for my own flesh and blood. (*As the happy couple kiss, Claus wipes away a suspicious moisture and turns to the other gnomes.*) Boys, do you know what day tomorrow is?

GNOMES (*crowding around expectantly*). Christmas!

CLAUS. Correct. When you look in your envelopes tonight, you'll find a little present from me—a forty-per-cent pay cut. And the first one who opens his trap—gets this. (*As he holds up a tear-gas bomb and beams at them, the gnomes utter cries of joy, join hands, and dance around him, shouting exultantly. All except Riskin and Briskin, that is, who exchange a quick glance and go underground.*)

FOR (OR AGAINST) CHILDREN

Our first idea was to collect a section of humor from books written for children. We gave it up because, except for "The Peterkin Papers" and "Uncle Remus," we did not find much humor in early juvenile literature, and the humor in modern books for children is for the most part picture-book humor. So this turned into a section quite as much about children as for them. Incidentally, it also has a good deal to say about parents.

Cross reference: A number of stories about real children will be found in this book under "Reminiscence."

Lucretia P. Hale

THE PETERKINS CELEBRATE THE
FOURTH OF JULY

The day began early.

A compact had been made with the little boys the evening before.

They were to be allowed to usher in the glorious day by the blowing of horns exactly at sunrise. But they were to blow them for precisely five minutes only, and no sound of the horns should be heard afterward till the family were downstairs.

It was thought that a peace might thus be bought by a short, though crowded, period of noise.

The morning came. Even before the morning, at half-past three o'clock, a terrible blast of the horns aroused the whole family.

Mrs. Peterkin clasped her hands to her head and exclaimed: "I am thankful the lady from Philadelphia is not here!" For she had been invited to stay a week, but had declined to come before the Fourth of July, as she was not well, and her doctor had prescribed quiet.

And the number of the horns was most remarkable! It was as though every cow in the place had arisen and was blowing through both her own horns!

"How many little boys are there? How many have we?" exclaimed Mr. Peterkin, going over their names one by one mechanically, thinking he would do it, as he might count imaginary sheep jumping over a fence, to put himself to sleep. Alas! the counting could not put him to sleep now, in such a din.

And how unexpectedly long the five minutes seemed! Elizabeth Eliza was to take out her watch and give the signal for the end of the five minutes, and the ceasing of the horns. Why did not the signal come? Why did not Elizabeth Eliza stop them?

And certainly it was long before sunrise; there was no dawn to be seen!

"We will not try this plan again," said Mrs. Peterkin.

305

"If we live to another Fourth," added Mr. Peterkin, hastening to the door to inquire into the state of affairs.

Alas! Amanda, by mistake, had waked up the little boys an hour too early. And by another mistake the little boys had invited three or four of their friends to spend the night with them. Mrs. Peterkin had given them permission to have the boys for the whole day, and they understood the day as beginning when they went to bed the night before. This accounted for the number of horns.

It would have been impossible to hear any explanation; but the five minutes were over, and the horns had ceased, and there remained only the noise of a singular leaping of feet, explained perhaps by a possible pillow-fight, that kept the family below partially awake until the bells and cannon made known the dawning of the glorious day,—the sunrise, or "the rising of the sons," as Mr. Peterkin jocosely called it when they heard the little boys and their friends clattering down the stairs to begin the outside festivities.

They were bound first for the swamp, for Elizabeth Eliza, at the suggestion of the lady from Philadelphia, had advised them to hang some flags around the pillars of the piazza. Now the little boys knew of a place in the swamp where they had been in the habit of digging for "flag-root," and where they might find plenty of flag flowers. They did bring away all they could, but they were a little out of bloom. The boys were in the midst of nailing up all they had on the pillars of the piazza, when the procession of the Antiques and Horribles passed along. As the procession saw the festive arrangements on the piazza, and the crowd of boys, who cheered them loudly, it stopped to salute the house with some especial strains of greeting.

Poor Mrs. Peterkin! They were directly under her windows! In a few moments of quiet, during the boys' absence from the house on their visit to the swamp, she had been trying to find out whether she had a sick-headache, or whether it was all the noise, and she was just deciding it was the sick-headache, but was falling into a light slumber, when the fresh noise outside began.

There were the imitations of the crowing of cocks, and braying of donkeys, and the sound of horns, encored and increased by the cheers of the boys. Then began the torpedoes, and the Antiques and Horribles had Chinese crackers also.

And, in despair of sleep, the family came down to breakfast.

Mrs. Peterkin had always been much afraid of fireworks, and had never allowed the boys to bring gunpowder into the house. She was even afraid of torpedoes; they looked so much like sugar-plums she was sure some of the children would swallow them, and explode before anybody knew it.

She was very timid about other things. She was not sure even about pea-nuts. Everybody exclaimed over this: "Surely there was no danger in pea-nuts!" But Mrs. Peterkin declared she had been very much alarmed at the Centennial Exhibition, and in the crowded corners of the streets in Boston, at the pea-nut stands, where they had machines to roast the pea-nuts. She did not think it was safe. They might go off any time, in the midst of a crowd of people, too!

Mr. Peterkin thought there actually was no danger, and he should be sorry to give up the pea-nut. He thought it an American institution, something really belonging to the Fourth of July. He even confessed to a quiet pleasure in crushing the empty shells with his feet on the sidewalks as he went along the streets.

Agamemnon thought it a simple joy.

In consideration, however, of the fact that they had had no real celebration of the Fourth the last year, Mrs. Peterkin had consented to give over the day, this year, to the amusement of the family as a Centennial celebration. She would prepare herself for a terrible noise, —only she did not want any gunpowder brought into the house.

The little boys had begun by firing some torpedoes a few days beforehand, that their mother might be used to the sound, and had selected their horns some weeks before.

Solomon John had been very busy in inventing some fireworks. As Mrs. Peterkin objected to the use of gunpowder, he found out from the dictionary what the different parts of gunpowder are,— saltpetre, charcoal, and sulphur. Charcoal, he discovered, they had in the wood-house; saltpetre they would find in the cellar, in the beef barrel; and sulphur they could buy at the apothecary's. He explained to his mother that these materials had never yet exploded in the house, and she was quieted.

Agamemnon, meanwhile, remembered a recipe he had read some-where for making a "fulminating paste" of iron-filings and powder of brimstone. He had written it down on a piece of paper in his pocket-book. But the iron filings must be finely powdered. This they began upon a day or two before, and the very afternoon before laid out some of the paste on the piazza.

Pin-wheels and rockets were contributed by Mr. Peterkin for the evening. According to a programme drawn up by Agamemnon and Solomon John, the reading of the Declaration of Independence was to take place in the morning, on the piazza, under the flags.

The Bromwicks brought over their flag to hang over the door.

"That is what the lady from Philadelphia meant," explained Elizabeth Eliza.

"She said the flags of our country," said the little boys. "We thought she meant 'in the country.'"

Quite a company assembled; but it seemed nobody had a copy of the Declaration of Independence.

Elizabeth Eliza said she could say one line, if they each could add as much. But it proved they all knew the same line that she did, as they began:—

"When, in the course of—when, in the course of—when, in the course of human—when in the course of human events—when, in the course of human events, it becomes—when, in the course of human events, it becomes necessary—when, in the course of human events, it becomes necessary for one people"—

They could not get any farther. Some of the party decided that "one people" was a good place to stop, and the little boys sent off some fresh torpedoes in honor of the people. But Mr. Peterkin was not satisfied. He invited the assembled party to stay until sunset, and meanwhile he would find a copy, and torpedoes were to be saved to be fired off at the close of every sentence.

And now the noon bells rang and the noon bells ceased.

Mrs. Peterkin wanted to ask everybody to dinner. She should have some cold beef. She had let Amanda go, because it was the Fourth, and everybody ought to be free that one day; so she could not have much of a dinner. But when she went to cut her beef she found Solomon had taken it to soak, on account of the saltpetre, for the fireworks!

Well, they had a pig; so she took a ham, and the boys had bought tamarinds and buns and a cocoa-nut. So the company stayed on, and when the Antiques and Horribles passed again they were treated to pea-nuts and lemonade.

They sung patriotic songs, they told stories, they fired torpedoes, they frightened the cats with them. It was a warm afternoon; the red poppies were out wide, and the hot sun poured down on the alleyways in the garden. There was a seething sound of a hot day in the buzzing of insects, in the steaming heat that came up from the ground. Some neighboring boys were firing a toy cannon. Every time it went off Mrs. Peterkin started, and looked to see if one of the little boys was gone. Mr. Peterkin had set out to find a copy of the "Declaration." Agamemnon had disappeared. She had not a moment to decide about her headache. She asked Ann Maria if she were not anxious about the fireworks, and if rockets were not dangerous. They went up, but you were never sure where they came down.

And then came a fresh tumult! All the fire-engines in town rushed toward them clanging with bells, men and boys yelling! They were out for a practice, and for a Fourth-of-July show.

Mrs. Peterkin thought the house was on fire, and so did some of the guests. There was a great rushing hither and thither. Some thought they would better go home; some thought they would better stay. Mrs. Peterkin hastened into the house to save herself, or see what she could save. Elizabeth Eliza followed her, first proceeding to collect all the pokers and tongs she could find, because they could be thrown out of the window without breaking. She had read of people who had flung looking-glasses out of the window by mistake, in the excitement of the house being on fire, and had carried the pokers and tongs carefully into the garden. There was nothing like being prepared. She had always determined to do the reverse. So with calmness she told Solomon John to take down the looking-glasses. But she met with a difficulty,—there were no pokers and tongs, as they did not use them. They had no open fires; Mrs. Peterkin had been afraid of them. So Elizabeth Eliza took all the pots and kettles up to the upper windows, ready to be thrown out.

But where was Mrs. Peterkin? Solomon John found she had fled to the attic in terror. He persuaded her to come down, assuring her it was the most unsafe place; but she insisted upon stopping to collect some bags of old pieces, that nobody would think of saving from the general wreck, she said, unless she did. Alas! this was the result of fireworks on Fourth of July! As they came downstairs they heard the voices of all the company declaring there was no fire; the danger was past. It was long before Mrs. Peterkin could believe it. They told her the fire company was only out for show, and to celebrate the Fourth of July. She thought it already too much celebrated.

Elizabeth Eliza's kettles and pans had come down through the windows with a crash, that had only added to the festivities, the little boys thought.

Mr. Peterkin had been roaming about all this time in search of a copy of the Declaration of Independence. The public library was shut, and he had to go from house to house; but now, as the sunset bells and cannon began, he returned with a copy, and read it, to the pealing of the bells and sounding of the cannon. Torpedoes and crackers were fired at every pause. Some sweet-marjoram pots, tin cans filled with crackers which were lighted, went off with great explosions.

At the most exciting moment, near the close of the reading, Agamemnon, with an expression of terror, pulled Solomon John aside.

"I have suddenly remembered where I read about the 'fulminating paste' we made. It was in the preface to 'Woodstock,' and I have been round to borrow the book, to read the directions over again, because I was afraid about the 'paste' going off. READ THIS QUICKLY! and tell me, *Where is the fulminating paste?*"

Solomon John was busy winding some covers of paper over a little parcel. It contained chlorate of potash and sulphur mixed. A friend had told him of the composition. The more thicknesses of paper you put round it the louder it would go off. You must pound it with a hammer. Solomon John felt it must be perfectly safe, as his mother had taken potash for a medicine.

He still held the parcel as he read from Agamemnon's book: "This paste, when it has lain together about twenty-six hours, will *of itself* take fire, and burn all the sulphur away with a blue flame and a bad smell."

"Where is the paste?" repeated Solomon John, in terror.

"We made it just twenty-six hours ago," said Agamemnon.

"We put it on the piazza," exclaimed Solomon John, rapidly recalling the facts, "and it is in front of our mother's feet!"

He hastened to snatch the paste away before it should take fire, flinging aside the packet in his hurry. Agamemnon, jumping upon the piazza at the same moment, trod upon the paper parcel, which exploded at once with the shock, and he fell to the ground, while at the same moment the paste "fulminated" into a blue flame directly in front of Mrs. Peterkin!

It was a moment of great confusion. There were cries and screams. The bells were still ringing, the cannon firing, and Mr. Peterkin had

ust reached the closing words: "Our lives, our fortunes, and our
acred honor."

"We are all blown up, as I feared we should be," Mrs. Peterkin
t length ventured to say, finding herself in a lilac-bush by the side
of the piazza. She scarcely dared to open her eyes to see the scattered
imbs about her.

It was so with all. Even Ann Maria Bromwick clutched a pillar
of the piazza, with closed eyes.

At length Mr. Peterkin said, calmly, "Is anybody killed?"

There was no reply. Nobody could tell whether it was because
everybody was killed, or because they were too wounded to answer.
It was a great while before Mrs. Peterkin ventured to move.

But the little boys soon shouted with joy, and cheered the success
of Solomon John's fireworks, and hoped he had some more. One
of them had his face blackened by an unexpected cracker, and Elizabeth Eliza's muslin dress was burned here and there. But no one was
hurt; no one had lost any limbs, though Mrs. Peterkin was sure she
had seen some flying in the air. Nobody could understand how, as
she had kept her eyes firmly shut.

No greater accident had occurred than the singeing of the tip of
Solomon John's nose. But there was an unpleasant and terrible odor
from the "fulminating paste."

Mrs. Peterkin was extricated from the lilac-bush. No one knew
how she got there. Indeed, the thundering noise had stunned everybody. It had roused the neighborhood even more than before. Answering explosions came on every side, and, though the sunset light had
not faded away, the little boys hastened to send off rockets under
cover of the confusion. Solomon John's other fireworks would not
go. But all felt he had done enough.

Mrs. Peterkin retreated into the parlor, deciding she really did
have a headache. At times she had to come out when a rocket went
off, to see if it was one of the little boys. She was exhausted by the
adventures of the day, and almost thought it could not have been
worse if the boys had been allowed gunpowder. The distracted lady
was thankful there was likely to be but one Centennial Fourth in her
lifetime, and declared she should never more keep anything in the
house as dangerous as saltpetred beef, and she should never venture
to take another spoonful of potash.

Sally Benson

APPRECIATION OF ART

The auditorium of the Carlton School was crowded and noisy. The children from the lower grades had marched in and were seated in the front rows, where they twisted and uttered unintelligible, piercing cries. Occasionally Miss Moffatt, who taught American history, walked down the aisle and frowned at them, putting her finger to her lips. For a few minutes they would be still. Then they would begin to move and rustle again, and pull and shove at one another.

The performance of "The Tempest" given by the girls of the Junior School was scheduled to begin at eight-thirty, and at a quarter past eight almost every seat was filled. Lois Graves, who was usher in Aisle 3, had put her coat across two of the best seats in the twelfth row, so that when her parents arrived, fashionably late, she was ready for the emergency. She met them at the door and smiled at them politely. She wore a powder-blue taffeta evening dress that swept the floor, and stretched diagonally over one shoulder was a dark-green satin ribbon on which the word "Usher" was printed in large gold letters. In one hand she carried a flashlight and in the other she held some programs.

"Well, dear," Mrs. Graves said. She looked quickly at the other ushers to see if Lois's dress was quite suitable, and sighed with relief as she noted other taffeta dresses in pink, turquoise blue, and pale green. She noticed that little Mildred Farney's dress pulled too tightly across her breasts, and that Jane Turner had on an unbecoming shade of blue. "Well, dear," she repeated.

Lois turned away, brisk and professional, and led the way down the aisle. She walked neatly in her high heels, and when she reached the seats over which she had thrown her coat, she pressed the button of her flashlight and focussed the beam on the floor.

"Say," Mr. Graves said appreciatively, "this is great!"

Lois leaned over them. "You'd better hold my coat so that people won't—you know."

The woman in the adjoining seat stared at them and muttered, "Well, I *must* say!"

"Oh," Mrs. Graves said. "Do you think you should have, Lois?"

"Nuts," Lois whispered. "Don't pay any attention to that old gorilla. She's just mad because she wanted to sit on the aisle and I told her these seats were taken."

With a whirl of her skirts and a rustle of silk, she was gone.

Mrs. Graves put her hand on her husband's sleeve. "It was thoughtful of her just the same."

Mr. Graves opened his program and fished in his pocket for his glasses. "I don't believe I've ever seen 'The Tempest.' What's it about?"

"I'm sure I don't know," Mrs. Graves answered. "I've never even read it. Judy's playing Stephano. It's a boy's part." She held her program two feet away from her eyes and frowned. "Here it is. Here's her name. Judith Graves."

Mr. Graves adjusted his glasses. "Stephano, a drunken Butler," he read aloud.

"Well!" Mrs. Graves exclaimed. "Well!"

A sharp memory of a talk he had had with Judy a week before flashed into Mr. Graves' mind. "Daddy," she had asked, "how many drinks do you have to have before you get drunk?" And he had answered, "It all depends. A person might get drunk on one drink, and then again it might take twenty." "I suppose," Judy had persisted, "if you were used to it, it would take twenty." He had said he imagined it would. And Judy seemed satisfied.

Mrs. Graves looked at him anxiously. "I suppose they know what they're doing. Giving a part like that to a little girl, I mean."

"Oh, sure," he said.

She glanced at her program thoughtfully. "I think it would have been nice if they had decided to give 'The Mikado.' They planned to at first. Except there weren't enough girls who could sing. Here's Fuffy Adams' name. She's going to be Trinculo, a Jester."

"I saw Pete Adams when we came in. He's putting on weight."

"They rented the costumes. Even the wigs."

"Have you seen Judy's costume?" Mr. Graves asked.

"No," she answered. "They only got them yesterday, in time for dress rehearsal. I haven't even heard her lines. She said them for Hilda, but it was the night we played bridge with the Conovers. I heard her in the kitchen, though, and she seemed to be shouting."

"I wouldn't worry."

"Oh, I'm not worrying. After all, Miss Lucy Smith is coaching them, and she must know what she's doing."

There were signs of excitement among the children in the first rows, and at a signal from a slender, faded, blonde woman who appeared from a door at the left, fifteen of them arose and marched up the stairs onto the stage. They stood there swallowing nervously, their arms hanging limply at their sides. Their dresses had become mussed and their eyes were glassy. The blonde woman, a Miss Avery, sat down at the piano and struck an opening chord.

"It's the school song," Mrs. Graves whispered. "I suppose we ought to stand."

According to the program, the words to the school song had been written by a Miss Dorothy Brewer, '09, but the tune was "Flow Gently, Sweet Afton."

Mrs. Graves watched the young faces of the Junior Glee Club tenderly, and her heart melted within her. They started to sing slightly off key, but the sound of their own voices gave them reassurance, and the words rang out clear and sweet:

> The mem'ries of school days will never grow old,
> So raise high the colors, the green and the gold.

For no reason at all, her eyes smarted, and she fumbled in her evening bag for a handkerchief.

> Our dear Alma Mater, our own Carlton School,
> May she evermore flourish and over us rule.

As the song ended there was a burst of applause, which stopped abruptly as Miss Avery swung into the opening bars of "The Star-Spangled Banner." The audience joined enthusiastically in the singing.

"I imagine the play will begin now," Mrs. Graves said, rearranging her evening wrap on the back of the seat. "I wonder when Judy comes on. It would be funny if we didn't recognize her, wouldn't it?"

"We'll know her all right," Mr. Graves said.

The girls of the Junior Glee Club marched back to their places

and the lights grew dim. The curtains parted, showing a black
backdrop. There was a flash of lightning from above and the sound
of tinny thunder. The play had begun.

"They've got the stage awfully dark," Mrs. Graves whispered. "Can
you see Judy?"

"I think this crowd are supposed to be sailors. They look as though
they're pulling at ropes."

The voices of the girls were lost in the rolls of thunder, and the
curtain fell.

"Well, that was short, anyway," Mr. Graves said. "The next scene
is on an island."

The curtain rose again; the backdrop had been lifted and the stage
was larger. In the direct centre at the rear was an opening surrounded
by unbleached muslin that had been dyed gray with green spots
to represent a rocky entrance to a cave, and to the right of this stood
a small spruce tree in a tub. From the wings came two figures, both
strictly feminine, although one of them wore a long, gray, matted
beard, a shaggy white wig, black tights, and a doublet. "Prospero,"
Mrs. Graves said. "And that's Miranda with him. The Burchell child."

Miranda had on a black wig bound with a fillet. It was made of
the blackest hair Mrs. Graves had ever seen, and from under it Polly
Burchell's face peered, small and round. She walked with the slow,
forlorn gait of an overworked chambermaid in a second-rate hotel,
but as she began to speak she came to life and gestured with her arms.
When she finished her lines, she lapsed into a coma and stared out
into the audience during the time Prospero took up the plot. The
scene was long, and Mrs. Graves was glad when Ariel danced from
the wings. Ariel's tunic was embarrassingly short, and she seemed
to be suffering from an acute form of St. Vitus's dance.

"What's the matter with her?" Mr. Graves asked.

"I imagine Miss Smith told her to keep moving, the poor little
thing. She's a sprite, you see."

The play dragged on. As each character appeared for the first time,
there was a burst of applause from relatives and school friends. Mrs.
Graves sat tensely, waiting for Judy's entrance. But Act I ended and
there had been no sign of her.

"She probably has just a small part," Mrs. Graves said when the
lights went up. "The girls *do* mutter, don't they?" She clapped half-
heartedly. "I don't see how Judy can be a *drunken* butler. After all,

it's supposed to be an almost deserted island, and there couldn't very well be any liquor on it. At least, I don't see where it would come from. The ship is wrecked. Besides, I don't think Judy would know how to act drunk. As far as I know, she's never even seen anyone very drunk."

"Of course she hasn't," Mr. Graves said. "A little high, maybe, but not boiled."

They waited for her entrance until Act II, Scene 2. A small, fat Caliban, dressed in what looked to be a fur union suit, and Fuffy Adams as Trinculo were talking together when Mrs. Graves heard a voice singing in the wings. It was the first completely audible voice in the performance, and it was Judy's. She reeled onto the stage, a bottle in her hand. Her smooth, dark-brown hair was covered with a straw-colored wig, the tip of her nose was painted a bright red. Her clothes were awry and she looked as tight as an owl.

"This is a very scurvy tune to sing at a man's funeral. Well, here's my comfort," she shouted, and, lifting the bottle to her lips, she took a healthy swig.

The children in the audience broke into delighted laughter, and Judy, hearing them, lifted the bottle again and staggered across the stage, throwing a heavy arm around Fuffy Adams, who giggled with abandon.

The force of Judy's entrance took Caliban off guard and struck her dumb. She forgot her rôle of savage and deformed slave and stood by as quietly as a baby panda in her furry suit, watching Judy's antics. Each time Judy lifted the bottle to her lips the laughter from the lower grades got louder. Over the noise, Judy's voice rang out, blurred with drink, loud and insinuating. She spun around, crying, "Prithee, do not turn me about. My stomach is not constant." And as an added touch, she put her hand on her small, firm stomach and hiccoughed.

When the curtain fell, the applause was deafening. It continued until Judy stood alone on the stage. She lifted the bottle to her lips and reeled again.

Mr. and Mrs. Graves were silent as the lights went on. Finally, Mrs. Graves spoke. "I can't believe it. I can't imagine what's got into her." She looked at her husband and saw that he was smiling.

"You could hear her, anyway," he said.

"Oh, you could hear her all right."

They sat through the next three acts and watched Judy faithfully portray various stages of intoxication; she fought, she laughed senselessly, she was sad, she lapsed into self-pity, and her last line, spoken in a maudlin whine—"O! touch me not. I am not Stephano, but a cramp"—brought down the house.

She gave a superb performance. She took four curtain calls and her cheeks were flushed and her eyes bright. The flowers that Mr. Graves had sent were delivered over the footlights, and she stood holding them in one hand while she clutched the bottle with the other.

Mrs. Graves slipped her wrap over her shoulders. "I wonder where Lois is. I hope she isn't minding too much."

"Judy was good," Mr. Graves said. "She was damned good."

They walked up the aisle. At the door, Pete Adams stopped them and clapped Mr. Graves on the shoulders. "Best thing I ever saw, the act your daughter put on!" he cried. "Reminded me of you, Harry." He wiped the tears from his eyes and coughed convulsively. "Congratulations, Grace! Congratulations!"

Mrs. Graves caught sight of Miss Lucy Smith and glanced hastily away. But Miss Smith bore down on them. She was a plump, white-haired woman, and she was smiling. "Wasn't Judy marvellous?" she said. "I had no idea she had it in her. She didn't act at all like that at rehearsals. To tell you the truth"—she lowered her voice—"I thought she made the other girls seem a trifle *wooden*."

The door to the basement opened and the members of the cast streamed out. In the centre of the group was Judy. She had taken off her wig and her soft hair fell to her shoulders. She carried the property bottle in one hand and her face was streaked with makeup. In her eyes shone a look of utter joy and pride. With her, holding tightly to her arm, was Lois, who caught sight of her father and mother. "Here she is!" she called. "Here's Judy! Talk about your Moscow Art Theatre for real swell acting!"

Judy ran toward them and Mrs. Graves caught her in her arms. She smelled of grease paint, perspiration, and moth balls, and she was trembling.

For an instant she buried her face against her mother, and Mrs. Graves knew that she was close to tears. "You were lovely, Judy darling," she whispered.

"You were great!" Mr. Graves said, and patted her head roughly. Children crowded around them and teachers and parents stopped to congratulate them. Judy seemed to be living in a dream. She leaned closer to her mother and then shook herself free. "Here," she said, and handed the bottle to her father. "Miss Smith says I can keep this for a souvenir. Hold it for me, will you, while I change my clothes?"

Mr. Graves took the bottle, which was made of papier-mâché, and tucked it proudly under his arm. "You run along," he said. "We'll wait here for you. And take your time. There's no hurry."

Booth Tarkington

WHITEY

Penrod and Sam made a gloomy discovery one morning in mid-October. All the week had seen amiable breezes and fair skies until Saturday, when, about breakfast-time, the dome of heaven filled solidly with gray vapour and began to drip. The boys' discovery was that there is no justice about the weather.

They sat in the carriage-house of the Schofields' empty stable; the doors upon the alley were open, and Sam and Penrod stared torpidly at the thin but implacable drizzle which was the more irritating because there was barely enough of it to interfere with a number of things they had planned to do.

"Yes; this is *nice!*" Sam said, in a tone of plaintive sarcasm. "This is a *perty* way to do!" (He was alluding to the personal spitefulness of the elements.) "I'd like to know what's the sense of it—ole sun pourin' down every day in the week when nobody needs it, then cloud up and rain all Saturday! My father said it's goin' to be a three days' rain."

"Well, nobody with any sense cares if it rains Sunday and Monday," said Penrod. "I wouldn't care if it rained every Sunday as long I lived; but I just like to know what's the reason it had to go and rain to-day. Got all the days o' the week to choose from and goes and picks on Saturday. That's a fine biz'nuss!"

"Well, in vacation——" Sam began, but at a sound from a source invisible to him he paused. "What's that?" he said, somewhat startled.

It was a curious sound, loud and hollow and unhuman, yet it seemed to be a cough. Both boys rose, and Penrod asked uneasily:

"Where'd that noise come from?"

"It's in the alley," said Sam.

Perhaps if the day had been bright, both of them would have stepped immediately to the alley doors to investigate; but their actual procedure was to move a little distance in the opposite direction. The strange cough sounded again.

"*Say!*" Penrod quavered. "What *is* that?"

Then both boys uttered smothered exclamations and jumped, for the long, gaunt head which appeared in the doorway was entirely unexpected. It was the cavernous and melancholy head of an incredibly thin, old, whitish horse. This head waggled slowly from side to side; the nostrils vibrated; the mouth opened, and the hollow cough sounded again.

Recovering themselves, Penrod and Sam underwent the customary human reaction from alarm to indignation.

"What you want, you ole horse, you?" Penrod shouted. "Don't you come coughin' around *me!*"

And Sam, seizing a stick, hurled it at the intruder.

"Get out o' here!" he roared.

The aged horse nervously withdrew his head, turned tail, and made a rickety flight up the alley, while Sam and Penrod, perfectly obedient to inherited impulse, ran out into the drizzle and uproariously pursued. They were but automatons of instinct, meaning no evil. Certainly they did not know the singular and pathetic history of the old horse who had wandered into the alley and ventured to look through the open door.

This horse, about twice the age of either Penrod or Sam, had lived to find himself in a unique position. He was nude, possessing neither harness nor halter; all he had was a name, Whitey, and he would have answered to it by a slight change of expression if any one had thus properly addressed him. So forlorn was Whitey's case, he was actually an independent horse; he had not even an owner. For two days and a half he had been his own master.

Previous to that period he had been the property of one Abalene Morris, a person of colour, who would have explained himself as engaged in the hauling business. On the contrary, the hauling business was an insignificant side line with Mr. Morris, for he had long ago given himself, as utterly as fortune permitted, to that talent which, early in youth, he had recognized as the greatest of all those surging in his bosom. In his waking thoughts and in his dreams, in health and in sickness, Abalene Morris was the dashing and emotional practitioner of an art probably more than Roman in antiquity. Abalene was a crap-shooter. The hauling business was a disguise.

A concentration of events had brought it about that, at one and the same time, Abalene, after a dazzling run of the dice, found the hauling business an actual danger to the preservation of his liberty. He won seventeen dollars and sixty cents, and within the hour found himself in trouble with an officer of the Humane Society on account of an altercation with Whitey. Abalene had been offered four dollars for Whitey some ten days earlier; wherefore he at once drove to the shop of the junk-dealer who had made the offer and announced his acquiescence in the sacrifice.

"*No,* suh!" said the junk-dealer, with emphasis. "I awready done got me a good mule fer my deliv'ry hoss, 'n'at ole Whitey hoss ain' wuff no fo' dollah nohow! I 'uz a fool when I talk 'bout th'owin' money roun' that a-way. *I* know what *you* up to, Abalene. Man come by here li'l bit ago tole me all 'bout white man try to 'rest you, ovah on the avvynoo. Yessuh; he say white man goin' to git you yit an' th'ow you in jail 'count o' Whitey. White man tryin' to fine out who you *is*. He say, nemmine, he'll know Whitey ag'in, even if he don' know you! He say he ketch you by the hoss; so you come roun' tryin' fix me up with Whitey so white man grab me, th'ow *me* in 'at jail. G'on 'way f'um hyuh, you Abalene! You cain' sell an' you cain' give Whitey to no cullud man 'n 'is town. You go an' drowned 'at ole hoss, 'cause you sutny goin' to jail if you git ketched drivin' him."

The substance of this advice seemed good to Abalene, especially as the seventeen dollars and sixty cents in his pocket lent sweet colours to life out of jail at this time. At dusk he led Whitey to a broad common at the edge of town, and spoke to him finally.

"G'on, 'bout you biz'nis," said Abalene; "you ain' *my* hoss. Don' look roun' at me, 'cause *I* ain' got no 'quaintance wif you. I'm a man o' money, an' I got my own frien's; I'm a-lookin' fer bigger cities, hoss. You got you' biz'nis an' I got mine. Mista' Hoss, good-night!"

Whitey found a little frosted grass upon the common and remained there all night. In the morning he sought the shed where Abalene had kept him, but that was across the large and busy town, and Whitey was hopelessly lost. He had but one eye, a feeble one, and his legs were not to be depended upon; but he managed to cover a great deal of ground, to have many painful little adventures, and to get monstrously hungry and thirsty before he happened to look in upon Penrod and Sam.

When the two boys chased him up the alley they had no intention to cause pain; they had no intention at all. They were no more cruel than Duke, Penrod's little old dog, who followed his own instincts, and, making his appearance hastily through a hole in the back fence, joined the pursuit with sound and fury. A boy will nearly always run after anything that is running, and his first impulse is to throw a stone at it. This is a survival of primeval man, who must take every chance to get his dinner. So, when Penrod and Sam drove the hapless Whitey up the alley, they were really responding to an impulse thousands and thousands of years old—an impulse founded upon the primordial observation that whatever runs is likely to prove edible. Penrod and Sam were not "bad"; they were never that. They were something which was not their fault; they were historic.

At the next corner Whitey turned to the right into the cross-street; thence, turning to the right again and still warmly pursued, he zig-zagged down a main thoroughfare until he reached another cross-street, which ran alongside the Schofields' yard and brought him to the foot of the alley he had left behind in his flight. He entered the alley, and there his dim eye fell upon the open door he had previously investigated. No memory of it remained, but the place had a look associated in his mind with hay, and as Sam and Penrod turned the corner of the alley in panting yet still vociferous pursuit, Whitey stumbled up the inclined platform before the open doors, staggered thunderously across the carriage-house and through another open door into a stall, an apartment vacant since the occupancy of Mr. Schofield's last horse, now several years deceased.

The two boys shrieked with excitement as they beheld the coincidence of this strange return. They burst into the stable, making almost as much noise as Duke, who had become frantic at the invasion. Sam laid hands upon a rake.

"You get out o' there, you ole horse, you!" he bellowed. "I ain't afraid to drive him out. I——"

"*Wait* a minute!" shouted Penrod. "Wait till I——"

Sam was manfully preparing to enter the stall.

"You hold the doors open," he commanded, "so's they won't blow shut and keep him in here. I'm goin' to hit him with——"

"Quee-*yut!*" Penrod shouted, grasping the handle of the rake so that Sam could not use it. "Wait a *minute,* can't you " He turned with ferocious voice and gestures upon Duke. *"Duke!"* And Duke, in spite of his excitement, was so impressed that he prostrated himself in silence, and then unobtrusively withdrew from the stable. Penrod ran to the alley doors and closed them.

"My gracious!" Sam protested. "What you goin' to do?"

"I'm goin' to keep this horse," said Penrod, whose face showed the strain of a great idea.

"What *for?*"

"For the reward," said Penrod simply.

Sam sat down in the wheelbarrow and stared at his friend almost with awe.

"My gracious," he said, "I never thought o' that. How—how much do you think we'll get, Penrod?"

Sam's thus admitting himself to a full partnership in the enterprise met no objection from Penrod, who was absorbed in the contemplation of Whitey.

"Well," he said judicially, "we might get more and we might get less."

Sam rose and joined his friend in the doorway opening upon the two stalls. Whitey had preëmpted the nearer, and was hungrily nuzzling the old frayed hollows in the manger.

"Maybe a hundred dollars—or sumpthing?" Sam asked in a low voice.

Penrod maintained his composure and repeated the new-found expression which had sounded well to him a moment before. He recognized it as a symbol of the non-committal attitude that makes people looked up to. "Well"—he made it slow, and frowned—"we might get more and we might get less."

"More'n a hundred *dollars?*" Sam gasped.

"Well," said Penrod, "we might get more and we might get less." This time, however, he felt the need of adding something. He put a question in an indulgent tone, as though he were inquiring, not to add to his own information but to discover the extent of Sam's. "How much do you think horses are worth, anyway?"

"I don't know," said Sam frankly, and unconsciously, he added, "They might be more and they might be less."

"Well, when our ole horse died," said Penrod, "papa said he wouldn't take five hundred dollars for him. That's how much *horses* are worth!"

"My gracious!" Sam exclaimed. Then he had a practical after-thought. "But maybe he was a better horse than this'n. What colour was he?"

"He was bay. Looky here, Sam"—and now Penrod's manner changed from the superior to the eager—"you look what kind of horses they have in a circus, and you bet a circus has the *best* horses, don't it? Well, what kind of horses do they have in a circus? They have some black and white ones, but the best they have are white all over. Well, what kind of a horse is this we got here? He's perty near white right now, and I bet if we washed him off and got him fixed up nice he *would* be white. Well, a bay horse is worth five hundred dollars, because that's what papa said, and this horse——"

Sam interrupted rather timidly.

"He—he's awful bony, Penrod. You don't guess that'd make any—"

Penrod laughed contemptuously.

"Bony! All he needs is a little food and he'll fill right up and look good as ever. You don't know much about horses, Sam, I expect. Why, *our* ole horse—"

"Do you expect he's hungry now?" asked Sam, staring at Whitey.

"Let's try him," said Penrod. "Horses like hay and oats the best, but they'll eat most anything."

"I guess they will. He's tryin' to eat that manger up right now, and I bet it ain't good for him."

"Come on," said Penrod, closing the door that gave entrance to the stalls. "We got to get this horse some drinkin'-water and some good food."

They tried Whitey's appetite first with an autumnal branch which they wrenched from a hardy maple in the yard. They had seen horses nibble leaves, and they expected Whitey to nibble the leaves of this branch, but his ravenous condition did not allow him time for cool discriminations. Sam poked the branch at him from the passageway, and Whitey, after one backward movement of alarm, seized it venomously.

"Here! You stop that!" Sam shouted. "You stop that, you ole horse, you!"

"What's the matter?" called Penrod from the hydrant, where he was filling a bucket. "What's he doin' now?"

"Doin'! He's eatin' the wood part, too! He's chewin' up sticks as big as baseball bats! He's crazy!"

Penrod rushed to see this sight, and stood aghast.

"Take it away from him, Sam!" he commanded sharply.

"Go on, take it away from him yourself!" was the prompt retort of his comrade.

"You had no biz'nuss to give it to him," said Penrod. "Anybody with any sense ought to know it'd make him sick. What'd you want to go and give it to him for?"

"Well, you didn't say not to."

"Well, what if I didn't? I never said I did, did I? You go on in that stall and take it away from him."

"*Yes,* I will!" Sam returned bitterly. Then, as Whitey had dragged the remains of the branch from the manger to the floor of the stall, Sam scrambled to the top of the manger and looked over. "There ain't much left to *take* away! He's swallered it all except some splinters. Better give him the water to try and wash it down with." And, as Penrod complied, "My gracious, look at that horse *drink!*"

They gave Whitey four buckets of water, and then debated the question of nourishment. Obviously, this horse could not be trusted with branches, and, after getting their knees black and their backs sodden, they gave up trying to pull enough grass to sustain him. Then Penrod remembered that horses like apples, both "cooking-apples" and "eating-apples," and Sam mentioned the fact that every autumn his father received a barrel of "cooking-apples" from a cousin who owned a farm. That barrel was in the Williams' cellar now, and the cellar was providentially supplied with "outside doors," so that it could be visited without going through the house. Sam and Penrod set forth for the cellar.

They returned to the stable bulging, and, after a discussion of Whitey's digestion (Sam claiming that eating the core and seeds, as Whitey did, would grow trees in his inside), they went back to the cellar for supplies again—and again. They made six trips, carrying each time a capacity cargo of apples, and still Whitey ate in a famished manner. They were afraid to take more apples from the barrel, which began to show conspicuously the result of their raids, wherefore Penrod made an unostentatious visit to the cellar of his own house. From the inside he opened a window and passed vege-tables out to Sam, who placed them in a bucket and carried them hurriedly to the stable, while Penrod returned in a casual manner through the house. Of his *sang-froid* under a great strain it is sufficient to relate that, in the kitchen, he said suddenly to Della, the cook, "Oh, look behind you!" and by the time Della discovered that there was nothing unusual behind her, Penrod was gone, and a loaf of bread from the kitchen table was gone with him.

Whitey now ate nine turnips, two heads of lettuce, one cabbage, eleven raw potatoes, and the loaf of bread. He ate the loaf of bread last and he was a long time about it; so the boys came to a not unreasonable conclusion.

"Well, sir, I guess we got him filled up at last!" said Penrod. "I bet he wouldn't eat a saucer of ice-cream now, if we'd give it to him!"

"He looks better to me," said Sam, staring critically at Whitey. "I think he's kind of begun to fill out some. I expect he must like us, Penrod; we been doin' a good deal for this horse."

"Well, we got to keep it up," Penrod insisted rather pompously. "Long as *I* got charge o' this horse, he's goin' to get good treatment."

"What we better do now, Penrod?"

Penrod took on the outward signs of deep thought.

"Well, there's plenty to *do,* all right. I got to think."

Sam made several suggestions, which Penrod—maintaining his air of preoccupation—dismissed with mere gestures.

"Oh, *I* know!" Sam cried finally. "We ought to wash him so's he'll look whiter'n what he does now. We can turn the hose on him acrost the manger."

"No; not yet," said Penrod. "It's too soon after his meal. You ought to know that yourself. What we got to do is to make up a bed for him—if he wants to lay down or anything."

"Make up a what for him?" Sam echoed, dumfounded. "What you talkin' about? How can—"

"Sawdust," said Penrod. "That's the way the horse we used to have used to have it. We'll make this horse's bed in the other stall, and then he can go in there and lay down whenever he wants to."

"How we goin' to do it?"

"Look, Sam; there's the hole into the sawdust-box! All you got to do is walk in there with the shovel, stick the shovel in the hole till it gets full of sawdust, and then sprinkle it around on the empty stall."

"All *I* got to do!" Sam cried. "What are you goin' to do?"

"I'm goin' to be right here," Penrod answered reassuringly. "He won't kick or anything, and it isn't goin' to take you half a second to slip around behind him to the other stall."

"What makes you think he won't kick?"

"Well, I *know* he won't, and, besides, you could hit him with the shovel if he tried to. Anyhow, I'll be right here, won't I?"

"I don't care where you are," Sam said earnestly. "What difference would that make if he ki—"

"Why, you were goin' right in the stall," Penrod reminded him. "When he first came in, you were goin' to take the rake and—"

"I don't care if I was," Sam declared. "I was excited then."

"Well, you can get excited now, can't you?" his friend urged. "You can just as easy get—"

He was interrupted by a shout from Sam, who was keeping his eye upon Whitey throughout the discussion.

"Look! Looky there!" And undoubtedly renewing his excitement, Sam pointed at the long, gaunt head beyond the manger. It was disappearing from view. "Look!" Sam shouted. "He's layin' down!"

"Well, then," said Penrod, "I guess he's goin' to take a nap. If he wants to lay down without waitin' for us to get the sawdust fixed for him, that's his lookout, not ours."

On the contrary, Sam perceived a favourable opportunity for action.

"I just as soon go and make his bed up while he's layin' down," he volunteered. "You climb up on the manger and watch him, Penrod, and I'll sneak in the other stall and fix it all up nice for him, so's he can go in there any time when he wakes up, and lay down again, or anything; and if he starts to get up, you holler and I'll jump out over the other manger."

Accordingly, Penrod established himself in a position to observe the recumbent figure. Whitey's breathing was rather laboured but regular, and, as Sam remarked, he looked "better," even in his slumber. It is not to be doubted that, although Whitey was suffering from a light attack of colic, his feelings were in the main those of contentment. After trouble, he was solaced; after exposure, he was sheltered; after hunger and thirst, he was fed and watered. He slept.

The noon whistles blew before Sam's task was finished, but by the time he departed for lunch there was made a bed of such quality that Whitey must needs have been a born faultfinder if he complained of

it. The friends parted, each urging the other to be prompt in returning, but Penrod got into threatening difficulties as soon as he entered
the house.

"Penrod," said his mother, "what did you do with that loaf of bread
Della says you took from the table?"

"Ma'am? *What* loaf o' bread?"

"I believe I can't let you go outdoors this afternoon," Mrs. Schofield
said severely. "If you were hungry, you know perfectly well all you
had to do was to—"

"But I wasn't hungry; I—"

"You can explain later," said Mrs. Schofield. "You'll have all afternoon."

Penrod's heart grew cold.

"I *can't* stay in," he protested. "I've asked Sam Williams to come
over."

"I'll telephone Mrs. Williams."

"Mamma!" Penrod's voice became agonized. "I *had* to give that
bread to a—to a poor ole man. He was starving and so were his children and his wife. They were all just *starving*—and they couldn't wait
while I took time to come and ask you, mamma. I *got* to go outdoors
this afternoon. I *got* to! Sam's—"

She relented.

In the carriage-house, half an hour later, Penrod gave an account of
the episode.

"Where'd we been, I'd just like to know," he concluded, "if I
hadn't got out here this afternoon?"

"Well, I guess I could managed him all right," said Sam. "I was in
the passageway, a minute ago, takin' a look at him. He's standin' up
again. I expect he wants more to eat."

"Well, we got to fix about that," said Penrod. "But what I mean—
if I'd had to stay in the house, where would we been about the most
important thing in the whole biz'nuss?"

"What you talkin' about?"

"Well, why can't you wait till I tell you?" Penrod's tone had become
peevish. For that matter, so had Sam's; they were developing one of
the little differences, or quarrels, that composed the very texture of
their friendship.

"Well, why don't you tell me, then?"

"Well, how can I?" Penrod demanded. "You keep talkin' every minute."

"I'm not talkin' *now*, am I?" Sam protested. "You can tell me *now*, can't you? I'm not talk—"

"You are, too!" shouted Penrod. "You talk all the time! You—"

He was interrupted by Whitey's peculiar cough. Both boys jumped and forgot their argument.

"He means he wants some more to eat, I bet," said Sam.

"Well, if he does, he's got to wait," Penrod declared. "We got to get the most important thing of all fixed up first."

"What's that, Penrod?"

"The reward," said Penrod mildly. "That's what I was tryin' to tell you about, Sam, if you'd ever give me half a chance."

"Well, I *did* give you a chance. I kept *tellin'* you to tell me, but—"

"You never! You kept sayin'—"

They renewed this discussion, protracting it indefinitely; but as each persisted in clinging to his own interpretation of the facts, the question still remained unsettled. It was abandoned, or rather, it merged into another during the later stages of the debate, this other being concerned with which of the debaters had the least "sense." Each made the plain statement that if he were more deficient than his opponent in that regard, self-destruction would be his only refuge. Each declared that he would "rather die than be talked to death"; and then, as the two approached a point bluntly recriminative, Whitey coughed again, whereupon they were miraculously silent, and went into the passageway in a perfectly amiable manner.

"I got to have a good look at him, for once," said Penrod, as he stared frowningly at Whitey. "We got to fix up about that reward."

"I want to take a good ole look at him myself," said Sam.

After supplying Whitey with another bucket of water, they returned to the carriage-house and seated themselves thoughtfully. In truth, they were something a shade more than thoughtful; the adventure to which they had committed themselves was beginning to be a little overpowering. If Whitey had been a dog, a goat, a fowl, or even a stray calf, they would have felt equal to him; but now that the earlier glow of their wild daring had disappeared, vague apprehensions stirred. Their "good look" at Whitey had not reassured them—he seemed large, Gothic, and unusual.

Whisperings within them began to urge that for boys to undertake an enterprise connected with so huge an animal as an actual horse was perilous. Beneath the surface of their musings, dim but ominous prophecies moved; both boys began to have the feeling that, somehow, this affair was going to get beyond them and that they would be in heavy trouble before it was over—they knew not why. They knew why no more than they knew why they felt it imperative to keep the fact of Whitey's presence in the stable a secret from their respective families, but they did begin to realize that keeping a secret of that size was going to be attended with some difficulty. In brief, their sensations were becoming comparable to those of the man who stole a house.

Nevertheless, after a short period given to unspoken misgivings, they returned to the subject of the reward. The money-value of bay horses, as compared to white, was again discussed, and each announced his certainty that nothing less than "a good ole hunderd dollars" would be offered for the return of Whitey.

But immediately after so speaking they fell into another silence, due to sinking feelings. They had spoken loudly and confidently, and yet they knew, somehow, that such things were not to be. According to their knowledge, it was perfectly reasonable to suppose that they would receive this fortune, but they frightened themselves in speaking of it; they knew that they *could* not have a hundred dollars for their own. An oppression, as from something awful and criminal, descended upon them at intervals.

Presently, however, they were warmed to a little cheerfulness again by Penrod's suggestion that they should put a notice in the paper. Neither of them had the slightest idea how to get it there, but such details as that were beyond the horizon; they occupied themselves with the question of what their advertisement ought to "say." Finding that they differed irreconcilably, Penrod went to a cache of his in the sawdust-box and brought two pencils and a supply of paper. He gave one of the pencils and several sheets to Sam; then both boys bent themselves in silence to the labour of practical composition. Penrod produced the briefer paragraph. (See Fig. I.) Sam's was more ample. (See Fig. II.)

Neither Sam nor Penrod showed any interest in what the other had written, but both felt that something praiseworthy had been accomplished. Penrod exhaled a sigh, as of relief, and, in a manner he had observed his father use sometimes, he said:

FIG I

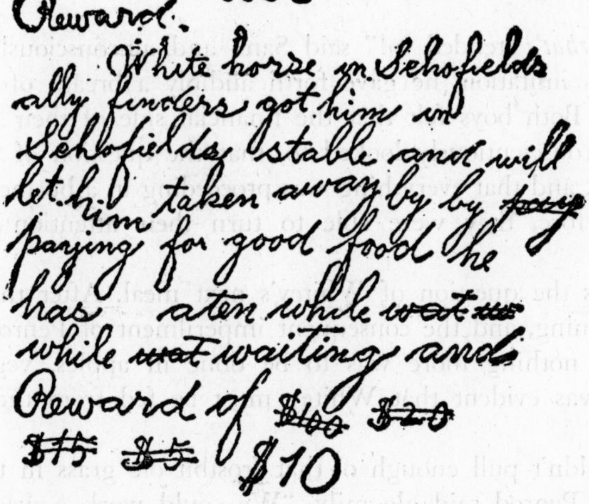

Reward.

White horse in Schofields ally finders got him in Schofieldsy stable and will let him taken away by by pay paying for good food he has aten while wat wa while wat waiting and Reward of $100 $20 $15 $5 $10

FIG II

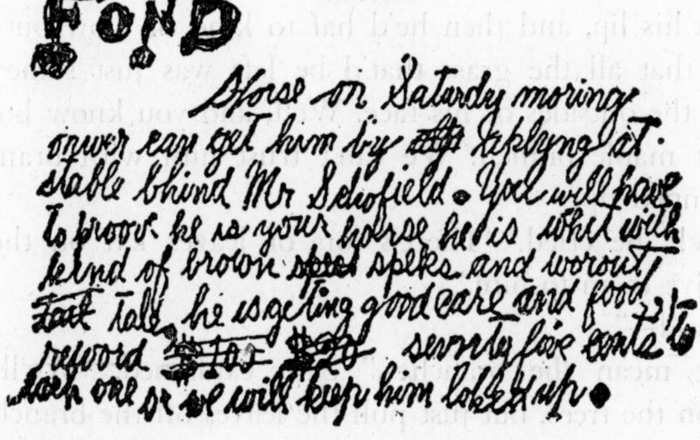

FOND

Horse on Saturday moring onwer can get him by sky aplying at stable bhind Mr Schofield. You will have to proov he is your horse he is whet with kfind of broon spot speks and worout tait tale he is geting good care and food reword $100 $20 seventy five cents each one or we will keep him lokt up.

"Thank goodness, *that's* off my mind, anyway!"

"What we goin' do next, Penrod?" Sam asked deferentially, the borrowed manner having some effect upon him.

"I don't know what *you're* goin' to do," Penrod returned, picking up the old cigarbox which had contained the paper and pencils. *"I'm* goin' to put mine in here, so's it'll come in handy when I haf to get at it."

"Well, I guess. I'll keep mine there, too," said Sam. Thereupon he deposited his scribbled slip beside Penrod's in the cigarbox, and the box was solemnly returned to the secret place whence it had been taken.

"There, *that's* 'tended to!" said Sam, and, unconsciously imitating his friend's imitation, he gave forth audibly a breath of satisfaction and relief. Both boys felt that the financial side of their great affair had been conscientiously looked to, that the question of the reward was settled, and that everything was proceeding in a businesslike manner. Therefore, they were able to turn their attention to another matter.

This was the question of Whitey's next meal. After their exploits of the morning, and the consequent imperilment of Penrod, they decided that nothing more was to be done in apples, vegetables, or bread; it was evident that Whitey must be fed from the bosom of nature.

"We couldn't pull enough o' that frostbit ole grass in the yard to feed him," Penrod said gloomily. "We could work a week and not get enough to make him swaller more'n about twice. All we got this morning, he blew most of it away. He'd try to scoop it in toward his teeth with his lip, and then he'd haf to kind of blow out his breath, and after that all the grass that'd be left was just some wet pieces stickin' to the outsides of his face. Well, and you know how he acted about that maple branch. We can't trust him with branches."

Sam jumped up.

"*I* know!" he cried. "There's lots of leaves left on the branches. We can give them to him."

"I just said—"

"I don't mean the branches," Sam explained. "We'll leave the branches on the trees, but just pull the leaves off the branches and put 'em in the bucket and feed 'em to him out the bucket."

Penrod thought this plan worth trying, and for three-quarters of an hour the two boys were busy with the lower branches of various trees in the yard. Thus they managed to supply Whitey with a fair quantity of wet leaves, which he ate in a perfunctory way, displaying little of his earlier enthusiasm. And the work of his purveyors might have been more tedious if it had been less damp, for a boy is seldom bored by anything that involves his staying-out in the rain without protection. The drizzle had thickened; the leaves were heavy with water, and at every jerk the branches sent fat drops over the two collectors. They attained a noteworthy state of sogginess.

Finally, they were brought to the attention of the authorities indoors, and Della appeared upon the back porch.

"Musther Penrod," she called, "y'r mamma says ye'll c'm in the house this minute an' change y'r shoes an' stockin's an' everythun' else ye got on! D'ye hear me?"

Penrod, taken by surprise and unpleasantly alarmed, darted away from the tree he was depleting and ran for the stable.

"You tell her I'm dry as toast!" he shouted over his shoulder.

Della withdrew, wearing the air of a person gratuitously insulted; and a moment later she issued from the kitchen, carrying an umbrella. She opened it and walked resolutely to the stable.

"She says I'm to bring ye in the house," said Della, "an' I'm goin' to bring ye!"

Sam had joined Penrod in the carriage-house, and, with the beginnings of an unnamed terror, the two beheld this grim advance. But they did not stay for its culmination. Without a word to each other they hurriedly tiptoed up the stairs to the gloomy loft, and there they paused, listening.

They heard Della's steps upon the carriage-house floor.

"Ah, there's plenty places t'hide in," they heard her say; "but I'll show ye! She tole me to bring ye, and I'm—"

She was interrupted by a peculiar sound—loud, chilling, dismal, and unmistakably not of human origin. The boys knew it for Whitey's cough, but Della had not their experience. A smothered shriek reached their ears; there was a scurrying noise, and then, with horror, they heard Della's footsteps in the passageway that ran by Whitey's manger. Immediately there came a louder shriek, and even in the anguish of knowing their secret discovered, they were shocked to hear distinctly the words, "O Lard in hivvin!" in the well-known voice of Della. She shrieked again, and they heard the rush of her footfalls across the carriage-house floor. Wild words came from the outer air, and the kitchen door slammed violently. It was all over. She had gone to "tell."

Penrod and Sam plunged down the stairs and out of the stable. They climbed the back fence and fled up the alley. They turned into Sam's yard, and, without consultation, headed for the cellar doors, nor paused till they found themselves in the farthest, darkest, and gloomiest recess of the cellar. There, perspiring, stricken with fear, they sank down upon the earthen floor, with their moist backs against the stone wall.

Thus with boys. The vague apprehensions that had been creeping upon Penrod and Sam all afternoon had become monstrous; the unknown was before them. How great their crime would turn out to be (now that it was in the hands of grown people), they did not know, but, since it concerned a horse, it would undoubtedly be considered of terrible dimensions.

Their plans for a reward, and all the things that had seemed both innocent and practical in the morning, now staggered their minds as manifestations of criminal folly. A new and terrible light seemed to play upon the day's exploits; they had chased a horse belonging to strangers, and it would be said that they deliberately drove him into the stable and there concealed him. They had, in truth, virtually stolen him, and they had stolen food for him. The waning light through the small window above them warned Penrod that his inroads upon the vegetables in his own cellar must soon be discovered. Della, that Nemesis, would seek them in order to prepare them for dinner, and she would find them not. But she would recall his excursion to the cellar, for she had seen him when he came up; and also the truth would be known concerning the loaf of bread. Altogether, Penrod felt that his case was worse than Sam's—until Sam offered a suggestion which roused such horrible possibilities concerning the principal item of their offense that all thought of the smaller indictments disappeared.

"Listen, Penrod," Sam quavered: "What—what if that—what if that ole horse maybe b'longed to a—policeman!" Sam's imagination was not of the comforting kind. "What'd they—do to us, Penrod, if it turned out he was some policeman's horse?"

Penrod was able only to shake his head. He did not reply in words, but both boys thenceforth considered it almost inevitable that Whitey *had* belonged to a policeman, and in their sense of so ultimate a disaster, they ceased for a time to brood upon what their parents would probably do to them. The penalty for stealing a policeman's horse would be only a step short of capital, they were sure. They would not be hanged; but vague, looming sketches of something called the penitentiary began to flicker before them.

It grew darker in the cellar, so that finally they could not see each other.

"I guess they're huntin' for us by now," Sam said huskily. "I don't —I don't like it much down here, Penrod."

Penrod's hoarse whisper came from the profound gloom:

"Well, who ever said you did?"

"Well—" Sam paused; then he said plaintively, "I wish we'd never seen that dern ole horse."

"It was every bit his fault," said Penrod. *"We* didn't do anything. If he hadn't come stickin' his ole head in our stable, it'd never happened at all. Ole fool!" He rose. "I'm goin' to get out of here; I guess I've stood about enough for one day."

"Where—where you goin', Penrod? You aren't goin' *home,* are you?"

"No; I'm not! What you take me for? You think I'm crazy?"

"Well, where *can* we go?"

How far Penrod's desperation actually would have led him is doubtful, but he made this statement:

"I don't know where *you're* goin', but *I'm* goin' to walk straight out in the country till I come to a farmhouse and say my name's George and live there!"

"I'll do it, too," Sam whispered eagerly. "I'll say my name's Henry."

"Well, we better get started," said the executive Penrod. "We got to get away from here, anyway."

But when they came to ascend the steps leading to the "outside doors," they found that those doors had been closed and locked for the night.

"It's no use," Sam lamented, "and we can't bust 'em, 'cause I tried to, once before. Fanny always locks 'em about five o'clock—I forgot. We got to go up the stairway and try to sneak out through the house."

They tiptoed back, and up the inner stairs. They paused at the top, then breathlessly stepped out into a hall which was entirely dark. Sam touched Penrod's sleeve in warning, and bent to listen at a door.

Immediately that door opened, revealing the bright library, where sat Penrod's mother and Sam's father.

It was Sam's mother who had opened the door.

"Come into the library, boys," she said. "Mrs. Schofield is just telling us about it."

And as the two comrades moved dumbly into the lighted room, Penrod's mother rose, and, taking him by the shoulder, urged him close to the fire.

"You stand there and try to dry off a little, while I finish telling Mr. and Mrs. Williams about you and Sam," she said. "You'd better make Sam keep near the fire, too, Mrs. Williams, because they both got wringing wet. Think of their running off just when most people would have wanted to stay! Well, I'll go on with the story, then. Della told me all about it, and what the cook next door said *she'd* seen, how they'd been trying to pull grass and leaves for the poor old thing all day—and all about the apples they carried from *your* cellar, and getting wet and working in the rain as hard as they could—and they'd given him a loaf of bread! Shame on you, Penrod!" She paused to laugh, but there was a little moisture round her eyes, even before she laughed. "And they'd fed him on potatoes and lettuce and cabbage and turnips out of *our* cellar! And I wish you'd see the sawdust bed they made for him! Well, when I'd telephoned, and the Humane Society man got there, he said it was the most touching thing he ever knew. It seems he *knew* this horse, and had been looking for him. He said ninety-nine boys out of a hundred would have chased the poor old thing away, and he was going to see to it that this case didn't go unnoticed, because the local branch of the society gives little silver medals for special acts like this. And the last thing he said before he led the poor old horse away was that he was sure Penrod and Sam each would be awarded one at the meeting of the society next Thursday night."

. . . On the following Saturday morning a yodel sounded from the sunny sidewalk in front of the Schofields' house, and Penrod, issuing forth, beheld the familiar figure of Samuel Williams in waiting.

Upon Sam's breast there glittered a round bit of silver suspended by a white ribbon from a bar of the same metal. Upon the breast of Penrod was a decoration precisely similar.

" 'Lo, Penrod," said Sam. "What you goin' to do?"

"Nothin'."

"I got mine on," said Sam.

"I have, too," said Penrod. "I wouldn't take a hunderd dollars for mine."

"I wouldn't take two hunderd for mine," said Sam.

Each glanced pleasantly at the other's medal. They faced each other without shame. Neither had the slightest sense of hypocrisy either in himself or in his comrade. On the contrary!

Penrod's eyes went from Sam's medal back to his own; thence they wandered, with perhaps a little disappointment, to the lifeless street and to the empty yards and spectatorless windows of the neighbour-hood. Then he looked southward toward the busy heart of the town, where multitudes were.

"Let's go down and see what time it is by the court-house clock," said Penrod.

Mark Twain

HUCK AND JIM TALK ABOUT KINGS*

By and by, when we got up, we turned over the truck the gang had stole off of the wreck, and found boots, and blankets, and clothes, and all sorts of other things, and a lot of books, and a spy-glass, and three boxes of seegars. We hadn't ever been this rich before in neither of our lives. The seegars was prime. We laid off all the afternoon in the woods talking, and me reading the books, and having a general good time. I told Jim all about what happened inside the wreck and at the ferryboat, and I said these kinds of things was adventures; but he said he didn't want no more adventures. He said that when I went in the texas and he crawled back to get on the raft and found her gone he nearly died, because he judged it was all up with *him* anyway it could be fixed; for if he didn't get saved he would get drownded; and if he did get saved, whoever saved him would send him back home so as to get the reward, and then Miss Watson would sell him South, sure. Well, he was right; he was most always right; he had an uncommon level head for a nigger.

I read considerable to Jim about kings and dukes and earls and such, and how gaudy they dressed, and how much style they put on, and called each other your majesty, and your grace, and your lord-ship, and so on, 'stead of mister; and Jim's eyes bugged out, and he was interested. He says:

"I didn' know dey was so many un um. I hain't hearn 'bout none un um, skasely, but ole King Sollermun, onless you counts dem kings dat's in a pack er k'yards. How much do a king git?"

"Get?" I says; "why, they get a thousand dollars a month if they want it; they can have just as much as they want; everything belongs to them."

This conversation takes place when Huck and Jim are hiding out on an island in the Mississippi. It is Chapter 14 of "The Adventures of Huckleberry Finn."

"*Ain'* dat gay? En what dey got to do, Huck?"

"*They* don't do nothing! Why, how you talk! They just set around."

"No; is dat so?"

"Of course it is. They just set around—except, maybe, when there's a war; then they go to the war. But other times they just lazy around; or go hawking—just hawking and sp— Sh!—d'you hear a noise?"

We skipped out and looked; but it warn't nothing but the flutter of a steamboat's wheel away down, coming around the point; so we come back.

"Yes," says I, "and other times, when things is dull, they fuss with the parlyment; and if everybody don't go just so he whacks their heads off. But mostly they hang round the harem."

"Roun' de which?"

"Harem."

"What's de harem?"

"The place where he keeps his wives. Don't you know about the harem? Solomon had one; he had about a million wives."

"Why, yes, dat's so; I—I'd done forgot it. A harem's a bo'd'n-house, I reck'n. Mos' likely dey has rackety times in de nussery. En I reck'n de wives quarrels considable; en dat 'crease de racket. Yit dey say Sollermun de wises' man dat ever live'. I doan' take no stock in dat. Bekase why: would a wise man want to live in de mids' er sich a blim-blammin' all de time? No—'deed he wouldn't. A wise man 'ud take en buil' a biler-factry; en den he could shet *down* de biler-factry when he want to res'."

"Well, but he *was* the wisest man, anyway; because the widow she told me so, her own self."

"I doan' k'yer what de widder say, he *warn't* no wise man nuther. He had some er de dad-fetchedes' ways I ever see. Does you know 'bout dat chile dat he 'uz gwyne to chop in two?"

"Yes, the widow told me all about it."

"*Well,* den! Warn' dat de beatenes' notion in de worl'? You jes' take en look at it a minute. Dah's de stump, dah—dat's one er de women; heah's you—dat's de yuther one; I's Sollermun; en dish yer dollar bill's de chile. Bofe un you claims it. What does I do? Does I shin aroun' mongs' de neighbors en fine out which un you de bill *do* b'long to, en han' it over to de right one, all safe en soun', de way dat anybody dat had any gumption would? No; I take en whack de bill in *two,* en give half un it to you, en de yuther half to de yuther woman. Dat's de way Sollermun was gwyne to do wid de chile. Now I want to ast you: what's de use er dat half a bill?—can't buy noth'n wid it. En what use is a half a chile? I wouldn' give a dern for a million un um."

"But hang it, Jim, you've clean missed the point—blame it, you've missed it a thousand mile."

"Who? Me? Go 'long. Doan' talk to *me* 'bout yo' pints. I reck'n I knows sense when I sees it; en dey ain' no sense in sich doin's as dat. De 'spute warn't 'bout a half a chile, de 'spute was 'bout a whole chile; en de man dat think he kin settle a 'spute 'bout a whole chile wid a half a chile doan' know enough to come in out'n de rain. Doan' talk to me 'bout Sollermun, Huck, I knows him by de back."

"But I tell you you don't get the point."

"Blame de pint! I reck'n I knows what I knows. En mine you, de *real* pint is down furder—it's down deeper. It lays in de way Sollermun was raised. You take a man dat's got on'y one or two chillen; is dat man gwyne to be waseful o' chillen? No, he ain't; he can't 'ford it. *He* know how to value 'em. But you take a man dat's got 'bout five million chillen runnin' roun' de house, en it's diffunt. *He* as soon chop a chile in two as a cat. Dey's plenty mo'. A chile er two, mo' er less, warn't no consekens to Sollermun, dad fetch him!"

I never see such a nigger. If he got a notion in his head once, there warn't no getting it out again. He was the most down on Solomon of any nigger I ever see. So I went to talking about other kings, and let Solomon slide. I told about Louis Sixteenth that got his head cut off in France long time ago; and about his little boy the dolphin, that would 'a' been a king, but they took and shut him up in jail, and some say he died there.

"Po' little chap."

"But some says he got out and got away, and come to America."

"Dat's good! But he'll be pooty lonesome—dey ain' no kings here, is dey, Huck?"

"No."

"Den he cain't git no situation. What he gwyne to do?"

"Well, I don't know. Some of them gets on the police, and some of them learns people how to talk French."

"Why, Huck, doan' de French people talk de same way we does?"

"*No,* Jim; you couldn't understand a word they said—not a single word."

"Well, now, I be ding-busted! How do dat come?"

"*I* don't know; but it's so. I got some of their jabber out of a book. S'pose a man was to come to you and say Polly-voo-franzy—what would you think?"

"I wouldn' think nuffn; I'd take en bust him over de head—dat is, if he warn't white. I wouldn't 'low no nigger to call me dat."

"Shucks, it ain't calling you anything. It's only saying, do you know how to talk French?"

"Well, den, why couldn't he say it?"

"Why, he *is* a-saying it. That's a Frenchman's *way* of saying it."

"Well, it's a blame ridicklous way, en I doan' want to hear no mo' 'bout it. Dey ain' no sense in it."

"Looky here, Jim; does a cat talk like we do?"

"No, a cat don't."

"Well, does a cow?"

"No, a cow don't, nuther."

"Does a cat talk like a cow, or a cow talk like a cat?"

"No, dey don't."

"It's natural and right for 'em to talk different from each other, ain't it?"

"Course."

"And ain't it natural and right for a cat and a cow to talk different from *us?*"

"Why, mos' sholy it is."

"Well, then, why ain't it natural and right for a *Frenchman* to talk different from us? You answer me that."

"Is a cat a man, Huck?"

"No."

"Well, den, dey ain't no sense in a cat talkin' like a man. Is a cow a man?—er is a cow a cat?"

"No, she ain't either of them."

"Well, den, she ain't got no business to talk like either one er the yuther of 'em. Is a Frenchman a man?"

"Yes."

"*Well,* den! Dad blame it, why doan' he *talk* like a man? You answer me *dat!*"

I see it warn't no use wasting words—you can't learn a nigger to argue. So I quit.

Ogden Nash

TO A SMALL BOY STANDING ON MY SHOES WHILE I AM WEARING THEM

Let's straighten this out, my little man,
And reach an agreement if we can.
I entered your door as an honored guest.
My shoes are shined and my trousers are pressed,
And I won't stretch out and read you the funnies
And I won't pretend that we're Easter bunnies.
If you must get somebody down on the floor,
What in the hell are your parents for?
I do not like the things that you say
And I hate the games that you want to play.
No matter how frightfully hard you try,
We've little in common, you and I.
The interest I take in my neighbor's nursery
Would have to grow, to be even cursory,
And I would that performing sons and nephews
Were carted away with the daily refuse,
And I hold that frolicsome daughters and nieces
Are ample excuse for breaking leases.
You may take a sock at your daddy's tummy
Or climb all over your doting mummy,
But keep your attentions to me in check
Or, sonny boy, I will wring your neck.
A happier man today I'd be
Had someone wrung it ahead of me.

Clifford Orr

SAVAGE HOMECOMING

'rieda came back last week from her first summer at Camp Conomo,
nd her mother isn't sure whether it will be quite wise to send her
mother year. She's different somehow, her mother says.

First of all, right in the station, there was that little incident about
ne berries. She came down the platform followed by a porter with
er bags, still shining new, and let her mother kiss her with what
eemed to be a bit of sufferance.

"How are you, darling?" her mother cried.

"*Mokka-lo-cakki,*" said Frieda. At least, that's what her mother
hought she said.

"What, darling?" asked her mother.

"That means 'The-health-spirit-is-smiling,'" said Frieda. "It's Indian.
's what you say when someone says '*Wo-manni-no?*' to you."

"I see," said her mother.

"That means 'How-sits-your-stomach?'"

"Hush, darling!" said her mother.

"It's all right," said Frieda. "It's Indian. Miss McClintock says it.
he used to yell it right across the lake. Sound carries on the water."

"Well," said her mother, "you're certainly looking well. You're
rown as a berry."

"Name one," said Frieda.

"What, dear?" her mother asked.

"Berries," said Frieda, "are red, blue, black, white, and green. They're
eldom or never brown, and if you say that anything is brown as a
erry, you could never be an Eagle in Elementary Nature. You'd be
ιcky if you even got to be a Nuthatch."

"I see, dear," said her mother.

Nothing really untoward happened during dinner. Frieda talked,
er mother said, in a rather strange sort of jargon, but her mother

refrained from any leading questions. She did, however, notice the frequency with which Miss McClintock's name came into the conversation, and finally she got up sufficient courage to ask about her.

"Miss McClintock is Head Counselor of the Otters. Those are the girls who live between the basketball court and the Grand Canyon. The girls on the other side, over near Yosemite and the cookhouse, are Beavers. The Otters are much the best. I wouldn't be a Beaver for anything. The Beavers haven't won Woodcraft for three years."

Her mother clucked, disparagingly.

"Miss McClintock goes to Wellesley," Frieda continued. "I've decided to go to Wellesley."

"But Frieda, dear," said her mother, "you always wanted to go to Vassar, and Father and I registered you when you were just a little thing. Mother would like to have you go where she went."

"Wellesley is best," said Frieda. "Miss McClintock can chin herself nineteen times."

"I'm sure that Miss McClintock is very nice," said her mother, "but we shouldn't let things like—"

"There's a Vassar girl who's one of the counselors of the Beavers," Frieda interrupted. "Miss Fellows. She teaches Basketry."

"Well, she's nice, isn't she?" her mother asked, a trifle timidly.

"She can't clean fish," said Frieda.

Somehow, her mother thought, Frieda's standards had changed. So, it became apparent at bedtime, had her habits. It had always before been a bit of an ordeal to get her upstairs at the appropriate hour, but tonight she discovered that it was eight-thirty all by herself.

"Kama-bo," she said, standing in the doorway.

Her mother guessed that this meant "Good night," so she said it herself, "Kama-bo!," and was rewarded by a smile of understanding as Frieda lifted three outstretched fingers in what was evidently a gesture of benison. She disappeared, but in a moment she was at the door again.

"Mother," she asked, "in case you need anything in the night, do you know the Cry of Distress?"

"I'm sure I shan't need anything, Frieda. Thank you just the same."

"Well, this is it, anyway," said Frieda. "If you cry 'Conomo!' just once, why that's just a greeting or to let people know you're in the neighborhood, and friendly, see?"

"Yes, dear."

"If you do it twice—'*Conomo! Conomo!*'—that means that you've found a new Specimen or have located the next Cairn, and the others should try to come where you are. Is that clear?"

"Perfectly, dear, but I doubt very much if tonight—"

"But if you cry it three times, with a note of alarm," Frieda went on, "like this—'*Conomo! Conomo! Conomo!*'—that's the Cry of Distress, and I'll come at double-time with a first-aid kit and, if possible, a hand axe and a piece of rope."

"I see, dear," her mother said. "I'll try to remember, and I'm sure you'll be of great help if Mother calls."

"The rope, of course," said Frieda, rather ominously, "is in case of Quicksand."

It was eleven o'clock when Frieda's mother went up to bed. It was after twelve-thirty when she woke up with a dry throat, a tickling in her nostrils, and a slowly reached conviction that she was smelling smoke. In less than a minute, after rushing from her room and half-way down the stairs, sniffing, she had thrown open Frieda's door and had been greeted by a cloud of it rolling out.

"Frieda! Frieda!" she called. "Frieda!"

"Tent Number Eight," said Frieda's sleepy voice from the bed. "All present."

Pawing her way through the smoke and finding the light switch, her mother eventually discovered that there was a small and sullen blaze in the fireplace, and that was all. The fire had been laid and unused all summer and the chimney draught evidently kept closed. But the smoke was almost unbearable. By practically main force, she dragged Frieda from the room and closed the door behind them. She would wake Annie and send her in to open the draught. Frieda was coughing and choking a bit, too, if sleepily. She was coherent enough, though, when her mother had put her into her father's bed and opened the windows wide.

"I was making a smudge," said Frieda.

"You certainly were," said her mother. "What on earth did you light the fire for, and why didn't you open the draught?"

"I felt a mosquito," said Frieda, "so I closed the draught and made a smudge."

"But Frieda, dear, there couldn't have been any mosquitoes. We haven't had any all summer. The screens are brand-new."

"I opened the screens," said Frieda. "Screens are symbols of civilization."

Her mother sat there, pondering this for a while, and finally Frieda spoke again.

"I used a match to light the fire, though," she said, more slowly and more faintly. "I didn't have any tinder. I might have scraped the furniture, only it's maple. Ash is best for tinder."

Her mother sat for another moment, and then rose and switched off the light.

"Good night, Frieda," she said.

There was a long pause.

"*Kama-bo*, Miss McClintock," said Frieda.

SATIRE—BROAD AND OTHERWISE

To satirize is to comment upon something with some keenness and imagination, perhaps in a rather roundabout or indirect fashion, sometimes savagely. Almost all humor is, roughly, satire. Obviously this section of the book could have been swelled to enormous proportions if there had been room. Some of our readers may quibble about the presence of the Franklin letters under this heading, since it appears (according to Mr. Carl Van Doren, anyway) that the old fellow actually wanted to marry the lady. But even in love, Franklin was a master of satiric persiflage.

The piece called "Mother Taft's Chickens" is simply an oddity—a bit of deadpan research, the sort of thing The New Yorker *has done with good effect many times.*

Artemus Ward

THE SHAKERS

he Shakers is the strangest religious sex I ever met. I'd hearn tell of
·m and I'd seen 'em, with their broad brim'd hats and long wastid
oats; but I'd never cum into immejit contack with 'em, and I'd sot
·m down as lackin intelleck, as I'd never seen 'em to my Show—least-
vays, if they cum they was disgised in white peple's close, so I didn't
now 'em.

But in the Spring of 18—, I got swampt in the exterior of New York
tate, one dark and stormy night, when the winds Blue pityusly, and
was forced to tie up with the Shakers.

I was toilin threw the mud, when in the dim vister of the futer I
bsarved the gleams of a taller candle. Tiein a hornet's nest to my off
oss's tail to kinder encourage him, I soon reached the place. I knockt
t the door, which it was opened unto me by a tall, slick-faced, solum
ookin individooal, who turn'd out to be a Elder.

"Mr. Shaker," sed I, "you see before you a Babe in the Woods, so
o speak, and he axes shelter of you."

"Yay," sed the Shaker, and he led the way into the house, another
·haker bein sent to put my hosses and waggin under kiver.

A solum female, lookin sumwhat like a last year's bean-pole stuck
nto a long meal-bag, cum in and axed me was I athurst and did I
ounger, to which I urbanely anserd "a few." She went orf and I en-
leverd to open a conversashun with the old man.

"Elder, I spect?" sed I.

"Yay," he sed.

"Helth's good, I reckon?"

"Yay."

"What's the wages of a Elder, when he understans his bizness—or
lo you devote your sarvices gratooitus?"

"Yay."

"Stormy night, sir."

349

"Yay."

"If the storm continners there'll be a mess underfoot, hay?"

"Yay."

"It's onpleasant when there's a mess underfoot."

"Yay."

"If I may be so bold, kind sir, what's the price of that pecooler kin of weskit you wear, incloodin trimmins?"

"Yay."

I pawsd a minit, and then, thinkin I'd be faseshus with him an see how that would go, I slapt him on the shoulder, bust into a hart larf, and told him that as a *yayer* he had no livin ekal.

He jumpt up as if Bilin water had bin squirted into his ears, groaned rolled his eyes up tords the sealin and sed: "You're a man of sin!" H then walkt out of the room.

Jest then the female in the meal-bag stuck her hed into the room and statid that refreshments awaited the weary traveler, and I sed if was vittles she ment the weary traveler was agreeable, and I follered her into the next room.

I sot down to the table and the female in the meal-bag pored ou sum tea. She sed nothin, and for five minutes the only live thing i that room was a old wooden clock, which tickt in a subdood an bashful manner in the corner. This dethly stillness made me oneasy and I determined to talk to the female or bust. So sez I, "Marrige i agin your rules, I bleeve, marm?"

"Yay."

"The sexes liv strickly apart, I spect?"

"Yay."

"It's kinder singler," sez I, puttin on my most sweetest look an speakin in a winnin voice, "that so fair a made as thou never go hitched to some likely feller." [N.B.—She was upards of 40 and homel as a stump fence, but I thawt I'd tickil her.]

"I don't like men!" she sed, very short.

"Wall, I dunno," sez I, "they're a rayther important part of th populashun. I don't scarcely see how we could git along without 'em.

"Us poor wimin folks would git along a grate deal better if ther was no men!"

"You'll excoos me, marm, but I don't think that air would work. I wouldn't be regler."

"I'm fraid of men!" she sed.

"That's onnecessary, marm, *You* ain't in no danger. Don't fret yourself on that pint."

"Here we're shot out from the sinful world. Here all is peas. Here we air brothers and sisters. We don't marry and consekently we have no domestic difficulties. Husbans don't abooze their wives—wives don't worrit their husbans. There's no children here to worrit us. Nothin to worrit us here. No wicked matrimony here. Would thow like to be a Shaker?"

"No," sez I, "it ain't my stile."

I had now histed in as big a load of pervishuns as I could carry comfortable, and, leanin back in my cheer, commenst pickin my teeth with a fork. The female went out, leavin me all alone with the clock. I hadn't sot thar long before the Elder poked his hed in at the door. "You're a man of sin!" he sed, and groaned and went away.

Direckly thar cum in two young Shakeresses, as putty and slick lookin gals as I ever met. It is troo they was drest in meal-bags like the old one I'd met previsly, and their shiny, silky har was hid from sight by long white caps, sich as I spose female Josts wear; but their eyes sparkled like diminds, their cheeks was like roses, and they was charming enuff to make a man throw stuns at his granmother, if they axed him to. They commenst clearin away the dishes, castin shy glances at me all the time. I got excited. I forgot Betsy Jane in my rapter, and sez I, "My pretty dears, how air you?"

"We air well," they solumly sed.

"Whar's the old man?" sed I, in a soft voice.

"Of whom dost thow speak—Brother Uriah?"

"I mean the gay and festiv cuss who calls me a man of sin. Shouldn't wonder if his name was Uriah."

"He has retired."

"Wall, my pretty dears," sez I, "let's hav sum fun. Let's play Puss in the corner. What say?"

"Air you a Shaker, sir?" they axed.

"Wall, my pretty dears, I haven't arrayed my proud form in a long weskit yit, but if they was all like you perhaps I'd jine 'em. As it is, I'm a Shaker pro-temporary."

They was full of fun. I seed that at fust, only they was a leetle skeery. I tawt 'em Puss in the corner and sich like plase, and we had a nice time, keepin quiet of course so the old man shouldn't hear.

When we broke up, sez I, "My pretty dears, ear I go you hav no objections, hav you, to a innersent kiss at partin?"

"Yay," thay sed, and I *yay'd*.

I went up stairs to bed. I spose I'd bin snoozin half a hour when I was woke up by a noise at the door. I sot up in bed, leanin on my elbers and rubbin my eyes, and I saw the follerin picter: The Elder stood in the doorway, with a taller candle in his hand. He hadn't no wearin appeerel on except his night close, which fluttered in the breeze like a Seseshun flag. He sed, "You're a man of sin!" then groaned and went away.

I went to sleep agin, and drempt of runnin orf with the pretty little Shakeresses, mounted on my Californy Bar. I thawt the Bar insisted on steerin strate for my dooryard in Baldinsville, and that Betsy Jane cum out and giv us a warm recepshun with a panful of Bilin water. I was woke up arly by the Elder. He sed refreshments was reddy for me down stairs. Then sayin I was a man of sin, he went groanin away.

As I was goin threw the entry to the room where the vittles was, I cum across the Elder and the old female I'd met the night before, and what d'ye spose they was up to? Huggin and kissin like young lovers in their gushingist state. Sez I, "My Shaker friends, I reckon you'd better suspend the rules, and git marrid!"

"You must excoos Brother Uriah," sed the female; "he's subjeck to fits, and hain't got no command over hisself when he's into 'em."

"Sartinly," sez I; "I've bin took that way myself frequent."

"You're a man of sin!" said the Elder.

Arter breakfust my little Shaker frends cum in agin to clear away the dishes.

"My pretty dears," sez I, "shall we *yay* agin?"

"Nay," they sed, and I *nay'd*.

The Shakers axed me to go to their meetin, as they was to hav sarvices that mornin, so I put on a clean biled rag and went. The meetin house was as neat as a pin. The floor was white as chalk and smooth as glass. The Shakers was all on hand, in clean weskits and meal-bags, ranged on the floor like milingtery companies, the mails on one side of the room and the females on tother. They commenst clappin their hands and singin and dancin. They danced kinder slow at fust, but as they got warmed up they shaved it down very brisk, I tell you. Elder Uriah, in particler, exhiberted a right smart chance of spryness in his legs, considerin his time of life, and as he cum a dubble shuffle near where I sot, I rewarded him with a approvin smile, and sed: "Hunky boy! Go it, my gay and festiv cuss!"

"You're a man of sin!" he sed, continnerin his shuffle.

The Sperret, as they called it, then moved a short fat Shaker to say a few remarks. He sed they was Shakers and all was ekal. They was the purest and seleckest peple on the yearth. Other peple was sinful as they could be, but Shakers was all right. Shakers was all goin kerslap to the Promist Land, and nobody wa'nt goin to stand at the gate to bar 'em out; if they did they'd git run over.

The Shakers then danced and sung agin, and arter thay was threw, one of 'em axed me what I thawt of it.

Sez I, "What duz it siggerfy?"

"What?" sez he.

"Why this jumpin up and singin? This long-weskit bizniss, and this anty-matrimony idee? My frends, you air neat and tidy. Your lands is flowin with milk and honey. Your brooms is fine, and your apple sass is honest. When a man buys a kag of apple sass of you he don't find a grate many shavins under a few layers of sass—a little Game I'm sorry to say sum of my New Englan ancesters used to practiss. Your garding seeds is fine, and if I should sow 'em on the rock of Gibralter probly I should raise a good mess of garding sass. You air honest in your dealins. You air quiet and don't distarb nobody. For all this I givs you credit. But your religion is small pertaters, I must say. You mope away your lives here in single retchidness, and as you air all by yourselves nothing ever conflicks with your pecooler idees, except when Human Nater busts out among you, as I understan she sumtimes do. (I give Uriah a sly wink here, which made the old feller squirm like a speared Eel.) You wear long weskits and long faces, and lead a gloomy life indeed. No children's prattle is ever hearn around your harthstuns—you air in a dreary fog all the time, and you treat the jolly sunshine of life as tho' it was a thief, drivin it from your doors by them weskits, and meal-bags, and pecooler noshuns of yourn. The gals among you, sum of which air as slick pieces of caliker as I ever sot eyes on, air syin to place their heds agin weskits which kiver honest, manly harts, while you old heds fool yerselves with the idee that they air fulfillin their mishun here, and air contented. Here you air, all pend up by yerselves, talkin about the sins of a world you don't know nothin of. Meanwhile said world continners to resolve round on her own axeltree onct in every 24 hours, subjeck to the Constitution of the United States, and is a very plesant place of residence. It's a unnatral, onreasonable and dismal life you're leadin here. So it strikes me. My Shaker frends, I now bid you a welcome adoo. You hav treated me exceedin well. Thank you kindly, one and all."

"A base exhibiter of depraved monkeys and onprincipled wax works!" sed Uriah.

"Hello, Uriah," sez I, "I'd most forgot you. Wall, look out for them fits of yourn, and don't catch cold and die in the flour of your youth and beauty."

And I resoomed my jerney.

James Thurber

THE GREATEST MAN IN THE WORLD *

Looking back on it now, from the vantage point of 1940, one can only marvel that it hadn't happened long before it did. The United States of America had been, ever since Kitty Hawk, blindly constructing the elaborate petard by which, sooner or later, it must be hoist. It was inevitable that some day there would come roaring out of the skies a national hero of insufficient intelligence, background, and character successfully to endure the mounting orgies of glory prepared for aviators who stayed up a long time or flew a great distance. Both Lindbergh and Byrd, fortunately for national decorum and international amity, had been gentlemen; so had our other famous aviators. They wore their laurels gracefully, withstood the awful weather of publicity, married excellent women, usually of fine family, and quietly retired to private life and the enjoyment of their varying fortunes. No untoward incidents, on a worldwide scale, marred the perfection of their conduct on the perilous heights of fame. The exception to the rule was, however, bound to occur and it did, in July, 1935, when Jack ("Pal") Smurch, erstwhile mechanic's helper in a small garage in Westfield, Iowa, flew a second-hand, single-motored Bresthaven Dragon-Fly III monoplane all the way around the world, without stopping.

Never before in the history of aviation had such a flight as Smurch's ever been dreamed of. No one had even taken seriously the weird floating auxiliary gas tanks, invention of the mad New Hampshire professor of astronomy, Dr. Charles Lewis Gresham, upon which Smurch placed full reliance. When the garage worker, a slightly built, surly, unprepossessing young man of twenty-two, appeared at Roosevelt Field early in July, 1935, slowly chewing a great quid of scrap tobacco, and announced "Nobody ain't seen no flyin' yet," the news-

* *This satiric prophecy was written in 1931, up to which date our national heroes had been well behaved.*

355

papers touched briefly and satirically upon his projected twenty-five-thousand-mile flight. Aëronautical and automotive experts dismissed the idea curtly, implying that it was a hoax, a publicity stunt. The rusty, battered, second-hand plane wouldn't go. The Gresham auxiliary tanks wouldn't work. It was simply a cheap joke.

Smurch, however, after calling on a girl in Brooklyn who worked in the flap-folding department of a large paper-box factory, a girl whom he later described as his "sweet patootie," climbed nonchalantly into his ridiculous plane at dawn of the memorable seventh of July, 1935, spit a curve of tobacco juice into the still air, and took off, carrying with him only a gallon of bootleg gin and six pounds of salami.

When the garage boy thundered out over the ocean the papers were forced to record, in all seriousness, that a mad, unknown young man—his name was variously misspelled—had actually set out upon a preposterous attempt to span the world in a rickety, one-engined contraption, trusting to the long-distance refuelling device of a crazy schoolmaster. When, nine days later, without having stopped once, the tiny plane appeared above San Francisco Bay, headed for New York, spluttering and choking, to be sure, but still magnificently and miraculously aloft, the headlines, which long since had crowded everything else off the front page—even the shooting of the Governor of Illinois by the Capone gang—swelled to unprecedented size, and the news stories began to run to twenty-five and thirty columns. It was noticeable, however, that the accounts of the epoch-making flight touched rather lightly upon the aviator himself. This was not because facts about the hero as a man were too meagre, but because they were too complete.

Reporters, who had been rushed out to Iowa when Smurch's plane was first sighted over the little French coast town of Serly-le-Mer, to dig up the story of the great man's life, had promptly discovered that the story of his life could not be printed. His mother, a sullen short-order cook in a shack restaurant on the edge of a tourists' camping ground near Westfield, met all inquiries as to her son with an angry "Ah, the hell with him; I hope he drowns." His father appeared to be in jail somewhere for stealing spotlights and laprobes from tourists' automobiles; his young brother, a weakminded lad, had but recently escaped from the Preston, Iowa, Reformatory and was already wanted in several Western towns for the theft of money-order blanks from post offices. These alarming discoveries were still piling up at the very time that Pal Smurch, the greatest hero of the twentieth century, blear-eyed, dead for sleep, half-starved, was piloting his crazy junkheap high above the region in which the lamentable story of his private life was being unearthed, headed for New York and a greater glory than any man of his time had ever known.

The necessity for printing some account in the papers of the young man's career and personality had led to a remarkable predicament. It was of course impossible to reveal the facts, for a tremendous popular feeling in favor of the young hero had sprung up, like a grass fire, when he was halfway across Europe on his flight around the globe. He was, therefore, described as a modest chap, taciturn, blond, popular with his friends, popular with girls. The only available snapshot of Smurch, taken at the wheel of a phony automobile in a cheap photo studio at an amusement park, was touched up so that the little vulgarian looked quite handsome. His twisted leer was smoothed into a pleasant smile. The truth was, in this way, kept from the youth's ecstatic compatriots; they did not dream that the Smurch family was despised and feared by its neighbors in the obscure Iowa town, nor that the hero himself, because of numerous unsavory exploits, had come to be regarded in Westfield as a nuisance and a menace. He had, the reporters discovered, once knifed the principal of his high school—not mortally, to be sure, but he had knifed him; and on another occasion, surprised in the act of stealing an altarcloth from a church, he had bashed the sacristan over the head with a pot of Easter lilies; for each of these offences he had served a sentence in the reformatory.

Inwardly, the authorities, both in New York and in Washington, prayed that an understanding Providence might, however awful such a thing seemed, bring disaster to the rusty, battered plane and its illustrious pilot, whose unheard-of flight had aroused the civilized world to hosannas of hysterical praise. The authorities were convinced that the character of the renowned aviator was such that the limelight of adulation was bound to reveal him, to all the world, as a congenital hooligan mentally and morally unequipped to cope with his own prodigious fame. "I trust," said the Secretary of State, at one of many secret Cabinet meetings called to consider the national dilemma, "I trust that his mother's prayer will be answered," by which he referred to Mrs. Emma Smurch's wish that her son might be drowned. It was, however, too late for that—Smurch had leaped

the Atlantic and then the Pacific as if they were millponds. At three
minutes after two o'clock on the afternoon of July 17, 1935, the
garage boy brought his idiotic plane into Roosevelt Field for a perfect
three-point landing.

It had, of course, been out of the question to arrange a modest little
reception for the greatest flier in the history of the world. He was
received at Roosevelt Field with such elaborate and pretentious ceremonies as rocked the world. Fortunately, however, the worn and
spent hero promptly swooned, had to be removed bodily from his
plane, and was spirited from the field without having opened his
mouth once. Thus he did not jeopardize the dignity of this first
reception, a reception illumined by the presence of the Secretaries
of War and the Navy, Mayor Michael J. Moriarity of New York,
the Premier of Canada, Governors Fanniman, Groves, McFeely,
and Critchfield, and a brilliant array of European diplomats. Smurch
did not, in fact, come to in time to take part in the gigantic hullabaloo
arranged at City Hall for the next day. He was rushed to a secluded
nursing home and confined in bed. It was nine days before he was
able to get up, or to be more exact, before he was permitted to get
up. Meanwhile the greatest minds in the country, in solemn assembly,
had arranged a secret conference of city, state, and government officials,
which Smurch was to attend for the purpose of being instructed in the
ethics and behavior of heroism.

On the day that the little mechanic was finally allowed to get up
and dress and, for the first time in two weeks, took a great chew of
tobacco, he was permitted to receive the newspapermen—this by way
of testing him out. Smurch did not wait for questions. "Youse guys,"
he said—and the *Times* man winced—"youse guys can tell the cock-
eyed world dat I put it over on Lindbergh, see? Yeh—an' made an
ass o' them two frogs." The "two frogs" was a reference to a pair
of gallant French fliers who, in attempting a flight only halfway
round the world, had, two weeks before, unhappily been lost at sea.
The *Times* man was bold enough, at this point, to sketch out for
Smurch the accepted formula for interviews in cases of this kind;
he explained that there should be no arrogant statements belittling
the achievements of other heroes, particularly heroes of foreign nations.
"Ah, the hell with that," said Smurch. "I did it, see? I did it, an'
I'm talkin' about it." And he did talk about it.

None of this extraordinary interview was, of course, printed. On the contrary, the newspapers, already under the disciplined direction of a secret directorate created for the occasion and composed of statesmen and editors, gave out to a panting and restless world that "Jacky," as he had been arbitrarily nicknamed, would consent to say only that he was very happy and that anyone could have done what he did. "My achievement has been, I fear, slightly exaggerated," the *Times* man's article had him protest, with a modest smile. These newspaper stories were kept from the hero, a restriction which did not serve to abate the rising malevolence of his temper. The situation was, indeed, extremely grave, for Pal Smurch was, as he kept insisting, "rarin' to go." He could not much longer be kept from a nation clamorous to lionize him. It was the most desperate crisis the United States of America had faced since the sinking of the Lusitania.

On the afternoon of the twenty-seventh of July, Smurch was spirited away to a conference-room in which were gathered mayors, governors, government officials, behaviorist psychologists, and editors. He gave them each a limp, moist paw and a brief unlovely grin. "Hah ya?" he said. When Smurch was seated, the Mayor of New York arose and, with obvious pessimism, attempted to explain what he must say and how he must act when presented to the world, ending his talk with a high tribute to the hero's courage and integrity. The Mayor was followed by Governor Fanniman of New York, who, after a touching declaration of faith, introduced Cameron Spottiswood, Second Secretary of the American Embassy in Paris, the gentleman selected to coach Smurch in the amenities of public ceremonies. Sitting in a chair, with a soiled yellow tie in his hand and his shirt open at the throat, unshaved, smoking a rolled cigarette, Jack Smurch listened with a leer on his lips. "I get ya, I get ya," he cut in, nastily. "Ya want me to ack like a softy, huh? Ya want me to ack like that — ——— baby-face Lindbergh, huh? Well, nuts to that, see?" Everyone took in his breath sharply; it was a sigh and a hiss. "Mr. Lindbergh," began a United States Senator, purple with rage, "and Mr. Byrd—" Smurch, who was paring his nails with a jackknife, cut in again. "Byrd!" he exclaimed. "Aw fa God's sake, *dat* big—" Somebody shut off his blasphemies with a sharp word. A newcomer had entered the room. Everyone stood up, except Smurch, who, still busy with his nails, did not even glance up. "Mr. Smurch," said someone, sternly, "the President of the United States!" It had been thought that the presence of the Chief Executive might have a chastening effect upon the young hero, and the former had been, thanks to the remarkable coöperation of the press, secretly brought to the obscure conference-room.

A great, painful silence fell. Smurch looked up, waved a hand at the President, "How ya comin'?" he asked, and began rolling a fresh cigarette. The silence deepened. Someone coughed in a strained way. "Geez, it's hot, ain't it?" said Smurch. He loosened two more shirt buttons, revealing a hairy chest and the tattooed word "Sadie" enclosed in a stencilled heart. The great and important men in the room, faced by the most serious crisis in recent American history, exchanged worried frowns. Nobody seemed to know how to proceed. "Come awn, come awn," said Smurch. "Let's get the hell out of here! When do I start cuttin' in on de parties, huh? And what's they goin' to be *in* it?" He rubbed a thumb and forefinger together meaningly. "Money!" exclaimed a state senator, shocked, pale. "Yeh, money," said Pal, flipping his cigarette out of a window. "An' big money." He began rolling a fresh cigarette. "Big money," he repeated, frowning over the rice paper. He tilted back in his chair, and leered at each gentleman, separately, the leer of an animal that knows its power, the leer of a leopard loose in a bird-and-dog shop. "Aw fa God's sake, let's get some place where it's cooler," he said. "I been cooped up plenty for three weeks!"

Smurch stood up and walked over to an open window, where he stood staring down into the street, nine floors below. The faint shouting of newsboys floated up to him. He made out his name. "Hot dog!" he cried, grinning, ecstatic. He leaned out over the sill. "You tell 'em, babies!" he shouted down. "Hot diggity dog!" In the tense little knot of men standing behind him, a quick, mad impulse flared up. An unspoken word of appeal, of command, seemed to ring through the room. Yet it was deadly silent. Charles K. L. Brand, secretary to the Mayor of New York City, happened to be standing nearest Smurch; he looked inquiringly at the President of the United States. The President, pale, grim, nodded shortly. Brand, a tall, powerfully built man, once a tackle at Rutgers, stepped forward, seized the greatest man in the world by his left shoulder and the seat of his pants, and pushed him out the window.

"My God, he's fallen out the window!" cried a quick-witted editor.

"Get me out of here!" cried the President. Several men sprang to his side and he was hurriedly escorted out of a door toward a side-entrance of the building. The editor of the Associated Press took charge, being used to such things. Crisply he ordered certain men to leave, others to stay; quickly he outlined a story which all the papers were to agree on, sent two men to the street to handle that end of the tragedy, commanded a Senator to sob and two Congressmen to go to pieces nervously. In a word, he skillfully set the stage for the gigantic task that was to follow, the task of breaking to a grief-stricken world the sad story of the untimely, accidental death of its most illustrious and spectacular figure.

The funeral was, as you know, the most elaborate, the finest, the solemnest, and the saddest ever held in the United States of America. The monument in Arlington Cemetery, with its clean white shaft of marble and the simple device of a tiny plane carved on its base, is a place for pilgrims, in deep reverence, to visit. The nations of the world paid lofty tributes to little Jacky Smurch, America's greatest hero. At a given hour there were two minutes of silence throughout the nation. Even the inhabitants of the small, bewildered town of Westfield, Iowa, observed this touching ceremony; agents of the Department of Justice saw to that. One of them was especially assigned to stand grimly in the doorway of a little shack restaurant on the edge of the tourists' camping ground just outside the town. There, under his stern scrutiny, Mrs. Emma Smurch bowed her head above two hamburger steaks sizzling on her grill—bowed her head and turned away, so that the Secret Service man could not see the twisted, strangely familiar, leer on her lips.

Benjamin Franklin

THREE LOVE LETTERS*

(From Franklin to Madame Helvétius)

I

Mr. Franklin is sorry to have caused the least harm to that beautiful hair, which he always admires with so much Pleasure. If that Lady likes to pass her Days with him, he in turn would like to pass his Nights with her; & as he has already given her many of his days, though he has so few left to give, she appears ungrateful never to have given him a single one of her nights, which steadily pass as a pure loss, without giving happiness to anyone, except Poupon. He nevertheless embraces her heartily, for he loves her infinitely in spite of all her faults.

II

Mr. Franklin having risen, washed, shaved, combed and beautified himself as much as possible, all dressed and on the point of going out, with his head full of the 4 Mesdames Helvétius, & of the sweet kisses which he planned to get from her, is much mortified to find the Possibility of this Felicity put off till next Sunday. However, he will bear up with what Patience he can, hoping to see one of these Ladies at M. de Chaumont's on Wednesday. He will be there early, to see her enter with that Grace & Dignity which so charmed him seven Weeks ago in the same place. He even plans to stop her there & to keep her at his house for life. Her three other selves remaining at Auteil will suffice for the Canary-birds & the Abbés.

The originals are in French, and are here translated by Paul McPharlin. The first was dated Passy, Sept. 19, 1779; the third letter was printed by Franklin at his Passy press. When he wrote them he was United States Minister to France. Madame Helvétius was the attractive widow of a French philosopher.

III

Nettled by your barbarous Resolution, so emphatically stated yesterday evening, to remain single for life in honour of your dear husband, I returned home, fell upon my Bed thinking myself dead, and found myself in the Elysian Fields.

I was asked whether I wished to see any People in particular. 'Take me to the Philosophers.' 'There are two who live near here in this Garden: they are very good Neighbours and Friends to each other.' 'Who are they?' 'Socrates and Helvétius.' 'I hold them both in tremendous Esteem; but let me first see Helvétius, for I understand a little French and not a Word of Greek.' He received me with great Courtesy, having known me, he said, by Reputation for some time. He asked me a thousand things about the War, and the present state of Religion, of Liberty, and of Government in France. 'You do not inquire about your dear one Madame Helvétius; though she however still loves you exceedingly, and it was not an hour ago that I was with her. 'Ah!' said he, 'you stir the Memory of my old Happiness. But that must be forgotten in order to be content here. For several years at first, I thought only of her. But at length I was consoled. I took another Wife. The most like her that I could find. She is not, 'tis true, altogether so beautiful, but she has as much good Sense, a little more Humour, and she loves me without End. She is forever studying to please me; and she has just gone out to find the best Nectar and Ambrosia to regale me this evening; stay with me and you shall see.' 'I perceive,' said I, 'that your old Companion is more faithful than you, for several good Matches have been offered her, all of which she has refused. I confess that I myself have loved her madly; but she has been adamant to my Attentions, and has definitely rejected me because of her love for you.'

'I take Pity,' said he, 'on your Plight, for she is truly a good and beautiful Woman and very lovable. But do not the Abbé de la Roche and the Abbé Morellet still come to her house occasionally? To be sure they do; for she has not lost a single one of our Friends. Had you won over the Abbé Morellet (with Coffee and Cream) to speak for you, perhaps you would have succeeded; for he is a Reasoner as subtle as Duns Scotus or St. Thomas; he puts his Arguments in such good Order that they become almost irresistable. Or if the Abbé de la Roche had been won over (by some pretty Edition of an old Classic to speak against you, that would have been even better: for I have always observed, that when he advised one thing, she had a strong Inclination to do the opposite.'

At these Words there entered the new Madame Helvétius with the Nectar: instantly I recognised her to be Mistress Franklin, my old American Helpmate. I would have owned her. But she said coldly, 'I was your good Wife forty-nine years and four Months, almost half a century; be content with that. Here I have formed a new Bond, which will last for Eternity.'

Displeased with this Refusal by my Euridice, I straightway made up my Mind to quit those ungrateful Shades, to come back to this good World, again to see the Sun and you. Here I am! Let us be avenged.

H. L. Mencken

THE WEDDING: A STAGE DIRECTION

The scene is a church in an American city of about half a million
population, and the time is about eleven o'clock of a fine morning in
early spring. The neighborhood is well-to-do, but not quite fashion-
able. That is to say, most of the families of the vicinage keep two
servants (alas, more or less intermittently!), and eat dinner at half-
past six, and about one in every four boasts a colored butler (who
attends to the fires, washes windows and helps with the sweeping),
and a last year's automobile. The heads of these families are merchan-
dise brokers; jobbers in notions, hardware and drugs; manufacturers
of candy, hats, badges, office furniture, blank books, picture frames,
wire goods and patent medicines; managers of steamboat lines; dis-
trict agents of insurance companies; owners of commercial printing
offices, and other such business men of substance—and the prosperous
lawyers and popular family doctors who keep them out of trouble.
In one block live a Congressman and two college professors, one of
whom has written an unimportant textbook and got himself into
"Who's Who in America." In the block above lives a man who once
ran for Mayor of the city, and came near being elected.

The wives of these householders wear good clothes and have a
liking for a reasonable gayety, but very few of them can pretend to
what is vaguely called social standing, and, to do them justice, not
many of them waste any time lamenting it. They have, taking one
with another, about three children apiece, and are good mothers. A
few of them belong to women's clubs or flirt with the suffragettes,
but the majority can get all of the intellectual stimulation they crave
in the Ladies' Home Journal and the Saturday Evening Post, with
Vogue added for its fashions. Most of them, deep down in their hearts,
suspect their husbands of secret frivolity, and about ten per cent.
have the proofs, but it is rare for them to make rows about it, and
the divorce rate among them is thus very low. Themselves indifferent

cooks, they are unable to teach their servants the art, and so the food they set before their husbands and children is often such as would make a Frenchman cut his throat. But they are diligent housewives otherwise; they see to it that the windows are washed, that no one tracks mud into the hall, that the servants do not waste coal, sugar, soap and gas, and that the family buttons are always sewed on. In religion these estimable wives are *pious in habit but somewhat nebulous in faith. That is to say, they regard any person who specifically refuses to go to church as a heathen, but they themselves are by no means regular in attendance, and not one in ten of them could tell you whether transubstantiation is a Roman Catholic or a Dunkard doctrine. About two per cent. have dallied more or less gingerly with Christian Science, their average period of belief being one year.

The church we are in is like the neighborhood and its people: well-to-do but not fashionable. It is Protestant in faith and probably Episcopalian. The pews are of thick, yellow-brown oak, severe in pattern and hideous in color. In each there is a long, removable cushion of a dark, purplish, dirty hue, with here and there some of its hair stuffing showing. The stained-glass windows, which were all bought ready-made and depict scenes from the New Testament, commemorate the virtues of departed worthies of the neighborhood, whose names appear, in illegible black letters, in the lower panels. The floor is covered with a carpet of some tough, fibrous material, apparently a sort of grass, and along the center aisle it is much worn. The normal smell of the place is rather less unpleasant than that of most other halls, for on the one day when it is regularly crowded practically all of the persons gathered together have been very recently bathed.

On this fine morning, however, it is full of heavy, mortuary perfumes, for a couple of florist's men have just finished decorating the chancel with flowers and potted palms. Just behind the chancel rail, facing the center aisle, there is a prie-dieu, and to either side of it are great banks of lilies, carnations, gardenias and roses. Three or four feet behind the prie-dieu and completely concealing the high altar, there is a dense jungle of palms. Those in the front rank are authentically growing in pots, but behind them the florist's men have artfully placed some more durable, and hence more profitable, sophistications. Anon the rev. clergyman, emerging from the vestry-room to the right, will pass along the front of this jungle to the prie-dieu, and o, framed in flowers, face the congregation with his saponaceous smile.

The florist's men, having completed their labors, are preparing to depart. The older of the two, a man in the fifties, shows the ease of an experienced hand by taking out a large plug of tobacco and gnawing off a substantial chew. The desire to spit seizing him shortly, he proceeds to gratify it by a trick long practised by gasfitters, musicians, caterer's helpers, piano movers and other such alien invaders of the domestic hearth. That is to say, he hunts for a place where the carpet is loose along the chancel rail, finds it where two lengths join, deftly turns up a flap, spits upon the bare floor, and then lets the flap fall back, finally giving it a pat with the sole of his foot. This done, he and his assistant leave the church to the sexton, who has been sweeping the vestibule, and, after passing the time of day with the two men who are putting up a striped awning from the door to the curb, disappear into a nearby saloon, there to wait and refresh themselves until the wedding is over, and it is time to take away their lilies, their carnations and their synthetic palms.

It is now a quarter past eleven, and two flappers of the neighborhood, giggling and arm-in-arm, approach the sexton and inquire of him if they may enter. He asks them if they have tickets and when they say they haven't, he tells them that he ain't got no right to let them in, and don't know nothing about what the rule is going to be. At some weddings, he goes on, hardly nobody ain't allowed in, but then again, sometimes they don't scarcely look at the tickets at all. The two flappers retire abashed, and as the sexton finishes his sweeping, there enters the organist.

The organist is a tall, thin man of melancholy, uræmic aspect, wearing a black slouch hat with a wide brim and a yellow overcoat that barely reaches to his knees. A pupil, in his youth, of a man who had once studied (irregularly and briefly) with Charles-Marie Widor, he acquired thereby the artistic temperament, and with it a vast fondness for malt liquor. His mood this morning is acidulous and depressed, for he spent yesterday evening in a Pilsner ausschank with two former members of the Boston Symphony Orchestra, and it was 3 A.M. before they finally agreed that Johann Sebastian Bach, all things considered, was a greater man than Beethoven, and so parted amicably. Sourness is the precise sensation that wells within him. He feels vinegary; his blood runs cold; he wishes he could immerse himself in bicarbonate of soda. But the call of his art is more potent *than the protest of his poisoned and quaking liver, and so he manfully climbs the spiral stairway to his organ-loft.*

Once there, he takes off his hat and overcoat, stoops down to blow the dust off the organ keys, throws the electrical switch which sets the bellows going, and then proceeds to take off his shoes. This done, he takes his seat, reaches for the pedals with his stockinged feet, tries an experimental 32-foot CCC, and then wanders gently into a Bach toccata. It is his limbering-up piece: he always plays it as a prelude to a wedding job. It thus goes very smoothly and even brilliantly, but when he comes to the end of it and tackles the ensuing fugue he is quickly in difficulties, and after four or five stumbling repetitions of the subject he hurriedly improvises a crude coda and has done. Peering down into the church to see if his flounderings have had an audience, he sees two old maids enter, the one very tall and thin and the other somewhat brisk and bunchy.

They constitute the vanguard of the nuptial throng, and as they proceed hesitatingly up the center aisle, eager for good seats but afraid to go too far, the organist wipes his palms upon his trousers legs, squares his shoulders, and plunges into the program that he has played at all weddings for fifteen years past. It begins with Mendelssohn's Spring Song, pianissimo. Then comes Rubinstein's Melody in F, with a touch of forte toward the close, and then Nevin's "Oh, That We Two Were Maying," and then the Chopin waltz in A flat, Opus 69, No. 1, and then the Spring Song again, and then a free fantasia upon "The Rosary" and then a Moszkowski mazurka, and then the Dvořák Humoresque (with its heart-rending cry in the middle), and then some vague and turbulent thing (apparently the disjecta membra of another fugue), and then Tschaikowsky's "Autumn," and then Elgar's "Salut d'Amour," and then the Spring Song a third time, and then something or other from one of the Peer Gynt suites, and then an hurrah or two from the Hallelujah chorus, and then Chopin again, and Nevin, and Elgar, and—

But meanwhile, there is a growing activity below. First comes a closed automobile bearing the six ushers and soon after it another automobile bearing the bridegroom and his best man. The bridegroom and the best man disembark before the side entrance of the church and make their way into the vestryroom, where they remove their hats and coats, and proceed to struggle with their cravats and collars before a mirror which hangs on the wall. The room is very dingy. A baize-covered table is in the center of it, and around the table stand six or eight chairs of assorted designs. One wall is completely covered by a bookcase, through the glass doors of which one may discern piles of cheap Bibles, hymn-books and back numbers of the parish magazine. In one corner is a small washstand. The best man takes a flat flask of whiskey from his pocket, looks about him for a glass, finds it on the washstand, rinses it at the tap, fills it with a policeman's drink, and hands it to the bridegroom. The latter downs it at a gulp. Then the best man pours out one for himself.

The ushers, reaching the vestibule of the church, have handed their silk hats to the sexton, and entered the sacred edifice. There was a rehearsal of the wedding last night, but after it was over the bride ordered certain incomprehensible changes in the plan, and the ushers are now completely at sea. All they know clearly is that the relatives of the bride are to be seated on one side and the relatives of the bridegroom on the other. But which side for one and which for the other? They discuss it heatedly for three minutes and then find that they stand three for putting the bride's relatives on the left side and three for putting them on the right side. The debate, though instructive, is interrupted by the sudden entrance of seven women in a group. They are headed by a truculent old battleship, possibly an aunt or something of the sort, who fixes the nearest usher with a knowing, suspicious glance, and motions to him to show her the way.

He offers her his right arm and they start up the center aisle, with the six other women following in irregular order, and the five other ushers scattered among the women. The leading usher is tortured damnably by doubts as to where the party should go. If they are aunts, to which house do they belong, and on which side are the members of that house to be seated? What if they are not aunts, but merely neighbors? Or perhaps an association of former cooks, parlor maids, nurse girls? Or strangers? The sufferings of the usher are relieved by the battleship, who halts majestically about twenty feet from the altar, and motions her followers into a pew to the left. They file in silently and she seats herself next the aisle. All seven settle back and wriggle for room. It is a tight fit.

(Who, in point of fact, are these ladies? Don't ask the question! The ushers never find out. No one ever finds out. They remain a joint mystery for all time. In the end they become a sort of tradition, and years hence, when two of the ushers meet, they will cackle over

old dreadnaught and her six cruisers. The bride, grown old and fat, will tell the tale to her daughter, and then to her granddaughter. It will grow more and more strange, marvelous, incredible. Variorum versions will spring up. It will be adapted to other weddings. The dreadnaught will become an apparition, a witch, the Devil in skirts. And as the years pass, the date of the episode will be pushed back. By 2017 it will be dated 1150. By 2475 it will take on a sort of sacred character, and there will be a footnote referring to it in the latest Revised Version of the New Testament.)

It is now a quarter to twelve, and of a sudden the vestibule fills with wedding guests. Nine-tenths of them, perhaps even nineteen-twentieths, are women, and most of them are beyond thirty-five. Scattered among them, hanging on to their skirts, are about a dozen little girls—one of them a youngster of eight or thereabout, with spindle shanks and shining morning face, entranced by her first wedding. Here and there lurks a man. Usually he wears a hurried, unwilling, protesting look. He has been dragged from his office on a busy morning, forced to rush home and get into his cutaway coat, and then marched to the church by his wife. One of these men, much hustled, has forgotten to have his shoes shined. He is intensely conscious of them, and tries to hide them behind his wife's skirt as they walk up the aisle. Accidentally he steps upon it, and gets a look over the shoulder which lifts his diaphragm an inch and turns his liver to water. This man will be court-martialed when he reaches home, and he knows it. He wishes that some foreign power would invade the United States and burn down all the churches in the country, and that the bride, the bridegroom and all the other persons interested in the present wedding were dead and in hell.

The ushers do their best to seat these wedding guests in some sort of order, but after a few minutes the crowd at the doors becomes so large that they have to give it up, and thereafter all they can do is to hold out their right arms ingratiatingly and trust to luck. One of them steps on a fat woman's skirt, tearing it very badly, and she has to be helped back to the vestibule. There she seeks refuge in a corner, under a stairway leading up to the steeple, and essays to repair the damage with pins produced from various nooks and crevices of her person. Meanwhile the guilty usher stands in front of her, mumbling apologies and trying to look helpful. When she finishes her work and emerges from her improvised drydock, he again offers her his arm, but she sweeps past him without noticing him, and proceeds grandly to a seat far forward. She is a cousin to the bride's mother, and will make a report to every branch of the family that all six ushers disgraced the ceremony by appearing at it far gone in liquor.

Fifteen minutes are consumed by such episodes and divertisements. By the time the clock in the steeple strikes twelve the church is well filled. The music of the organist, who has now reached Mendelssohn's Spring Song for the third and last time, is accompanied by a huge buzz of whispers, and there is much craning of necks and long-distance nodding and smiling. Here and there an unusually gorgeous hat is the target of many converging glances, and of as many more or less satirical criticisms. To the damp funeral smell of the flowers at the altar, there has been added the cacodorous scents of forty or fifty different brands of talcum and rice powder. It begins to grow warm in the church, and a number of women open their vanity bags and duck down for stealthy dabs at their noses. Others, more reverent, suffer the agony of augmenting shines. One, a trickster, has concealed powder in her pocket handkerchief, and applies it dexterously while pretending to blow her nose.

The bridegroom in the vestry-room, entering upon the second year (or is it the third?) of his long and ghastly wait, grows increasingly nervous, and when he hears the organist pass from the Spring Song into some more sonorous and stately thing he mistakes it for the wedding march from "Lohengrin," and is hot for marching upon the altar at once. The best man, an old hand, restrains him gently, and administers another sedative from the bottle. The bridegroom's thoughts turn to gloomy things. He remembers sadly that he will never be able to laugh at benedicts again; that his days of low, rabelaisian wit and care-free scoffing are over; that he is now the very thing he mocked so gaily but yesteryear. Like a drowning man, he passes his whole life in review—not, however, that part which is past, but that part which is to come. Odd fancies throng upon him. He wonders what his honeymoon will cost him, what there will be to drink at the wedding breakfast, what a certain girl in Chicago will say when she hears of his marriage. Will there be any children? He rather hopes not, for all those he knows appear so greasy and noisy, but he decides that he might conceivably compromise on a boy. But how is he going to make sure that it will not be a girl? The thing, as yet, is a medical impossibility—but medicine is making rapid strides. Why not wait until the secret is discovered? This sapient compromise pleases the bridegroom, and he proceeds to a consideration of various problems of finance. And then, of a sudden, the organist swings unmistakably into "Lohengrin" and the best man grabs him by the arm.

There is now great excitement in the church. The bride's mother, two sisters, three brothers and three sisters-in-law have just marched up the center aisle and taken seats in the front pew, and all the women in the place are craning their necks toward the door. The usual electrical delay ensues. There is something the matter with the bride's train, and the two bridesmaids have a deuce of a time fixing it. Meanwhile the bride's father, in tight pantaloons and tighter gloves, fidgets and fumes in the vestibule, the six ushers crowd about him inanely, and the sexton rushes to and fro like a rat in a trap. Finally, all being ready, with the ushers formed two abreast, the sexton pushes a button, a small buzzer sounds in the organ loft, and the organist, as has been said, plunges magnificently into the fanfare of the "Lohengrin" march. Simultaneously the sexton opens the door at the bottom of the main aisle, and the wedding procession gets under weigh.

The bride and her father march first. Their step is so slow (about one beat to two measures) that the father has some difficulty in maintaining his equilibrium, but the bride herself moves steadily and erectly, almost seeming to float. Her face is thickly encrusted with talcum in its various forms, so that she is almost a dead white. She keeps her eyelids lowered modestly, but is still acutely aware of every glance fastened upon her—not in the mass, but every glance individually. For example, she sees clearly, even through her eyelids, the still, cold smile of a girl in Pew 8 R—a girl who once made an unwomanly attempt upon the bridegroom's affections, and was routed and put to flight by superior strategy. And her ears are open, too: she hears every "How sweet!" and "Oh, lovely!" and "Ain't she pale!" from the latitude of the last pew to the very glacis of the altar of God.

While she has thus made her progress up the hymeneal chute, the bridegroom and his best man have emerged from the vestryroom and begun the short march to the prie-dieu. They walk haltingly, clumsily, uncertainly, stealing occasional glances at the advancing bridal party. The bridegroom feels of his lower right-hand waistcoat pocket; the ring is still there. The best man wriggles his cuffs. No one, however, pays any heed to them. They are not even seen, indeed, until the bride and her father reach the open space in front of the altar. There the bride and the bridegroom find themselves standing side by side, but not a word is exchanged between them, nor even a look of recognition. They stand motionless, contemplating the ornate cushion at their feet, until the bride's father and the bridesmaids file to the left of the bride and the ushers, now wholly disorganized and imbecile, drape themselves in an irregular file along the altar rail. Then, the music having died down to a faint murmur and a hush having fallen upon the assemblage, they look up.

Before them, framed by foliage, stands the reverend gentleman of God who will presently link them in indissoluble chains—the estimable rector of the parish. He has got there just in time; it was, indeed, a close shave. But no trace of haste or of anything else of a disturbing character is now visible upon his smooth, glistening, somewhat feverish face. That face is wholly occupied by his official smile, a thing of oil and honey all compact, a balmy, unctuous illumination—the secret of his success in life. Slowly his cheeks puff out, gleaming like soap-bubbles. Slowly he lifts his prayer-book from the prie-dieu and holds it droopingly. Slowly his soft caressing eyes engage it. There is an almost imperceptible stiffening of his frame. His mouth opens with a faint click. He begins to read.

The Ceremony of Marriage has begun.

Clarence Day

THOUGHTS WITHOUT WORDS

I

Down in the Pits of Feeling
The Female lies, bedeck'd,
Till Man arrives, revealing
The Light of Intellect.

II

Oh who that ever lived and loved
Can look upon an egg unmoved?
The egg it is the source of all.
'Tis everyone's ancestral hall.
The bravest chief that ever fought,
The lowest thief that e'er was caught,
The harlot's lip, the maiden's leg,
They each and all came from an egg.

The rocks that once by ocean's surge
Beheld the first of eggs emerge—
Obscure, defenseless, small and cold—
They little knew what eggs could hold.
The gifts the reverent Magi gave,
Pandora's box, Aladdin's cave,
Wars, loves, and kingdoms, heaven and hell
All lay within that tiny shell.

Oh, join me gentlemen, I beg,
In honoring our friend, the egg.

III

Who drags the fiery artist down?
What keeps the pioneer in town?
Who hates to let the seaman roam?
It is the wife, it is the home.

IV

The story of his life.

V

Here's Bishop Briskoe Pettifogg.
Is he in—or on—the hands of God?

VI

When eras die, their legacies
 Are left to strange police.
Professors in New England guard
 The glory that was Greece.

Kenneth Fearing

PORTRAIT

The clear brown eyes, kindly and alert, with 20-20 vision,
give confident regard to the passing world through R. K.
Lampert & Company lenses framed in gold
    his soul, however, is all his own
        Arndt Brothers necktie and hat (with feather)
        supply a touch of youth

With his soul his own, he drives, drives, chats and drives
    the second and third bicuspids, lower right, replaced
    by bridgework, while two incisors have porcelain
    crowns

(Render unto federal, state, and city Caesar, but not
unto time
    render nothing unto time until Amalgamated Death
    serves final notice, in proper form

The vault is ready
    the will has been drawn by Clagget, Clagget, Clag-
get & Brown
        the policies are adequate, Confidential's best,
        reimbursing for disability, partial or complete,
        with double indemnity should the end be a
        pure and simple accident)

Nothing unto time
    nothing unto change
        nothing unto fate
            nothing unto you, and nothing unto me,
            or to any other known or unknown party
            or parties, living or deceased

But Mercury shoes, with special arch supports, take
much of the wear and tear
    on the course, a custombuilt driver corrects a tend-
    ency to slice
        love's ravages have been repaired (it was a text-
        book case) by Drs. Schultz, Lightner, Mann-
        heim, and Goode
            while all of it is enclosed in excellent
            tweed, with Mr. Baumer's personal atten-
            tion to the shoulders and the waist

And all of it now roving, chatting amiably through space
in a Plymouth 6
    with his soul (his own) at peace, soothed by Walter
    Lippmann, and sustained by Haig & Haig.

e. e. cummings

the Cambridge ladies

the Cambridge ladies who live in furnished souls
are unbeautiful and have comfortable minds
(also, with the church's protestant blessings
daughters, unscented shapeless spirited)
they believe in Christ and Longfellow, both dead,
are invariably interested in so many things—
at the present writing one still finds
delighted fingers knitting for the is it Poles?
perhaps. While permanent faces coyly bandy
scandal of Mrs. N and Professor D
.... the Cambridge ladies do not care, above
Cambridge if sometimes in its box of
sky lavender and cornerless, the
moon rattles like a fragment of angry candy

Ogden Nash

BANKERS ARE JUST LIKE ANYBODY ELSE, EXCEPT RICHER

This is a song to celebrate banks,
Because they are full of money and you go into them
    and all you hear is clinks and clanks,
Or maybe a sound like the wind in the trees on the hills,
Which is the rustling of the thousand-dollar bills.
Most bankers dwell in marble halls,
Which they get to dwell in because they encourage
    deposits and discourage withdralls,
And particularly because they all observe one rule which
    woe betides the banker who fails to heed it,
Which is you must never lend any money to anybody
    unless they don't need it.
I know you, you cautious conservative banks!
If people are worried about their rent it is your duty to
    deny them the loan of one nickel, yes, even one
    copper engraving of the martyred son of the late
    Nancy Hanks;
Yes, if they request fifty dollars to pay for a baby you
    must look at them like Tarzan looking at an uppity
    ape in the jungle,
And tell them what do they think a bank is, anyhow,
    they had better go get the money from their wife's
    aunt or ungle.
But suppose people come in and they have a million
    and they want another million to pile on top of it,
Why, you brim with the milk of human kindness and
    you urge them to accept every drop of it,
And you lend them the million so then they have two
    million and this gives them the idea that they
    would be better off with four,

So they already have two million as security so you have
   no hesitation in lending them two more,
And all the vice-presidents nod their heads in rhythm,
And the only question asked is do the borrowers want
   the money sent or do they want to take it withm.
But please do not think that I am not fond of banks,
Because I think they deserve our appreciation and
   thanks,
Because they perform a valuable public service in elimi-
   nating the jackasses who go around saying that health
   and happiness are everything and money isn't essential,
Because as soon as they have to borrow some unimportant
   money to maintain their health and happiness they starve
   to death so they can't go around any more sneering at
   good old money, which is nothing short of providential.

FIRST FAMILIES, MOVE OVER!

Carry me back to Ole Virginny,
And there I'll meet a lot of people from New York,
There the Ole Marsa of the Hounds is from Smithtown or
   Peapack or Millbrook,
And the mocking bird makes music in the sunshine accompanied
   by the rattling shaker and the popping cork.

All up and down the old plantation
Socialites are riding hell-for-leather like witches and war-
   locks,
And there is only one thing that keeps the squirearchy from
   being a genuine reproduction,
Which is that the peasantry's hair is kinky so they
   haven't any forelocks so they can't tug their
   forelocks.

In the evening by the bright light you can hear those
   darkies singing,
How the white folks do enjoy it and call the attention

of their friends from Piping Rock to the natural
    musical talent of the dusky proletariat.
You can hear those banjos ringing because the hands
    have been ordered to exchange their saxophones
    for banjos,
And they wish they were singing Lookie lookie lookie,
    here comes Cookie, but their instructions are to
    sing Swing Low Sweet Chariot.

Oh what is more beautiful and more Southern than a
    Southern beauty from Philadelphia or Rumson,
And indeed where was Southern beauty before the
    advent of Schiaparelli and Elizabeth Arden?
And what is more gracious than a hostess calling you
    you-all in the singular and plural indiscriminately,
And what has more local color than a lovely girl in
    jodhpurs telling you about her gyarrrden?

Oh the long happy days spent huntin' or shootin' or
    fishin',
Or in any other sport provided it's lackin' in g's!
Oh the long happy evenings spent sniffing jasmine and
    poring over the shiny new family Bible,
And figuring out that after all this is really your home
    because great-grandmother Wilkins was a Filkins
    and the Filkinses were related by marriage to the
    Randolphs or the Lees!

So please somebody carry me back to Ole Virginny,
Where gentlemen are gentlemen and a lady is known by
    the product she endorses,
Where the atmosphere is as Southern as an advertisement
    for a medium-priced rye whiskey,
And where the Virginians from Virginia have to ride automo-
    biles because the Virginians from Long Island are the
    only ones who can afford to ride horses.

Russell Maloney

INFLEXIBLE LOGIC

When the six chimpanzees came into his life, Mr. Bainbridge was
thirty-eight years old. He was a bachelor and lived comfortably in
a remote part of Connecticut, in a large old house with a carriage
drive, a conservatory, a tennis court, and a well-selected library. His
income was derived from impeccably situated real estate in New
York City, and he spent it soberly, in a manner which could give
offence to nobody. Once a year, late in April, his tennis court was
resurfaced, and after that anybody in the neighborhood was welcome
to use it; his monthly statement from Brentano's seldom ran below
seventy-five dollars; every third year, in November, he turned in his
old Cadillac coupé for a new one; he ordered his cigars, which were
mild and rather moderately priced, in shipments of one thousand,
from a tobacconist in Havana; because of the international situation
he had cancelled arrangements to travel abroad, and after due thought
had decided to spend his travelling allowance on wines, which seemed
likely to get scarcer and more expensive if the war lasted. On the
whole, Mr. Bainbridge's life was deliberately, and not too unsuccess-
fully, modelled after that of an English country gentleman of the late
eighteenth century, a gentleman interested in the arts and in the
expansion of science, and so sure of himself that he didn't care if
some people thought him eccentric.

Mr. Bainbridge had many friends in New York, and he spent
several days of the month in the city, staying at his club and looking
around. Sometimes he called up a girl and took her out to a theatre
and a night club. Sometimes he and a couple of classmates got a little
tight and went to a prizefight. Mr. Bainbridge also looked in now
and then at some of the conservative art galleries, and liked occasionally
to go to a concert. And he liked cocktail parties, too, because of the
fine footling conversation and the extraordinary number of pretty
girls who had nothing else to do with the rest of their evening. It

was at a New York cocktail party, however, that Mr. Bainbridge kept his preliminary appointment with doom. At one of the parties given by Hobie Packard, the stockbroker, he learned about the theory of the six chimpanzees.

It was almost six-forty. The people who had intended to have one drink and go had already gone, and the people who intended to stay were fortifying themselves with slightly dried canapés and talking animatedly. A group of stage and radio people had coagulated in one corner, near Packard's Capehart, and were wrangling about various methods of cheating the Collector of Internal Revenue. In another corner was a group of stockbrokers, talking about the greatest stock-broker of them all, Gauguin. Little Marcia Lupton was sitting with a young man, saying earnestly, "Do you really want to know what my greatest ambition is? I want to be myself," and Mr. Bainbridge smiled gently, thinking of the time Marcia had said that to him. Then he heard the voice of Bernard Weiss, the critic, saying, "Of course he wrote one good novel. It's not surprising. After all, we know that if six chimpanzees were set to work pounding six type-writers at random, they would, in a million years, write all the books in the British Museum."

Mr. Bainbridge drifted over to Weiss and was introduced to Weiss's companion, a Mr. Noble. "What's this about a million chimpanzees, Weiss?" he asked.

"Six chimpanzees," Mr. Weiss said. "It's an old cliché of the mathe-maticians. I thought everybody was told about it in school. Law of averages, you know, or maybe it's permutation and combination. The six chimps, just pounding away at the typewriter keys, would be bound to copy out all the books ever written by man. There are only so many possible combinations of letters and numerals, and they'd produce all of them—see? Of course they'd also turn out a mountain of gibberish, but they'd work the books in, too. All the books in the British Museum."

Mr. Bainbridge was delighted; this was the sort of talk he liked to hear when he came to New York. "Well, but look here," he said, just to keep up his part in the foolish conversation, "what if one of the chimpanzees finally did duplicate a book, right down to the last period, but left that off? Would that count?"

"I suppose not. Probably the chimpanzee would get around to doing the book again, and put the period in."

"What nonsense!" Mr. Noble cried.

"It may be nonsense, but Sir James Jeans believes it," Mr. Weiss said, huffily. "Jeans or Lancelot Hogben. I know I ran across it quite recently."

Mr. Bainbridge was impressed. He read quite a bit of popular science, and both Jeans and Hogben were in his library. "Is that so?" he murmured, no longer feeling frivolous. "Wonder if it has ever actually been tried? I mean, has anybody ever put six chimpanzees in a room with six typewriters and a lot of paper?"

Mr. Weiss glanced at Mr. Bainbridge's empty cocktail glass and said drily, "Probably not."

Nine weeks later, on a winter evening, Mr. Bainbridge was sitting in his study with his friend James Mallard, an assistant professor of mathematics at New Haven. He was plainly nervous as he poured himself a drink and said, "Mallard, I've asked you to come here—Brandy? Cigar?—for a particular reason. You remember that I wrote you some time ago, asking your opinion of . . . of a certain mathematical hypothesis or supposition."

"Yes," Professor Mallard said, briskly. "I remember perfectly. About the six chimpanzees and the British Museum. And I told you it was a perfectly sound popularization of a principle known to every schoolboy who had studied the science of probabilities."

"Precisely," Mr. Bainbridge said. "Well, Mallard, I made up my mind . . . It was not difficult for me, because I have, in spite of that fellow in the White House, been able to give something every year to the Museum of Natural History, and they were naturally glad to oblige me. . . . And after all, the only contribution a layman can make to the progress of science is to assist with the drudgery of experiment. . . . In short, I—"

"I suppose you're trying to tell me that you have procured six chimpanzees and set them to work at typewriters in order to see whether they will eventually write all the books in the British Museum. Is that it?"

"Yes, that's it," Mr. Bainbridge said. "What a mind you have, Mallard. Six fine young males, in perfect condition. I had a—I suppose you'd call it a dormitory—built out in back of the stable. The typewriters are in the conservatory. It's light and airy in there, and I moved most of the plants out. Mr. North, the man who owns th rcus, very obligingly let me engage one of his best animal men. eally, it was no trouble at all."

Professor Mallard smiled indulgently. "After all, such a thing is not aheard of," he said. "I seem to remember that a man at some uni-rsity put his graduate students to work flipping coins, to see if heads d tails came up an equal number of times. Of course they did."

Mr. Bainbridge looked at his friend very queerly. "Then you believe at any such principle of the science of probabilities will stand up der an actual test?"

"Certainly."

"You had better see for yourself." Mr. Bainbridge led Professor allard downstairs, along a corridor, through a disused music room, d into a large conservatory. The middle of the floor had been cleared plants and was occupied by a row of six typewriter tables, each one pporting a hooded machine. At the left of each typewriter was a at stack of yellow copy paper. Empty wastebaskets were under each ble. The chairs were the unpadded, spring-backed kind favored by perienced stenographers. A large bunch of ripe bananas was hang-g in one corner, and in another stood a Great Bear water-cooler and rack of Lily cups. Six piles of typescript, each about a foot high, ere ranged along the wall on an improvised shelf. Mr. Bainbridge cked up one of the piles, which he could just conveniently lift, and t it on a table before Professor Mallard. "The output to date of himpanzee A, known as Bill," he said simply.

"'"Oliver Twist," by Charles Dickens,'" Professor Mallard read t. He read the first and second pages of the manuscript, then fever-ly leafed through to the end. "You mean to tell me," he said, "that is chimpanzee has written—"

"Word for word and comma for comma," said Mr. Bainbridge. oung, my butler, and I took turns comparing it with the edition I vn. Having finished 'Oliver Twist,' Bill is, as you see, starting the ciological works of Vilfredo Pareto, in Italian. At the rate he has been ing, it should keep him busy for the rest of the month."

"And all the chimpanzees"—Professor Mallard was pale, and enun-ated with difficulty—"they aren't all—"

"Oh, yes, all writing books which I have every reason to believe are the British Museum. The prose of John Donne, some Anatole ance, Conan Doyle, Galen, the collected plays of Somerset Maugham, arcel Proust, the memoirs of the late Marie of Rumania, and a monograph by a Dr. Wiley on the marsh grasses of Maine and Massa chusetts. I can sum it up for you, Mallard, by telling you that since started this experiment, four weeks and some days ago, none of th chimpanzees has spoiled a single sheet of paper."

Professor Mallard straightened up, passed his handkerchief acros his brow, and took a deep breath. "I apologize for my weakness," h said. "It was simply the sudden shock. No, looking at the thing scien tifically—and I hope I am at least as capable of that as the next ma —there is nothing marvellous about the situation. These chimpanzee or a succession of similar teams of chimpanzees, would in a millio years write all the books in the British Museum. I told you some tim ago that I believed that statement. Why should my belief be altere by the fact that they produced some of the books at the very outset After all, I should not be very much surprised if I tossed a coin hundred times and it came up heads every time. I know that if I kep at it long enough, the ratio would reduce itself to an exact fifty p cent. Rest assured, these chimpanzees will begin to compose gibberis quite soon. It is bound to happen. Science tells us so. Meanwhile, advise you to keep this experiment secret. Uninformed people migl create a sensation if they knew."

"I will, indeed," Mr. Bainbridge said. "And I'm very grateful fc your rational analysis. It reassures me. And now, before you go, yo must hear the new Schnabel records that arrived today."

During the succeeding three months, Professor Mallard got into th habit of telephoning Mr. Bainbridge every Friday afternoon at fiv thirty, immediately after leaving his seminar room. The Professc would say, "Well?," and Mr. Bainbridge would reply, "They're still : it, Mallard. Haven't spoiled a sheet of paper yet." If Mr. Bainbridg had to go out on Friday afternoon, he would leave a written messag with his butler, who would read it to Professor Mallard: "Mr. Bain bridge says we now have Trevelyan's 'Life of Macaulay,' the Confe sions of St. Augustine, 'Vanity Fair,' part of Irving's 'Life of Georg Washington,' the Book of the Dead, and some speeches delivered i Parliament in opposition to the Corn Laws, sir." Professor Mallar would reply, with a hint of a snarl in his voice, "Tell him to remen ber what I predicted," and hang up with a clash.

The eleventh Friday that Professor Mallard telephoned, Mr. Bain bridge said, "No change. I have had to store the bulk of the manu script in the cellar. I would have burned it, except that it probably has some scientific value."

"How dare you talk of scientific value?" The voice from New Haven roared faintly in the receiver. "Scientific value! You—you—chimpanzee!" There were further inarticulate sputterings, and Mr. Bainbridge hung up with a disturbed expression. "I am afraid Mallard is overtaxing himself," he murmured.

Next day, however, he was pleasantly surprised. He was leafing through a manuscript that had been completed the previous day by Chimpanzee D, Corky. It was the complete diary of Samuel Pepys, and Mr. Bainbridge was chuckling over the naughty passages, which were omitted in his own edition, when Professor Mallard was shown into the room. "I have come to apologize for my outrageous conduct on the telephone yesterday," the Professor said.

"Please don't think of it any more. I know you have many things on your mind," Mr. Bainbridge said. "Would you like a drink?"

"A large whiskey, straight, please," Professor Mallard said. "I got rather cold driving down. No change, I presume?"

"No, none. Chimpanzee F, Dinty, is just finishing John Florio's translation of Montaigne's essays, but there is no other news of interest."

Professor Mallard squared his shoulders and tossed off his drink in one astonishing gulp. "I should like to see them at work," he said. "Would I disturb them, do you think?"

"Not at all. As a matter of fact, I usually look in on them around this time of day. Dinty may have finished his Montaigne by now, and it is always interesting to see them start a new work. I would have thought that they would continue on the same sheet of paper, but they don't, you know. Always a fresh sheet, and the title in capitals."

Professor Mallard, without apology, poured another drink and slugged it down. "Lead on," he said.

It was dusk in the conservatory, and the chimpanzees were typing by the light of student lamps clamped to their desks. The keeper lounged in a corner, eating a banana and reading *Billboard*. "You might as well take an hour or so off," Mr. Bainbridge said. The man left.

Professor Mallard, who had not taken off his overcoat, stood with his hands in his pockets, looking at the busy chimpanzees. "I wonder if you know, Bainbridge, that the science of probabilities takes everything into account," he said, in a queer, tight voice. "It is certainly almost beyond the bounds of credibility that these chimpanzees should write books without a single error, but that abnormality may be corrected by—*these!*" He took his hands from his pockets, and each one held a .38 revolver. "Stand back out of harm's way!" he shouted.

"Mallard! Stop it!" The revolvers barked, first the right hand, then the left, then the right. Two chimpanzees fell, and a third reeled into a corner. Mr. Bainbridge seized his friend's arm and wrested one of the weapons from him.

"Now I am armed, too, Mallard, and I advise you to stop!" he cried. Professor Mallard's answer was to draw a bead on Chimpanzee E and shoot him dead. Mr. Bainbridge made a rush, and Professor Mallard fired at him. Mr. Bainbridge, in his quick death agony, tightened his finger on the trigger of his revolver. It went off, and Professor Mallard went down. On his hands and knees he fired at the two chimpanzees which were still unhurt, and then collapsed.

There was nobody to hear his last words. "The human equation ... always the enemy of science ..." he panted. "This time ... vice versa ... I, a mere mortal ... savior of science ... deserve a Nobel ..."

When the old butler came running into the conservatory to investigate the noises, his eyes were met by a truly appalling sight. The student lamps were shattered, but a newly risen moon shone in through the conservatory windows on the corpses of the two gentlemen, each clutching a smoking revolver. Five of the chimpanzees were dead. The sixth was Chimpanzee F. His right arm disabled, obviously bleeding to death, he was slumped before his typewriter. Painfully, with his left hand, he took from the machine the completed last page of Florio's Montaigne. Groping for a fresh sheet, he inserted it, and typed with one finger, "UNCLE TOM'S CABIN, by Harriet Beecher Stowe. Chapte ..." Then he, too, was dead.

Finley Peter Dunne

MR. DOOLEY ON THE EDUCATION OF THE YOUNG

*"If ye had a boy wud ye sind him to colledge?" asked Mr. Hennessy.
"Well," said Mr. Dooley, "at th' age whin a boy is fit to be in colledge
I wudden't have him around th' house."*

* * *

The troubled Mr. Hennessy had been telling Mr. Dooley about the
difficulty of making a choice of schools for Packy Hennessy, who at
the age of six was at the point where the family must decide his
career.

" 'Tis a big question," said Mr. Dooley, "an' wan that seems to be
worryin' th' people more thin it used to whin ivry boy was designed
f'r th' priesthood, with a full undherstandin' be his parents that th'
chances was in favor iv a brick yard. Nowadays they talk about th'
edycation iv th' child befure they choose th' name. 'Tis: 'Th' kid talks
in his sleep. 'Tis th' fine lawyer he'll make.' Or, 'Did ye notice him
admirin' that photygraph? He'll be a gr-reat journalist.' Or, 'Look at
him fishin' in Uncle Tim's watch pocket. We must thrain him f'r a
banker.' Or, 'I'm afraid he'll niver be sthrong enough to wurruk. He
must go into th' church.' Befure he's baptized too, d'ye mind. 'Twill
not be long befure th' time comes whin th' soggarth'll christen th'
infant: 'Judge Pathrick Aloysius Hinnissy, iv th' Northern District iv
Illinye,' or 'Profissor P. Aloysius Hinnissy, LL.D., S.T.D., P.G.N., iv
th' faculty iv Northre Dame.' Th' innocent child in his cradle, won-
dherin' what ails th' mist iv him an' where he got such funny lookin'
parents fr'm, has thim to blame that brought him into the wurruld if
he dayvilops into a sicond story man befure he's twinty-wan an' is
took up be th' polis. Why don't you lade Packy down to th' occylist an'
have him fitted with a pair iv eye-glasses? Why don't ye put goloshes
on him, give him a blue umbrelly an' call him a doctor at wanst an'
be done with it?

"To my mind, Hinnissy, we're wastin' too much time thinkin' iv th'
future iv our young, an' thryin' to larn thim early what they oughtn't

393

to know till they've growed up. We sind th' childher to school as if 'twas a summer garden where they go to be amused instead iv a pinitinchry where they're sint f'r th' original sin. Whin I was a la-ad I was put at me ah-bee abs, th' first day I set fut in th' school behind th' hedge an' me head was sore inside an' out befure I wint home. Now th' first thing we larn th' future Mark Hannas an' Jawn D. Gateses iv our naytion is waltzin', singin', an' cuttin' pitchers out iv a book. We'd be much betther teachin' thim th' sthrangle hold, f'r that's what they need in life.

"I know what'll happen. Ye'll sind Packy to what th' Germans call a Kindygarten, an' 'tis a good thing f'r Germany, because all a German knows is what some wan tells him, and his grajation papers is a certy-ficate that he don't need to think annymore. But we've inthrajooced it into this counthry, an' whin I was down seein' if I cud injooce Raf-ferty, th' Janitor iv th' Isaac Muggs Grammar School, f'r to vote f'r Riordan—an' he's goin' to—I dhropped in on Cassidy's daughter, Mary Ellen, an' see her kindygartnin'. Th' childher was settin' ar-round on th' flure an' some was moldin' dachshunds out iv mud an' wipin' their hands on their hair, an' some was carvin' figures iv a goat out iv paste-board an' some was singin' an some was sleepin' an' a few was dancin' an' wan la-ad was pullin' another la-ad's hair. 'Why don't ye take th' coal shovel to that little barbaryan, Mary Ellen?' says I. 'We don't believe in corporeal punishment,' says she. 'School shud be made pleasant f'r th' childher,' she says. 'Th' child who's hair is bein' pulled is larnin' patience,' she says, 'an' th' child that's pullin' th' hair is dis-coverin' th' footility iv human indeavor,' says she. 'Well, oh, well,' says I, 'times has changed since I was a boy,' I says. 'Put thim through their exercises,' says I. 'Tommy,' says I, 'spell cat,' I says. 'Go to th' divvle,' says th' cheerub. 'Very smartly answered,' says Mary Ellen. 'Ye shud not ask thim to spell,' she says. 'They don't larn that till they get to colledge,' she says, 'an',' she says, 'sometimes not even thin,' she says. 'An' what do they larn?' says I. 'Rompin',' she says, 'an' dancin',' she says, 'an' indepindance iv speech, an' beauty songs, an' sweet thoughts, an' how to make home home-like,' she says. 'Well,' says I, 'I didn't take anny iv thim things at colledge, so ye needn't unblanket thim,' I says. 'I won't put thim through anny exercise to-day,' I says. 'But whisper, Mary Ellen,' says I, 'Don't ye niver feel like bastin' the seeraphims?' 'Th' teachin's iv Freebull and Pitzotly is conthrary to that,' she says. 'But I'm goin' to be marrid an' lave th' school on

Choosdah, th' twinty-sicond iv Janooary,' she says, 'an' on Mondah, th' twinty-first, I'm goin' to ask a few iv th' little darlin's to th' house an',' she says, 'stew thim over a slow fire,' she says. Mary Ellen is not a German, Hinnissy.

"Well, afther they have larned in school what they ar're licked f'r larnin' in th' back yard—that is squashin' mud with their hands—they're conducted up through a channel iv free an' beautiful thought till they're r-ready f'r colledge. Mamma packs a few doylies an' tidies into son's bag, an' some silver to be used in case iv throuble with th' landlord, an' th' la-ad throts off to th' siminary. If he's not sthrong enough to look f'r high honors as a middleweight pugilist he goes into th' thought departmint. Th' prisidint takes him into a Turkish room, gives him a cigareet an' says: 'Me dear boy, what special branch iv larnin' wud ye like to have studied f'r ye be our compitint profissors? We have a chair iv Beauty an' wan iv Puns an' wan iv Pothry on th' Changin' Hues iv th' Settin' Sun, an' wan on Platonic Love, an' wan on Non-sense Rhymes, an' wan on Sweet Thoughts, an' wan on How Green Grows th' Grass, an' wan on th' Relation iv Ice to th' Greek Idee iv God,' he says. 'This is all ye'll need to equip ye f'r th' perfect life, onless,' he says, 'ye intind bein' a dintist, in which case,' he says, 'we won't think much iv ye, but we have a good school where ye can larn that disgraceful thrade,' he says. An' th' la-ad makes his choice, an' ivry mornin' whin he's up in time he takes a whiff iv hasheesh an' goes off to hear Profissor Maryanna tell him that 'if th' dates iv human knowledge must be rejicted as subjictive, how much more must they be subjicted as rejictive if, as I think, we keep our thoughts fixed upon th' inanity iv th' finite in comparison with th' onthinkable truth with th' ondivided an' onimaginable reality. Boys, ar-re ye with me?' . . ."

"I don't undherstand a wurrud iv what ye'r sayin'," said Mr. Hennessy.

"No more do I," said Mr. Dooley. "But I believe 'tis as Father Kelly says: 'Childher shuddn't be sint to school to larn, but to larn how to larn. I don't care what ye larn thim so long as 'tis onpleasant to thim.' 'Tis thrainin' they need, Hinnissy. That's all. I niver cud make use iv what I larned in colledge about thrigojoomethry an'—an'—grammar an' th' welts I got on th' skull fr'm th' schoolmasther's cane I have niver been able to turn to anny account in th' business, but 'twas th' bein' there an' havin' to get things to heart without askin' th' meanin' iv

thim an' goin' to school cold an' comin' home hungry, that made th'
man iv me ye see befure ye."

"That's why th' good woman's throubled about Packy," said Hennessy.

"Go home," said Mr. Dooley.

MR. DOOLEY ON GOLF

"Well, sir," said Mr. Dooley, "I don't want to say annything that wud
hurt a frind, but I do think th' authorities ar-re very lax in lavin'
Hogan at large, as they ar-re doin'."

"An' what ails Hogan?" Mr. Hennessy asked.

"He's got what th' dock calls a fixed deelusion," said Mr. Dooley.
"He thinks he's a goluf player. No, he don't play th' game. Nobody
does that. They wurruk at it. But Hogan he slaves at it. He don't
think iv annything else. He takes it down to th' wather-office with
him in th' mornin', an' he carries it home with him at night an'
sleeps with it. If ye go over to his house at this minyit ye'll find him
in th' front parlor swingin' a poker an' tellin' the good woman how
he played th' eighth hole. There's nawthin' more excitin' to th' mother
iv siven at th' end of a complete wash-day thin to listen to an account
iv a bum goluf game fr'm th' lips iv her lifemate. 'Tis almost as
absorbin' as th' invintory iv a grocery store. I was over there th' other
night, an' he broke three panes iv glass showin' me what he calls a
mashie shot, an' he near took an ear off his aunt Bridget practisin' with
a war-club that he calls a nibbelick. I wudden't be harsh with him,
but a few months or aven years in a well upholstered cell with a ball
an' chain on his leg, might restore him to himself an' make him again
th' safe an' bashful husband an' father he wanst was.

"But 'tis a gr-reat game, a gr-rand, jolly, hail-fellow-well-met spoort.
With th' exciption maybe iv th' theery iv infant damnation, Scotland
has given nawthin' more cheerful to th' wurruld thin th' game iv goluf.
Whin 'twas first smuggled into this counthry, I cudden't make out
what 'twas like. I thought whin I first read about it that it was in-
tinded f'r people with a hackin' cough, an' that no wan who was
robust enough to play 'Twinty Questions' in a wheel-chair, wud engage in it without a blush. I had it in me mind that 'twas played iv a
rainy afthernoon in th' front parlor. Th' two athletes got out their

needles an' their embroidery canvas, give a shout iv glee an' flew at it. Th' results was submitted to th' 'Ladies Home Journal,' an' me frind Eddie Bok decided who was champeen, an' give him a goold thimble f'r a prize.

"But I know betther now. 'Tis a rough an' angry game, full of ondacint remarks an' other manly charackteristics, d'ye mind. An' whin 'tis over it laves as much bad blood as a German submarine. At th' end iv ivry goluf match th' player loathes himsilf, is not on speakin' terms with th' fellow he played agin, cud kill his own caddy an' his opponent's, an' hates th' criminal that laid out th' coorse, th' game itsilf, th' Jook iv Argyll, each wan iv his clubs, th' little bur-rd that twittered whin he was shootin', th' pretty wild flowers on th' margin iv th' links, an' each separate spear iv grass on th' puttin'-green. If that Dutch pote that wrote th' 'Hymn iv Hate' wants to write an-other on th' same subjeck with a rale punch in it he ought to larn goluf. 'Twuld help him.

"How's it played, says ye? I don't exactly know. I niver studied law. But ye can get th' rules iv th' game in th' public library, in siven volumes edited be th' Lord Chief Justice iv Scotland. If ye have a dispute over th' rules, th' quickest way to get a decision is to hire a lawyer, make a test case, an' carry it to th' supreem coort. In a gin'ral way, all I can say about it is that it's a kind iv a game iv ball that ye play with ye'er own worst inimy which is ye'ersilf, an' a man ye don't like goes around with ye an' gloats over ye, an' a little boy follows ye to carry th' clubs an' hide th' ball afther ye've hit it. Th' ball is small, made iv injy rubber an' filled with a pizinous substance, an' if ye hit it a good smash it busts an' puts out ye'er eye. Ye're supposed to smash this little grenade fr'm place to place an' here an' there an' up an' down an' hither an' yon with an enormous insthrument iv wood or iron, ontill in due time ye get to what is called a puttin'-green. There's a little hole with a tin can in it in th' middle iv this place, an' whin ye're within a fut or two iv this hole ye take a small hammer out iv th' bag, an' ye hit th' ball four or five times till it tumbles into th' hole. Thin ye wipe th' cold sweat fr'm ye'er brow, write down '5' on a little card, an' walk away a few feet an' do it all over again.

"So far so good. But that ain't nearly all. Ye've got along pretty well, pokin th' ball down th' pretty grass, whin wan day ye see a dark, evil-lookin' man watchin' ye. Ye mark him at wanst as ye'er inimy, an' well it is ye do, f'r he's th' expert that is layin' out the coorse. He marks the spot where ye'er best shot goes, an' says he, with a scowl, 'I'll fix that crokey-playin' plumber.' An' he digs a hole five feet deep an' dumps a wagon iv soft coal ashes into it. Thin he picks out th' other places where ye loved to land, an' he puts in railroad ties, barbed wire, ditches, mounds, pizen-ivy, blackberry bushes, thrailin'-arbutus, a swamp, an' a field iv thistles, tears down a hill an' builds a mountain, gashes th' fair face iv nature with gapin' caverns an' chasms filled with gravel, cigaret stumps, brick-bats, sardine cans, hairpins, an' futprints, calls thim bunkers, an' goes his way. This pro-fissyonal torturer is what is known as a goluf archytect. If ye left a thurly good goluf archytect in th' garden iv Eden f'r an hour he'd make it look like Bilgium afther th' war.

"Well, ye play wanst through this jungle that a wire-haired tarryer cudden't get into, an' ye're told be a frind that ye ought to take a lesson. So ye pick out a bright-faced Scotch lad with a head shaped like a alligator pear an' who can hit th' ball a mile blindfolded an' ye give him what change ye have an' ask him to pint out ye'er faults. He pints out all ye'er wife has told ye about an' manny dark wans besides. I see Hogan takin' a goluf lesson wanst, an' how he iver dared to lift his head again is more thin I cud undherstand. Afther th' pro-fissyonal has recited th' catalog iv ye'er sins an' vices, an' ye've made an act iv conthrition, he tells ye how to hit th' ball. Ye'd think that ought to be aisy. Just go up an' give it a cuff.

"But it ain't annything like as soft as that. There ar-re forty different things ye have to think iv with each shot, an' if ye do wan iv thim wrong, ye're a lost soul. When ye'er idjication is completed ye go out an' do all th' things he told ye, but nineteen, an' th' ball skips lightly into a pit. Now is ye'er time to escape. If ye lave it lie there, turn ye'er back on it, run to th' parish-house an' ask f'r th' prayers iv th' congregation, it may not be too late. Ye may be saved. Fly, weak an' wretched man, while ye have th' strenth! But if ye delay, if ye step but wan fut into th' thrap, ye're doomed an' on'y th' kindly hand iv death will release ye fr'm a life iv shame.

"Oh, 'tis th' jolly game, th' jolly ol' Scotch game. No wondher it's played all over th' counthry. Th' next pleasantest feelin' in the wurruld to bein' perfectly happy is bein' perfectly cross. That's why it's took up be middle-aged gintlemen. They want a chanst to go into a towerin' rage in th' open an' undher th' blue sky. To a goluf player, Hinnissy, th' spreadin' ellum three, a bloomin' rose bush, or a purlin' brook ar-re not what they seem to us. He don't use what ye call figures of speech about thim. No, sir, he uses a nibblelick or a fish-net.

"Another gr-reat injoocement to men to spind their Sundays on th' goluf-coorse is th' prisince iv th' fair sect. Hogan tells me there's nawthin' so pleasant to a tired player as to come up on a tee an' find in front iv him four beautiful ladies. Niver excipt in a sleepin'-car in th' mornin' ar-re ladies so atthractive as whin ye see thim fr'm a tee, with their lovely hair out iv curl, their tender faces tanned a lively pink or vermilion, an' a lumber jack's boots on their dainty feet, while they dab pitcheresquely at th' herbage or stand in graceful attichoods on th' puttin'-green correctin' each other's scoors. Their presence lights up th' whole landscape an' gives th' men players a chanst to rest an' gnash their teeth.

"Yes, sir, th' bravest an' th' best an' th' fairest can be seen, east or west, or north or south, beltin' away winter an' summer at this noble game or hallucynation or rite or whativer ye call it—sinitors, judges, congressmen, gr-reat iditors, preachers, th' prisidint himsilf. Whin a reporter wants to see Dock Wilson he don't look f'r him in th' White House. No, sir. But ye r-read: A riprisintative iv th' 'Daily Gloom' found th' prisidint on th' eighteenth green. He seemed in very good spirits. Whin told that Count von Bernstorff had set fire to th' threasury departmint, Ambassador Gerard had been pizened be th' Kaiser, an' American battleship had been sunk be Cap Boy-Ed in th' North River, an' Dernburg was ladin' a charge iv th' turn-d'ye-mind armed with dumb-bells an' bowlin'-pins on Governor's Island, he laughed good naturedly an' said: 'We mustn't get too excited about this kind iv play-fulness. I'll write thim a little letter th' first time we have a rainy day. By th' way, me boy, whin ye go down to ye'er office, I'd like ye to turn in this scoor an' tell th' spoortin' editor I missed a short putt f'r an eight at th' sixteenth. Otherwise I niver played betther.'

"Did I iver see th' game played? Faith, I did. Th' other mornin' I see Hogan go out with his kit iv tools. In other games wan bat is enough, but in goluf ye have to own twinty. All th' money that used to go f'r shoes in Hogan's fam'ly now goes f'r goluf-clubs. If he man-ages to hit th' ball with a club, he tells ye he wudden't part with that club f'r a hundherd dollars an' asts ye to feel it an' say ain't that a nice club. Whin he misses it he says th' club has gone back on him an' he buys a new wan. He has as manny implymints iv this new thrade iv his as a tinker. He has a hammer to beat th' ball into th' ground with, an' a pick to get it out, an' a little shovel to scrape it fr'm th' sand, an' a little hatchet to knock it into th' hole whin he gets near it. 'Where ar-re ye goin' with th' hardware?' says I. 'Is it to open a safe or build a battleship?' says I. 'I'm goin' to play goluf,' says he angrily. 'This is th' day I hang Larkin's hide on th' fence,' he says.

"So I followed him out to Douglas Park, an' there we met Larkin, who had a bag iv akel size. Hogan used to be champeen caber tosser iv th' ward an' Larkin was a sthructural ir'n-wurruker befure his health give out an' he become a horseshoer, but they groaned undher their burdens. Fortchnitly at that moment two bright little boys iv about eight years stepped up an' relieved thim iv their burden. 'What are these pigmies goin' to do with this here year's output iv th' Gary mills?' says I. 'They're goin' to carry thim,' says Larkin. 'They're caddies,' he says. 'Well,' says I, ' 'tis very nice iv th' little toddlers. Th' young cannot start too arly in helpin' th' aged. But,' I says, 'why don't ye get up on their backs an' have thim carry ye around? A little more weight wudden't make much difference,' says I. 'Hush up,' says Hogan.

"Th' poor fellow was standin' on what they call th' tee, which is where ye take th' first lick at th' ball. He had a pole in his hand an' was swingin' it at a dandeline an' missin'. Ivinchooly he stepped up to where th' ball roosted on a little pile iv sand, stood with his legs apart like th' statue he calls th' Goloshes iv Rhodes, waggled th' stick in th' air, p'inted it tords th' pole, cried out, 'Stand away, Larkin, get round behind me, Martin, stop shufflin' there, boy,' an' screamed 'Fore' at a fat old gintleman that was at wurruk in a thrench three city blocks ahead. Thin he hauled off with th' bat, muttherin' to himsilf: 'Eye on th' ball, slow back, keep th' lift arm sthraight, pivot on th' right foot, folly through.' Up crept th' dhread insthrument slow an' cautious an' down it came with a blow that wud've foorced th' Dardanelles. I expicted to see th' ball splintered into a thousan' pieces or disappear into space. But it didn't. It left th' tee ridin' on a piece iv turf th' size iv ye'er hat, floated lazily off to wan side, dhropped, bounced twice, an' nestled in a bush. 'Watch it, boy,' yells Hogan. 'Watch it. Go right to it. Oh,' says he, 'what did I do that was wrong, what *did* I do?' says he, wringin' his hands. 'Ye dhropped ye're right shouldher,' says Larkin. 'Took ye're eye off it,' says Larkin's caddy. 'Toed it,' says an innocint bystander. 'Ye made a mistake thryin' to hit at all. Ye shud've kicked it,' says I. Hogan stood by, his face convulsed with mortyfication ontil Larkin, a man whose Sunday mornin' recreation used to be raisin' a kag iv beer over his head fifty times, give a lunge at th' ball, done a complete spin an' missed it altogether. Thin a wan smile come to Hogan's lips. 'What ar-re ye haw-hawin' about?' says Larkin. They niver spoke again. Most iv th' time they weren't in speakin' distance iv each other. Fr'm time to time they wud meet be chanst on a puttin'-green an' Hogan wud say to himsilf: 'I'm down in twelve,' an' Larkin wud kick his ball over to th' next tee. So they wint rollickin' on. Hogan spoke to me wanst. He said: 'Dammit, stop coughin'.' Whin I left thim at th' sivinth hole th' excitement was at its hite. Larkin' was lookin' f'r his ball in a geeranyum bush, an' Hogan was choppin' down an evergreen three with wan iv his little axes. 'Where ar-re ye goin'?' says he. 'I don't know,' says I, 'but I may dhrop in at th' morgue an' listen to an inquest,' says I. 'I've got to spend me holiday someway,' says I.

"I see Hogan th' next day an' asked him why he played. 'Why,' says I, 'd'ye make a joke iv ye'ersilf at ye'er time iv life, an' ye a man with a family?' says I. 'That's just it,' says he. 'I do it because iv me time iv life an' me fam'ly cares,' says he. 'I defy anny man in th' wurruld to get a bad lie in a bunker an' think iv annything else. He's that mad all his other sorrows, his debts, his sins, an' his future, disappears,' he says, 'like a summer cloud in a hur'cane. I'm that onhappy nawthin' bothers me. If a man come up an' told me me house was afire I'd not hear him. I don't know what it is,' says he, 'onless,' he says, 'it's th' feelin' that ye're bein' persecuted. It's ye'er sinse iv injustice that's stirred up in ye, that makes ye injye a round,' says he."

"Is th' Prisidint a good goluf player, d'ye know, at all?" asked Mr. Hennessy after a moment of judicial silence.

"As a goluf player he cud give Lincoln a sthroke a hole," said Mr. Dooley.

Geoffrey Hellman

MOTHER TAFT'S CHICKENS

Quite a few people have told me, and I have often seen it in print, that the main object of formal education is not so much to inculcate certain facts and dates as to teach you where to go to find out things you want to know. I can find out practically anything I want to know by calling up the *Times,* the Public Library's information desk, the British Library of Information, the French Information Center, or by asking my sister, and I have never precisely understood the connection between this easy ability of mine and the years I spent on algebra, geometry, geology, corrective posture, and Greek. Several months ago I asked the Public Library's information people just what they supposed the connection was, and they said they had no idea offhand but would call me back. I haven't heard from them yet.

My suspicion that the dissection of a frog teaches you, at best, how to dissect a frog, and not a thing more, received a regrettable boost the other day when I came across a printed list, headed "Lost Alumni," sent out by the Taft School, of Watertown, Connecticut, to several hundred of its graduates and ex-students. Taft, as anyone up on educational affairs knows, is one of the best-regarded prep schools in the country, with a student body recruited largely from thoughtful, substantial families and with an admirably low college-entrance-examination mortality record. Its annual algebra contests with Hotchkiss, discontinued a few years ago because of the terrible feeling they engendered, were at one time a lively feature of the Eastern scholastic scene. The list of lost Taft alumni which I have been studying contains four hundred and eleven names, ranging from William Tatlock, class of 1891, to John Ordway, of the class of 1939, who seems to have dropped out of sight like a plummet. The list is accompanied by a statement which reads in part, "You will help us by sending in addresses of any of those listed on the enclosure."

Well, I have every sympathy with Taft's inability to put its finger on Linson E. Tsao, 1914, and I don't suppose that John L. Lewis, 1907, can be the man I keep reading about in the papers, but some of the other lost characters strike me as being surprisingly accessible. Lawrence H. Nott, 1923, for example, is living at 108 East Eighty-second Street, New York, New York; Frederick B. Gleason, Jr., 1927, is at 315 East Sixty-eighth Street; and Alexis C. Coudert, 1931, is at 103 East Eighty-sixth Street. Horace H. Work, Jr., 1936, has an office at 535 Fifth Avenue, and I imagine that the whereabouts of Manfred W. Ehrich, Jr., one of the fifteen missing members of the class of 1933, could be ascertained by sending a postcard to his father at 20 Exchange Place. I am in a position to give this information about Taft's stormy petrels as a result of having spent a few minutes with the New York telephone book, without stirring from my desk.

Comparatively few Taft men come from New York, and perhaps for this reason a number of alumni have managed to conceal themselves right on Park Avenue. Thus, William H. Symington, 1908, listed as lost, is at 1021 Park, while Stockton Green and William S. Begg, Taft 1925 and Yale 1929 both of them, are living with their families at 1120 and 1192 Park, respectively. Leonard Cox, 1911, in what seems a more likely effort to throw the school off his trail, is hiding out in the Village, at 63 East Eleventh Street. Richard C. Plater, Jr., a Watertown classmate of Mr. Green and Mr. Begg and similarly listed as lost, is at 301 Nehoiden Avenue, Needham, Massachusetts, and at least two missing alumni are safe and sound in Connecticut—Warner Bishop, 1912, at 301 Park Place, Bridgeport, and John H. Lynch, Jr., 1921, at his place, Mountain Greenery, in Ridgefield. Another 1921 man-wanted, Mark H. Haight, is at 179-58 Selover Road, St. Albans, Long Island. I can't keep this up much longer, as J. Edgar Hoover is waiting in the reception room to take me out to lunch, but as an indication that my powers of raising the lost aren't confined to Greater New York and New England, I would like to reveal that William H. Woodin, son of the late Secretary of the Treasury and one of twenty missing members of the Taft class of 1919, is at Wilmot Road, Tucson, Arizona, while Spelman Prentice, 1929, a grandson of the late John D. Rockefeller whom Taft is unable to locate, is receiving mail, if not his class notices, at Wolf Pen Road, Prospect, Kentucky. The addresses of Messrs. Woodin and Prentice, and those of all the other lost alumni listed in this paragraph, appear in the current issue of the New York *Social Register,* a copy of which, along with the telephone book, is surely available in Watertown.

I haven't looked up Ambrose Bierce, but if he isn't in one of them, it's only because he didn't go to Taft.

Frank Sullivan

THE JUKES FAMILY

The air is so cluttered with homely little radio programs recounting the daily heartaches and joys of a multitude of families—"The Green Family," "The Brown Family," "This Man's Family," "That Man's Family," and so on—that I have decided to climb on the band wagon with my own program, "The Jukes Family." It will recount, from day to day, the joys and sorrows of an average, homey, not-quite-bright family of the lower lower class.

The matriarch is Ma Jukes, a friendly old party of forty-five who has brought fifteen or twenty children into the world and has learned to take things as they come. She does the best she can to manage her unruly brood, each of whom has some characteristic that sets him or her apart from the herd. For instance, it has long been a subject of frank discussion in the family whether the ears on Laddie, the seventh boy, extend above the top of his head or whether the plateau of his head simply fails to rise to the top of his ears.

The fourth child, Slim, age twenty-two, has a penchant for bigamy which frequently brings upon him the good-natured raillery of the rest of the family. Another of the boys, Timmy, is doing a stretch in Sing Sing, and Mayzetta, the third girl, is in her sophomore year at the Dobbville Home for Delinquent Females. But the glamour girl of the Jukes Family is Babs—tall, striking, with dark, flashing eyes and a head of hair five and a half feet long. And every single strand of it a natural emerald green! Ma Jukes' family (she was a Cabot) all had hair of vivid yellow. Pa's folks' hair had been Alice blue. Nature's alchemy had combined the two colors happily in Babs.

Now then, as our first program opens, we find Ma Jukes setting a kettle of water to boil. A dozen or so of the youngsters, among them her first-born, Jeddie, a fine-looking chap of thirty with white hair and pink eyes, romp boisterously under her feet as she putters about the stove. There is a scuffle among the bairns. Ma intervenes.

"Monongahela!" she admonishes a strapping girl of about ten. "You give Jeddie back his doll. Ain't you ashamed to be playin' with dolls, a big gal like you. . . . Tarnation take it, git out from under my feet afore ye git scalded. Oh, it's you, Chub."

Chub is an attractive child of nineteen, always hanging around the stove because he *likes* to be scalded. Ma goodnaturedly ladles a teaspoonful of hot water on him.

"Now, thar, that's enough. Git along an' quit pesterin' yer pore ole ma."

Chub scampers off with a happy scream of agony.

"I declar'," says Ma, philosophizing in the manner of all the Mas on the family radio programs, "I don't know what the younger generation's a-comin' to. When I was a young un we hung around our ma to git the scrapin's from the cake bowl, not to git hot water thrun on us. Now, whatever's a-keepin' yer pa?"

"I'm hungry," cries Eglantine Jukes, a comely sprite of fifteen without a chin.

Here the voice of Chuckles Gladsome, the announcer, is heard. Ma winces. In the cheery voice of the typical family-program announcer, Chuckles says that if little Eglantine is "hongry," she had just better get herself a good, big, heapin' ole dish of rich, creamy, juicy, delicious, nourishing Dwerps, the Sweetheart of Breakfast Foods. "So go to your corner grocery store tonight, or at the very latest tomorrow morning, etc., etc.," concludes Chuckles.

"I'm still hungry," says Eglantine.

"Well, yer pa oughta be here any minnit now with the chicken," says Ma. "Wonder what's a-keepin' him? Oh, here he is!"

Pa Jukes enters. He is a jovial soul who takes the responsibilities of a large family in his stride. His face, if you can call it a face, is unlined by the years, and its frank, open expression is enhanced rather than marred by an almost complete absence of chin.

"Howdy, Pa," says Ma. "Where's the chicken? You said you was a-goin' to snag us a chicken fer supper."

"Shucks, Ma, there ain't none," apologizes Pa. "Dad rat it, I was lucky I got out of Ole Man Eddy's hencoop 'thout gettin' a hideful o' buckshot."

Ma's face falls at this news, but only for an instant. She quickly hides her disappointment and presents a brave front to the children.

All mothers on family programs are constantly presenting brave fronts in the face of domestic problems. "Tarnation take the ornery ole cuss!" she says. "Can't even leave a neighbor have a measly ole chicken. An' after the way we all pitched in an' helped, the night his barn took fire."

"Now, Ma," says Pa, "you know we wa'n't doin' no mor'n our plain duty in helpin' put that fire out. You know 's well 's I do, 'twas our Buster set that barn afire."

Buster is the firebug of the Jukes family, a gay, irresponsible Puck of thirteen with the typical Jukes no-chin, and regarded by the neighbors as quite a tease because of his habit of setting buildings afire every so often.

"Well," says Ma, "I kind o' had my face fixed fer chicken, but I guess we c'n manage. Here, Lump, you run down to Perkins' grocery and fetch up a few cans salmon an' any other vittles ye think might tech the spot."

"Not me," Lump says. "Jedge tole me ef I got caught swipin' any more stuff out'n stores, he'd send me to state's prison sure 'nough."

"That so, young Mister High-an'-Mighty!" snaps Pa Jukes. "Well, lemme tell you one thing, you young whippersnapper, ef state's prison's good enough fer yer brother Timmy, it's plenty good enough fer you."

"Now, Pa," says Ma, soothingly.

"Well, dad rat it, Ma, jest don't let him git so uppity, that's all. I don't know what's got into the younger generation lately. Why, there ain't a nicer crowd o' boys you'd want to meet than the boys at Sing Sing. Leastwise, 'twas so in my day thar."

"Pa, mebbe one o' the children that ain't never been pinched better go," advises Ma. "It'll look better."

There are shouts from the kiddies of "Me, Ma! Let me go! I wanna go, Ma!"

At this point the door bursts open and in comes Wash Jukes, an attractive, coffee-colored lad of fourteen.

"Guess what, Ma!" Wash exults. "The jedge jes' pernounced me a ju-vile delinquent!"

Wash's brothers and sisters are agog with admiration and Ma glows with maternal pride, but Brother Lump is in the clutch of the green-eyed monster.

"Shucks!" says Lump. "I was a ju-vile delinquent when I was ten year old, wa'n't I, Ma?"

"Go on, po' white trash," sneers Wash.

"Wash Jukes!" Ma rebukes. "You lemme hear you call yer brother po' white trash again an' I'll slap ye down. Now git along to the store and fetch back some vittles." She sighs.

"What's wrong, Ma?" asks Pa.

"Pa, I'm a-worrit about Babs. I wa'n't fixin' to tell ye, because I didn't aim to fret ye none, but she ain't been hum now fer two days and two nights."

"Shucks, Ma, she prob'ly stopped off at some gal friend's house on her way hum from school."

"She hadn't oughta gone an' done it 'thout lettin' me know. I declar', I don't know what the younger generation's a-comin' to. When I was a gal Babs' age, ef I stayed away from hum fer more'n one night a-runnin', I got Hail Columbia from the matron."

"Don't ye fret none about Babs, Ma. She's jest young an' full o' fun. Leave her have her fling. She'll be old soon enough."

"Mebbe yer right, Pa, but it seems to me the young uns don't pay no heed to their elders nowadays nohow. Mebbe I'm a-gettin' old-fashioned, but I kind o' like to know whar my children is o' nights. Say, that reminds me, I got a letter from Timmy today."

"Ye did? Then he's out o' solitary. They don't let ye write no letters when yer in solitary. Leastwise, they didn't in my day at Sing Sing. What's he say?"

"Tarnation take it, how do I know? That's why I'm a-waitin' for Babs to come hum, so's she can read it to me. Buster!"

"Yes, Ma!"

"Quit settin' fire to Chub!"

"But he ast me to set him afire, Ma," Buster says.

"Sure I did, Ma," says Chub.

"Makes no difference," says Ma, sternly. " 'Tain't good fer ye. Ye want to grow up all charred?"

"Yes," says Chub, eagerly.

"Well, I swan to glory, I don't know what the younger generation's a-comin' to. Pa, put out Chub, will ye?"

With a good-natured chuckle, Pa throws a pail of water over Chub just as Wash returns from his trip to Perkins' store. The hungry brood crowds around him eagerly.

"Any luck, Wash?" says Ma.

"Naw," says Wash. "Ole Perkins was a-watchin' me all the time. All I could git was this." He takes a ham from beneath his blouse.

"Well," says Ma, "'tain't much, but it's somethin'."

"And this." Wash produces another package.

"A flitch o' bacon," says Ma. "Now, that's real nice." Ma's tone is cheery. She is presenting a brave front.

"And these," says Wash, and he unloads from various crannies of his person a quantity of canned goods, fresh vegetables, assorted table delicacies, a watermelon, and a case of soft drinks.

"That all ye got?" asks Ma, striving to keep the disappointment from her voice. "Well, ye done the best ye could. We'll manage somehow."

Now the door opens and who bursts in but Babs, her handsome eyes flashing and her green hair flying in the wind.

"Ma," cries Babs, "guess what!"

"Babs Jukes, whar you been?" says Ma, severely. "Go tidy up yer hair. Look at ye!"

"Ma!" cries Babs. "I got a job!"

Pa winces at the sound of the ugly three-letter word.

"Whar's the job?" Ma inquires, coldly, after a pause.

"In the circus! Lady Godiva!"

An artistic career! Well, that's different. Not quite to be classed as work. The alarm subsides, and the family is agog to hear about Babs' job.

"My sakes!" says Ma. "To think we got a real, gen-wine actress in the family!"

"Babs, c'n I have yer autograph?" asks little Monongahela.

Ma is thinking happily how she will come it over her neighbor up the alley, Mrs. Kallikak, who has been insufferable ever since her son got the hot squat for the axe murder of seven.

"Reason I ain't been hum," says Babs, "is I had to go to New York right away an' sign up. Guess they was afraid some other circus might grab me."

"I allus knew Babs'd go places," says Pa, with pride.

"Gee Whittaker, I'm tired," says Babs. "I set up on that train from New York the hull night."

"Set down, child," urges Ma. "I'll git ye a cup o' tea."

Babs sinks into a chair and the youngsters crowd around their distinguished sister, beseeching her for details of her new career and entreating her to get them jobs as freaks in the sideshow.

Suddenly, above the childish babble, there is heard a shriek, then a sinister crackling noise, and cries of alarm as the children scurry to safety.

"Buster! You quit that!" Ma shouts, as is her wont whenever she hears crackling, but it is too late. This time Buster's prank has succeeded all too well. By the time rescue measures have been taken, Babs' once-glorious mane is a smoldering ruin, naught of it remaining save a charred stubble.

Babs is inconsolable.

"Don't you fret none, dearie," Ma attempts to comfort her. "It'll grow in again in no time at all. Onct, when I had the type-ford fever—"

But here the voice of Chuckles Gladsome interrupts Ma.

"Well, folks," says he, "all I can say is, if Babs Jukes wants that hair to grow again in time for her to join the circus, she had just better go tonight, or tomorrow morning at the very latest, to the nearest drugstore and get a bottle of Stickney's Famous Hair Restorer. Ladies, if your hair bothers you, if it is dull, dry, and hard to manage—"

A shot rings out.

When the smoke clears, Ma Jukes is standing over poor Chuckles with Pa's shotgun in her right hand.

"Got him, by cracky!" she announces, with grim pleasure.

"Ma," Pa says. "Ye hadn't ought to o' gone an' done that. The law says 'tain't legal to shoot a buck announcer out o' season. Now ye've let ye'se'f in fer a good fine, and whar ye're a-goin' to raise the dough, I don't know."

Well, what will happen to Ma? Will any jury convict? Will any Fish and Game Commission slap a fine on her for shooting an announcer, in season or out? Is Ma on her way to the clink? And how about Babs' hair? Will it grow back in time for her to join the circus? Follow the adventures of that happy-go-lucky, madcap, lovable, charming, irresponsible bunch, the Jukes Family! Tune in on this station tomorrow afternoon at this same hour and find out what happened to Ma Jukes. Your announcer is Paul Parks, substituting for Chuckles Gladsome. Bi-ing, ba-ang, bo-ong!

THE VANDERBILT CONVENTION

Undoubtedly, the Vanderbilts constitute one of the most interesting families this country has produced. Intertwined as they are with the industrial development of the country they have, in addition, a romantic interest that intrigues the great mass of their newspaper-reading countrymen.

Some Vanderbilt, somewhere, is always doing something that arouses the curiosity of his fellow-Americans. One roams the oceans in search of rare specimens of deep-sea fauna. Another drives an old-fashioned coach and four at Newport. One is at the Rota, in Rome, pleading for an annulment of her marriage. One flouts tradition to enter trade as a newspaper-publisher. But whatever the Vanderbilts do, they are, as a newspaper chap I know would put it, "good copy."

There is one difficulty. The descendants of the doughty old Commodore have grown to be almost as numerous as the proverbial sands of the sea. Indeed, he who attempts to explain which Vanderbilt is which is tackling a man-sized problem. Who married whom? When were they divorced and who got the custody of what? How many Willie K.'s are there? Is it Cornelia or Muriel who rides horseback astride? Is Harold married? When did Mrs. Belmont cease being Mrs. Vanderbilt? They are, in truth, a complicated group.

What follows here is an attempt to explain the Vanderbilt family tree simply and briefly. I shall not go into the more remote branches; that would indeed be a Herculean task. My aim, rather, will be to explain and identify the various Vanderbilts who have figured, more or less, in the public eye.

The Commodore, the original Cornelius Vanderbilt, married, first, Sophia Johnson, and, second, Frances Crawford. His son, William Henry Vanderbilt, inheritor of the bulk of the doughty Commodore's fortune, married Maria Louisa Kissam. They had issue as follows: four sons, Cornelius, Frederick, William Kissam, and George, and four daughters, who became Mrs. Elliot Shepard, Mrs. Henry White, Mrs. Hamilton McKay Twombly, and Mrs. William Seward Webb.

William Kissam married, first, an Alabama girl from an old family named Smith. She later married O. H. P. Belmont. William Kissam then married Mrs. Anne Rutherford Harriman Sands. No. Mrs. Anne Sands Harriman Rutherford. No, that's not right either; let's get this straight. He married, secondly, Mrs. *Anne Harriman Sands Ruth-erford*. She then became, by a process of elimination, Mrs. Anne Harriman Sands Rutherford Vanderbilt.

Cornelius Vanderbilt married Alice Gwynne. That is, not the *first* Cornelius. The first Cornelius was the Commodore and he married, first, Frances Crawford, and, second, Sophia Johnson. No, it's the other way round; he married, first, Sophia Johnson, and, second, Frances Crawford. And his grandson, William Kissam, married Anne Harriman Sands Rutherford.

Now then. The Cornelius Vanderbilt who married Alice Gwynne was not the Cornelius whose yacht recently blew up in the East River. No. The Cornelius whose yacht blew up in the East River is the Cornelius who married Grace Wilson, and they had issue as follows: Cornelius Vanderbilt, Jr., and Grace Vanderbilt (Mrs. Henry Gassaway Davis III). Cornelius Vanderbilt, Jr., son of the Cornelius whose yacht blew up, is the Cornelius whose newspapers blew up. His grandfather, Cornelius Vanderbilt, is the Cornelius who married Alice Gwynne. There is no record of anything belonging to this Cornelius ever having blown up.

Now then. Cornelius and Alice Gwynne Vanderbilt had issue as follows: Cornelius, Alfred Gwynne (named after his mother), Reginald, Gertrude, and Gladys.

Gertrude married a Hungarian nobleman, Count Lâszló Széchényi. No, it couldn't have been Gertrude who married the Count. Gertrude is the sculptor, isn't she? Well then, if she's the sculptor, she's the one who married Payne Whitney, because that one is the one who's the sculptor. I remember distinctly reading *that*. No, that's not right, either. It wasn't Payne Whitney that Gladys—I mean Gertrude—married; it was *Harry* Payne Whitney. You see, *Payne* Whitney and *Harry* Payne Whitney—well, maybe it would be better to clear up the Vanderbilts today and leave the Whitneys for some other day.

Now then. It was Birdie Vanderbilt who married the Hungarian Count. No, Birdie is the sculptor. No, it's Gladys who's the sculptor; what am I thinking of! Her statue blew up. No, it was her yacht that blew up.

No, it was Cornelius' yacht that blew up. Birdie married William K. Not the William K. that married, first, Mrs. O. H. P. Belmont, *née* Smith, and, second, Mrs. Anne Harriman Sands Rutherford. Not that one. Birdie married the William K. who married, first, Virginia

Fair. Cathleen is their daughter. No, Cathleen is Reginald's daughter. Reginald married, first, Ellen French, and, second, Margaret Emerson McKim Mead and White. No, that wasn't Reginald.

Suppose we start *all* over again and get this thing straight. Let's begin once more with the doughty old Commodore. He married, first, Sophia Johnson, and, second, Frances Crawford. William Henry Vanderbilt was their son. Not the William Henry Vanderbilt who gives all the clambakes; the other one, the one who married Maria Louisa Kissam.

Now, if William Henry and Maria Louisa Kissam, after getting married, had let it go at that, things wouldn't have become so complicated. But they didn't. They had issue: eight children. These eight children had children and these children in turn had children, so that in the due course of time there came to be so many Vanderbilts that the family became known as the Vanderbilt Convention. And the doughty old Commodore had started practically on a shoestring!

Now then. What I am trying to do here is simply to give an explanation of which Vanderbilt is which, so that the reader who is interested may be able to distinguish them.

Damn it all, why the hell should people want to distinguish the Vanderbilts, anyhow? This country is supposed to be a democracy, isn't it? When our forefathers gathered at Boston—no, it wasn't Boston. It was Philadelphia. Well, it was either New York or Philadelphia. I don't *care* which one it was. It was on some Sub-Treasury steps, and our forefathers, when they gathered to free the Vanderbilts from the tyranny of George II—no, George III—stipulated, didn't they, that each person in the new nation should be conceived in liberty and dedicated to the proposition that all men are entitled to the pursuit of life, liberty, and the pursuit of happiness.

All right then, why harry the poor Vanderbilts this way? Why not let them alone once in a while? Whose business is it which of them is which? The trouble with this country is that there are a lot of morons in this country who can't mind their own business. They have to be always reading intimate details about the lives of other people. They want everything explained to them. What business is it of theirs which Vanderbilt is which? It's the sensational tabloids, and these physical-culture magazines, that encourage all this morbid curiosity. Why can't the Vanderbilts come and go in peace, same as any other citizen? Who do they think they are, anyhow? Why, for that matter, the old man, the doughty old Commodore, who married Sophia Johnson, first, and Frances Crawford, second, was in trade. He ran a ferry between Staten Island and Manhattan!

His son was William Henry Vanderbilt, who married William Kissam—no, Louisa Maria Kissam, and they had issue (eight children) and then somewhere down the line someone of them married Count Lâszló Széchényi. They have five children and he fought a duel. But Reginald Vanderbilt married Cathleen Neilson and their daughter, Cathleen, married Henry Gassaway Davis III.

No. It wasn't Cathleen who married Henry Gassaway Davis III. Cathleen married Harry C. Cushing III. It was Grace, daughter of the Cornelius whose yacht blew up, who married Henry Gassaway Cushing III.

If only each Vanderbilt would arrange to have something of his, some little bit of personal property, easily distinguishable, blown up, it would be so much easier to tell them apart. "Ah, there goes Phyllis Vanderbilt. Which one is she, you ask? Why, she's the one whose first husband blew up."

It seems to me that somewhere, some time, some Vanderbilt married Irving Berlin III. On second thought, I guess not. I guess I'm thinking either of Cornelia, daughter of Mrs. George W. Vanderbilt (Mrs. Peter Goelet Gerry) who married the Hon. John Francis Amherst Cecil, or of Mary Cadogan, who married the Marquis of Blandford, son of the Duchess of Marlborough who was Consuelo Vanderbilt (Mrs. Jacques Balsan), daughter of the William Kissam Vanderbilt who married Mrs. O. H. P. Belmont and, later, Mrs. Anne Harriman Sands Rutherford Vanderbilt.

Consuelo, erstwhile Duchess of Marlborough (Mrs. Jacques Balsan), would therefore be the aunt of the Consuelo who married Earl E. T. Smith.

Now, there was a time when the Smiths outnumbered the Vanderbilts by two to one, but that era is passing. The Vanderbilts are beginning to absorb the Smiths, although as yet no Vanderbilt has overtly married a Jones. Still, you never can tell. The descendants of the doughty old Commodore are an impulsive and passionate race and if one of them ever chanced upon an unusually comely Jones there is no telling what might ensue.

I trust I have made everything clear.

—CHOLLY SULLIVAN

Ring Lardner

ON CONVERSATION

The other night I happened to be comeing back from Wilmington, Del. to wherever I was going and was setting in the smokeing compartment or whatever they now call the wash room and overheard a conversation between two fellows who we will call Mr. Butler and Mr. Hawkes. Both of them seemed to be from the same town and I only wished I could repeat the conversation verbatim but the best I can do is report it from memory. The fellows evidently had not met for some three to fifteen years as the judges say.

"Well," said Mr. Hawkes, "if this isn't Dick Butler!"

"Well," said Mr. Butler, "if it isn't Dale Hawkes."

"Well, Dick," said Hawkes, "I never expected to meet you on this train."

"No," replied Butler. "I genally always take Number 28. I just took this train this evening because I had to be in Wilmington today."

"Where are you headed for?" asked Hawkes.

"Well, I am going to the big town," said Butler.

"So am I, and I am certainly glad we happened to be in the same car."

"I am glad too, but it is funny we happened to be in the same car."

It seemed funny to both of them but they successfully concealed it so far as facial expression was conserned. After a pause Hawkes spoke again:

"How long since you been back in Lansing?"

"Me?" replied Butler. "I ain't been back there for 12 years."

"I ain't been back there either myself for ten years. How long since you been back there?"

"I ain't been back there for twelve years."

"I ain't been back there myself for ten years. Where are you headed for?"

416

"New York," replied Butler. "I have got to get there about once
year. Where are you going?"

"Me?" asked Hawkes. "I am going to New York too. I have got
o go down there every little wile for the firm."

"Do you have to go there very often?"

"Me? Every little while. How often do you have to go there?"

"About once a year. How often do you get back to Lansing?"

"Last time I was there was ten years ago. How long since you was
back?"

"About twelve years ago. Lot of changes there since we left there."

"That's the way I figured it. It makes a man seem kind of old to
go back there and not see nobody you know."

"You said something. I go along the streets there now and don't
ee nobody I know."

"How long since you was there?"

"Me?" said Hawkes. "I only get back there about once every ten
ears. By the way what become of old man Kelsey?"

"Who do you mean, Kelsey?"

"Yes, what become of him?"

"Old Kelsey? Why he has been dead for ten years."

"Oh, I didn't know that. And what become of his daughter? I
mean Eleanor."

"Why Eleanor married a man named Forster or Jennings or some-
hing like that from Flint."

"Yes, but I mean the other daughter, Louise."

"Oh, she's married."

"Where are you going now?"

"I am headed for New York on business for the firm."

"I have to go there about once a year myself—for the firm."

"Do you get back to Lansing very often?"

"About once in ten or twelve years. I hardly know anybody there
now. It seems funny to go down the street and not know nobody."

"That's the way I always feel. It seems like it was not my old home
own at all. I go up and down the street and don't know anybody
nd nobody speaks to you. I guess I know more people in New York
now than I do in Lansing."

"Do you get to New York often?"

"Only about once a year. I have to go there for the firm."

"New York isn't the same town it used to be neither."

"No, it is changeing all the time. Just like Lansing. I guess they all change."

"I don't know much about Lansing any more. I only get there about once in ten or twelve years."

"What are you reading there?"

"Oh, it is just a little article in Asia. They's a good many interesting articles in Asia."

"I only seen a couple copies of it. This thing I am reading is a little article on 'Application' in the American."

"Well, go ahead and read and don't let me disturb you."

"Well, I just wanted to finish it up. Go ahead and finish what you're reading yourself."

"All right. We will talk things over later. It is funny we happened to get on the same car."

FOLKLORE AND TALL STORIES

Folklore and tall stories, accumulating from generation to generation, are our humorous heritage from the early unsophisticated America. There have been many scholarly analyses of this source material of our national humor. And there have been good collections of regional stuff—Negro, cowboy, early New England, early Southern. For example, we first encountered M's "Going to Bed Before a Young Lady" in Franklin J. Meine's "Tall Tales of the Southwest."

Since it has been so well covered, we are presenting only a moderate amount of folk humor, in proportion to the amount available. Also, we found that a good many of the tales were merely quaint, not funny. There is a tendency in this whole field to confuse quaintness with humor—the two are not interchangeable. Some of the great legendary figures, real or mythical, such as David Crockett, Mike Fink, Pecos Bill— the rangy swashbucklers—are genuinely interesting to read about, but it takes lots of space to account for all the bears Davy Crockett could shoot in a week.

It should be noted that the Paul Bunyan story printed here was written for children. For some reason, the simple-minded editors of this anthology found it better reading than the adult versions of the Bunyan legends.

Marc Connelly

A FISH FRY*

In the darkness many voices are heard singing "Rise, Shine, Give God The Glory." They sing it gayly and rapidly. The lights go up as the second verse ends. The chorus is being sung diminuendo by a mixed company of angels. That is they are angels in that they wear brightly colored robes and have wings protruding from their backs. Otherwise they look and act like a company of happy Negroes at a fish fry. The scene itself is a pre-Creation Heaven with compromises. In the distance is an unbroken stretch of blue sky. Companionable vari-colored clouds billow down to the floor of the stage and roll overhead to the branches of a live oak tree which is up left. The tree is leafy and dripping with Spanish moss, and with the clouds makes a frame for the scene. In the cool shade of the tree are the usual appurtenances of a fish fry; a large kettle of hot fat set on two small parallel logs, with a fire going underneath, and a large rustic table formed by driving four stakes into the ground and placing planks on top of the small con-necting boards. On the table are piles of biscuits and corn bread and the cooked fish in dish pans. There are one or two fairly large cedar or crock "churns" containing boiled custard, which looks like milk. There is a gourd dipper beside the churns and several glasses and cups of various sizes and shapes from which the custard is drunk.

The principal singers are marching two by two in a small area at the right of the stage. Two MAMMY ANGELS *are attending to the frying*

---

* *This is Part I, Scene 2, of "The Green Pastures." In an author's note Marc Connelly says: "'The Green Pastures' is an attempt to present certain aspects of a living religion in the terms of its believers. The religion is that of thousands of Negroes in the deep South. With terrific spiritual hunger and the greatest humility these untutored black Christians—many of whom cannot even read the book which is the treasure house of their faith—have adapted the contents of the Bible to the consistencies of their everyday lives....The author is indebted to Mr. Roark Bradford, whose retelling of several of the Old Testament stories in 'Ol' Man Adam an' His Chillun' first stimulated his interest in this point of view."*

beside the kettle. Behind the table a MAN ANGEL *is skinning fish and passing them to the cooks. Another is ladling out the custard. A* MAMMY ANGEL *is putting fish on bread for a brood of cherubs, and during the first scene they seat themselves on a grassy bank upstage. Another* MAMMY ANGEL *is clapping her hands disapprovingly and beckoning a laughing* BOY CHERUB *down from a cloud a little out of her reach. Another* MAMMY ANGEL *is solicitously slapping the back of a girl cherub who has a large fish sandwich in her hand and a bone in her throat. There is much movement about the table, and during the first few minutes several individuals go up to the table to help themselves to the food and drink. Many of the women angels wear hats and a few of the men are smoking cigars. A large boxful is on the table. There is much laughter and chatter as the music softens, but continues, during the early part of the action. The following short scenes are played almost simultaneously.*

FIRST COOK (*at kettle; calling off*). Hurry up, Cajey. Dis yere fat's cryin' fo' mo' feesh.

A VOICE (*off stage*). We comin', fas' we kin. Dey got to be ketched ain't dey? We cain't say, "C'm'on little fish. C'm'on an' git fried,' kin we?

SECOND COOK (*at table*). De trouble is de mens is all worm fishin'

FIRST MAN ANGEL (*at table*). Whut dif'runce do it make? Yo' all de time got to make out like somebody's doin' somethin' de wrong way.

SECOND COOK (*near table*). I s'pose you got de perfec' way fo' makin bait.

FIRST MAN ANGEL. I ain't sayin' dat. I is sayin' what's wrong wid worm fishin'.

SECOND COOK. Whut's wrong wid worm fishin'? Ever'thing, dat's all Dey's only one good way fo' catfishin', an' dats minny fishin' Anybody know dat.

FIRST MAN ANGEL. Well, it jest so happen dat minny fishin' is de doggondest fool way of fishin' dey is. You kin try minny fishin' to de cows come home an' all you catch'll be de backache. De trouble wid you, sister, is you jest got minny fishin' on de brain.

SECOND COOK. Go right on, loud mouf. You tell me de news. My, my You jest de wisest person in de worl'. First you, den de Lawd God

FIRST MAN ANGEL (*to the custard ladler*). You cain't tell dem nothin'. (*Walks away to the custard churn.*) Does you try to 'splain some simple fac' dey git man-deaf.

FIRST MAMMY ANGEL (*to* CHERUB *on the cloud*). Now, you heerd me. (*The* CHERUB *assumes several mocking poses, as she speaks.*) You fly down yere. You wanter be put down in de sin book? (*She goes to the table, gets a drink for herself and points out the* CHERUB *to one of the men behind the table.*) Dat baby must got imp blood in him he so vexin'. (*She returns to her position under the cloud.*) You want me to fly up dere an' slap you down? Now, I tol' you. (*The* CHERUB *starts to come down.*)

STOUT ANGEL (*to the* CHERUB *with a bone in her throat*). I tol' you you was too little fo' catfish. What you wanter git a bone in you' froat fo'? (*She slaps the* CHERUB's *back.*)

SLENDER ANGEL (*leisurely eating a sandwich as she watches the back-slapping*). What de trouble wid Leonetta?

STOUT ANGEL. She got a catfish bone down her froat. (*To the* CHERUB.) Doggone, I tol' you to eat grinnel instead.

SLENDER ANGEL. Ef'n she do git all dat et, she gonter have de bellyache.

STOUT ANGEL. Ain't I tol' her dat? (*To* CHERUB). Come on now; let go dat bone. (*She slaps* CHERUB's *back again. The bone is dislodged and the* CHERUB *grins her relief.*) Dat's good.

SLENDER ANGEL (*comfortingly.*) Now she all right.

STOUT ANGEL. Go on an' play wid yo' cousins. (*The* CHERUB *joins the* CHERUBS *sitting on the embankment. The concurrency of scenes ends here.*) I ain't see you lately, Lily. How you been?

SLENDER ANGEL. Me, I'm fine. I been visitin' my mammy. She waitin' on de welcome table over by de throne of grace.

STOUT ANGEL. She always was pretty holy.

SLENDER ANGEL. Yes, ma'am. She like it dere. I guess de Lawd's took quite a fancy to her.

STOUT ANGEL. Well, dat's natural. I declare yo' mammy one of de finest lady angels I know.

SLENDER ANGEL. She claim you de best one she know.

STOUT ANGEL. Well, when you come right down to it, I suppose we is all pretty near perfec'.

SLENDER ANGEL. Yes, ma'am. Why is dat, Mis' Jenny?

STOUT ANGEL. I s'pose it's caize de Lawd he don' 'low us 'sociatin' wid de devil any mo' so dat dey cain' be no mo' sinnin'.

SLENDER ANGEL. Po' ol' Satan. Whutevah become of him?

STOUT ANGEL. De Lawd put him some place I s'pose.

SLENDER ANGEL. But dey ain't any place but Heaven, is dey?

STOUT ANGEL. De Lawd could make a place, couldn't he?

SLENDER ANGEL. Dat's de truth. Dey's one thing confuses me though.

STOUT ANGEL. What's dat?

SLENDER ANGEL. I do a great deal of travelin' an' I ain't never come across any place but Heaven anywhere. So if de Lawd kick Satan out of Heaven jest whereat did he go? Dat's my question.

STOUT ANGEL. You bettah let de Lawd keep his own secrets, Lily. De way things is goin' now dey ain't been no sinnin' since dey give dat scamp a kick in de pants. Nowadays Heaven's free of sin an' if a lady wants a little constitutional she kin fly till she wing-weary widout gittin' insulted.

SLENDER ANGEL. I was jest a baby when Satan lef'. I don't even 'member what he look like.

STOUT ANGEL. He was jest right fo' a devil. (*An* ARCHANGEL *enters. He is older than the others and wears a white beard. His clothing is much darker than that of the others and his wings a trifle more imposing.*) Good mo'nin', Archangel.

(*Others say good morning.*)

ARCHANGEL. Good mo'nin', folks. I wonder kin I interrup' de fish fry an' give out de Sunday school cyards? (*Cries of "Suttingly!" "Mah goodness, yes"—etc. The marching* CHOIR *stops.*) You kin keep singin' if you want to. Why don' you sing "When de Saints Come Marchin' In"? Seem to me I ain' heard dat lately. (*The* CHOIR *begins "When the Saints Come Marching In," rather softly, but does not resume marching. The* ARCHANGEL *looks off left.*) All right, bring 'em yere. (*A prim-looking* WOMAN TEACHER-ANGEL *enters, shepherding ten* BOY *and* GIRL CHERUBS. *The* TEACHER *carries ten beribbonned diplomas, which she gives to the* ARCHANGEL. *The* CHERUBS *are dressed in stiffly starched white suits and dresses, the little girls having enormous ribbons at the backs of their dresses and smaller ones in their hair and on the tips of their wings. They line up in front of the* ARCHANGEL *and receive the attention of the rest of the company. The* CHOIR *sings through the ceremony.*) Now den cherubs, why is you yere?

CHILDREN. Because we so good.

ARCHANGEL. Dat's right. Now who de big boss?

CHILDREN. Our dear Lawd.

ARCHANGEL. Dat's right. When you all grow up what you gonter be?

CHILDREN. Holy angels at de throne of grace.

ARCHANGEL. Dat's right, Now, you passed yo' 'xaminations and it gives me great pleasure to hand out de cyards for de whole class. Gineeva Chaproe. (*The* FIRST GIRL CHERUB *goes to him and gets her diploma. The* CHOIR *sings loudly and resumes marching, as the* ARCHANGEL *calls out another name—and presents diplomas.*) Corey Moulter. (SECOND GIRL CHERUB *gets her diploma.*) Nootzie Winebush. (THIRD GIRL CHERUB.) Harriet Prancy. (FOURTH GIRL CHERUB.) I guess you is Brozain Stew't. (*He gives the* FIFTH GIRL CHERUB *the paper. Each of the presentations has been accompanied by handclapping from the bystanders.*) Now you boys know yo' own names. Suppose you come yere and help me git dese 'sorted right?

(BOY CHERUBS *gather about him and receive their diplomas. The little* GIRLS *have scattered about the stage, joining groups of the adult angels. The angel* GABRIEL *enters. He is bigger and more elaborately winged than even the* ARCHANGEL, *but he is also much younger and beardless. His costume is less conventional than that of the other men, resembling more the Gabriel of the Doré drawings. His appearance causes a flutter among the others. They stop their chattering with the children. The* CHOIR *stops as three or four audible whispers of "Gabriel!" are heard. In a moment the heavenly company is all attention.*)

GABRIEL (*lifting his hand.*) Gangway! Gangway for de Lawd God Jehovah! (*There is a reverent hush as* GOD *enters. He is the tallest and biggest of them all. He wears a white shirt with a white bow tie, a long Prince Albert coat of black alpaca, black trousers and congress gaiters. He looks at the assemblage. There is a pause. He speaks in a rich, bass voice.*)

GOD. Is you been baptized?

OTHERS (*chanting*). Certainly, Lawd.

GOD. Is you been baptized?

OTHERS. Certainly, Lawd.

GOD (*with the beginning of musical notation*). Is you been baptized?

OTHERS (*now half-singing*). Certainly, Lawd. Certainly, certainly, certainly, Lawd. (*They sing the last two verses with equivalent part division.*)

Is you been redeemed?
Certainly, Lawd.
Is you been redeemed?
Certainly, Lawd.
Is you been redeemed?
Certainly, Lawd. Certainly, certainly, certainly, Lawd.

Do you bow mighty low?
Certainly, Lawd.
Do you bow mighty low?
Certainly, Lawd.
Do you bow mighty low?
Certainly, Lawd. Certainly, certainly, certainly, Lawd.

(*As the last response ends all heads are bowed.* GOD *looks at them for a moment; then lifts His hand.*)

GOD. Let de fish fry proceed.

(EVERYONE *rises. The* ANGELS *relax and resume their inaudible conversations. The activity behind the table and about the cauldron is resumed. Some of the* CHOIR *members cross to the table and get sandwiches and cups of the boiled custard. Three or four of the* CHILDREN *in the Sunday School class and the* LITTLE GIRL *who had the bone in her throat affectionately group themselves about* GOD *as He speaks with the* ARCHANGEL. *He pats their heads, they hang to His coat-tails, etc.*)

ARCHANGEL. Good mo'nin', Lawd.

GOD. Good mo'nin', Deacon. You lookin' pretty spry.

ARCHANGEL. I cain' complain. We jest been givin' our cyards to de chillun.

GOD. Dat's good.

(*A small* CHERUB, *his feet braced against one of* GOD's *shoes, is using* GOD's *coat-tail as a trapeze. One of the* COOKS *offers a fish sandwich which* GOD *politely declines.*)

FIRST MAMMY ANGEL. Now, you leave go de Lawd's coat, Herman. You heah me?

GOD. Dat's all right, sister. He jest playin'.

FIRST MAMMY ANGEL.—He playin' too rough. (GOD *picks up the* CHERUB *and spanks him good-naturedly. The* CHERUB *squeals with delight and runs to his mother.* GABRIEL *advances to* GOD *with a glass of the custard.*)

GABRIEL. Little b'iled custud, Lawd?

GOD. Thank you very kindly. Dis looks nice.

CUSTARD MAKER (*offering a box*). Ten cent seegar, Lawd?

GOD (*taking it*). Thank you, thank you. How de fish fry goin'? (*Ad lib. cries of "O. K., Lawd," "Fine an' dandy, Lawd," "De best one yit, Lawd," etc. To the* CHOIR.) How you shouters gittin' on?

CHOIR LEADER. We been marchin' and singin' de whole mo'nin'.

GOD. I heerd you. You gettin' better all de time. You gittin' as good as de one at de throne. Why don' you give us one dem ol' time jump-ups?

CHOIR LEADER. Anythin' you say, Lawd. (*To the others.*) "So High!" (*The* CHOIR *begins to sing "So High You Can't Get Over It." They sing softly, but do not march. An* ANGEL *offers his cigar to* GOD *from which He can light His own.*)

GOD. No, thanks. I'm gonter save dis a bit. (*He puts the cigar in his pocket and listens to the singers a moment. Then he sips his custard. After a second sip, a look of displeasure comes on his face.*)

GABRIEL. What's de matter, Lawd?

GOD (*sipping again.*) I ain't jest sure, yit. Dey's something 'bout dis custard. (*Takes another sip.*)

CUSTARD MAKER. Ain't it all right, Lawd?

GOD. It don't seem seasoned jest right. You make it?

CUSTARD MAKER. Yes, Lawd, I put everythin' in it like I allus do. It's supposed to be perfec'.

GOD. Yeah. I kin taste de eggs and de cream and de sugar. (*Suddenly.*) I know what it is. It needs jest a little bit mo' firmament.

CUSTARD MAKER. Dey's firmament in it, Lawd.

GOD. Maybe, but it ain' enough.

CUSTARD MAKER. It's all we had, Lawd. Dey ain't a drap in de jug.

GOD. Dat's all right. I'll jest r'ar back an' pass a miracle. (CHOIR *stops singing.*) Let it be some firmament! An' when I say let it be some firmament, I don't want jest a little bitty dab o' firmament caize I'm sick an' tired of runnin' out of it when we need it. Let it be a whole mess of firmament! (*The stage has become misty until* GOD *and the heavenly company are obscured. As he finishes the speech there is a burst of thunder. As the stage grows darker.*) Dat's de way I like it.

(*Murmurs from the others: "Dat's a lot of firmament." "My, dat is firmament!" "Look to me like he's created rain," etc.*)

FIRST MAMMY ANGEL (*when the stage is dark*.) Now, look Lawd, dat's too much firmament. De cherubs is gettin' all wet.

SECOND MAMMY ANGEL. Look at my Carlotta, Lawd. She's soaked to de skin. Dat's *plenty* too much firmament.

GOD. Well, 'co'se we don't want de chillun to ketch cold. Can't you dreen it off?

GABRIEL. Dey's no place to dreen it, Lawd.

FIRST MAMMY ANGEL. Why don't we jest take de babies home, Lawd?

GOD. No, I don' wanta bust up de fish fry. You angels keep quiet an' I'll pass another miracle. Dat's always de trouble wid miracles. When you pass one you always gotta r'ar back an' pass another. (*There is a hush*.) Let dere be a place to dreen off this firmament. Let dere be mountains and valleys an' let dere be oceans an' lakes. An' let dere be rivers and bayous to dreen it off in, too. As a matter of fac' let dere be de earth. An' when dat's done let dere be de sun, an' let it come out and dry my cherubs' wings.

(*The lights go up until the stage is bathed in sunlight. On the embankment upstage there is now a waist-high wrought-iron railing such as one sees on the galleries of houses in the French quarter of New Orleans. The* CHERUBS *are being examined by their parents and there is an ad lib. murmur of, "You all right, honey?" "You feel better now, Albert?" "Now you all dry, Vangy?" until the* ARCHANGEL, *who has been gazing in awe at the railing, drowns them out*.)

ARCHANGEL. Look yere!

(*There is a rush to the embankment accompanied by exclamations, "My goodness!" "What's dis?" "I declah!" etc.* GABRIEL *towers above the group on the middle of the embankment.* GOD *is wrapped in thought, facing the audience. The* CHOIR *resumes singing "So High You Can't Get Over It" softly. The babbling at the balustrade dies away as the people lean over the railing.* GABRIEL *turns and faces* GOD *indicating the earth below the railing with his left hand*.)

GABRIEL. Do you see it, Lawd?

GOD (*quietly, without turning his head upstage*). Yes, Gabriel.

GABRIEL. Looks mighty nice, Lawd.

GOD. Yes.

(GABRIEL *turns and looks over the railing*.)

GABRIEL (*gazing down*). Yes, suh. Dat'd make mighty nice farming country. Jest look at dat South forty over dere. You ain't going to let dat go to waste is you Lawd? Dat would be a pity an' a shame.

GOD (*not turning*). It's good earth. (GOD *turns, room is made for him beside* GABRIEL *on the embankment.*) Yes. I ought to have some-body to enjoy it. (*He turns, facing the audience. The others, save for the* CHOIR *who are lined up in two rows of six on an angle up right, continue to look over the embankment.*) Gabriel! (GOD *steps down from the embankment two paces.*)

GABRIEL (*joining him.*) Yes, Lawd.

GOD. Gabriel, I'm goin' down dere.

GABRIEL. Yes, Lawd.

GOD. I want you to be my working boss yere while I'm gone.

GABRIEL. Yes, Lawd.

GOD. You know dat matter of dem two stars?

GABRIEL. Yes, Lawd.

GOD. Git dat fixed up! You know dat sparrow dat fell a little while ago? 'Tend to dat, too.

GABRIEL. Yes, Lawd.

GOD. I guess dat's about all. I'll be back Saddy. (*To the choir.*) Quiet, angels. (*The* CHOIR *stops singing. Those on the embankment circle down stage.* GOD *goes to embankment. Turns and faces the company.*) I'm gonter pass one more miracle. You all gonter help me an' not make a soun' caize it's one of de most impo'tant miracles of all. (*Nobody moves.* GOD *turns, facing the sky and raises His arms above his head.*) Let there be man.

(*There is growing roll of thunder as stage grows dark. The* CHOIR *bursts into "Hallelujah," and continues until the lights go up on the next scene.*)

Mark Twain

A MISSISSIPPI PILOT *

There used to be an excellent pilot on the river, a Mr. X., who was a somnambulist. It was said that if his mind was troubled about a bad piece of river, he was pretty sure to get up and walk in his sleep and do strange things. He was once fellow-pilot for a trip or two with George Ealer, on a great New Orleans passenger packet. During a considerable part of the first trip George was uneasy, but got over it by and by, as X. seemed content to stay in his bed when asleep. Late one night the boat was approaching Helena, Ark.; the water was low, and the crossing above the town in a very blind and tangled condition. X. had seen the crossing since Ealer had, and as the night was particularly drizzly, sullen, and dark, Ealer was considering whether he had not better have X. called to assist in running the place, when the door opened and X. walked in. Now, on very dark nights, light is a deadly enemy to piloting; you are aware that if you stand in a lighted room, on such a night, you cannot see things in the street to any purpose; but if you put out the lights and stand in the gloom you can make out objects in the street pretty well. So, on very dark nights, pilots do not smoke; they allow no fire in the pilot-house stove, if there is a crack which can allow the least ray to escape; they order the furnaces to be curtained with huge tarpaulins and the skylights to be closely blinded. Then no light whatever issues from the boat. The undefinable shape that now entered the pilot-house had Mr. X.'s voice. This said:

"Let me take her, George; I've seen this place since you have, and it is so crooked that I reckon I can run it myself easier than I could tell you how to do it."

"It is kind of you, and I swear I am willing. I haven't got another drop of perspiration left in me. I have been spinning around and

* *This tall story was told as fact in "Life on the Mississippi." Maybe it was fact.*

around the wheel like a squirrel. It is so dark I can't tell which way she is swinging till she is coming around like a whirligig."

So Ealer took a seat on the bench, panting and breathless. The black phantom assumed the wheel without saying anything, steadied the waltzing steamer with a turn or two, and then stood at ease, coaxing her a little to this side and then to that, as gently and as sweetly as if the time had been noonday. When Ealer observed this marvel of steering, he wished he had not confessed! He stared, and wondered, and finally said:

"Well, I thought I knew how to steer a steamboat, but that was another mistake of mine."

X. said nothing, but went serenely on with his work. He rang for the leads; he rang to slow down the steam; he worked the boat carefully and neatly into invisible marks, then stood at the center of the wheel and peered blandly out into the blackness, fore and aft, to verify his position; as the leads shoaled more and more, he stopped the engines entirely, and the dead silence and suspense of "drifting" followed; when the shoalest water was struck, he cracked on the steam, carried her handsomely over, and then began to work her warily into the next system of shoal-marks; the same patient, heedful use of leads and engines followed, the boat slipped through without touching bottom, and entered upon the third and last intricacy of the crossing; imperceptibly she moved through the gloom, crept by inches into her marks, drifted tediously till the shoalest water was cried, and then, under a tremendous head of steam, went swinging over the reef and away into deep water and safety!

Ealer let his long-pent breath pour in a great relieving sigh, and said:

"That's the sweetest piece of piloting that was ever done on the Mississippi River! I wouldn't believe it could be done, if I hadn't seen it."

There was no reply, and he added:

"Just hold her five minutes longer, partner, and let me run down and get a cup of coffee."

A minute later Ealer was biting into a pie, down in the "texas," and comforting himself with coffee. Just then the night watchman happened in, and was about to happen out again, when he noticed Ealer and exclaimed:

"Who is at the wheel, sir?"

"X."

"Dart for the pilot-house, quicker than lightning!"

The next moment both men were flying up the pilot-house companion-way, three steps at a jump! Nobody there! The great steamer was whistling down the middle of the river at her own sweet will! The watchman shot out of the place again; Ealer seized the wheel, set an engine back with power, and held his breath while the boat reluctantly swung away from a "towhead," which she was about to knock into the middle of the Gulf of Mexico!

By and by the watchman came back and said:

"Didn't that lunatic tell you he was asleep, when he first came up here?"

"No."

"Well, he was. I found him walking along on top of the railings, just as unconcerned as another man would walk a pavement; and I put him to bed; now just this minute there he was again, away astern, going through that sort of tight-rope deviltry the same as before."

"Well, I think I'll stay by next time he has one of those fits. But I hope he'll have them often. You just ought to have seen him take this boat through Helena crossing. *I* never saw anything so gaudy before. And if he can do such gold-leaf, kid-glove, diamond-breastpin piloting when he is sound asleep, what *couldn't* he do if he was dead!"

Joel Chandler Harris

MISS COW FALLS A VICTIM TO MR. RABBIT

"Uncle Remus," said the little boy, "what became of the Rabbit after he fooled the Buzzard, and got out of the hollow tree?"

"Who? Brer Rabbit? Bless yo' soul, honey, Brer Rabbit went skippin' 'long home, he did, des ez sassy ez a jay-bird at a sparrer's nes'. He went gallopin' 'long, he did, but he feel mighty tired out, en stiff in his jints, en he wuz mighty nigh dead for sumpin fer ter drink, en bimeby, w'en he got mos' home, he spied ole Miss Cow feedin' roun' in a fiel', he did, en he 'termin' fer ter try his han' wid 'er. Brer Rabbit know mighty well dat Miss Cow won't give 'im no milk, kaze she done 'fuse 'im mo'n once, en w'en his ole 'oman wuz sick, at dat. But never mind dat. Brer Rabbit sorter dance up 'long side er de fence, he did, en holler out:

" 'Howdy, Sis Cow,' sez Brer Rabbit, sezee.

" 'W'y, howdy, Brer Rabbit,' sez Miss Cow, sez she.

" 'How you fine yo'se'f deze days, Sis Cow?' sez Brer Rabbit, sezee.

" 'I'm sorter toler'ble, Brer Rabbit; how you come on?' sez Miss Cow, sez she.

" 'Oh, I'm des toler'ble myse'f, Sis Cow; sorter linger'n' twix' a bauk en a break-down,' sez Brer Rabbit, sezee.

" 'How yo' fokes, Brer Rabbit?' sez Miss Cow, sez she.

" 'Dey er des middlin', Sis Cow; how Brer Bull gittin' on?' sez Brer Rabbit, sezee.

" 'Sorter so-so', sez Miss Cow, sez she.

" 'Dey er some mighty nice 'simmons up dis tree, Sis Cow,' sez Brer Rabbit, sezee, 'en I'd like mighty well fer ter have some un um,' sezee.

" 'How you gwineter git um, Brer Rabbit?' sez she.

" 'I 'low'd maybe dat I might ax you fer ter butt 'gin de tree, en shake some down, Sis Cow,' sez Brer Rabbit, sezee.

"C'ose Miss Cow don't wanter diskommerdate Brer Rabbit, en she march up ter de 'simmon tree, she did, en hit it a rap wid'er horns—blam! Now, den," continued Uncle Remus, tearing off the corner of a plug of tobacco and cramming it into his mouth—"now, den, dem 'simmons wuz green ez grass, en na'er one never drap. Den Miss Cow butt de tree—blim! Na'er 'simmon drap. Den Miss Cow sorter back off little, en run agin de tree—blip! No 'simmons never drap. Den Miss Cow back off little fudder, she did, en hi'st her tail on 'er back, en come agin de tree, kerblam! en she come so fas', en she come so hard, twel one 'er her horns went spang thoo de tree, en dar she wuz. She can't go forreds, en she can't go backerds. Dis zackly w'at Brer Rabbit waitin' fer, en he no sooner seed ole Miss Cow all fas'en'd up dan he jump up, he did, en cut de pidjin-wing.

" 'Come he'p me out, Brer Rabbit,' sez Miss Cow, sez she.

" 'I can't clime, Sis Cow,' sez Brer Rabbit, sezee, 'but I'll run'n tell Brer Bull,' sezee; en wid dat Brer Rabbit put out fer home, en 'twan't long 'fo here he come wid his ole 'oman en all his chilluns, en de las' one er de fambly wuz totin' a pail. De big uns had big pails, en de little uns had little pails. En dey all s'roundid ole Miss Cow, dey did, en you hear me, honey, dey milk't 'er dry. De ole uns milk't en de young uns milk't, en den w'en dey done got nuff, Brer Rabbit, he up'n say, sezee:

" 'I wish you mighty well, Sis Cow. I 'low'd bein's how dat you'd hatter sorter camp out all night dat I'd better come en swaje yo' bag,' sezee."

"Do which, Uncle Remus?" asked the little boy.

"Go 'long, honey! Swaje 'er bag. W'en cows don't git milk't, der bag swells, en youk'n hear um a moanin' en a beller'n des like dey wuz gittin' hurtid. Dat's w'at Brer Rabbit done. He 'sembled his family, he did, en he swaje ole Miss Cow's bag.

"Miss Cow, she stood dar, she did, en she study en study, en strive fer ter break loose, but de horn done bin jam in de tree so tight dat twuz way 'fo day in de mornin' 'fo she loose it. Anyhow hit wuz endurin' er de night, en atter she git loose she sorter graze 'roun', she did, fer ter jestify 'er stummuck. She 'low'd, ole Miss Cow did, dat Brer Rabbit be hoppin' 'long dat way fer ter see how she gittin' on, en she tuck'n lay er trap fer 'im; en des 'bout sunrise wat'd ole Miss Cow do but march up ter de 'simmon tree en stick er horn back in de hole? But, bless yo' soul, honey, w'ile she wuz croppin' de grass, she tuck one moufull too menny, kaze w'en she hitch on ter de 'simmon tree agin, Brer Rabbit wuz settin' in de fence cornder a watchin' un 'er. Den Brer Rabbit he say ter hisse'f:

"'Heyo,' sezee, 'w'at dis yer gwine on now? Hole yo' hosses, Sis Cow, twel you hear me comin',' sezee.

"En den he crope off down de fence, Brer Rabbit did, en bimeby here he come—lippity-clippity, clippity-lippity—des a sailin' down de big road.

"'Mornin', Sis Cow,' sez Brer Rabbit, sezee, 'how you come on dis mornin'?' sezee.

"'Po'ly, Brer Rabbit, po'ly,' sez Miss Cow, sez she. 'I ain't had no res' all night,' sez she. 'I can't pull loose,' sez she, 'but ef you'll come en ketch holt er my tail, Brer Rabbit,' sez she, 'I reckin may be I kin fetch my horn out,' sez she. Den Brer Rabbit, he come up little closer, but he ain't gittin' too close.

"'I speck I'm nigh nuff, Sis Cow,' sez Brer Rabbit, sezee. 'I'm a mighty puny man, en I might git trompled,' sezee. 'You do de pullin', Sis Cow,' sezee, 'en I'll do de gruntin',' sezee.

"Den Miss Cow, she pull out 'er horn, she did, en tuck atter Brer Rabbit, en down de big road dey had it, Brer Rabbit wid his years laid back, en Miss Cow wid 'er head down en 'er tail curl. Brer Rabbit kep' on gainin', en bimeby he dart in a brier-patch, en by de time Miss Cow come 'long he had his head stickin' out, en his eyes look big ez Miss Sally's chany sassers.

"'Heyo, Sis Cow! Whar you gwine?' sez Brer Rabbit, sezee.

"'Howdy, Brer Big-Eyes,' sez Miss Cow, sez she. 'Is you seed Brer Rabbit go by?'

"'He des minit pass,' sez Brer Rabbit, sezee, 'en he look mighty sick,' sezee.

"En wid dat, Miss Cow tuck down de road like de dogs wuz atter 'er, en Brer Rabbit, he des lay down dar in de brier-patch en roll en laugh twel his sides hurtid 'im. He bleedzd ter laff. Fox atter 'im, Buzzard atter 'im, en Cow atter 'im, en dey ain't kotch 'im yit."

"M"

GOING TO BED BEFORE A YOUNG LADY *

As I was saying, ten years ago, Judge Douglass, of Illinois, was a beardless youth of twenty years of age, freshly come amongst the people of the "Sucker State," with an air about him suspiciously red-olent of Yankeeland. A mere youthful adventurer amongst those "square" Suckers—one would deem the position embarrassing. Not so with the judge; he had come on business. A political fortune was to be made, and no time lost. He was about launching on the sea of popular favour, and he commenced a general coast survey the day he arrived. He soon made himself District Attorney, member of the Legislature, Register of the U. S. Land Office, Secretary of State, and Judge of the Supreme Court.

"How do you adapt yourself," said I, "Judge, to the people? How did you 'naturalize' yourself, as it were?"

"Oh, nothing easier; you see I like it. It's democratic. But it did come awkward at first. You know I am, or rather was, bashful to rather a painful degree. Well, now, nine-tenths of my constituents despise luxuries, and have no such thing as a second room in their houses. In beating up votes, I live with my constituents, eat with my constituents, drink with them, lodge with them, pray with them, laugh, hunt, dance and work with them; I eat their corn dodgers and fried bacon, and sleep two in a bed with them. Among my first acquaintances were the L———s, down under the Bluffs. Fine fellows, the L———s,—by the way, I am sure of five votes there. Well, you perceive, I had to live there: and I did live there. But, sir, I was frightened the first night I slept there. I own it; yes, sir, I acknowledge the corn. An ice in August is something: but I was done to

---

* This sketch was reprinted in The Spirit of the Times (1845) and was credited to a New York paper—The Evening Mirror. The author is not known. The "Judge Douglass" of the story was, presumably, Stephen A. Douglas.

an icicle; had periodical chills for ten days. Did you ever see a Venus in linsey-woolsey?"

"No!"

"Then you shall see Serena L——s. They call her the 'White Plover'; seventeen:—plump as a pigeon, and smooth as a persimmon. How the devil, said I to myself, soliloquizing the first night I slept there, am I to go to bed before this young lady? I do believe my heart was topsyturvied, for the idea of pulling off my boots before the girl was death. And as to doffing my other fixtures, I would sooner have my leg taken off with a wood-saw. The crisis was tremendous. It was nearly midnight, and the family had been hours in bed. Miss Serena alone remained. Bright as the sun, the merry minx talked on. It was portentously obvious to me at last, that she had determined to outsit me. By repeated spasmodic efforts, my coat, waistcoat, cravat, boots and socks were brought off. During the process, my beautiful neighbor talked to me with unaverted eyes, and with that peculiar kind of placidity employed by painters to imbody their idea of the virgin. I dumped myself down in a chair, in a cold perspiration. A distressing thought occurred to me. Does not the damsel stand on a point of local etiquette? It may be the fashion of these people to see strangers in bed before retiring themselves. May I not have kept those beautiful eyes open, from ignorance of what these people deem good breeding? Neither the lady's eyes nor tongue had indeed be- trayed fatigue. Those large jet eyes seemed to dilate and grow brighter as the blaze of the wood fire died away; but doubtless this was from kind consideration for the strange wakefulness of her guest. The thing was clear. I determined to retire, and without delay. I arose with firmness, unloosed my suspenders, and in a voice not altogether steady, said:

" 'Miss Serena, I think I will retire.'

" 'Certainly, sir,' she quietly observed, 'you will lodge there, sir'; inclining her beautiful head towards a bed standing a few yards from where she was sitting. I proceeded to uncase; entrenching myself behind a chair the while, fondly imagining the position offered some security. It is simply plain to a man in his senses, that a chair of the fashion of the one I had thrown between myself and 'the enemy,' as a military man would say, offered almost no security at all. No more, in fact, than standing up behind a ladder—nothing in the way of the artillery of bright eyes, as a poet would say, sweeping one down by platoons. Then I had a dead open space of ten feet between me and the bed; a sort of Bridge of Lodi passage which I was forced to make, exposed to a cruel raking fire fore and aft. Although I say it, who should not say it, an emergency never arose for which I had not a resource. I had one for this. The plan was the work of a moment, I de—"

"Ah! I see, you stormed the battery and s—"

"Bah! don't interrupt me. No; I determined, by a bold ruse de guerre, to throw her attention out of the window, clear the perilous passage, and fortify myself under the counterpane before she recovered her surprise. The plan failed. You see I am a small man, physically speaking. Body, limbs, and head, setting up business on one hundred and seven and a half pounds, all told, of flesh, blood, and bones, cannot, individually or collectively, set up any very ostentatious pretensions. I believe the young lady must have been settling in her mind some philosophical point on that head. Perhaps her sense of justice wished to assure itself of a perfectly fair distribution of the respective motives. Perhaps she did not feel easy until she knew that a kind Providence had not added to general poverty individual wrong. Certain it was, she seemed rather pleased with her speculations; for when I arose from a stooping posture finally, wholly disencumbered of cloth, I noticed mischievous shadows playing about the corners of her mouth. It was the moment I had determined to direct her eye to some astonishing circumstance out of the window. But the young lady spoke at the critical moment.

" 'Mr. Douglass,' she observed, 'you have got a mighty small chance of legs there.'

"Men seldom have any notice of their own powers, I never made any pretensions to skill in ground and lofty tumbling; but it is strictly true, I cleared, at one bound, the open space, planted myself on the centre of the bed, and was buried in the blankets in a twinkling."

"I congratulate you, my boy," said I, poising a cube of the crimson core of the melon on the point of my knife; "a lucky escape truly! But was the young lady modest?"

"Modest, sir!—there is not in Illinois a more modest, or more sensible girl. It's habit—all habit. I think nothing of it now. Why, it's only last week I was at a fine wedding party, and a large and fine assembly of both sexes lodged in the same room, with only three feet or so of neutral territory between them."

"You astonish me, Mr. Douglass."

"Fact, sir, upon my honour. You see these people are the very soul of hospitality, and never allow a fine social party to turn out at twelve o'clock at night to go long distances home. All that is more cleverly managed here. An Illinois bed has a power of elongation or expansion perfectly enigmatical to strangers. One bed four feet wide, will, on occasion, flank one whole side of the house, and is called a field-bed, and large parties will range themselves on opposite sides of the house as economically as candles in a box."

"But, my dear fellow, this is drouthy prose, introduce yourself to that little fellow in the corner, and pass him over; and now tell me all about old Canandaigua."

Glen Rounds

WHY THERE ARE NO TREES
ON THE DESERT*

For many years in his spare time Ol' Paul had fooled around cross-breeding plants in a small way. At first he tried to cross an apple tree, a yellow pine, and a sawmill to get a tree that would keep the best features of all three. The idea was that if he could have a tree that would grow lumber already cut, the boards hanging like apples, he could get rid of all his loggers and hire apple or apricot pickers instead. Which of course would be a big saving, as everyone knows that fruit pickers work cheaper than lumberjacks, and feed themselves, which in itself is no small item. Besides that, he could deal direct with the consumer, as the Plankavos, as he hoped to call them, would do away with the sawmills, except for the few needed to provide sawdust for butcher shops and saloons.

I don't know exactly what ever happened to the Plankavo, but while he was fooling around he somehow accidentally crossed a Douglas fir, a California redwood, and a desert cactus. The tree he got was as tall as a redwood, the wood couldn't be told from fir, and it grew well in the dryest desert. The main trouble was the fact that it had thorns seventy feet long, instead of branches. This made Ol' Paul sore, so he didn't breed any more trees. However, a great many years later these trees had grown to a great size, covering the desert with a deep forest.

One day Ol' Paul gets a letter from the Government telling him he'll have to log the desert off. It seems that the Tired Eastern Business Women going out there for their vacations, were complaining that they couldn't see the desert because of the trees, and the cowboys on the dude ranches were all the time coming home with their clothes snagged up by the thorns. Along with the letter is a hand-painted

* A Paul Bunyan story as told for children by Glen Rounds.

440

picture, showing him what the Government thinks a desert should look like.

As soon as Paul gets the letter he hitches Babe to the south end of the section of land the camp is on, and hauls it down to Nevada. He often moved camp this way as it was quicker than any other, and besides, the men never got homesick for the old camp.

Next morning he takes a look at the timber and knows he's in for plenty of trouble for sure, on account of those seventy-foot thorns. At first they try to tunnel under the thorns and cut the trees off at the roots, but the thorns keep the trees from falling over even after they're cut off.

Then he decides to dynamite, and what a job that is! First they dig out a powder chamber under the roots, then carry in four thousand five hundred and four cases of dynamite and two thousand and four cans of giant powder. The idea is to blast off a township at a time. All the time the heat is affecting the men something fierce, so they can only work in four-hour shifts. Even working shifts day and night and holidays, it takes three weeks and nine days to get the giant blast ready. The last case of dynamite is packed, the percussion caps are wired, and the men all move back out of danger. Ol' Paul looks around and hollers: "Let her go!"

Well sir, the shock throws every man in camp flat on his back, knocks the cupolas off three barns in Iowa, and the smoke and dust go up in a column thirty-four miles high. When the air clears somewhat the men see there's nothing left but the holes. The trees've been blown clean out of sight. As it's nearly supper time, Ol' Paul says they might as well knock off for the day, but first he reaches up and feels around on top of the smoke column, which is still standing. He finds half a wagon load of wild ducks up there.

It seems that a big flock had been flying over when the blast went off. It has shot the air full of sand the exact size of bird shot and killed them all instantly, except one drake who was flying well in the lead. The sand missed him, but the force of the blast put a curl in his tail feathers that has never come out.

That night the men go to bed with their stomachs full of roast duck, and naturally very well satisfied. But the next morning when they go out, they find the trees fallen back to the ground, right side up and in the holes where they were before!

There seems to be nothing for Paul to do but give the men a day off and figure what to do. The trees couldn't be cut down. They couldn't be blasted down. They had been fire-proofed the Year of the Dry Rains, and couldn't be burned down. Ol' Paul chews his nails down to the quick and still can't figure what to do. He thinks and thinks. He thinks standing up, then he thinks sitting down, but this isn't so good as the ground is too hot. So he goes and sits down in the shade of the blacksmith shop and starts whittling.

He whittles a full-rigged clipper ship, full size, and tries all afternoon to get it inside a beer bottle, like the old sailors do. He gets so interested in this business that he forgets about his real problem until near supper time, and never does get the blamed thing into the bottle. So the next morning he gives the men another day off and goes into his office and thinks without whittling. Even so, it is three days before he comes tearing out with his arms full of blueprints, hollering for the straw bosses to get the men together. He's going to make a speech.

"Boys," he says, "the Gov'ment's dependin' on us. If we fail, them plans is blowed higher'n Gilroy's kite. We'll build the biggest piledriver ever seen. And by the Great Ringtailed Catamount, we'll drive them trees down like tent pegs!"

You see, this idea would make a story to be told in every camp this side of Mexico. Ol' Paul liked to do a job like that occasionally, even if there was no profit in it, just to remind folks he was no ordinary logger.

For thirty-nine weeks they work on the great pile-driver. It stands so high that the clouds going by are all the time knocking the upper half off, so he puts a hinge in the middle and lets the upper half down when he sees a cloud coming. For a weight he uses one of the Rocky Mountain peaks. (When he gets done he tosses it up into Colorado, where it sets to this day, right behind Colorado Springs.)

When everything is ready, they set the machine up over a thorn tree, and Babe, grunting mightily, hauls the weight to the top. It comes down and strikes with a crash that is heard for one hundred and three miles. The tree is driven clear to bed rock, its top being sixteen feet below the ground.

Ol' Paul reckons that'll do, and they go to work in real earnest. The noise and dust are terrific, as they drive a tree every three minutes, and Babe is sweating from every pore. The sweat pours down off his sides and down his legs and runs in streams across the desert. It washes big gullies in the soft soil that can be seen to this day. These streams running every which way hinder the work, so Paul grabs a shovel and digs a ditch for them to drain into. This is now known as the Grand Canyon. After Paul left the country the Government ran the Colorado River through it.

As soon as he gets the pile-driver crew working smoothly, Paul goes back to camp to catch up with a number of smaller problems that've piled up while he's busy with the cactus trees. On account of the heat, the men want ice tea every meal, and the cooks need ice to keep the meat from spoiling. But there's no ice to be had.

Suddenly Ol' Paul remembers something. That, by the way was one of the secrets of his success, that habit of remembering things even when they didn't seem worth remembering at the time.

It seems that while they had been building the pile-driver, Babe had been allowed to run loose, and had come back from Alaska with a small snowstorm snagged on one horn. Paul had taken it off, and having no use for a snowstorm round camp at the time, had put it in an old sheep pen in a dry lake-bed a few miles from camp, and forgotten it completely.

So now he decides to go and see how it's getting along. He sort of expects to find it pretty much wilted from the heat, but instead he finds the dry lake frozen from bank to bank. In the center of it the snowstorm's dug a burrow, and is as happy as a clam. Paul breaks off a piece of the ice and finds that it's much colder than ordinary ice, and when it melts it leaves a dry spot. This puzzles him for a bit, then he sees that it's dry ice. Naturally, if you freeze a dry lake you can get nothing but dry ice from it—it stands to reason. So Paul keeps the snowstorm there all the time he's logging off the desert, and the cooks never have to worry about the icebox pans running over.

A. J. Liebling

NATURAL HISTORY

"Fish is brain food," Fritz Strohschneider, a waiter and a friend of mine told me, "but around cities they is brainier. It is just like people, the city fish is more slicker as the country fish.

"I don't go fishing more," he went on without encouragement, "since they exploded Heinrich Heine.

"In the old days it was so nice on Sunday to fish for tommys from the docks. Tommys and eelses. On 96th Street dock we used to sit, me and my friend Jack Poppberger, with a case of beer and our clarinets. It was the most convenient fishing.

"Each one would have four, five lines. The lines are tied to wires and on each wire there is a bell. When a fish bites, the bell rings, like an elevator. You pull him up and it is sport.

"So one Sunday we was sitting on the dock, and we had eight lines out. Suddenly, along comes Heinrich Heine.

"It seems between those bells was musical gradations, by chance of the length of the wires, and as I am sitting tuning my clarinet, so I hear played wonder good on the bells the scale. 'Do, re, mi, fa, sol,' and the rest of it. 'My God, Jake,' I says, 'what is this for a fish?'

"Back it comes the other way the scale—being a fish the scale was its specialty—and then 'dingle, dingle,'—it was trying to pick out 'Annie Laurie.'

"Jake wanted to pull up the line, but I said, 'What, you would murder a musician?'

"We looked down it shouldn't be boys in a boat under the pier, but there was nothing. The next Sunday we came to the same spot. We set the lines and soon it gave 'Ich Weiss Nicht Was Soll Es Bedeuten.' Then I named the fish Heinrich Heine. So we played on our clarinets and Heinrich Heine would accompany us.

"Every Sunday new tunes we were teaching him, and sometimes he even offered for us original compositions. So nice it was in the sunset

444

to sit there with a case of empty beer bottles and play 'Love's Old Sweet Song.' "

Fritz sighed. He flicked listlessly at an imaginary speck of dust with his towel.

"I never saw Heinrich Heine," he said. "I don't know whether he was a tommy or whether an eel. But in a way I helped kill him. Among the tunes we taught him was 'Die Wacht Am Rhein.' We didn't mean no harm. It was before America went in the war. Scotchers, Englishers, Irishers used to come down to the pier. It made them mad to hear the fish play so nice the German antler.

"But when this country went in the war a battleship came in the river. A bright Sunday morning Heinrich Heine commenced to play. 'Ta-tum-tee-um-tee-um-Die Wacht Am Rhein.' The battleship shot a torpedo and exploded Heinrich Heine. Since then I go no more fishing."

George W. Harris

MRS. YARDLEY'S QUILTING *

"Thar's one durn'd nasty muddy job, an' I is jis' glad enuf tu take a ho'n ur two, on the straingth ove hit."

"What have you been doing, Sut?"

"Helpin tu salt ole Missis Yardley down."

"What do you mean by that?"

"Fixin her fur rotten cumfurtably, kiverin her up wif sile, tu keep the buzzards frum cheatin the wurms."

"Oh, you have been helping to bury a woman."

"That's hit, by golly! Now why the devil can't I 'splain mysef like yu? I ladles out my words at randum, like a calf kickin at yaller-jackids; yu jis' rolls em out tu the pint, like a feller a-layin bricks— every one fits. How is it that bricks fits so clost enyhow? Rocks won't ni du hit."

"Becaze they'se all ove a size," ventured a man with a wen over his eye.

"The devil yu say, hon'ey-head! haint reapin-mersheens ove a size? I'd like tu see two ove em fit clost. You wait ontil yu sprouts tuther ho'n, afore yu venters tu 'splain mix'd questions. George, did yu know ole Missis Yardley?"

"No."

"Well, she wer a curious 'oman in her way, an' she wore shiney specks. Now jis' listen: Whenever yu see a ole 'oman ahine a par ove *shiney* specks, yu keep yer eye skinn'd; they am dang'rus in the extreme. Thar is jis' no knowin what they ken du. I hed one a-stradil ove me onst, fur kissin her gal. She went fur my har, an' she went fur my skin, ontil I tho't she ment tu kill me, an' wud a-dun hit, ef my hollerin hadent fotch ole Dave Jordan, a *bacheler,* tu my aid. He, like a durn'd fool, cotch her by the laig, an' drug her back'ards ofen me. She jis' kivered him, an' I run, by golly! The nex time I seed him he

* A "Sut Lovingood" yarn.

wer bald headed, an' his face looked like he'd been a-fitin wild-cats.

"Ole Missis Yardley wer a great noticer ove littil things, that nobody else ever seed. She'd say right in the middil ove sumbody's serious talk: 'Law sakes! thar goes that yaller slut ove a hen, a-flingin straws over her shoulder; she' arter settin now, an' haint laid but seven aigs. I'll disapint *her*, see ef I don't; I'll put a punkin in her nes', an' a feather in her nose. An' bless my soul! jis' look at that cow wif the wilted ho'n, a-flingin up dirt an' a-smellin the place whar hit cum frum, wif the rale ginuine still-wurim twis' in her tail, too; what upon the face ove the yeath kin she be arter now, the ole fool? watch her, Sally. An' sakes alive! jis' look at that ole sow; she's a-gwine in a fas' trot, wif her empty bag a-floppin agin her sides. Thar, she hes stop't, an's a-listenin! Massy on us! what a long yearnis' grunt she gin; hit cum frum way back ove her kidneys. Thar she goes agin; she's arter no good, sich kerryin on means no good.'

"An' so she wud gabble, no odds who wer a-listenin. She looked like she mout been made at fust 'bout four foot long, an' the common thickness ove wimen when they's at tharsefs, an' then had her har tied tu a stump, a par ove steers hitched to her heels, an' then straiched out a-mos' two foot more—mos' ove the straichin cumin outen her laigs an' naik. Her stockins, a-hangin on the clothes-line tu dry, looked like a par ove sabre scabbards, an' her naik looked like a dry beef shank smoked, an' mout been ni ontu es tough. I never felt hit mysef, I didn't, I jis' jedges by looks. Her darter Sal wer bilt at fust 'bout the laingth ove her mam, but wer never straiched eny by a par ove steers, an' she wer fat enuf tu kill; she wer taller lyin down than she wer a-standin up. Hit wer her who gin me the 'hump shoulder.' Jis' look at me; haint I'se got a tech ove the dromedary back thar bad? haint I humpy? Well, a-stoopin tu kiss that squatty lard-stan ove a gal is what dun hit tu me. She wer the fairest-lookin gal I ever seed. She allers wore thick woolin stockins 'bout six inches too long fur her laig; they rolled down over her garters, lookin like a par ove life presarvers up thar. I tell yu she wer a tarin gal enyhow. Luved kissin, wrastlin, an' biled cabbige, an' hated tite clothes, hot weather, an' suckit-riders. B'leved strong in married folk's ways, cradles, an' the remishun ove sins, an' didn't b'leve in corsets, fleas, peaners, nur the fashun plates."

"What caused the death of Mrs. Yardley, Sut?"

"Nuffin, only her heart stop't beatin 'bout losing a nine dimunt quilt.

True, she got a skeer'd hoss tu run over her, but she'd a-got over that ef a quilt hadn't been mix'd up in the catastrophy. Yu see quilts wer wun ove her speshul gifts; she run strong on the bed-kiver question. Irish chain, star ove Texas, sun-flower, nine dimunt, saw teeth, checker board, an' shell quilts; blue, an' white, an' yaller an' black coverlids; an' callickercumfurts reigned triumphan' 'bout her hous'. They wer packed in drawers, layin in shelfs full, wer hung four dubbil on lines in the lof, packed in chists, piled on cheers, an' wer everywhar, even ontu the beds, an' wer changed every bed-makin. She told everybody she cud git tu listen tu hit that she ment tu give every durn'd one ove them tu Sal when she got married. Oh, lordy! what es fat a gal es Sal Yardley cud ever du wif half ove em, an' sleeping wif a husbun at that, is more nor I ever cud see through. Jis' think ove her onder twenty layer ove quilts in July, an' you in thar too. Gewhillikins! George, look how I is sweatin' now, an' this is December. I'd 'bout es lief be shet up in a steam biler wif a three hundred pound bag ove lard, es tu make a bisiness ove sleepin wif that gal—'twould kill a glass-blower.

"Well, tu cum to the serious part ove this conversashun, that is how the old quilt-mersheen an' coverlidloom cum tu stop operashuns on this yeath. She hed narrated hit thru the neighborhood that nex Saterday she'd gin a quiltin—three quilts an' one cumfurt tu tie. 'Goblers, fiddils, gals, an' whisky,' wer the words she sent tu the men-folk, an' more tetchin ur wakenin words never drap't ofen an 'oman's tongue. She sed tu the gals, 'Sweet toddy, huggin, dancin, an' huggers in 'bundance.' Them words struck the gals rite in the pit ove the stumick, an' spread a ticklin sensashun bof ways, ontil they scratched thar heads wif one han, an' thar heels wif tuther.

"Everybody, he an' she, what were baptized b'levers in the righteousnes ove quiltins wer thar, an' hit jis' so happen'd that everybody in them parts, frum fifteen summers tu fifty winters, wer unannamu b'levers. Strange, warn't hit? Hit wer the bigges' quiltin ever Missis Yardley hilt, an' she hed hilt hundreds; everybody wer thar, 'scept th constibil an' suckit-rider, two dam easily-spared pussons; the number ni ontu even too; jis' a few more boys nur gals; that made hit mor exhitin, fur hit gin the gals a chance tu kick an' squeal a littil, wifou runnin eny risk ove not gittin kissed at all, an' hit gin reasonab grouns fur a few scrimmages amung the he's. Now es kissin an' fiti am the pepper an' salt ove all soshul getherins, so hit wer mor

espishully wif this ove ours. Es I swung my eyes over the crowd,
George, I thought quiltins, managed in a morril an' sensibil way,
truly am good things—good fur free drinkin, good fur free eatin, good
fur free huggin, good fur free dancin, good fur free fitin, an' goodest
ove all fur poperlatin a country fas'.

"Thar am a fur-seein wisdum in quiltins, ef they has proper trimmins: 'vittils, fiddils, an' sperrits in 'bundance.' One holesum quiltin
am wuf three old pray'rmeetins on the poperlashun pint, purtickerly
ef hits hilt in the dark ove the moon, an' runs intu the night a few
hours, an' April ur May am the time chosen. The moon don't suit
quiltins whar everybody is well acquainted an' already fur along in
courtin. She dus help pow'ful tu begin a courtin match onder, but
when hit draws ni ontu a head, nobody wants a moon but the old
mammys.

"The mornin cum, still, saft, sunshiney; cocks crowin, hens singin,
birds chirpin, tuckeys gobblin—jis' the day tu sun quilts, kick, kiss,
squeal, an' make love.

"All the plow-lines an' clothes-lines were straiched tu every post an'
tree. Quilts purvailed. Durn my gizzard ef two acres roun that ar
house warn't jis' one solid quilt, all out a-sunnin, an' tu be seed. They
dazzled the eyes, skeered the hosses, gin wimen the heart-burn, an'
perdominated.

"To'ards sundown the he's begun tu drap in. Yearnis' needil-drivin
cummenced tu lose ground; threads broke ofen, thimbils got los', an'
quilts needed anuther roll. Gigglin, winkin, whisperin, smoofin ove
har, an' gals a-ticklin one anuther, wer a-gainin every inch ove groun
what the needils los'. Did yu ever notis, George, at all soshul getherins,
when the he's begin tu gather, that the young she's begin tu tickil one
anuther an' the ole maids swell thar tails, roach up thar backs, an'
sharpen thar nails ontu the bed-posts an' door jams, an' spit an' groan
sorter like cats a-courtin? Dus hit mean *rale* rath, ur is hit a dare tu
the he's, sorter kivered up wif the outside signs ove danger? I honestly
b'leve that the young she's ticklin means, 'Cum an' take this job ofen
our hans.' But that swellin I jis' don't onderstan; dus yu? Hit looks
skeery, an' I never tetch one ove em when they am in the swellin way.
I may be mistaken'd 'bout the ticklin bisiness too; hit may be dun like
a feller chaws poplar bark when he haint got any terbacker, a-sorter
better nur nun make-shif. I dus know one thing tu a certainty: that is,
when the he's take hold the ticklin quits, an' ef yu gits one ove the

old maids out tu hersef, then she subsides an' is the smoofes, sleekes, saft thing yu ever seed, an' dam ef yu can't hear her purr, jes' es plain!

"But then, George, gals an' ole maids haint the things tu fool time away on. Hits widders, by golly, what am the rale sensibil, steady-goin, never-skeerin, never-kickin, willin, sperrited, smoof pacers. They cum clost up tu the hoss-block, standin still wif thar purty silky years playin, an' the naik-veins a-throbbin, an' waits fur the words, which ove course yu gives, arter yu finds yer feet well in the stirrup, an' away they moves like a cradil on cushioned rockers, ur a spring buggy runnin in damp san'. A tetch ove the bridil, an' they know yu wants em tu turn, an' they dus hit es willin es ef the idear wer thar own. I be dod rabbited ef a man can't 'propriate happiness by the skinful ef he is in contack wif sumbody's widder, an' is smart. Gin me a willin widder, the yeath over: what they don't know, haint worth larnin. They hes all been tu Jamakey an' larnt how sugar's made, an' know how tu sweeten wif hit; an' by golly, they is always ready to use hit. All yu hes tu du is tu find the spoon, an' then drink cumfort till yer blind. Nex tu good sperrits an' my laigs, I likes a twenty-five year old widder, wif roun ankils, an' bright eyes, honestly an' squarly lookin intu yurn, an' sayin es plainly es a partrige sez 'Bob White,' 'Don't be afraid ove me; I hes been thar; yu know hit ef yu hes eny sense, an' thar's no use in eny humbug, ole feller—cum ahead!'

"Ef yu onderstands widder nater, they ken save yu a power ove troubil, onsartinty, an' time, an' ef yu is interprisin yu gits mons'rous well paid fur hit. The very soun ove thar littil shoe-heels speak full trainin, an' hes a knowin click as they tap the floor; an' the rustil ove thar dress sez, 'I dar yu tu ax me.'

"When yu hes made up yer mind tu court one, jis' go at hit like hit wer a job ove rail-maulin. Ware yer workin close, use yer common, everyday moshuns an' words, an' abuv all, fling away yer cinamint ile vial an' burn all yer love songs. No use in tryin tu fool em, fur they sees plum thru yu, a durn'd sight plainer than they dus thru thar veils. No use in a pasted shut; she's been thar. No use in borrowin a cavortin fat hoss; she's been thar. No use in har-dye; she's been thar. No use in cloves, tu kill whisky breff; she's been thar. No use in buying clost curtains fur yer bed, fur she has been thar. Widders am a speshul means, George, fur ripenin green men, killin off weak ones, an makin 'ternally happy the soun ones.

"Well, es I sed afore, I flew the track an' got ontu the widders. The fellers begun tu ride up an' walk up, sorter slow, like they warn't in a hurry, the durn'd 'saitful raskils, hitchin thar critters tu enything they cud find. One red-comb'd, long-spurr'd, dominecker feller, frum town, in a red an' white grid-iron jackid an' patent leather gaiters, hitched his hoss, a wild, skeery, wall-eyed devil, inside the yard palins, tu a cherry tree lim'. Thinks I, that hoss hes a skeer intu him big enuf tu run intu town, an' perhaps beyant hit, ef I kin only tetch hit off; so I sot intu thinkin.

"One aind ove a long clothes-line, wif nine dimunt quilts ontu hit, wer tied tu the same cherry tree that the hoss wer. I tuck my knife and socked hit thru every quilt, 'bout the middil, an' jis' below the rope, an' tied them thar wif bark, so they cudent slip. Then I went tu the back aind, an' ontied hit frum the pos', knottin in a hoe-handil, by the middil, tu keep the quilts frum slippin off ef my bark strings failed, an' laid hit on the groun. Then I went tu the tuther aind: thar wer 'bout ten foot tu spar, a-lyin on the groun arter tyin tu the tree. I tuck hit atwix Wall-eye's hine laigs, an' tied hit fas' tu bof stirrups, an' then cut the cherry tree lim' betwix his bridil an' the tree, almos' off. Now, mine yu thar were two ur three uther ropes full ove quilts atween me an' the hous', so I were purty well hid frum thar. I jis' tore off a palin frum the fence, an' tuck hit in bof hans, an' arter raisin hit 'way up yander, I fotch hit down, es hard es I cud, flatsided to'ards the groun, an' hit acksidentally happen'd tu hit Wall-eye, 'bout nine inches ahead ove the root ove his tail. Hit landed so hard that hit made my hans tingle, an' then busted intu splinters. The first things I did, wer tu feel ove mysef, on the same spot whar hit hed hit the hoss. I cudent help duin hit tu save my life, an' I swar I felt sum ove Wall-eye's sensashun, jis' es plain. The fust thing he did, wer tu tare down the lim' wif a twenty-foot jump, his head to'ards the hous'. Thinks I, now yu hev dun hit, yu durn'd wall-eyed fool! tarin down that lim' wer the beginin ove all the troubil, an' the hoss did hit hissef; my conshuns felt clar es a mountin spring, an' I wer in a frame ove mine tu obsarve things es they happen'd, an' they soon begun tu happen purty clost arter one anuther rite then, an' thar, an' tharabouts, clean ontu town, thru hit, an' still were a-happenin, in the woods beyant thar ni ontu eleven mile from ole man Yardley's gate, an' four beyant town.

"The fust line ove quilts he tried tu jump, but broke hit down; the nex one he ran onder; the rope cotch ontu the ho'n ove the saddil, broke at bof ainds, an' went along wif the hoss, the cherry tree lim' an' the fust line ove quilts, what I hed proverdensally tied fas' tu the rope. That's what I calls foresight, George. Right furnint the frunt door he cum in contack wif old Missis Yardley hersef, an' anuther ole 'oman; they wer a-holdin a nine dimunt quilt spread out, a-'zaminin hit, an' a-praisin hits perfeckshuns. The durn'd onmanerly, wall-eyed fool run plum over Missis Yardley, frum ahine, stompt one hine foot through the quilt, takin hit along, a-kicken ontil he made hits corners snap like a whip. The gals screamed, the men hollered wo! an' the ole 'oman wer toted intu the hous' limber es a wet string, an' every word she sed wer, 'Oh, my preshus nine dimunt quilt!'

"Wall-eye busted thru the palins, an' Dominicker sed 'im, made a mortal rush fur his bitts, wer too late fur them, but in good time fur the strings ove flying quilts, got tangled amung em, an' the gridiron jackid patren wer los' tu my sight amung star an' Irish chain quilts; he went frum that quiltin at the rate ove thuty miles tu the hour. Nuffin lef on the lot ove the hole consarn, but a nine biler hat, a par ove gloves, an' the jack ove hearts.

"What a onmanerly, suddin way ove leavin places sum folks hev got, enyhow.

"Thinks I, well, that fool hoss, tarin down that cherry tree lim', hes dun sum good, enyhow; hit hes put the ole 'oman outen the way fur the balance ove the quiltin, an' tuck Dominicker outen the way an' outen danger, fur that gridiron jackid wud a-bred a scab on his nose afore midnite; hit wer morrily boun tu du hit.

"Two months arterwards, I tracked the route that hoss tuck in his kalamatus skeer, by quilt rags, tufts ove cotton, bunches ove har (human an' hoss), an' scraps ove a gridiron jackid stickin ontu the bushes, an' plum at the aind ove hit, whar all signs gin out, I foun a piece ove watch chain an' a hosses head. The places what know'd Dominicker, know'd im no more.

"Well, arter they'd tuck the ole 'oman up stairs an' camfired her tu sleep, things begun tu work agin. The widders broke the ice, an' arter a littil gigilin, goblin, an' gabblin, the kissin begun. *Smack!*—'Thar, now,' a widder sed that. *Pop!*—'Oh, don't!' *Pfip!*—'Oh, yu quit!' *Plosh!*—'Go *way* yu awkerd critter, yu kissed me in the eye!' anuther widder sed that. *Bop!* 'Now yu ar satisfied, I recon, big mouf!' *Vip!*—'That haint fair!' *Spat!*—'Oh, lordy! May, cum pull Bill away; he's a-tanglin my har'. *Thut!*—'I jis' d-a-r-e yu tu du that agin!' a widder sed that, too. Hit sounded all 'roun that room like poppin co'n in a hot skillet, and wer pow'ful sujestif.

"Hit kep on ontil I be durn'd ef *my* bristils didn't begin tu rise, an' sumthin like a cold buckshot wud run down the marrow in my back-bone 'bout every ten secons, an' then run up agin, tolerabil hot. I kep a swallerin wif nuthin tu swaller, an' my face felt swell'd; an' yet I wer fear'd tu make a bulge. Thinks I, I'll ketch one out tu hersef torreckly, an' then I guess we'll rastil. Purty soon Sal Yardley started fur the smoke-'ous, so I jis' gin my head a few short shakes, let down one ove my wings a-trailin, an' sirkiled roun her wif a side twis' in my naik, steppin side-wise, an' a-fetchin up my hinemos' foot wif a sorter jerkin slide at every step. Sez I, 'Too coo-took a-too.' She onderstood hit, an stopt, sorter spreadin her shoulders. An' jis' es I hed pouch'd out my mouf, an' wer a-reachin forrid wif hit, fur the article hitsef, sunthin nterfared wif me, hit did. George, wer yu ever ontu yer hans an' knees, an' let a hell-tarin big, mad ram, wif a ten-yard run, but yu yearnis'ly, is onst, right squar ontu the pint ove yer back-bone?"

"No, you fool; why do you ask?"

"Kaze I wanted tu know ef yu cud hev a realizin' noshun ove my shock. Hits scarcely worth while tu try to make yu onderstan the case by words only, onles yu hev been tetched in that way. Gr-eat golly! the fust thing I felt, I tuck hit tu be a back-ackshun yeath-quake; an' the fust thing I seed wer my chaw'r terbacker a-flying over Sal's head like a skeer'd bat. My mouf wer pouch'd out, ready fur the article hitsef, yu know, an' hit went outen the roun hole like the wad outen a pop-gun—thug! an' the fust think I know'd, I wer a flying over Sal's head too, an' a-gainin on the chaw'r terbacker fast. I wer strait-ened out strait, toes hinemos', middil finger-nails foremos', an' the fust thing I hearn wer, 'Yu dam Shanghi!' Great Jerus-a-lam! I lit ontu my all fours jis' in time tu but the yard gate ofen hits hinges, an' skeer loose sum more hosses—kep on in a four-footed gallop, clean acrost the lane afore I cud straiten up, an' yere I cotch up wif my chaw'r ter-backer, stickin flat agin a fence-rail. I hed got so good a start that I thot hit a pity tu spile hit, so I jis' jump'd the fence an' tuck thru the orchurd. I tell yu I dusted these yere close, fur I tho't hit wer arter me.

"Arter running a spell, I ventered tu feel roun back thar, fur sum signs ove what hed happened tu me. George, arter two pow'ful hard-tugs, I pull'd out the vamp an' sole ove one ove ole man Yardley's big brogans, what he hed los' amung my coat-tails. Dre'ful! dre'ful! Arter

I got hit away frum thar, my flesh went fas' asleep, frum abuv my
kidneys tu my knees; about now, fur the fust time, the idear struck
me, what hit wer that hed interfar'd wif me, an' los' me the kiss. Hit
wer ole Yardley hed kicked me. I walked fur a month like I were
straddlin a thorn hedge. Sich a shock, at sich a time, an' on sich a place
—jis' think ove hit! hit am tremenjus, haint hit? The place feels num,
right now."

"Well, Sut, how did the quilting come out?"

"How the hell du yu 'speck me tu know? I warn't thar eny more."

Alfred Henry Lewis

THE MAN FROM YELLOWHOUSE

That's straight, son; you shorely should have seen Jack Moore,"
ontinued the Old Cattleman, after a brief pause, as he hitched his
hair into a comfortable position; "not seein' Jack is what any gent
might call deeprivation.

"Back in the old days," he went on, "Jack Moore, as I relates, is
ettle-tender an' does the rope work of the Stranglers. Whatever is the
tranglers? Which you asks some late. I mentions this assembly a heap
requent yeretofore. Well, some folks calls 'em the 'vig'lance com-
nittee'; but that's long for a name, so in Wolfville we allers allooded
o 'em as 'Stranglers.' This yere is brief, an' likewise sheds some light.

"This Jack Moore—which I'm proud to say he's my friend—I reck-
ns is the most *pro bono publico* gent in the Southwest. He's out to
o anythin' from fight to fiddle at a dance, so's it's a public play.

"An' then his idees about his dooties is wide. He jest scouts far an'
ear, an' don't pay no more heed to distance an' fatigue than a steer
oes to cobwebs.

" 'A offishul,' says Jack, 'who don't diffuse himse'f 'round none, an'
onfines his endeavors to his own bailiwick, is reestricted an' oneffec-
ooal, an' couldn't keep down crime in a village of prairie-dogs.' An'
nen he'd cinch on his saddle, an' mebby go curvin' off as far north
s the Flint Hills, or east to the Turkey-track.

"That's right; when it comes to bein' active, Jack is what you might
ll an all-round seelection. An' clean strain? Game as hornets. Never
nowed him to quit anythin' in his life—not even whiskey. I says to
im myse'f one time: 'Jack; whyever don't you renig on whiskey?
ooks like it's sorter gettin' behind you some, ain't it? Some day
iebby it outholds you when you can't stand to lose.'

" 'Sometimes I thinks I'll pass it up, myse'f,' says Jack, 'but don't
ou know, I can't do it. I'm too sperited, that a-way, an' chivalrous.
'hat's whatever! I'm too chivalrous.' An' I shore reckons he was.

455

"But as for doin' his dooty! Which the same is simply relaxation t
Jack Moore. I recalls one instance speshul. One day thar comes traili
along into Wolfville a party from down 'round Yallerhouse some'er
This yere Yallerhouse gent looks disperited an' off color as to healt
But of course we-alls don't refer none to it; for whether this stranger
sick or well is his business, not ours; leastwise in its first stages. Th
yere's before Doc Peets inhabits Wolfville or he'd informed us touchi
this party's that a-way.

"Which the Yallerhouse gent tracks along into the Red Light, a
tells the barkeep to set out the nose-paint. He drinks alone, not invitin
of the pop'lace, whereby we knows for shore he's offen his feed.

"Well, after he corrals his forty drops, this invalid camps down i
one corner of the stage station, an' next mornin' he wakes up oute
his head an' plumb locoed.

" 'This yere Yallerhouse man,' says Dan Boggs, comin' along int
the Red Light about first-drink time the same mornin', an' speakin
general, 'is what conserv'tive opinion might call "some sick." I stops
minute ago an' asks him how he's stackin' up like, but it ain't no us
He's plumb off his mental reservation, an' crazy as a woman's watch

" 'Whatever do you allow is the matter of him, Boggs?' asks Ol
Man Enright.

" 'Smallpox,' says Boggs, mighty confident.

" 'Smallpox!' repeats Enright; 'be you shore?'

" 'That's what I says,' answers Boggs; 'an' you can gamble my lon
suit is pickin' out smallpox every time. I knows the signal smoke lik
my own campfire.'

" 'Well, see yere,' says Dave Tutt, who's come in, 'I jest now round
up them symptoms of this Yallerhouse gent; an' talkin' of smallpox,
offers a hundred dollars even he ain't got no smallpox. Bein' out sole
for legit'mate sport,' continues Tutt, 'an' not aimin' to offend Bogg
none, I willin'ly calls it fifty to one hundred he ain't got nothin'.'

" 'Which I takes both bets,' says Boggs, 'an' deems 'em easy. Whic
both is like robbin' a bird's-nest. Yere's the circ'latin' medium. Tha
cover it an' file it away with the barkeep to wait results.' So Tutt a
Boggs makes their bets mighty eager, an' the barkeep holds the stake

"As soon as it gets blown through Wolfville this Yallerhouse part
has smallpox, everybody comes canterin' over to the Red Light, gets
drink, an' wants to hold a mass meetin' over it. By partic'lar reque
Enright takes the chair an' calls 'em to order.

" 'This yere meetin',' says Enright, meanwhile beatin' with the butt
of his six-shooter on the poker-table, 'is some sudden an' permiscus;
but the objects is easy an' plain. We-alls convenes ourse'fs to consider
the physical condition of this party from Yallerhouse, which report
says is locoed an' can't talk none for himself. To make this inquiry a
success, we-alls oughter see this Yallerhouse gent; an' as thar is fewer
of him than of us, I app'ints Jack Moore, Dan Boggs, an' Short Creek
Dave, a committee, of three, to bring him before us in a body. Pendin'
the return of the committee the meetin' will take a drink with the
hair.'

"In about no time back comes the outfit, packin' the Yallerhouse
man all easy enough in a blanket, an' spreads him out on the floor.
He looks sorter red 'round in spots, like somethin's being stingin' of
him, but it's evident, as Boggs says, he's locoed. He lays thar, rollin'
his eyes an' carryin' on to himse'f, but he don't address the chair or
offer to take no part in the meetin'. Enright quaffs his drink all slow
an' dignified, an' gazes at the Yallerhouse man on the floor.

" 'Well, gents,' says Enright at last, settin' down his glass, an' givin'
the poker-table a little tap with his gun, 'yere's the party, an' the
question is now: "What's he got?" Do I hear any remarks?'

" 'Bein' in the lines, Mister Pres'dent,' says Boggs, 'of previous assertion, an' for the purpose of bringin' the question squar' before this
house, I now moves you this yere Yallerhouse party has the smallpox.
I ain't aimin' herein at playin' it low on Tutt, an' su'gests that the
chair, in puttin' the question, also informs the meetin' as to them
wagers; which the money tharof is now in the war-bags of the barkeep.
I believes in givin' every gent all necessary light wherein to make up
his mind; an', as I says, to open the game all logical, I ag'in moves this
Yallerhouse man has the smallpox.'

" 'Yo tambien,' yells a Mexican over near the door.

" 'Put that Greaser out!' shouts Enright, at the same time bangin'
the table. 'This ain't no international incident at all, an' nothin' but
the clean-strain American wolf is eligible to howl.'

"The Greaser goes out on his saddle-colored head, an' Enright puts
Boggs's motion.

" 'Every gent,' says Enright, 'in favor of this Yallerhouse man havin'
the smallpox, say "Aye"; contrary "No." '

"Everybody shouts 'Aye!'

" 'Which the "Ayes" has it unanimous,' says Enright. 'The Yaller-

house party has the smallpox, an' the next chicken on the parli⸗
mentary roost is the question: "Whatever is to be done to make thi⸗
yere malady a success?" Is thar any su'gestions?'

" 'Mister Pres'dent,' says Texas Thompson, risin' in his place, 'I'v⸗
done took no hand in these proceedin's so far, through ignorance c⸗
the purposes of this yere convocation. Said purposes bein' now for th⸗
first time lined out all right in my mind, an' the question bein⸗
"What's to be done with our captive?" I asks your indulgence. M⸗
first idee is that our dooty an' our path is plain; the same bein' simpl⸗
to take a lariat an' hang this Yallerhouse person to the dance-hall wind⸗
mill; but this course, on second thought, seems prematoor an' the of⸗
springs of nacheral impulse. Still, somethin' must be done; an' whil⸗
my mind is by no means cl'ar, I su'gests we turn the gent over to Jac⸗
Moore, which is the marshal hereof, to ride herd on him till furthe⸗
orders; an' I makes a motion to that effect.'

" 'Seconds the motion!' says Short Creek Dave.

" 'You don't have to put that motion, Mister Pres'dent,' says Jack⸗
'I've been circlin' the idee some myse'f, an' I reckons it's my dooty t⸗
take charge of this Yallerhouse gent. You can bet anythin' which get⸗
sawed onto me as my dooty goes, an' don't make no doubt about i⸗
Yere's how I trails out on this: If it ain't my dooty to take care of thi⸗
person, whose dooty is it? 'Tain't nobody's. Tharfore I plays the hand⸗

" 'Which the same bein' eminent satisfactory,' says Dave Tutt, risin⸗
as if he thinks of somethin' speshul, 'I now inquires whether this yer⸗
is held decisive of them bets I makes with Boggs. I holdin', meanwhile⸗
contrary views emphatic.'

" 'This bein' a question of priv'lege,' says Enright, 'the chair wil⸗
answer it. These proceedin's decides your bets with Boggs, an' th⸗
barkeep pays Boggs the *dinero*. This is a gov'ment of the people, fo⸗
the people, by the people, an' founded on a *vox populi* bluff. The voic⸗
of the majority goes. You tharfore lose your bets to Boggs; drinks o⸗
Boggs, of course. Thar is another matter,' continues Enright, 'a bet w⸗
overlooks. Takin' care of this Yallerhouse gent will cost a stack or two⸗
an' means must be provided. I tharfore makes as an order that yere⸗
after thar's to be a rake on tens-up or better, showed, to make a fun⸗
to back this play; said rake to go ontil Mister Moore reports sai⸗
Yallerhouse gent as safe or ceased to be.'

"Jack takes this Yallerhouse party over to the calaboose an' lays hin⸗
away on some blankets. The calaboose is dry, an' what you-alls migh⸗

call, commodious. It's a slam-up camp; yes indeed! Never has but Steve Stevenson in it. Puts Steve in one night when he's dead-drunk. The calaboose is new then, an' we-alls is that proud an' anxious to try it an' put it to some use, we couldn't resist, so in Steve goes.

"About four hours later Steve comes back up to the Red Light, hotter'n a burnt boot. Seems like he comes to, an' is that outraged an' indignant about bein' corralled that a-way, he busts the corner outen the calaboose an' issues forth a whole lot to find who does it.

"When he comes into the Red Light he revives himse'f with a drink, an' then inquires whether it's humorous, or do we mean it? Seein' how speshul low Steve takes it, we-alls allows it's a joke! an' Steve, while he evident feels some fretted, concloods to let it go at that.

"But on account of the hole through which Steve emerges, an' which he makes liberal an' big, the calaboose is a mighty commodious place. So Jack beds down the Yallerhouse man all right an' starts in to bringin' him through. The rest of us don't crowd 'round none to watch the play, don't hover over it that a-way, 'cause we ain't aimin' to acquire nothin' ourse'fs.

"Jack has a heap of trouble an' worry. Never sees no smallpox, do you? Folks locoed most usual,—clean off up in the air an' pitchin' on their ropes. Of course the Yallerhouse gent has all he needs. That rake on tens-up them days would have took care of a fam'ly. But he keeps Jack herdin' him all the time. Otherwise, not bein' watched, an' crazy that a-way, he's liable to come stampedin' over to the Red Light, or some'ers else, any time, an' skeer us up some.

"'He's a world-beater,' says Jack one day, when he comes over for a drink. 'He's shorely four kings an' an ace. You can't ride him with buckin'-straps an' a Spanish bit. It's got so now—his disease bein' at a crisis like—that I simply has to be with this Yallerhouse party day an' night. He'd shorely lay waste this camp if I didn't.'

"At last the Yallerhouse party an' Jack somehow beats the smallpox, but Yallerhouse comes out shy an eye. The smallpox gouges it out one of them times when Jack ain't lookin' out his game sharp. It's his pistol eye, too; which makes him feel the loss more keen, an' creates general sympathy. The Yallerhouse man gets some morose over it, which ain't, after all, onnacheral. A gent ain't got so many eyes he can afford to go short one on every little game he plays. So he finds fault with Jack a lot, an' allows if he has him back in the States he'd sue him for neglect of dooty.

" 'Which, I shorely likes that!' says Jack to the Yallerhouse party, gettin' peevish over his fault-findin'. 'Don't you know it's merely owin' to the mercy of hell an' my watchful care, you-all ain't bustin' your harp-strings an' raisin' all 'round discord among the heavenly hosts on high right now, instead of bein' safe an' well yere in Wolfville? You don't act like a gent who saveys when he makes a winnin'. S'pose you be an eye out; you're still lookin' at things terrestrial with the other. You talks of gross neglect of dooty! Now let me inform you of some-thin': You come pesterin' 'round me some more an' I'll bend a gun over your head.'

" 'Which if it ain't my six-shooter eye which's out,' says the Yaller-house party, mighty ugly, 'do you know what I'd do? Well, this yere would be the basis of a first-class gun-play. You can gamble thar wouldn't be no jim-crow marshal go pirootin' 'round, losin' no eye of mine an' gettin' away with it, an' then talk of bendin' guns on me; none whatever.'

"But it all preys on Jack. An' a-seein' of this Yallerhouse gent 'round camp a-lookin' at him in a fault-findin' way outen his one eye sorter aggravates Jack like it's a nightmare.

" 'I wouldn't mind it so much,' says Jack to me, confidential, 'if this Yallerhouse gent quits a laig or an arm behind, 'cause in which event we pieces him out with wood, easy. But about eyes, it's different. An eye out is an eye out; an' that settles it.'

"One day Jack can't b'ar it no longer, an', resolvin' to end it, he walks up to the Yallerhouse party in the Red Light, all brisk an' brief.

" 'It's a rough deal on a one-eyed gent,' says Jack, 'an' I shore asks pardon an' states regrets in advance. But things has got to a show-down. I'm slowly becomin' onfit for public dooty. Now yere's an offer, an' you can have either end. You-all can get a hoss an' a hundred dollars of me, an' pull your freight; or you can fix yourse'f with a gun an' have a mighty stirrin' an' eventful time with me right yere. As an outcome of the last, the public will have one of us to plant, an' mebby a vacancy to fill in the post of kettle-tender. Which is it, an' what do you say?'

" 'What for a hoss is she?' asked the Yallerhouse party.

" 'Which she's a *pinto*,' says Jack; 'as excellent a paint pony as ever is roped.'

" 'Does this yere threat you-all makes incloode a saddle an' spurs?' asks the Yallerhouse party.

" 'It shorely does,' replies Jack. 'Is it a go?'

" 'Well,' says the Yallerhouse man, after ponderin' it up one way an' down the other, 'this idee of settlin' for eyes for a hoss an' a hundred dollars is far from bein' usual with me. If I has my eye ag'in, I'd shorely stay an' shoot it out, an' admire to be present. But now sech thoughts is vanity. So round up your money an' your pony at the Red Light in fifteen minutes by the watch, an' as soon as I gets a bottle filled I'm ready to go. I shorely should not regret leavin' an outfit which puts folks in jail for bein' sick, an' connives by reckless an' criminal neglect of dooty at their bein' blinded for life.' "

Roark Bradford

THE ADULTERATION OF OLD KING DAVID *

Ole King David made a mighty king. He always had his armies out
fightin' for de Lawd, and he was always busy at home, holdin' cou't
and keepin' de women-folks straightened out.

Well, one day ole King David was settin' on de front po'ch, jest
settin' back, smokin' a cigar and lettin' his dinner settle. He was a
mighty king, but he acted jest like a natchal man, too.

So purty soon a messenger rid up and bowed down to de ground
and say, "Yo' Majesty King David, de enemies er de Lawd is done
whupped."

"Who say de enemies er de Lawd is whupped, messenger?" say
David.

"De General say dey's whupped," says de messenger.

"Well, I don't b'lieve hit," say ole King David. "Dem enemies er
de Lawd is a awful pack of liars, and I speck they git de General to
say they's whupped jest so's our boys won't fly in and give 'em a sho-
'nuff whuppin'. So you jest up and ride back and tell our boys to light
into de enemies ag'in and stay lit to dey hollers, 'Calf rope.'"

So de messenger went ridin' off and ole King David r'ared back
ag'in, smokin' his cigar and settlin' his dinner.

Well, David was a king and a mighty king. But David was a man,
jest like any yuther man. And whar you see a man, hit's bound to be
a woman hangin' round somewheres close by. So right across de road
was de house of a woman named Miz Uriah.

Miz Uriah was one er deseyar married womens which is good-
lookin' and don't keer who knows hit. She's jest de kind dat's always
waitin' for her husband to git outer de house so's she kin start messin'
round.

Her husband was in de armies er de Lawd, fightin' de enemies, and

* From "Ol' Man Adam an' His Chillun," Roark Bradford's book of Negro
Bible stories.

462

he left her home to look after de chickens and things while he gone. But dat gal ain' studdin' no chickens. She's got her mind on de menfolks.

And while ole King David is tawkin' to de messenger, she's hidin' behind de window blinds, a-watchin'. And soon as she see de messenger leave, she runs back and put on her Sunday dress and goes over to whar ole King David is settin'.

"Good mawnin', King David, Yo' Majesty," she say, sweetenin' up her voice.

"Good mawnin', sister," say ole King David. "What can I do for you dis mawnin'?"

"Well," say Miz Uriah, casual-like, "I comed over to ax you does you yar somethin' 'bout my husband. He ain't much husband, but he better'n no husband a-tall. I guess he's about all a ugly ole gal like me kin git, anyway. I wish I was a good-lookin' gal."

"You don't look so bad, gal," say ole King David.

"Aw, hysh up, Yo' Majesty," says Miz Uriah. "You know I ain't no good-lookin' gal. Jest look at 'at ole ugly laig. Look at 'at flat chest—" and she started twistin' herse'f round, showin' off.

But David is a good man and he know what she's up to, so he say: "Git on back home, gal, befo' I puts you in jail for tryin' to adulterate My Majesty. Git home! You yar me?"

Well, Miz Uriah got on back 'cross de road and ole King David sets down and writes a psa'm 'bout how he resisted temptation. But dat woman ain't started on him yit. She goes on 'cross de road and back in de house, and den de fust thing ole King David know, he sees her draggin' a big washtub out on de front po'ch and start pourin' water in hit.

"Gonter do some washin' today, Sister Uriah?" say ole King David.

"Some, Yo' Majesty," she say.

"I thought you washed yo' clothes on Monday," say de king.

"I does, Yo' Majesty," say Miz Uriah.

"Today's Sadday," say ole King David.

"I ain't said I was gonter wash no clothes today, Yo' Majesty," say Miz Uriah. "Dis is my bath day." And dat gal starts undressin' right out on de front po'ch, right in front er ole King David.

"Whyn't you git back in dat house to git naked, gal?" say ole King David. "You ain't got a lick er sense. S'pose somebody come down de road and sees you?"

"S'pose'n they does," says Miz Uriah. "They won't see nothin' but ole ugly me." And she went right on takin' off her clothes.

Ole King David set and watched her to de last stitch fell off and she stepped in de tub.

"Gal!" say ole King David, "ain't you got no shame? Whyn't you git back in dat house? Standin' out yar naked as a jay bird! Somebody comin' down dat road and see you, fust thing you know."

So Miz Uriah says, kinder baby-like: "Maybe you's right, Yo' Majesty, and I'm is mighty ashame'. But I can't tote dis tub back in de house all by myse'f. Efn Yo' Majesty'll he'p me tote hit in, I'll git back in de house."

Well, yar was ole King David tryin' to keep de kingdom f'm gittin' scandalized by dis fool gal takin' a bath on de front po'ch, and so hit wa'n't nothin' for him to do but go on and he'p her tote de tub back in de house. So he gits up and goes over to he'p her tote de tub back in de house, and dat's de last anybody seed of ole King David to Monday mawnin', when de Lawd come wawkin' up and seed him settin' out on his own front po'ch ag'in, lookin' mighty sad and sinful.

"Heyho, King David!" say de Lawd. "Been writin' any mo' psa'ms since I been round yar?"

"I writ one," say ole King David, "all 'bout how I was resistin' temptation f'm a fool woman."

"Dat sounds good," say de Lawd. "Wait'll I git settled down in dis cheer, and I wants you to read it at me."

"Can't," say ole King David. "I done tored hit up."

So de Lawd and ole King David sot on de po'ch, jest leanin' back and sayin' nothin', to finally yar come Miz Uriah draggin' her washtub out on de front po'ch ag'in, and pourin' water in hit.

Ole King David spotted her and he tried to signal to her to git back in de house, 'cause de Lawd was dar, but she didn't pay him no mind. She jest kept right on pourin' water in de tub. Den when she got de water in de tub, she brought out a bundle er clothes and started washin' 'em.

"Gonter do some washin', sister?" say de Lawd.

"Yes, Lawd. Monday's my regular washday," she say.

Den de Lawd turn to ole King David and say, "Dat's a mighty fine-lookin' neighbor you got over yonder. What's her name?"

"Dat's Uriah's wife," say King David.

"You mean hit's Uriah's widder," say de Lawd.

"Uriah's which?" say de king.

"Widder," say de Lawd. "Ole Uriah got mixed up wid one er my enemies, and when they got done wid him they had to haul him off in a sack."

"Naw?" say ole King David. "So she's a widder woman! Well I be doggone!" So he got up and started back in de house.

"Whar you goin' now, King David?" say de Lawd.

"To git my pencil and paper," say ole King David. "I'm gonter write another psa'm."

NONSENSE

When nonsense is good, it is divine. When it is bad, it is awful. Nonsense that doesn't quite come off is the dreariest stuff in the world. Many writers think they can write nonsense by omitting sense. They are victims of a terrible delusion.

Don Marquis satirized human beings by writing poems about a bug and a cat. The archy *and* mehitabel *pieces included here are perhaps nearer to satire than to pure nonsense; yet they are nonsensical, too, and have been brought into this section, where we found it convenient to stable most of our animals. Josh Billings' notes on the poodle and the mule are not precisely nonsense, either, but they seemed to belong alongside Oliver Herford's verses.*

S. J. Perelman, current headman of the zanies, who produces a rich yearly crop of nonsense, is here represented by two of his earlier and (we presume) less well-known pieces.

S. J. Perelman

IN OLD CHINATOWN

FRED BERKOWITZ, TRAPPED BY THE ALMOND-EYED PLOTTERS,
AGAIN GIVES THEM THE SLIP

The dinner dishes had been cleared away, and Benson and I were comfortably ensconced before a glowing can of Sterno. Jitters, Benson's man, was preparing our whiskies and soda, the kettle was steaming on the hob, and hobstairs and houtside the wind was whistling.

"Benson," I said, lazily puffing on my Trichinopoly cheroot, "they call you the most eminent surgeon in the world. Tell me about your most unusual case."

"That is a poser," laughed Benson. Benson is somewhat of a joker, although he looks more like the nine of clubs or one of the low face-cards. "Well, I should say that the Philip Forceps affair was the most peculiar." And closing his eyes and going to sleep, he told me the following story:

Philip Forceps was a young pair of pliers in the employ of John Greenblatt Whittier, author of "Snowbloom." He was an honest and upright pair of pincers whose duties were few; he would extract tacks and glass which had become imbedded in his master's legs and every fortnight he would trim Whittier's luxurious orange beard. But time passed and John Greenblatt Whittier fell on evil days. He was forced to trade Philip to one Leon Error for a handful of glass beads and Manhattan Island.

Error was at that time a dancer and Forceps used to stand in the wings and enviously watch Error's twinkling legs collapse to the applause of the multitude. One night he returned to his modest hall bedroom on Evans Street. He was about to leap into bed when he happened to spy himself in the full-length mirror. He was astounded. His legs, which had always been straight as an arrow, were now curved like a bow. He rushed to the theater to confront Error with the facts and found him out in the barn milking his cow, a Holbein.

Error offered to take Forceps into his act. "If I can't do it any other way, I'll have to use that brute Forceps," he admitted. The distraught young pair of pliers accepted and LEON ERROR & FORCEPS PHILIP opened, spotted next to the trained leopards. From the first they were a wow. When they played the Palace the waiting line stretched to Bedloe's Island and the Garden held the overflow. Flowers, jewels, beautiful women and rain rained in on the young pincers.

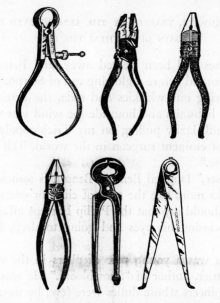

How Philip Forceps' legs were straightened

And then, at a musicale at Libby's baths, Forceps met Anne Margoulies. She was a young dental pincers in the first flush of radiant womanhood, alive, impressionable, dainty. Philip showered her with Lancias, orchids, and telephone calls. He took her to Chinatown, through the Holland Tunnel, through the great red network of sewers. He wined her, dined her, and shined her with steel wool. But she would have none of him, for his legs, curved, like parentheses they were curved, annoyed her. Frantic, Forceps took his problem to Error.

"Why don't you give her a booking?" suggested Error.

"She already has a booking," groaned Forceps with a groan.

His unrequited love was maddening him when, on the verge of insanity, a friend advised that he see Benson, the renowned physician. Benson, or Bensdorp, as he was then called, for he was in the cocoa racket, as we have already shown, was sympathetic, but held out little hope. He consented to do what he could, however, and prescribed a diet for Philip. He must eat no more horseshoes in between meals and he was forbidden to look at croquet wickets. He must not ride horseback and he must eschew arch glances. For this he was given a small pocket eschewer and ordered to eschew each arch glance thirty-two times.

Slowly, painfully, under Benson's tender care, he was won back. It was a hard and desperate fight, for his legs curled outward like hoops on the slightest provocation. But by degrees his ankles became less bowed and one sunny May morning Benson pronounced him normal again. Philip and Anne were married next day in the Little Church Around the Corner. The blushing bride carried a bouquet of magnets and the happy couple left for the Horseshoe Falls.

The Sterno embers were dying out with an eerie glow as the story ended. I awoke Benson.

"Yes," he murmured as we drank each other's health from a slipper. "It was another scalpel to hang at my beltel." And from the next room we heard the quaint cracked notes of Benson's well-tempered clavicle tinkling out the theme song from Olive Hasholem's opera:

> "Marriage by contract, I love you,
> Marriage by contract, you thrill me thro' and thro',
> Dreaming in the gloaming, bringing in the loam,
> Mammy and her gigolos, my old Kaintucky home."

THE IDOL'S EYE

I had been week-ending with Gabriel Snubbers at his villa in Cheyne-Stokes, on the edge of the Downs. Gabriel isn't seen about as much as he used to be; one hears that an eccentric aunt left him a tidy little sum and the lazy beggar refuses to leave his native haunts. Four of us had cycled down from London together: Gossip Gabril-owitsch, the Polish pianist; Downey Couch, the Irish tenor; Frank

Falcovsky, the Jewish prowler; and myself, Clay Modelling. Snubbers, his face beaming, met us at the keeper's lodge. His eyes were set in deep rolls of fat for our arrival, and I couldn't help thinking how well they looked. I wondered whether it was because his daring farce, "Mrs. Stebbins' Step-Ins," had been doing so well at the Haymarket.

"Deuced decent of you chaps to make this filthy trip," he told us, leading us up the great avenue of two stately alms toward the house. "Rum place, this." A surprise awaited us when we reached the house, for the entire left wing had just burned down. Snubbers, poor fellow, stared at it a bit ruefully, I thought.

"Just as well, it was only a plague-spot," sympathized Falcovsky. Snubbers was thoughtful.

"D'ye know, you chaps," he said suddenly, "I could swear an aunt of mine was staying in that wing." Falcovsky stirred the ashes with his stick and uncovered a pair of knitting needles and a half-charred corset.

"No, it must have been the other wing," dismissed Snubbers. "How about a spot of whisky and soda?" We entered and Littlejohn, Snubbers' man, brought in a spot of whisky on a piece of paper which we all examined with interest. A splendid fire was already roaring in the middle of the floor to drive out the warmth.

"Soda?" offered Snubbers. I took it to please him, for Gabriel's cellar was reputedly excellent. A second later I wished that I had drunk the cellar instead. Baking soda is hardly the thing after a three-hour bicycle trip.

"You drank that like a little soldier," he complimented, his little button eyes fastened on me. I was about to remark that I had never drunk a little soldier, when I noticed Littlejohn hovering in the doorway.

"Yes, that will be all," Snubbers waved, "and, oh, by the way, send up to London tomorrow for a new wing, will you?" Littlejohn bowed and left, silently, sleekly Oriental.

"Queer cove, Littlejohn," commented Snubbers. "Shall I tell you a story?" He did, and it was one of the dullest I have ever heard. At the end of it Falcovsky grunted. Snubbers surveyed him suspiciously.

"Why, what's up, old man?" he queried.

"What's up? Nothing's up," snarled Falcovsky. "Can't a man grunt in front of an open fire if he wants to?"

"But . . ." began Snubbers.

"But nothing," Falcovsky ground. "You haven't lived till you've grunted in front of an open fire. Just for that—grunt, grunt, grunt," and he grunted several times out of sheer spite. None of us dared remonstrate, for Falcovsky was reputedly the owner of great natural beds of Eskimo pies and would pay through the nose to keep his name free from scandal. The last was no idle boast—Falcovsky's was the only nose in England I have ever seen large enough to pay through, and had the Bank of England ever needed him, he could have made his fortune as a cashier's wicket.

"It's a funny thing," brooded Snubbers.

"Oh, it is, is it?" flared Falcovsky, throwing himself on Snubbers. We tore them apart and only ended the dispute by measuring the former's nose against Snubbers'. Of course Falcovsky won hands down—that is, hands down on his nose—and we resumed our drinking. The baking soda was beginning to tell on Snubbers.

"Remarkable thing happened the other day," he began. "I was pottering about in the garden . . ."

"Why must one always potter around in a garden?" demanded Couch. "Can't you potter around in an armchair just as well?"

"I did once," confessed Snubbers moodily, revealing a whitish scar on his chin. "Gad, sir, what a tigress she was!" He chewed his wad of carbon paper reminiscently. "Oh, well, never mind. But as I was saying—I was going through some of my great-grandfather's things the other day . . ."

"What things?" demanded Falcovsky, whose nose was beginning to heal.

"His bones, if you must know," Snubbers said coldly. "You know, Great-grandfather died under strange circumstances. He opened a vein in his bath."

"I never knew baths had veins," protested Gabrilowitsch.

"I never knew his great-grandfather had a ba—" began Falcovsky derisively. With a shout Snubbers threw himself on Falcovsky. It was the signal for Pandemonium, the upstairs girl, to enter and throw herself with a shout on Couch. The outcome of the necking bee was as follows: Canadians 12, Visitors 9. Krebs and Vronsky played footie, subbing for Gerber and Weinwald, who were disabled by flying antipasto.

We were silent after Snubbers had spoken; men who have wandered in far places have an innate delicacy about their great-grand-fathers' bones. Snubbers' face was a mask, his voice a harsh whip of pain in the stillness when he spoke again.

"I fancy none of you knew my great-grandfather," he said slowly. "Before your time, I daresay. A rare giant of a man with quizzical eyes and a great shock of wiry red hair, he had come through the Peninsular Wars without a scratch. Women loved this impetual Irish adventurer who would rather fight than eat and vice versa. The wars over, he turned toward cookery, planning to devote his failing years to the perfection of the welsh rarebit, a dish he loved. One night he was chaffing at The Bit, a tavern in Portsmouth, when he overheard a chance remark from a brawny gunner's mate in his cups. In Calcutta the man had heard native tales of a mysterious idol, whose single eye was a flawless ruby.

" 'Topscuttle my bamberger, it's the size of a bloomin' pigeon's egg!' spat the salt, shifting his quid to his other cheek. 'A bloomin' rajah's ransom and ye may lay to that, mateys!'

"The following morning the *Maid of Hull,* a frigate of the line mounting thirty-six guns, out of Bath and into bed in a twinkling, dropped downstream on the tide, bound out for Bombay, object matrimony. On her as passenger went my great-grandfather, an extra pair of nankeen pants his only baggage and a dirk in his throat ready for use. Fifty-three days later in Poona, he was heading for the interior of one of the Northern states. Living almost entirely on cameo brooches and the few ptarmigan which fell to the ptrigger of his pfowling-piece, he at last sighted the towers of Ishpeming, the Holy City of the Surds and Cosines, fanatic Mohammedan warrior sects. He disguised himself as a beggar and entered the gates.

"For weeks my great-grandfather awaited his chance to enter the temple of the idol. They were changing the guard one evening when he saw it. One of the native janissaries dropped his knife. My great-grandfather leaped forward with cringing servility and returned it to him, in the small of his back. Donning the soldier's turban, he quickly slipped into his place. Midnight found him within ten feet of his prize. Now came the final test. He furtively drew from the folds of his robes a plate of curry, a dish much prized by Indians, and set it in a far corner. The guards rushed upon it with bulging squeals of delight. A twist of his wrist and the gem was his. With an elaborately stifled yawn, my great-grandfather left under pretense of going out for a glass of water. The soldiers winked slyly but when he did not return after two hours, their suspicions were aroused. They hastily made a canvass of the places where water was served and their worst fears were realized. The ruby in his burnoose, Great-grandfather was escaping by fast elephant over the Khyber Pass. Dockside loungers in Yarmouth forty days later stared curiously at a mammoth of a man with flaming red hair striding abstractedly toward the Bull and Bloater Tavern. Under his belt lay the Ruby Eye.

"Ten years to that night had passed, and my great-grandfather, in seclusion under this very roof, had almost forgotten his daring escapade. Smoking by the fireplace, he listened to the roar of the wind and reviewed his campaigns. Suddenly he leaped to his feet—a dark face had vanished from the window. Too late my great-grandfather snatched up powder and ball and sent a charge of grape from his dueling-pistol hurtling into the night. The note pinned to the window drained the blood from his face.

"It was the first of a series. Overnight his hair turned from rose-red to snow-white. And finally, when it seemed as though madness were to rob them of their revenge, *they came.*"

Snubbers stopped, his eyes those of a man who had looked beyond life and had seen things best left hidden from mortal orbs. Falcovsky's hand was trembling as he pressed a pinch of snuff against his gums. "You—you mean?" he quavelled.

"Yes." Snubbers' voice had sunk to a whisper. "He fought with the strength of nine devils, but the movers took away his piano. You see," he added very gently, "Great-grandfather had missed the last four instalments." Gabrilowitsch sighed deeply and arose, his eyes fixed intently on Snubbers.

"And—and the ruby?" he asked softly, his delicate fingers closing around the fire-tongs.

"Oh, *that,*" shrugged Snubbers, "I just threw that in to make it interesting."

We bashed in the top of his conk and left him to the vultures.

Frances Warfield

FPAFM

I ordered ham and eggs, as I always do on the diner, and then, as I always do, looked around for pamphlets. There was one handy. "Echoes from Colonial Days," it was called, "being a little fouvenir iffued from time to time for the benefit of the guefts of The Baltimore & Ohio Railroad Company as a reminder of pleafant moments fpent ..." Involuntarily, my lips began to move. I reached for a pencil. But the man across from me already had his pencil out. He had written:

"Oh, fay can you fee?"

I said: "Fing Fomething Fimple."

"Filly, ifn't it?" he said, and kept on writing.

I wrote: "Fing a Fong of Fixpence."

"Oh, ftop the fongs," he said. "Too eafy." He wrote: "The Courtfhip of Miles Ftandifh," "I fee a fquirrel," "I undereftimate ftatefmanfhip," "My fifter feems fuperfenfitive," and seeing that I did not appreciate the last one, which he evidently thought very fine, he wrote: "Forry to fee you fo ftupid."

I ate my lunch grouchily. How could I help it if he was in practice and I was not? He had probably taken this train before.

"Pafs the falt," I said.

"Pleafe pafs the falt," he triumphed.

I paid no attention. "Waiter!" I said. The waiter did not budge.

"You muft fpeak the language," said the man opposite me. He called out: "Fay! Fteward!"

The waiter jumped to attention. "Fir?" he said.

"Pleafe fill the faltcellar."

"The falt-fhaker fhall be replenifhed inftantly," replied the waiter, with a superior gleam in his eyes.

I smiled and my companion unbent a little.

"Let's try for hard ones," he invited.

"Fure," I said.

476

"Farcafm," he said.

"Fubftance."

"Fubfiftence," he scored.

"Fcythe."

"S's inside now," he ruled.

"Perfuafive," I said instantly.

"Languifh."

"Bafilifk."

"Quiefcent."

"Nonfenfe," I finished. "Fon of a fpeckled fea monfter."

"Ftep-fon of a poifonous fnake!" he cried.

"You don't fay fo!" I retorted.

"I do fo fay fo!" he replied, getting up and leaving the diner.

"Fool!" I called after him, fniffling.

Morris Bishop

LIMERICKS LONG AFTER LEAR

[PICTURES BY RICHARD TAYLOR]

Said a fervent young lady of Hammels,
"I object to humanity's trammels!
   I want to be free!
   Like a bird! Like a bee!
Oh, why am I classed with the mammals?"

478

A youth who afflicts Essex Fells
Can yell university yells,
   From Abilene's hail
   To the frog call of Yale;
He also puts poison in wells.

A man who smokes hams in Shrub Oak
Hangs his wife in the smokehouse to smoke;
 "It's only to render
 Her tempting and tender,"
He says to censorious folk.

A joker who haunts Monticello
Is really a terrible fellow;
  In the midst of caresses
  He fills ladies' dresses
With garter snakes, ice cubes, and Jell-O.

When a lady returned from Big Moose,
Her husband exclaimed, "What the deuce!
　　I am quite reconciled
　　To the call of the wild,
But where did you get the papoose?"

A ghoulish old fellow in Kent
Encrusted his wife in cement;
   He said, with a sneer,
   "I was careful, my dear,
To follow your natural bent."

There's a girl out in Center Moriches
Who keeps all the neighbors in stitches;
    She swims down to Islip
    And borrows a dry slip,
And bicycles home without breeches.

A lady who rules Fort Montgomery
Says the wearing of clothes is mere mummery;
    She has frequently tea'd in
    The costume of Eden,
Appearing delightfully summery.

Ring Lardner

SIT STILL

One morning I was walking down Fifth Avenue alongside of the
Park and I stopped with the rest of the southbound traffic at Seventy-
second Street to allow the crosstown traffic to move, though God
knows what good it did them because it is a two-way street and there
were just as many going one way as the other, but during the wait I
happened to glance at the curb and saw a taxicab that I had never
seen before so I got in and the first thing I noticed was an autographed
picture of a man named Nathan Schwartz. The driver must have
heard me slam the door, for pretty soon he turned around and opened
the sliding window that separated his compartment from mine and
said where to.

"Where were you headed for?" I retorted.

"Nowhere a special," he said.

"Well," I said, "I figured we might as well ride together as long as
we were headed in the same direction. How did Mr. Schwartz come
to send you one of his pictures? Do you know him?"

"I'm one of his fans," said the driver. "What I'd appreciate now,
though, is where you want me to take you."

"You'll be one of the first people I'll tell as soon as I find out. Just
drive along a ways and if I hear anything I'll get in touch with you."

"All right," said the driver, "and maybe you'd better rap twice on
the window so I'll know it's you. That will be the signal. Have you
got it?"

"Two raps," I said.

"You pick things up quickly, but whether you remember them is
the question. Perhaps it will help you if you connect it in your mind
with some common fact, like how many legs on a man, or how many
rear wheels on a car."

"Or how many times I've been abroad," I chuckled.

"You've got it," said the driver.

The policeman jingled his bell and we were on our way. I was about to doze off when I observed a newspaper that had been left on the back seat by the people who had moved out. I picked it up and read an item about Jackie Coogan. He was in New York and staying at the Ritz (Forty-sixth and Madison). I rapped three times on the window, but the driver paid no attention. Then I remembered—"How many legs on a man?"—and rapped twice. The driver opened the window.

"Well?" he said.

"Take me to the Hotel Astor," I ordered, wondering why I had not thought of it before because I had wanted to see the Astor ever since moving to New York.

"That's on the Lincoln Highway, isn't it?" said the driver. "It's either on it or just off it. I'll find it anyhow; there must be plenty of signs."

We continued down the Avenue until we came to Forty-fifth Street.

"We could lose a little distance, by going to Forty-third Street," said the driver, "but Forty-fifth's worse at this time of the day, so I imagine it evens up in the end."

I was pretty hungry when we got to the Astor as I had gone without my lunch.

"Goodbye," I said to the driver.

"Goodbye," he said. "And don't forget—two legs to a man."

The car door was opened by a tall fellow who spoke to me, but I could not place him. I walked up the steps and into the hotel's front lobby, which seemed to be quite crowded, so crowded that I might never have been able to reach the desk without my training as a coxcomb at Yale.

"Have you got a room?" I said to a clerk, thinking of course they were filled up or why would there be such a crush in the lobby?

"Yes, sir. Kindly register and I'll fix you up," he replied.

There was nothing for me to do but write down my name and address. I was afraid to use the only other name I could think of, Nathan Schwartz; the clerk might be one of his fans, too, and know me for an impostor.

The clerk called a bellboy and gave him a key and the bellboy asked where I had left my baggage. I feigned temporary deafness and asked him in turn why, if the hotel had vacant rooms, there was such a crush in the lobby.

"Oh," he said, "that's just our waiting list."

"But why do they have to wait if I didn't?"

"They're not waiting for rooms. They're waiting to sit down," he said.

This statement interested me to such an extent that I spent the next few hours investigating, and I learned the following facts, which may or may not lessen the difficulty:

The lobby has four pillars or columns, which were originally placed there to keep the ceiling from bouncing up and down on the floor. ("Four men to a male quartette.") There are three chairs to each pillar, or twelve chairs in all. ("Twelve horsemen in the Notre Dame backfield.") The occupants of these chairs have been in them continuously for periods ranging from eight to sixty-six years. The man who has been sitting in his chair the shortest while (eight years) is a Mr. J. N. Purdy, but the others refer to him as "The Junior Partner" or "The Kid." He paid one hundred and twenty-five thousand dollars for his seat, a record price at the time, buying it from a Mr. Louis Bolton, who, after an occupancy of only four years and two months, yielded to a life-long ambition to take up window-shopping.

The oldest settler is the man who sits on the desk side of the pillar nearest the entrance to the florist's. No one knows his real name, but they call him "General Grant" because he sat down in 1864 and announced that he would sit it out in that chair if it took all century.

At the same pillar is Mr. Lyman Bates, who used to be an inveterate smoker. He had to give it up fourteen years ago when he ran out of cigars and money, and the bellboys refused to extend him credit. The other tenant of this pillar is a woman, Lucy Pond, who came into the hotel in 1887, expecting to meet a Harvard man and take lunch with him. She got tired standing after three months and, as there were no vacancies at the time, sat down in Mr. Bates' lap. In 1893, it was discovered that a Mr. Levings, who shared the pillar with Bates and "General Grant" at that time, had died quite a while previously. Bates made the discovery and managed to push Levings out of his chair. Miss Pond then moved into it, much to the relief of Bates, whose foot was asleep.

The only other woman squatter is Margaret Vesey. She has a chair at the pillar opposite the newsstand. They say she was quite an attractive girl when she sat down, in 1900, and that Barney Diehl, who had a seat at that column, showed an inclination to flirt with her. He was not rebuffed, but she insisted on his looking at her while he talked and he had to quit on account of stiff neck.

In the early days of Astor squatting it was necessary to put into effect a rule prohibiting standees from attempting to eject the settlers by physical means. The latter were in no condition to put up a battle and the thing was too unfair. But there was no law against the use of strategy and many tricks were employed successfully before it was overdone. For example, one of the standees would bribe a bellboy to shout, "Mr. Gordon is wanted on the telephone by Lily Langtry." Gordon, unable to resist the temptation, would jump out of his chair and the trickster would slip into it. Another effective ruse was starting a cry of "Fire!" The hotel people soon put a stop to that.

It is now understood that when a squatter has occupied one of the chairs for twenty-five years, it becomes his homestead and he is privileged to get up and move around without jeopardizing his rights. He is privileged to get up and move around, but he can't. Because he can't.

One of the bellboys told me of a remark recently made by Mr. Bates. He had overheard a standee speaking of Prof. Goozlequirt, a champion flagpole-sitter who had just come down off a flagpole in Madison Square Garden after sitting there for eighteen days and five hours.

"What makes those Danes so restless?" said Mr. Bates.

N. P. Willis

MISS ALBINA McLUSH

I have a passion for fat women. If there is anything I hate in life it is what dainty people call a *spirituelle*. Motion—rapid motion—a smart, quick, squirrel-like step, a pert, voluble tone—in short, a lively girl—is my exquisite horror! I would as lief have a *diable petit* dancing his infernal hornpipe on my cerebellum as to be in the room with one. I have tried before now to school myself into liking these parched peas of humanity. I have followed them with my eyes, and attended to their rattle till I was as crazy as a fly in a drum. I have danced with them, and romped with them in the country, and periled the salvation of my "white tights" by sitting near them at supper. I swear off from this moment. I do. I won't—no—hang me if ever I show another small, lively, *spry* woman a civility.

Albina McLush is divine. She is like the description of the Persian beauty by Hafiz: "Her heart is full of passion and her eyes are full of sleep." She is the sister of Lurly McLush, my old college chum, who, as early as his sophomore year, was chosen president of the *Dolce far niente* Society—no member of which was ever known to be surprised at anything (the college law of rising before breakfast excepted). Lurly introduced me to his sister one day, as he was lying upon a heap of turnips, leaning on his elbow with his head in his hand, in a green lane in the suburbs. He had driven over a stump, and been tossed out of his gig, and I came up just as he was wondering how in the d——l's name he got there! Albina sat quietly in the gig, and when I was presented, requested me, with a delicious drawl, to say nothing about the adventure—it would be so troublesome to relate it to everybody! I loved her from that moment. Miss McLush was tall, and her shape, of its kind, was perfect. It was not a *fleshy* one exactly, but she was large and full. Her skin was clear, fine-grained and transparent; her temples and forehead perfectly rounded and polished, and her lips and chin swelling into a ripe and tempting pout, like the cleft of a bursted apricot. And then her eyes—large, liquid and sleepy—they languished beneath their long black fringes as if they had no business with daylight—like two magnificent dreams, surprised in their jet embryos by some bird-nesting cherub. Oh! it was lovely to look into them!

She sat, usually, upon a *fauteuil,* with her large, full arm embedded in the cushion, sometimes for hours without stirring. I have seen the wind lift the masses of dark hair from her shoulders when it seemed like the coming to life of a marble Hebe—she had been motionless so long. She was a model for a goddess of sleep as she sat with her eyes half-closed, lifting up their superb lids slowly as you spoke to her, and dropping them again with the deliberate motion of a cloud, when she had murmured out her syllable of assent. Her figure, in a sitting posture, presented a gentle declivity from the curve of her neck to the instep of the small round foot lying on its side upon the ottoman. I remember a fellow's bringing her a plate of fruit one evening. He was one of your lively men—a horrid monster, all right angles and activity. Having never been accustomed to hold her own plate, she had not well extricated her whole fingers from her handkerchief before he set it down in her lap. As it began to slide slowly toward her feet, her hand relapsed into the muslin folds, and she fixed her eye upon it with a kind of indolent surprise, drooping her lids gradually till, as the fruit scattered over the ottoman, they closed entirely, and a liquid jet line was alone visible through the heavy lashes. There was an imperial indifference in it worthy of Juno.

Miss McLush rarely walks. When she does, it is with the deliberate majesty of a Dido. Her small, plump feet melt to the ground like snowflakes; and her figure sways to the indolent motion of her limbs with a glorious grace and yieldingness quite indescribable. She was idling slowly up the Mall one evening just at twilight, with a servant at a short distance behind her, who, to while away the time between his steps, was employing himself in throwing stones at the cows feeding upon the Common. A gentleman, with a natural admiration for her splendid person, addressed her. He might have done a more eccentric thing. Without troubling herself to look at him, she turned to her servant and requested him, with a yawn of desperate ennui, to knock that fellow down! John obeyed his orders; and, as his mistress resumed her lounge, picked up a new handful of pebbles, and tossing one at the nearest cow, loitered lazily after.

Such supreme indolence was irresistible. I gave in—I—who never before could summon energy to sigh—I—to whom a declaration was but a synonym for perspiration—I—who had only thought of love as a nervous complaint, and of women but to pray for a good deliverance —I—yes—I—knocked under. Albina McLush! Thou were too exquisitely lazy. Human sensibilities cannot hold out forever.

I found her one morning sipping her coffee at twelve, with her eyes wide open. She was just from the bath, and her complexion had a soft, dewy transparency, like the cheek of Venus rising from the sea. It was the hour, Lurly had told me, when she would be at the trouble of thinking. She put away with her dimpled forefinger, as I entered, a cluster of rich curls that had fallen over her face, and nodded to me like a waterlily swaying to the wind when its cup is full of rain.

"Lady Albina," said I, in my softest tone, "how are you?"

"Bettina," said she, addressing her maid in a voice as clouded and rich as the south wind on an Aeolian, "how am I today?"

The conversation fell into short sentences. The dialogue became a monologue. I entered upon my declaration. With the assistance of Bettina, who supplied her mistress with cologne, I kept her attention alive through the incipient circumstances. Symptoms were soon told. I came to the avowal. Her hand lay reposing on the arm of the sofa, half-buried in a muslin *foulard*. I took it up and pressed the cool soft fingers to my lips—unforbidden. I rose and looked into her eyes for confirmation. Delicious creature—she was asleep!

I never have had courage to renew the subject. Miss McLush seems to have forgotten it altogether. Upon reflection, too, I'm convinced she would not survive the excitement of the ceremony—unless, indeed, she should sleep between the responses and the prayer. I am still devoted, however, and if there should come a war or an earthquake, or if the millennium should commence, as is expected in 18—, or if anything happens that can keep her waking so long, I shall deliver a declaration, abbreviated for me by a scholar-friend of mine, which, he warrants, may be articulated in fifteen minutes—without fatigue.

Josh Billings

ANIMATED NATUR

THE POODLE

The poodle iz a small dog, with sore eyes, and hid amungst a good deal ov promiskuss hair.

They are sumtimes white for color, and their hair iz tangled all over them, like the hed ov a yung darkey.

They are kept az pets, and, like all other pets, are az stubborn az a setting hen.

A poodle iz a woman's pet, and that makes them kind ov sakred, for whatever a woman luvs she worships.

I hav seen poodles that i almost wanted tew swop places with, but the owners ov them didn't akt to me az tho they wanted tew trade for enny thing.

Thare iz but phew things on the face ov this earth more utterly worthless than a poodle, and yet i am glad thare iz poodles, for if thare wasn't thare iz some people who wouldn't hav enny objekt in living, and hav nothing tew luv.

Thare iz nothing in this world made in vain, and poodles are good for fleas.

Fleas are also good for poodles, for they keep their minds employed scratching, and almost every boddy else's too about the house.

I never knew a man tew keep a poodle. Man's natur iz too koarse for poodles. A poodle would soon fade and die if a man waz tew nuss him.

I don't expekt enny poodle, but if enny boddy duz giv me one he must make up his mind tew be tied onto a long stick every Saturday, and be used for washing the windows on the outside.

This kind of nussing would probably make the poodle mad, and probably he would quit, but i kant help it.

493

If i hav got to keep a poodle, he haz got tew help wash the windows every Saturday. I am solid on this pint.

Bully for me.

THE MULE

The mule is haf hoss and haf Jackass, and then kums tu a full stop, natur diskovering her mistake.

Tha weigh more, akordin tu their heft, than enny other kreetur, except a crow-bar.

Tha kant hear enny quicker, nor further than the hoss, yet their ears are big enuff for snow shoes.

You kan trust them with enny one whose life aint worth enny more than the mules. The only wa tu keep the mules into a paster, is tu turn them into a medder jineing, and let them jump out.

Tha are reddy for use, just as soon as they will du tu abuse.

Tha haint got enny friends, and will live on huckle berry brush, with an ockasional chanse at Kanada thistels.

Tha are a modern invenshun, i dont think the Bible deludes tu them at tall.

Tha sel for more money than enny other domestik animile. You kant tell their age by looking into their mouth, enny more than you could a Mexican cannons. Tha never have no dissease that a good club wont heal.

If tha ever die tha must kum rite tu life agin, for i never herd no-boddy sa "ded mule."

Tha are like sum men, verry korrupt at harte; ive known them tu be good mules for 6 months, just tu git a good chanse to kick sumbody.

I never owned one, nor never mean to, unless thare is a United Staits law passed, requiring it.

The only reason why tha are pashunt, is bekause tha are ashamed ov themselfs.

I have seen eddikated mules in a sirkus.

Tha kould kick, and bite, tremenjis. I would not sa what I am forced tu sa again the mule, if his birth want an outrage, and man want tu blame for it.

Enny man who is willing tu drive a mule, ought to be exempt by law from running for the legislatur.

Tha are the strongest creeturs on earth, and heaviest ackordin tu their sise; I herd tell ov one who fell oph from the tow path, on the Eri kanawl, and sunk as soon as he touched bottom, but he kept rite on towing the boat tu the nex stashun, breathing thru his ears, which stuck out ov the water about 2 feet 6 inches; i did'nt see this did, but an auctioneer told me ov it, and i never knew an auctioneer tu lie unless it was absolutely convenient.

Oliver Herford

MORE ANIMALS

THE COW

The Cow is too well known, I fear,
    To need an introduction here.
    If she should vanish from earth's face
It would be hard to fill her place;
For with the Cow would disappear
So much that every one holds Dear.
Oh, think of all the Boots and Shoes,
Milk Punches, Gladstone Bags and Stews,
And Things too numerous to count,
Of which, my child, she is the Fount.
Let's hope, at least, the Fount may last
Until *our* Generation's past.

A COW

THE GNU

Beware, My Dear, if ever you
Should chance to come across a Gnu!
You may be Fair, and Tall, and Svelte,
But do not hope the Gnu to melt.
You may be Gentle, Kind, and True,
These things mean nothing to the Gnu.
You may love Beasts, both Great and Small,
That won't affect the Gnu at all.
You may be Generous, you may
Subscribe to the S.P.C.A.,
All this of no avail will be,
The Only Thing's to Climb a Tree.
And if there *is* no Tree to Climb,
Don't say you were not warned in Time!

A Gnu.

THE HEN

Alas! my Child, where is the Pen
  That can do Justice to the Hen?
  Like Royalty, She goes her way,
Laying foundations every day,
Though not for Public Buildings, yet
For Custard, Cake and Omelette.
Or if too Old for such a use
They have their Fling at some Abuse,
As when to Censure Plays Unfit
Upon the Stage they make a Hit,
Or at elections Seal the Fate
Of an Obnoxious Candidate
No wonder, Child, we prize the Hen,
Whose Egg is Mightier than the Pen.

THE HORSE

This noble Beast—
 But, why discourse
Upon the Virtues of the Horse?
They are too numerous to tell
Save when you have a Horse to Sell.
No Beast has done so much as He
To elevate Society.
How *could* Society Get On
(Or off), my Child, if He were gone?
We Owe him Much, yet who can say
He ever asked us to Repay?
Ah, Child! How Bright the World would be,
If Creditors were All as He.

Ogden Nash

THE STRANGE CASE OF MR. FORTAGUE'S
DISAPPOINTMENT

Once upon a time there was a man name Mr. Lionel Fortague.

~~~

He didn't have very much to talk about.

~~~

In summer he used to ask people if it was hot enough for them.

~~~

It always was.

~~~

In winter he used to ask people if it was cold enough for them.

~~~

It always was.

~~~

Mr. Lionel Fortague got pretty sick of people it was hot enough for.

~~~

He got pretty sick of people it was cold enough for, too.

~~~

He decided he would arise and go now.

~~~

He decided he would go to Innisfree.

~~~

The people of Innisfree are different, thought Mr. Lionel Fortague.

~~~

As soon as he got to Innisfree he asked the people if it was cold enough
for them.

~~~

They asked him What? Was what cold enough for who?

~~~

Mr. Lionel Fortague was delighted.

~~~

knew Innisfree would be different, he said to himself.

~~~

He could hardly wait for summer to verify his conclusion.

~~~

As soon as summer came he asked everybody if it was hot enough for them.

~~~

Everybody said the question was familiar but they couldn't remember the answer.

~~~

Mr. Lionel Fortague said he would settle down on Innisfree, the home of iridescent chitchat.

~~~

He said he would a small cabin build there, of clay and wattles made.

~~~

Everybody said did he mean he would build a small cabin there, made of clay and wattles?

~~~

Mr. Lionel Fortague said yes, but his way of putting it was more poetic.

~~~

Everybody said maybe, but they were all out of wattles.

~~~

Mr. Lionel Fortague grew very angry at the people of Innisfree.

~~~

He a small cabin built there, of clay and beaverboard made.

~~~

He a fierce-looking dog at an annual clearance sale bought, and it the people of Innisfree one by one to bite he instructed.

~~~

My, he was disappointed.

~~~

He had forgotten that a bargain dog never bites.

~~~

REQUIEM

There was a young belle of old Natchez
Whose garments were always in patchez.
When comment arose
On the state of her clothes,
She drawled, When Ah itchez, Ah scratchez!

Will Cuppy

A SHORT HISTORY OF MAN

The Java Man

The Java Man lived in Java five hundred thousand or one million or two million years ago and was lower than we are. He was Lower Pleistocene and Lower Quaternary and knock-kneed. He was called *Pithecanthropus* ("Ape-Man") *erectus* because he walked with a slight stoop. He consisted of a calvarium, three teeth, and a femur. Professor Dubois made him a face which proves that he was dolichocephalic, or long-headed, instead of brachycephalic, or square-headed, and that he was 5 feet, 6½ inches high. The Java Man had immense supra-orbital ridges of solid bone and was conscious in spots. Does that remind you of anyone? His Broca's area was low. He could say that the evenings were drawing in and times were hard and his feet hurt. The spiritual life of the Java Man was low because he was only a beginner. He was just a child at heart and was perfectly satisfied with his polygamy, polygyny, polyandry, endogamy, exogamy, and totemism. How he ever became extinct is beyond me. The Java Man has been called the Missing Link by those who should know.

The Pekin Man

The Pekin Man shows that people were living in Asia long, long ago, as most of us knew already. He was discovered near Pekin, or Peiping, and was named *Sinanthropus pekinensis* to keep certain persons from calling him Peiping Tom. *Sin* means China, although the Chinese are no worse than other foreigners. The glabella was prominent, so he was probably a young male. The brain shows that the calvarium, or brain-case, was good. The skull was in perfect condition because the Pekin Man took better care of his skull than some of us. He had begun to think, or whatever the Chinese do. The pre-

503

frontal region resembles that found in some parts of the Middle West. The right horizontal ramus shows a tendency to do everything backward. The Pekin Man is lovable because he left no culture. He knew nothing about the Ming Dynasty and the Ch'ing Dynasty and the Sung Dynasty and he wrote no short poems stating that he got drunk and went out in a canoe and fell in. He had no imports and exports but he had fauna and flora. The Pekin Man was fond of overpopulation. We do not know whether he was religious or promiscuous or both.

THE PILTDOWN MAN

The Piltdown Man was called the Dawn Man, or Barmy Ned, because he was found in Great Britain. He was a great help because he left crude flint implements. These were used for making still cruder flint implements. The Piltdown Man had little to do. His skull is in small pieces which can be fitted together in various ways after choosing sides. This is called Badminton. The Piltdown Man had aspidistras, delphiniums, and sinus trouble. Already he was aiming at the stars and missing them. The manubrium indicates self-control but very little to control. The Piltdown Man had no chin and was rather toothy. It seems incredible that he had a private life, but those are just the ones who do. The young took after their parents. Anthropologists say that the Piltdown Man was stupider than any person of today. Anthropologists are people who are in museums. They lead sheltered lives. The Early Irish left few skulls. The Early Scotch left no skulls.

THE MODERN MAN

The Modern Man, or Nervous Wreck, is the highest of all Mammals because anyone can see that he is. There are about two billion Modern Men, or too many. The Modern Man's highly developed brain has made him what he is and you know what he is. The development of his brain is caused by his upright or bipedal position, as in the Penguin, the Dinosaur, and other extinct Reptiles. Modern Man has been called the Talking Animal because he talks more than any other three animals chosen at random. He has also been called the Reasoning Animal, but there may be a catch in this. The fissure of Sylvius and the fissure of Rolando enable him to argue in circles. His main pursuits in the order named are murder, robbery, kidnapping, body-snatching, barratry, nepotism, arson, and mayhem. This is known as the Good, the True, and the Beautiful. They mature slowly but make up for it later, generally from July 1 to June 30, inclusive. The females carry nickels and pins in their mouths. They are fond of glittering objects, bits of ribbon, and olives. All Modern Men are descended from a Wormlike Creature, but it shows more on some people. Modern Man will never become extinct if the Democrats can help it.

Don Marquis

ARCHY AND MEHITABEL

i the coming of archy

Dobbs Ferry possesses a rat which slips out of his lair at night and runs a typewriting machine in a garage. Unfortunately, he has always been interrupted by the watchman before he could produce a complete story.

It was at first thought that the power which made the typewriter run was a ghost, instead of a rat. It seems likely to us that it was both a ghost and a rat. Mme. Blavatsky's ego went into a white horse after she passed over, and someone's personality has undoubtedly gone into this rat. It is an era of belief in communications from the spirit land.

And since this matter had been reported in the public prints and seriously received we are no longer afraid of being ridiculed, and we do not mind making a statement of something that happened to our own typewriter only a couple of weeks ago.

We came into our room earlier than usual in the morning, and discovered a gigantic cockroach jumping about upon the keys.

He did not see us, and we watched him. He would climb painfully upon the framework of the machine and cast himself with all his force upon a key, head downward, and his weight and the impact of the blow were just sufficient to operate the machine, one slow letter after another. He could not work the capital letters, and he had a great deal of difficulty operating the mechanism that shifts the paper so that a fresh line may be started. We never saw a cockroach work so hard or perspire so freely in all our lives before. After about an hour of this frightfully difficult literary labor he fell to the floor exhausted, and we saw him creep feebly into a nest of the poems which are always there in profusion.

Congratulating ourself that we had left a sheet of paper in the ma-

chine the night before so that all this work had not been in vain, we
made an examination, and this is what we found:

> expression is the need of my soul
> i was once a vers libre bard
> but i died and my soul went into the body of a cockroach
> it has given me a new outlook upon life
> i see things from the under side now
> thank you for the apple peelings in the wastepaper basket
> but your paste is getting so stale i cant eat it
> there is a cat here called mehitabel i wish you would have
> removed she nearly ate me the other night why dont she
> catch rats that is what she is supposed to be for
> there is a rat here she should get without delay
>
> most of these rats here are just rats
> but this rat is like me he has a human soul in him
> he used to be a poet himself
> night after night i have written poetry for you
> on your typewriter
> and this big brute of a rat who used to be a poet
> comes out of his hole when it is done
> and reads it and sniffs at it
> he is jealous of my poetry
> he used to make fun of it when we were both human
> he was a punk poet himself
> and after he has read it he sneers
> and then he eats it
>
> i wish you would have mehitabel kill that rat
> or get a cat that is onto her job
> and i will write you a series of poems showing how things look
> to a cockroach
> that rats name is freddy
> the next time freddy dies i hope he wont be a rat
> but something smaller i hope i will be a rat
> in the next transmigration and freddy a cockroach
> i will teach him to sneer at my poetry then

dont you ever eat any sandwiches in your office
i havent had a crumb of bread for i dont know how long
or a piece of ham or anything but apple parings
and paste leave a piece of paper in your machine
every night you can call me archy

ii mehitabel was once cleopatra

boss i am disappointed in
some of your readers they
are always asking how does
archy work the shift so as to get a
new line or how does archy do
this or do that they
are always interested in technical
details when the main question is
whether the stuff is
literature or not
i wish you would leave
that book of george moores on
the floor

mehitabel the cat and i want to
read it i have discovered that
mehitabel s soul formerly inhabited a
human also at least that
is what mehitabel is claiming these
days it may be she got jealous of
my prestige anyhow she and
i have been talking it over in a
friendly way who were you
mehitabel i asked her i was
cleopatra once she said well i said i
suppose you lived in a palace you bet
she said and what lovely fish dinners
we used to have and licked her chops

mehitabel would sell her soul for
a plate of fish any day i told her i thought
you were going to say you were

the favorite wife of the emperor
valerian he was some cat nip eh
mehitabel but she did not get me
                          archy

iii the song of mehitabel

this is the song of mehitabel
of mehitabel the alley cat
as i wrote you before boss
mehitabel is a believer
in the pythagorean
theory of the transmigration
of the soul and she claims
that formerly her spirit
was incarnated in the body
of cleopatra
that was a long time ago
and one must not be
surprised if mehitabel
has forgotten some of her
more regal manners

i have had my ups and downs
but wotthehell wotthehell
yesterday sceptres and crowns
fried oysters and velvet gowns
and today i herd with bums
but wotthehell wotthehell
i wake the world from sleep
as i caper and sing and leap
when i sing my wild free tune
wotthehell wotthehell
under the blear eyed moon
i am pelted with cast off shoon
but wotthehell wotthehell

do you think that i would change
my present freedom to range
for a castle or moated grange

wotthehell wotthehell
cage me and i d go frantic
my life is so romantic
capricious and corybantic
and i m toujours gai toujours gai

i know that i am bound
for a journey down the sound
in the midst of a refuse mound
but wotthehell wotthehell
oh i should worry and fret
death and i will coquette
there s a dance in the old dame yet
toujours gai toujours gai

i once was an innocent kit
wotthehell wotthehell
with a ribbon my neck to fit
and bells tied onto it
o wotthehell wotthehell
but a maltese cat came by
with a come hither look in his eye
and a song that soared to the sky
and wotthehell wotthehell
and i followed adown the street
the pad of his rhythmical feet
o permit me again to repeat
wotthehell wotthehell

my youth i shall never forget
but there s nothing i really regret
wotthehell wotthehell
there s a dance in the old dame yet
toujours gai toujours gai

the things that i had not ought to
i do because i ve gotto
wotthehell wotthehell
and i end with my favorite motto
toujours gai toujours gai

boss sometimes i think
that our friend mehitabel
is a trifle too gay

iv the old trouper

i ran onto mehitabel again
last evening
she is inhabiting
a decayed trunk
which lies in an alley
in greenwich village
in company with the
most villainous tom cat
i have ever seen
but there is nothing
wrong about the association
archy she told me
it is merely a plutonic
attachment
and the thing can be
believed for the tom
looks like one of pluto s demons
it is a theatre trunk
archy mehitabel told me
and tom is an old theatre cat
he has given his life
to the theatre
he claims that richard
mansfield once
kicked him out of the way
and then cried because
he had done it and
petted him
and at another time
he says in a case
of emergency
he played a bloodhound
in a production of

uncle tom s cabin
the stage is not what it
used to be tom says
he puts his front paw
on his breast and says
they don t have it any more
they don t have it here
the old troupers are gone
there s nobody can troupe
any more
they are all amateurs nowadays
they haven t got it
here
there are only
five or six of us oldtime
troupers left
this generation does not know
what stage presence is
personality is what they lack
personality
where would they get
the training my old friends
got in the stock companies
i knew mr booth very well
says tom
and a law should be passed
preventing anybody else
from ever playing
in any play he ever
played in
there was a trouper for you
i used to sit on his knee
and purr when i was
a kitten he used to tell me
how much he valued my opinion
finish is what they lack
finish
and they haven t got it
here

and again he laid his paw
on his breast
i remember mr daly very
well too
i was with mr daly s company
for several years
there was art for you
there was team work
there was direction
they knew the theatre
and they all had it
here
for two years mr daly
would not ring up the curtain
unless i was in the
prompter s box
they are amateurs nowadays
rank amateurs all of them
for two seasons i played
the dog in joseph
jefferson s rip van winkle
it is true i never came
on the stage
but he knew i was just off
and it helped him
i would like to see
one of your modern
theatre cats
act a dog so well
that it would convince
a trouper like jo jefferson
but they haven t got it
nowadays
they haven t got it
here
jo jefferson had it he had it
here
i come of a long line
of theatre cats

my grandfather
was with forrest
he had it he was a real trouper
my grandfather said
he had a voice
that used to shake
the ferryboats
on the north river
once he lost his beard
and my grandfather
dropped from the
fly gallery and landed
under his chin
and played his beard
for the rest of the act
you don t see any theatre
cats that could do that
nowadays
they haven t got it they
haven t got it
here
once i played the owl
in modjeska s production
of macbeth
i sat above the castle gate
in the murder scene
and made my yellow
eyes shine through the dusk
like an owl s eyes
modjeska was a real
trouper she knew how to pick
her support i would like
to see any of these modern
theatre cats play the owl s eyes
to modjeska s lady macbeth
but they haven t got it nowadays
they haven t got it
here

mehitabel he says
both our professions
are being ruined
by amateurs

archy

THE CRITICS AT WORK

America today is a paradise for critics, there is so much work to be done. Everything which is created in this country immediately becomes the subject of a critical report. Music, books, plays, movies, art—these must all be analyzed, praised, and damned, in the press; also women's underclothes, wines, architecture, sports, wall papers, motor cars—dozens of things. The accepted American journalistic practice is to present a critical estimate of a work of art five or ten minutes after it has been completed, before the paint is dry on the canvas, before the last act curtain has descended. In the Nineteenth Century the critics believed that a work of art should age for a few days, or years, before being passed upon. For this section of our book we have hunted up reviews for which it seemed likely the critic had had at least twenty-four hours to prepare himself before pronouncing a verdict.

Humor is a handy tool on a critic's workbench. The truth is, almost every good humorist is a critic of sorts. A knave like Ogden Nash, who is classified as poet and wit, is certainly at heart a critic, who attends life's every opening night; and Mark Twain apparently never had more fun than when he was taking something or somebody apart.

As well as giving you reviews in this section we have

thrown in Alexander Woollcott's own subtreasury of criticism—an essay in which he has collected some of his favorite critical bon mots and left jabs to the heart. Benchley's critical article on the French newspapers, "La Presse Perverse," tickled us when we read it over, even though to read it in these times is a melancholy pleasure. We are putting it in the book confident that the newspapers of France will some day again be free and, to a visiting American, full of wonder.

Mark Twain

FENIMORE COOPER'S LITERARY OFFENSES

The Pathfinder and *The Deerslayer* stand at the head of Cooper's novels
s artistic creations. There are others of his works which contain parts as
erfect as are to be found in these, and scenes even more thrilling. Not one
an be compared with either of them as a finished whole.
The defects in both of these tales are comparatively slight. They were
ure works of art.—*Prof. Lounsbury.*
The five tales reveal an extraordinary fullness of invention.
. . . One of the very greatest characters in fiction, Natty Bumppo. . . .
The craft of the woodsman, the tricks of the trapper, all the delicate art
f the forest, were familiar to Cooper from his youth up.—*Prof. Brander
Matthews.*
Cooper is the greatest artist in the domain of romantic fiction yet pro-
uced by America.—*Wilkie Collins.*

It seems to me that it was far from right for the Professor of English
Literature in Yale, the Professor of English Literature in Columbia,
nd Wilkie Collins to deliver opinions on Cooper's literature without
aving read some of it. It would have been much more decorous to
eep silent and let persons talk who have read Cooper.

Cooper's art has some defects. In one place in *Deerslayer,* and in the
estricted space of two-thirds of a page, Cooper has scored 114 offenses
gainst literary art out of a possible 115. It breaks the record.

There are nineteen rules governing literary art in the domain of
omantic fiction—some say twenty-two. In *Deerslayer* Cooper violated
ighteen of them. These eighteen require:

1. That a tale shall accomplish something and arrive somewhere.
But the *Deerslayer* tale accomplishes nothing and arrives in the air.

2. They require that the episodes of a tale shall be necessary parts
f the tale, and shall help to develop it. But as the *Deerslayer* tale is
ot a tale, and accomplishes nothing and arrives nowhere, the episodes
ave no rightful place in the work, since there was nothing for them
o develop.

3. They require that the personages in a tale shall be alive, excep in the case of corpses, and that always the reader shall be able to te the corpses from the others. But this detail has often been overlooke in the *Deerslayer* tale.

4. They require that the personages in a tale, both dead and aliv shall exhibit a sufficient excuse for being there. But this detail also ha been overlooked in the *Deerslayer* tale.

5. They require that when the personages of a tale deal in conversa tion, the talk shall sound like human talk, and be talk such as huma beings would be likely to talk in the given circumstances, and have discoverable meaning, also a discoverable purpose, and a show of rele vancy, and remain in the neighborhood of the subject in hand, and b interesting to the reader, and help out the tale, and stop when th people cannot think of anything more to say. But this requirement ha been ignored from the beginning of the *Deerslayer* tale to the end of i

6. They require that when the author describes the character of personage in his tale, the conduct and conversation of that personag shall justify said description. But this law gets little or no attentio in the *Deerslayer* tale, as Natty Bumppo's case will amply prove.

7. They require that when a personage talks like an illustrated, gilt edged, tree-calf, hand-tooled, seven-dollar Friendship's Offering in th beginning of a paragraph, he shall not talk like a negro minstrel in th end of it. But this rule is flung down and danced upon in the *Deer slayer* tale.

8. They require that crass stupidities shall not be played upon th reader as "the craft of the woodsman, the delicate art of the forest," b either the author or the people in the tale. But this rule is persistentl violated in the *Deerslayer* tale.

9. They require that the personages of a tale shall confine themselve to possibilities and let miracles alone; or, if they venture a miracle, th author must so plausibly set it forth as to make it look possible an reasonable. But these rules are not respected in the *Deerslayer* tale.

10. They require that the author shall make the reader feel a deep interest in the personages of his tale and in their fate; and that he sha make the reader love the good people in the tale and hate the bac ones. But the reader of the *Deerslayer* tale dislikes the good people in it is indifferent to the others, and wishes they would all get drowne together.

11. They require that the characters in a tale shall be so clearly de

fined that the reader can tell beforehand what each will do in a given emergency. But in the *Deerslayer* tale this rule is vacated.

In addition to these large rules there are some little ones. These require that the author shall

12. *Say* what he is proposing to say, not merely come near it.

13. Use the right word, not its second cousin.

14. Eschew surplusage.

15. Not omit necessary details.

16. Avoid slovenliness of form.

17. Use good grammar.

18. Employ a simple and straightforward style.

Even these seven are coldly and persistently violated in the *Deerslayer* tale.

Cooper's gift in the way of invention was not a rich endowment; but such as it was he liked to work it, he was pleased with the effects, and indeed he did some quite sweet things with it. In his little box of stage-properties he kept six or eight cunning devices, tricks, artifices for his savages and woodsmen to deceive and circumvent each other with, and he was never so happy as when he was working these innocent things and seeing them go. A favorite one was to make a moccasined person tread in the tracks of the moccasined enemy, and thus hide his own trail. Cooper wore out barrels and barrels of moccasins in working that trick. Another stage-property that he pulled out of his box pretty frequently was his broken twig. He prized his broken twig above all the rest of his effects, and worked it the hardest. It is a restful chapter in any book of his when somebody doesn't step on a dry twig and alarm all the reds and whites for two hundred yards around. Every time a Cooper person is in peril, and absolute silence is worth four dollars a minute, he is sure to step on a dry twig. There may be a hundred handier things to step on, but that wouldn't satisfy Cooper. Cooper requires him to turn out and find a dry twig; and if he can't do it, go and borrow one. In fact, the Leatherstocking Series ought to have been called the Broken Twig Series.

I am sorry there is not room to put in a few dozen instances of the delicate art of the forest, as practised by Natty Bumppo and some of the other Cooperian experts. Perhaps we may venture two or three samples. Cooper was a sailor—a naval officer; yet he gravely tells us how a vessel, driving toward a lee shore in a gale, is steered for a particular spot by her skipper because he knows of an *undertow* there which will hold her back against the gale and save her. For just pure woodcraft, or sailorcraft, or whatever it is, isn't that neat? For several years Cooper was daily in the society of artillery, and he ought to have noticed that when a cannon-ball strikes the ground it either buries itself or skips a hundred feet or so; skips again a hundred feet or so—and so on, till finally it gets tired and rolls. Now in one place he loses some "females"—as he always calls women—in the edge of a wood near a plain at night in a fog, on purpose to give Bumppo a chance to show off the delicate art of the forest before the reader. These mislaid people are hunting for a fort. They hear a cannon-blast, and a cannon-ball presently comes rolling into the wood and stops at their feet. To the females this suggests nothing. The case is very different with the admirable Bumppo. I wish I may never know peace again if he doesn't strike out promptly and *follow the track* of that cannon-ball across the plain through the dense fog and find the fort. Isn't it a daisy? If Cooper had any real knowledge of Nature's way of doing things, he had a most delicate art in concealing the fact. For instance: one of his acute Indian experts, Chingachgook (pronounced Chicago, I think), has lost the trail of a person he is tracking through the forest. Apparently that trail is hopelessly lost. Neither you nor I could ever have guessed out the way to find it. It was very different with Chicago. Chicago was not stumped for long. He turned a running stream out of its course, and there, in the slush in its old bed, were that person's moccasin tracks. The current did not wash them away, as it would have done in all other like cases—no, even the eternal laws of Nature have to vacate when Cooper wants to put up a delicate job of woodcraft on the reader.

We must be a little wary when Brander Matthews tells us that Cooper's books "reveal an extraordinary fullness of invention." As a rule, I am quite willing to accept Brander Matthews's literary judgments and applaud his lucid and graceful phrasing of them; but that particular statement needs to be taken with a few tons of salt. Bless your heart, Cooper hadn't any more invention than a horse; and I don't mean a high-class horse, either; I mean a clothes-horse. It would be very difficult to find a really clever "situation" in Cooper's books, and still more difficult to find one of any kind which he has failed to render absurd by his handling of it. Look at the episodes of "the caves"; and at the celebrated scuffle between Maqua and those others on the table-land a few days later; and at Hurry Harry's queer water-transit from the castle to the ark; and at Deerslayer's half-hour with his first corpse; and at the quarrel between Hurry Harry and Deerslayer later; and at—but choose for yourself; you can't go amiss.

If Cooper had been an observer his inventive faculty would have worked better; not more interestingly, but more rationally, more plausibly. Cooper's proudest creations in the way of "situations" suffer noticeably from the absence of the observer's protecting gift. Cooper's eye was splendidly inaccurate. Cooper seldom saw anything correctly. He saw nearly all things as through a glass eye, darkly. Of course a man who cannot see the commonest little every-day matters accurately is working at a disadvantage when he is constructing a "situation." In the *Deerslayer* tale Cooper has a stream which is fifty feet wide where it flows out of a lake; it presently narrows to twenty as it meanders along for no given reason, and yet when a stream acts like that it ought to be required to explain itself. Fourteen pages later the width of the brook's outlet from the lake has suddenly shrunk thirty feet, and become "the narrowest part of the stream." This shrinkage is not accounted for. The stream has bends in it, a sure indication that it has alluvial banks and cuts them; yet these bends are only thirty and fifty feet long. If Cooper had been a nice and punctilious observer he would have noticed that the bends were oftener nine hundred feet long than short of it.

Cooper made the exit of that stream fifty feet wide, in the first place, for no particular reason; in the second place, he narrowed it to less than twenty to accommodate some Indians. He bends a "sapling" to the form of an arch over this narrow passage, and conceals six Indians in its foliage. They are "laying" for a settler's scow or ark which is coming up the stream on its way to the lake; it is being hauled against the stiff current by a rope whose stationary end is anchored in the lake; its rate of progress cannot be more than a mile an hour. Cooper describes the ark, but pretty obscurely. In the matter of dimensions "it was little more than a modern canal-boat." Let us guess, then, that it was about one hundred and forty feet long. It was of "greater breadth than common." Let us guess, then, that it was about sixteen feet wide. This leviathan had been prowling down bends which were but a third as long as itself, and scraping between banks where it had only two feet of space to spare on each side. We cannot too much admire this miracle. A low-roofed log dwelling occupies "two-thirds of the ark's length"—a dwelling ninety feet long and sixteen feet wide, let us say—a kind of vestibule train. The dwelling has two rooms— each forty-five feet long and sixteen feet wide, let us guess. One of them is the bedroom of the Hutter girls, Judith and Hetty; the other is the parlor in the daytime, at night it is papa's bedchamber. The ark is arriving at the stream's exit now, whose width has been reduced to less than twenty feet to accommodate the Indians—say to eighteen. There is a foot to spare on each side of the boat. Did the Indians notice that there was going to be a tight squeeze there? Did they notice that they could make money by climbing out of that arched sapling and just stepping aboard when the ark scraped by? No, other Indians would have noticed these things, but Cooper's Indians never notice anything. Cooper thinks they are marvelous creatures for noticing, but he was almost always in error about his Indians. There was seldom a sane one among them.

The ark is one hundred and forty-feet long; the dwelling is ninety feet long. The idea of the Indians is to drop softly and secretly from the arched sapling to the dwelling as the ark creeps along under it at the rate of a mile an hour, and butcher the family. It will take the ark a minute and a half to pass under. It will take the ninety-foot dwelling a minute to pass under. Now, then, what did the six Indians do? It would take you thirty years to guess, and even then you would have to give it up, I believe. Therefore, I will tell you what the Indians did. Their chief, a person of quite extraordinary intellect for a Cooper Indian, warily watched the canal-boat as it squeezed along under him, and when he had got his calculations fined down to exactly the right shade, as he judged, he let go and dropped. And *missed the house!* That is actually what he did. He missed the house, and landed in the stern of the scow. It was not much of a fall, yet it knocked him silly. He lay there unconscious. If the house had been ninety-seven feet long he would have made the trip. The fault was Cooper's, not his. The error lay in the construction of the house. Cooper was no architect.

There still remained in the roost five Indians. The boat has passed under and is now out of their reach. Let me explain what the five did —you would not be able to reason it out for yourself. No. 1 jumped for the boat, but fell in the water astern of it. Then No. 2 jumped for the boat, but fell in the water still farther astern of it. Then No. 3 jumped for the boat, and fell a good way astern of it. Then No. 4 jumped for the boat, and fell in the water *away* astern. Then even No. 5 made a jump for the boat—for he was a Cooper Indian. In the matter of intellect, the difference between a Cooper Indian and the Indian that stands in front of the cigar-shop is not spacious. The scow episode is really a sublime burst of invention; but it does not thrill, because the inaccuracy of the details throws a sort of air of fictitiousness and general improbability over it. This comes of Cooper's inadequacy as an observer.

The reader will find some examples of Cooper's high talent for inaccurate observation in the account of the shooting-match in *The Pathfinder*.

A common wrought nail was driven lightly into the target, its head having been first touched with paint.

The color of the paint is not stated—an important omission, but Cooper deals freely in important omissions. No, after all, it was not an important omission; for this nail-head is *a hundred yards from* the marksmen, and could not be seen by them at that distance, no matter what its color might be. How far can the best eyes see a common house-fly? A hundred yards? It is quite impossible. Very well; eyes that cannot see a house-fly that is a hundred yards away cannot see an ordinary nail-head at that distance, for the size of the two objects is the same. It takes a keen eye to see a fly or a nail-head at fifty yards—one hundred and fifty feet. Can the reader do it?

The nail was lightly driven, its head painted, and game called. Then the Cooper miracles began. The bullet of the first marksman chipped an edge of the nail-head; the next man's bullet drove the nail a little way into the target—and removed all the paint. Haven't the miracles gone far enough now? Not to suit Cooper; for the purpose of this whole scheme is to show off his prodigy, Deerslayer-Hawkeye-Long-Rifle-Leatherstocking-Pathfinder-Bumppo before the ladies.

"Be all ready to clench it, boys!" cried out Pathfinder, stepping into his friend's tracks the instant they were vacant. "Never mind a new nail; I can see that, though the paint is gone, and what I can see I can hit at a hundred yards, though it were only a mosquito's eye. Be ready to clench!"
The rifle cracked, the bullet sped its way, and the head of the nail was buried in the wood, covered by the piece of flattened lead.

There, you see, is a man who could hunt flies with a rifle, and command a ducal salary in a Wild West show to-day if we had him back with us.

The recorded feat is certainly surprising just as it stands; but it is not

surprising enough for Cooper. Cooper adds a touch. He has made
Pathfinder do this miracle with another man's rifle; and not only that,
but Pathfinder did not have even the advantage of loading it himself.
He had everything against him, and yet he made that impossible shot;
and not only made it, but did it with absolute confidence, saying, "Be
ready to clench." Now a person like that would have undertaken that
same feat with a brickbat, and with Cooper to help he would have
achieved it, too.

Pathfinder showed off handsomely that day before the ladies. His
very first feat was a thing which no Wild West show can touch. He
was standing with the group of marksmen, observing—a hundred
yards from the target, mind; one Jasper raised his rifle and drove
the center of the bull's-eye. Then the Quartermaster fired. The target
exhibited no result this time. There was a laugh. "It's a dead miss,"
said Major Lundie. Pathfinder waited an impressive moment or two;
then said, in that calm, indifferent, know-it-all way of his, "No, Major,
he has covered Jasper's bullet, as will be seen if any one will take the
trouble to examine the target."

Wasn't it remarkable! How *could* he see that little pellet fly through
the air and enter that distant bullet-hole? Yet that is what he did; for
nothing is impossible to a Cooper person. Did any of those people have
any deep-seated doubts about this thing? No; for that would imply
sanity, and these were all Cooper people.

The respect for Pathfinder's skill and for his *quickness and accuracy of
sight* [the italics are mine] was so profound and general, that the instant
he made this declaration the spectators began to distrust their own opinions, and a dozen rushed to the target in order to ascertain the fact. There,
sure enough, it was found that the Quartermaster's bullet had gone through
the hole made by Jasper's, and that, too, so accurately as to require a
minute examination to be certain of the circumstance, which, however, was
soon clearly established by discovering one bullet over the other in the
stump against which the target was placed.

They made a "minute" examination; but never mind, how could
they know that there were two bullets in that hole without digging
the latest one out? for neither probe nor eyesight could prove the
presence of any more than one bullet. Did they dig? No; as we shall
see. It is the Pathfinder's turn now; he steps out before the ladies,
takes aim, and fires.

But, alas! here is a disappointment; an incredible, an unimaginable disappointment—for the target's aspect is unchanged; there is nothing there but that same old bullet-hole!

"If one dared to hint at such a thing," cried Major Duncan, "I should say that the Pathfinder has also missed the target!"

As nobody had missed it yet, the "also" was not necessary; but never mind about that, for the Pathfinder is going to speak.

"No, no, Major," said he, confidently, "that *would* be a risky declaration. I didn't load the piece, and can't say what was in it; but if it was lead, you will find the bullet driving down those of the Quartermaster and Jasper, else is not my name Pathfinder."
A shout from the target announced the truth of this assertion.

Is the miracle sufficient as it stands? Not for Cooper. The Pathfinder speaks again, as he "now slowly advances toward the stage occupied by the females":

"That's not all, boys, that's not all; if you find the target touched at all, I'll own to a miss. The Quartermaster cut the wood, but you'll find no wood cut by that last messenger."

The miracle is at last complete. He knew—doubtless *saw*—at the distance of a hundred yards—that his bullet had passed into the hole *without fraying the edges*. There were now three bullets in that one hole—three bullets embedded processionally in the body of the stump back of the target. Everybody knew this—somehow or other—and yet nobody had dug any of them out to make sure. Cooper is not a close observer, but he is interesting. He is certainly always that, no matter what happens. And he is more interesting when he is not noticing what he is about than when he is. This is a considerable merit.

The conversations in the Cooper books have a curious sound in our modern ears. To believe that such talk really ever came out of people's mouths would be to believe that there was a time when time was of no value to a person who thought he had something to say; when it was the custom to spread a two-minute remark out to ten; when a man's mouth was a rolling-mill, and busied itself all day long in turning four-foot pigs of thought into thirty-foot bars of conversational railroad iron by attenuation; when subjects were seldom faithfully stuck to, but the talk wandered all around and arrived nowhere; when conversations consisted mainly of irrelevancies, with here and there a relevancy, a relevancy with an embarrassed look, as not being able to explain how it got there.

Cooper was certainly not a master in the construction of dialogue. Inaccurate observation defeated him here as it defeated him in so many other enterprises of his. He even failed to notice that the man who talks corrupt English six days in the week must and will talk it on the seventh, and can't help himself. In the *Deerslayer* story he lets Deerslayer talk the showiest kind of book-talk sometimes, and at other times the basest of base dialects. For instance, when some one asks him if he has a sweetheart, and if so, where she abides, this is his majestic answer:

"She's in the forest—hanging from the boughs of the trees, in a soft rain—in the dew on the open grass—the clouds that float about in the blue heavens—the birds that sing in the woods—the sweet springs where I slake my thirst—and in all the other glorious gifts that come from God's Providence!"

And he preceded that, a little before, with this:

"It consarns me as all things that touches a fri'nd consarns a fri'nd."

And this is another of his remarks:

"If I was Injin born, now, I might tell of this, or carry in the scalp and boast of the expl'ite afore the whole tribe; or if my inimy had only been a bear"—[and so on].

We cannot imagine such a thing as a veteran Scotch Commander-in-Chief comporting himself in the field like a windy melodramatic actor, but Cooper could. On one occasion Alice and Cora were being chased by the French through a fog in the neighborhood of their father's fort:

"Point de quartier aux coquins!" cried an eager pursuer, who seemed to direct the operations of the enemy.
"Stand firm and be ready, my gallant 6oths!" suddenly exclaimed a voice above them; "wait to see the enemy; fire low, and sweep the glacis."
"Father, father!" exclaimed a piercing cry from out of the mist; "it is I! Alice! thy own Elsie! spare, O! save your daughters!"
"Hold!" shouted the former speaker, in the awful tones of parental agony, the sound reaching even to the woods, and rolling back in solemn echo. " 'Tis she! God has restored me my children! Throw open the sally-port; to the field, 6oths, to the field! pull not a trigger, lest ye kill my lambs! Drive off these dogs of France with your steel!"

Cooper's word-sense was singularly dull. When a person has a poor ear for music he will flat and sharp right along without knowing it. He keeps near the tune, but it is *not* the tune. When a person has a poor ear for words, the result is a literary flatting and sharping; you perceive what he is intending to say, but you also perceive that he doesn't *say* it. This is Cooper. He was not a word-musician. His ear was satisfied with the *approximate* word. I will furnish some circumstantial evidence in support of this charge. My instances are gathered from half a dozen pages of the tale called *Deerslayer*. He uses "verbal" for "oral"; "precision" for "facility"; "phenomena" for "marvels"; necessary" for "predetermined"; "unsophisticated" for "primitive"; "preparation" for "expectancy"; "rebuked" for "subdued"; "dependent on" for "resulting from"; "fact" for "condition"; "fact" for "conjecture"; "precaution" for "caution"; "explain" for "determine"; "mortified" for "disappointed"; "meretricious" for "factitious"; "materially" for "considerably"; "decreasing" for "deepening"; "increasing" for "disappearing"; "embedded" for "inclosed"; "treacherous" for "hostile"; "stood" for "stooped"; "softened" for "replaced"; "rejoined" for "remarked"; "situation" for "condition"; "different" for "differing"; "insensible" for "unsentient"; "brevity" for "celerity"; "distrusted" for "suspicious"; "mental imbecility" for "imbecility"; "eyes" for "sight"; "counteracting" for "opposing"; "funeral obsequies" for "obsequies."

There have been daring people in the world who claimed that Cooper could write English, but they are all dead now—all dead but Lounsbury. I don't remember that Lounsbury makes the claim in so many words, still he makes it, for he says that *Deerslayer* is a "pure work of art." Pure, in that connection, means faultless—faultless in all details—and language is a detail. If Mr. Lounsbury had only compared Cooper's English with the English which he writes himself—but it is plain that he didn't; and so it is likely that he imagines until this day that Cooper's is as clean and compact as his own. Now I feel sure, deep down in my heart, that Cooper wrote about the poorest English that exists in our language, and that the English of *Deerslayer* is the very worst that even Cooper ever wrote.

I may be mistaken, but it does seem to me that *Deerslayer* is not a work of art in any sense; it does seem to me that it is destitute of every detail that goes to the making of a work of art; in truth, it seems to me that *Deerslayer* is just simply a literary *delirium tremens*.

A work of art? It has no invention; it has no order, system, sequence, or result; it has no life-likeness, no thrill, no stir, no seeming of reality; its characters are confusedly drawn, and by their acts and words they prove that they are not the sort of people the author claims that they are; its humor is pathetic; its pathos is funny; its conversations are—oh! indescribable; its love-scenes odious; its English a crime against the language.

Counting these out, what is left is Art. I think we must all admit that.

Ogden Nash

LET'S STAY HOME AND MAKE FRIENDS

May I give you a one-word comment on the average revue?
Pew!
Goodness sakes, couldn't they be a little less anatomical
And a little more comical?
Couldn't they have a few more jests
And a few less breasts?
Must they consist of nothing but scenes such as may be observed at
    the Zoo in the monkey- or yak-house,
And revelry suggestive less of Bacchus than the backhouse?
Must all their skits on l'amour
Be fished from the sour?
Can the producers think of no subtler way of easing themselves into
    Isottas and their girl-friends into sables
Than by luring a lot of people to pay a lot of money to look at a lot
    of other peoples' nabels?
The undersigned obviously stands in strong need of a physic
If he is expected to find the above mentioned an aphrodysic.
Not that he proposes that all of our spectacular extravaganzas
Should be of the type that could be legally presented in Wichita,
    Kansas;
Not that he insists that the female form should be fenced off as some-
    thing of unmentionable sacredness;
Only that he believes that a bare finger in private is fraught with more
    significance than any amount of public nacredness.

Alexander Woollcott

"MANHATTAN"

From time to time it is acrimoniously argued that the reviewers ought not measure the passing plays by their own perverse and epicurean taste nor commit themselves by applying any adjectives whatever—such as hilarious, febrile, dainty, narcotic, repulsive or the like—to the new piece of the night before. As a matter of fact, while much would be lost, something might be gained by barring adjectival indulgence from journalistic criticism, like firmly telling the cook that there must be no more thickening in the soup. One of the scribes, for instance, rather induced the impression that every new play was worth seeing the first six months after his first encounter with the word "intriguing" and the remote Louis Sherwin (before he shut his eyes, held his nose and jumped into the movies) was so abjectly devoted to the word "jejune" that he would lick it and paste it on every new play whether it was in the least jejune or not.

However, as we understand the contention, the desideratum is a severe, impersonal description of the play. Now it is quite impossible to accomplish that in terms of the first-night reception. If a first-nighter is pleased and entertained, he beats his palms together and laughs till he almost falls into the aisle. But watch him when he is bored. Then he beats his palms together and laughs till he almost falls into the aisle. So one is driven relentlessly back to bare description of the play's contents, its fabric, its design—in short, its plot.

Let us then consider the plot of the piece called "Manhattan," which launched one season at the Playhouse. The curtain rises on the library of the Van Norman home in Park Avenue. (It has been several years now since any dramatist has sheltered his more elegant characters on Riverside Drive or on Fifth or Madison Avenue. Only Clare Kummer —ever a bit wild and puckish in her fancy—has had the pioneer spirit to break from this tradition. Once, only once—it was in "The Robbery"—she went so far as to set the scene *in a cross street.* However, in most plays all the best people live on Park Avenue.)

Well, the aforesaid rising curtain reveals *Duncan Van Norman* busy writing an essay for *The Atlantic Monthly.* He is doing this in a snuggery so conveniently close to the front door that the butler has scarce disappeared in response to the door-bell when the room is a-swarm with laughing society folk, all eager to drag him off to some gayety. The *Van Normans,* as far as the play reveals, are a family of three—widowed mother, son and daughter. They have two bookcases and a butler. When *Miss Van Norman* has a burst of confidence, she does not skip up the plebeian stairs to her mother's boudoir and begin: "Mom, *what* do you think has happened?" Not she. Instead she rings for the butler and says: *"Paget,* tell my mother I wish to see her in the library and talk to her about something I want the audience to overhear." No, come to think of it, the last part of that sentence isn't actually spoken.

Well, *Duncan* isn't in the best of health. This is evidenced by his announcing that he does not care for any dinner beyond a biscuit and a glass of port—a dietetic arrangement which the authors in some way subtly associate with his writings for *The Atlantic.* However, both manifestations worry his gaudy old mother, who tries to persuade him that it is high time for him to go forth and cut up a bit. The same advice is then echoed by the family lawyer, who sends him a pretty little typist with the suggestion that he might seduce her, and, presumably, thereby become a contributor to *The Saturday Evening Post.* The typist arrives. She proves to be young, personable, poor. She is *Peg-o-My-Heart* all over again and again and again. She lacks the brogue and the red hair and Michael, to be sure, but she says "Gee" quite often; she is fond of poetry and she is so hard up that she agrees to copy "The Fourth Dimension in Ethics" for *The Atlantic.*

She copies it in a wretched little garret room south of Greenwich Village, which she shares with an Irish miss. This colleen is the good-natured kind who gives all her dinner to the poor starving girl next door. One gathers from the chit-chat of these three that a poor working-girl in New York has only to say the word—the word is "Yes" —to have sables and limousines galore. Indeed, one of their little circle appears to have said "Yes" recently, and they are all speculating on her happiness and wondering whether it was worth the price. There is some difference of opinion. Enter *Duncan Van Norman.* His arrival at this lowly spot might take the unsophisticated unawares, but the canny first-nighter knows full well that no manager, who has worked himself up to the point of paying Norman Trevor's salary, would ever allow an act to slip by without using him. Metaphorically speaking, *Duncan* has come in with a sable coat in one hand and a limousine in the other. He also mentions art, music, travel. He is spurned by the typist, who, however, does get five hundred dollars out of him for the poor starving girl next door and does consent to become his secretary.

The next act sees her thus installed in Park Avenue, where she takes hints from *Paget* and reads assiduously in *The Book of Etiquette,* all in an effort to "become a lady." Indeed, how she ever escaped from a novel by Frances Hodgson Burnett is one of the mysteries of modern letters. Well, naturally, you can imagine the talk caused in what the *Van Normans* call either "our world" or "the circle in which we move," when it is bruited up and down Park Avenue that *Duncan Van Norman* has a female secretary who comes right to his library every day and does his typing. There is so much scandal that *Duncan* offers marriage on the spot, which, despite his mother's efforts to buy the girl off, might settle matters and obviate the necessity of a last act, when in rushes that old family lawyer again, this time not to suggest that *Duncan* seduce some one else, but with the news that the little typist has just that moment inherited $450,000 of South African real estate. Of course, *Duncan* is horribly embarrassed by that, but she lands him at last by the expedient of locking herself in a room with him and throwing the key out the window.

And there you are. Though why "Manhattan"? To be sure, the scenes are *not* in Tallahassee, but then on that principle "Hamlet" might as well be called "Denmark" and "The First Year" might as well have been renamed "Redding, Illinois, and Joplin, Missouri." Why "Manhattan," do you suppose? Let's see. It's the name of an island and of a borough and of a transfer and of a cocktail and—oh, yes—of a storehouse.

CAPSULE CRITICISM

There is a popular notion that a dramatic criticism, to be worthy of the name, must be an article of at least one thousand words, mostly polysyllables and all devoted—perfectly devoted—to the grave discussion of some play as written and performed. To this notion, it must be sadly admitted, each generation of writers on the theater has lent some color.

In such an article it is presumed that there will be one judicious use of the word "adequate" and one resort to the expression "treading the boards"; also at least one regretful shaking of the head over the hopeless inferiority of the performance in question to (a) the way it was done in some other country two years before or (b) the way it would have been done in the critic's own country thirty years ago. Such ingredients are expected with reasonable confidence. But one thing is certain. The piece, to be real dramatic criticism, can scarcely be briefer than a thousand words.

The tradition of prolixity and the dullness in all such writing is as old as Aristotle and as lasting as William Archer. A man who will talk gaily of a play will yet feel a certain solemnity wetting down his spirits the moment he finds himself called upon to discuss it in print. Even Mr. Dickens, who could take his beloved theater lightly enough when he was weaving it into a novel and who always packed his letters full of the most engaging accounts of the farces and melodramas he was seeing, became rigid with self-importance and chill with scrupulosity the moment he knew he was reviewing a piece for publication. If he had undertaken to supply such comment to *The Examiner* or to our own *Atlantic,* a voice within him seemed to whisper, "Remember, now, you're a dramatic critic." And, lo! he was no more Dickensy than the merest penny-a-liner. This was true to some extent of Walt Whitman and certainly was true of Edgar Allan Poe. (The strangest people, it will be observed, have put in some time as dramatic critics; such people, for instance, as Eugene Field and Richard Harding Davis and Edward Bok and Elihu Root). Probably they were all verbose.

Yet I suspect it could be demonstrated that the most telling of all dramatic criticisms have found expression in less than fifty words. Also that the best of all were never written at all. To substantiate this, I have been raking my memory for the ones that have lodged there while longer and more majestical utterances have faded out of mind as completely as though they had never been written.

What we are looking for, of course, is the happy sentence that speaks volumes. As an example, consider the familiar problem presented by the players who can do everything on the stage except act. I have in mind a still celebrated beauty to whom that beauty opened wide the stage-door full thirty years ago. Since then she has devoted herself most painstakingly to justifying her admission. She has keen intelligence and great industry. She has learned every trick of voice and gesture that can be taught. She has acquired everything except some substitute for the inborn gift. Something to that effect, expressed, of course, as considerately as possible, ought, it seems to me, to be a part of any report on her spasmodic reappearances.

It usually takes about five hundred words. Yet Mr. Cohan managed it pretty well in a single sentence when he was passing on a similar case in one of his own companies. An attempt was made to argue with him that the veteran actor under review was a good fellow and all that. "He's a fine fellow, all right," Cohan assented amiably enough, and then added, with murderous good humor, "There's really only one thing I've got against him. He's stage-struck."

You see, often the perfection of these capsule criticisms are achieved by mere bluntness—are arrived at by the no more ingenious process than that of speaking out in meeting. I was struck with that on the melancholy occasion when John and Ethel Barrymore lent a momentary and delusive glamour to a piece called "Clair de Lune" by Michael Strange, the exquisitely beautiful poetess whom Mr. Barrymore had just married. By the time its third act had unfolded before the pained eyes of its first audience, there was probably not a single person in that audience who was not thinking that, with all the good plays lying voiceless on the shelf, Michael Strange's shambling and laboriously *macabre* piece would scarcely have been produced had it not been for the somewhat irrelevant circumstance of her having married Mr. Barrymore, the surest means, apparently, of engaging his priceless services for one's drama. Now, some such opinion, I say, was buzzing in every first-night head. All the critics thought just that. Yet they all described nervous circles around this central idea, dancing skittishly about it as though it had been a May-pole. Full of what Gladys Unger was once inspired to call "a dirty delicacy," reluctant, perhaps, to acknowledge the personal equation in criticism, and weighed down, probably, by an ancient respect for the marriage tie, they avoided all audible speculation as to why Mr. Barrymore had put the piece on at all. All, that is, except one. Mr. Whittaker of *The Chicago Tribune* —the same Mr. Whittaker, by the way, who married the fair Ina

Claire—cheerfully put the prevailing thought into three devastating
words. He entitled his review: "For the Love of Mike."

That is not the only time I have seen the very essence and spirit
of a review distilled in a single head-line. It happened on the occasion
when the late Sir Herbert Tree, ever and always recognizable behind
the most ornate make-ups, ever and always himself through all faint-
hearted efforts at disguise, appeared for the first time in London in
"The Merchant of Venice." It was on that occasion that his more illustrious brother, Max Beerbohm, then merely the dramatic critic of
The Saturday Review, went back-stage to felicitate the star but was
overlooked in the crush of notables who were crowding around. When
Tree chided him afterwards for unfraternal neglect, Max murmured:
"Ah, I was there but you did not know me in your beard." Of course
Max could not write the review of his own brother's performance—a
task delegated, therefore, to John Palmer, whose comment on the play
was awaited, naturally enough, with considerable interest. Palmer
wrote a polite, though mildly derisive, review of the production and
entitled it: "Shylock as Mr. Tree."

I find that the crispest reviews which come back in this effort at
memory have taken many forms. For instance, when it was quite
the leading American sin to attend the agitating performances of
"Sapho" by Olga Nethersole, Franklin P. Adams made his comment in
one quatrain:

> I love little Olga,
> Her plays are so warm.
> And if I don't see them
> They'll do me no harm.

The late Charles Frohman, on the other hand, was likely to sum
up plays most felicitously in telegrams. Once, when he was producing
an English comedy at his cherished Empire Theater in New York,
he received just after the première a cable of eager, though decently
nervous, inquiry from the author in London, who could not bear to
wait until the reviews and the box-office statements reached him.
"How's it going?" was the inquiry. Frohman cabled back: "It's gone."

Of course, many of the best capsule criticisms are classics. There was
Warren's tart comment on Joe Jefferson's performance as *Bob Acres*
in "The Rivals," a brilliant feat of comedic genius made out of whole
cloth, so little origin did it have in the rôle as originally written. "Ha!"

quoth Warren, "Sheridan twenty miles away." And there was the
feline stroke usually ascribed to Wilde—the one which said that Tree's
Hamlet was funny without being vulgar. And there was the much-
quoted knifing of still another *Hamlet* by an unidentified bandit who
said, after the performance, that it would have been a fine time to
settle the great controversy as to who wrote the play: one need merely
have watched beside the graves of Shakespere and Bacon to see which
one turned over.

Fairly familiar, also, are two ascribed by tradition to Eugene Field,
in the days when he was dramatic critic of "The Denver Post" and
used to go to the once-famous Tabor Grand to see "Modjesky ez
Cameel," the days when the peak of the season for him was marked
by the engagement of a vagrant, red-headed soubrette named Minnie
Maddern. Of one performance of "Hamlet" there, Field's entire review consisted of two short melancholy sentences. He wrote: "So-and-
so played Hamlet last night at the Tabor Grand. He played it till
one o'clock." And it was Field who haunted the declining years of
Creston Clarke with his review of that actor's *Lear*. Clarke, a journey-
ing nephew of Edwin Booth, passed through Denver and gave there a
singularly unimpressive and unregal performance in that towering
tragedy. Field couldn't bear it and finally vented his emotions in one
sentence. Said he: "Mr. Clarke played the King all evening as though
under constant fear that some one else was about to play the Ace."

Of course some beautiful capsule criticisms are doomed to a lesser
fame because it is so difficult to detach them from their circumstances
and their context. This is true, for instance, of several deft summaries
by Heywood Broun. When some years ago one Butler Davenport put
on a juvenilely obscene little play at his own little theater in New
York, Broun scowled and wrote, "Some one should spank young Mr.
Davenport and take away his piece of chalk." Then there was the
hilarious episode which grew out of the production for one afternoon
in the spring of 1917 of Wedekind's "Frühlingserwachen," which
Broun translated as "The Spring Offensive." In his little piece on the
subject, he mentioned casually that to his mind an actor named Stein
gave in the leading rôle the worst performance he had ever seen on
any stage. Stein sued for damages, but the court decided, after some
diverting testimony, that after all a critic was free to express his
esthetic judgment, however incompetent, or however painful it might
prove to the subject. Later it became Mr. Broun's embarrassing duty

to review another performance by the same aggrieved Stein in another play. Broun evaded the duty until the last sentence, where he could have been found murmuring, "Mr. Stein was not up to his standard."

I am inclined to think, however, that the best of the tabloid reviews have been oral. Coleridge's famous comment on Kean's *Hamlet* —that seeing it was like reading Shakspere by flashes of lightning— was said by him but written by somebody else, wasn't it? Certainly the two best of my day were oral criticisms. One was whispered in my ear by a comely young actress named Tallulah Bankhead, who was sitting incredulous before a deliberate and intentional revival of Maeterlinck's "Aglavaine and Sélysette," a monstrous piece of perfumed posturing, meaning exactly nothing. Two gifted young actresses and a considerable bit of scenery were involved, and much pretentious rumbling of voice and wafting of gesture had gone into the enterprise. Miss Bankhead, fearful, apparently, lest she be struck dead for impiety, became desperate enough to whisper, "There is less in this than meets the eye."

The other was tossed off by that delightful companon and variegated actor, Beerbohm Tree. Hurrying from California to New York, he joined at the eleventh hour the already elaborated rehearsals of "Henry VIII," into which he was to step in the familiar scarlet of *Wolsey*. He was expected to survey whatever had been accomplished by his delegates and pass judgment. He approved cheerfully enough of everything until he came to the collection of damsels that had been dragged into the theater as ladies in waiting to the queen. He looked at them in pained and prolonged dissatisfaction and then said what we have all wanted to say of the extra-women in nearly every throne-room and ball-room and school-room scene since the theater began. "Ladies," said Tree, peering at them plaintively through his monocle, "just a little more virginity, if you don't mind."

S. J. Perelman

DOWN WITH THE RESTORATION!

Does anybody here mind if I make a prediction? I haven't made a prediction since the opening night of "The Women" year before last, when I rose at the end of the third act and announced to my escort, a Miss Chicken-Licken, "The public will never take this to its bosom." Since the public has practically worn its bosom to a nubbin niggling up to "The Women," I feel that my predictions may be a straw to show the direction the wind is blowing away from. I may very well open up a cave and do business as a sort of Cumaean Sibyl in reverse. You can't tell me people would rather climb up that Aventine Hill and have a man mess around with the entrails of a lot of sacred chickens when they can come down into my nice cool cave and get a good hygienic prediction for a few cents. So just to stimulate trade and start the ball rolling, here goes my first prediction: One of these days two young people are going to stumble across a ruined farmhouse and leave it alone.... Well, what are you sitting there gaping at? You heard what I said. That's my prediction.

Honest Injun, I hate to sound crotchety, and the last thing in the world I want to do is throw the editors of all those home-making magazines like *Nook and Garden* and *The American Home-Owner* into an uproar, but the plain fact is that I've got a bellyful. For over two years now, every time I start leafing through one of those excellent periodicals, I fall afoul of another article about a couple of young people who stumble across a ruined farmhouse and remodel it on what is inelegantly termed spit and coupons. Or maybe it's the same article. I couldn't be reading the same issue over and over, could I?

All these remodelling articles are written by the remodellers themselves and never by the ruined farmer or the man who didn't get paid for the plastering, which accounts for their rather smug tone. They invariably follow the same pattern. A young couple named Mibs and Evan (and if you checked up, I'll bet they were never married at *all!*)

540

have decided to return to the land. I see Mibs as one of those girls on the short side, with stocky legs, a low-slung posterior, and an untidy bun of straw-colored hair continually unwinding on the nape of her neck. Before anyone ever heard of Salzburg, she wore a high-bodiced dress with full skirts, a sort of horrid super-dirndl with home-cooked hems that have a tendency to hang down in back. She is usually engaged in reading a book written by two unfrocked chemists which tells women how to make their own cold cream by mixing a little potash with a dram of glycerine and a few cloves. Evan is a full-haunched young man in a fuzzy woollen suit (I don't suppose there's any such thing as a fuzzy cotton suit, but you know what I mean) who is forever rubbing a briar pipe along his nose to show you the beauty of the grain. He smokes his own mixture of perique, Latakia, and Imperial Cube Cut, for the very good reason that nobody else will smoke it, and he has probably read more of Arthur Machen than any man alive.

Well, as I say, your average remodelling yarn begins with Mibs and Evan stumbling across the most adorable ruin of an eighteenth-century farmhouse. It doesn't *have* to be a farmhouse; it can be a gristmill, or a tobacco barn, or a Mennonite schoolhouse, or—if Mibs and Evan are really lucky—an abandoned ropewalk. It can even be an early Colonial hen house, with delightful hand-hewn beams and perfectly sweet old tar paper scaling off the sides. Apparently nobody previous to Mibs and Evan has realized its possibilities, but Evan takes one look at it and says in a guarded tone, "Two hundred dollars would restore that beautifully if you didn't go crazy putting in a lot of bathrooms you didn't need." "Oh, Evan!" breathes Mibs, her eyes shining above her adenoids and her brain reeling with visions of Cape Cod spatter floors. "Dare we ... ?" That night, at dinner in the Jumble Shop, they put their heads together—Evan removes the pipe from alongside his nose, of course—and decide to jump at the chance. It involves giving up that trip to Europe, a choice the characters in these stories always have to make, but Mibs has always dreamed of a sunny garden filled with old-fashioned flowers of the type her mother used to read about in Max Schling's catalogue. So they bravely draw two hundred dollars out of their little hoard, leaving a hundred in case they ever want to take a really long trip to some place like Bali, and lay it on the line.

After considerable excitement, in which everybody searches the title like mad and Mibs discovers the quaintest old parchment deed describing their land in terms of rods, chains, and poods, they are ready to take the "Before" snapshots. Evan digs up one of the cameras used by Brady at the battle of Antietam, waits for a good cloudy-day, and focuses across a mound of guano at the most ramshackle corner of the "manse," as Mibs calls it with irreverent gaiety. The article generally carries several gray smudges captioned "Southwest corner of the house before work began," and you can't help wondering where those giant oaks came from in the "After" photographs. Maybe they sprang up from acorns dropped by the workmen while they were having lunch.

The first thing the high-hearted pair decide on is a new roof. This fortunately costs only eight dollars, as they use second-hand wattles and hire a twelve-year-old scab—all right, maybe he only mislaid his union card—to tack them on. The outside walls are a problem, but an amazing stroke of good fortune comes to their rescue. Opening a trapdoor they hadn't investigated, Mibs and Evan stumble across countless bundles of lovely old hand-split shingles which have been overlooked by previous tenants, like the hens. Two superb Adam fireplaces, hitherto concealed by some matchboarding, now make their appearance, in one of them a box of dusty but otherwise well-preserved pieces of Sandwich and Stiegel glass. "The attic!" shout Mibs and Evan simultaneously, suddenly remembering their resolution to look through it some rainy day, and sure enough, there they find a veritable treasure trove of pewter ware, cherry escritoires, Chippendale wing chairs, sawbuck tables, and Field beds, hidden away by survivors of the Deerfield massacre. "It just didn't seem *possible,*" recalls Mibs candidly, up to her old trick of taking the words out of your mouth.

And now, suddenly, the place becomes a hive of activity. A salty old character named Lafe (who is really Paul Bunyan, no matter what *Nook and Garden* says) appears and does the work of ten men at the price of one. He pulls down trees with his bare hands, lays new floors, puts up partitions, installs electricity, diverts streams, forges the ironware, bakes porcelain sinks, and all but spins silk for the draperies. How this djinn ever escaped from his bottle, and where he is now, the article neglects to mention. The upshot is that in a little over two weeks, the last hooked rug—picked up by Mibs at an auction for ten cents after spirited bidding—is in place and the early Salem kettle is singing merrily on the hob. A fat orange tabby blinks before the fire and Evan, one arm around Mibs, is adding up a column of figures. "Think of it, lover," whispers Mibs with dancing eyes. "We did the whole thing for only *fifty-one dollars and eighteen cents!*" "Less than we'll get for that article in *The American Home-Owner*," murmurs Evan exultantly, reaming the cake from his pipe. "Tell me, does oo love its 'ittle—" ... And now would you hate me if I stole out very quietly? I'm afraid there's going to be just a wee bit of baby talk.

Clifton Fadiman

GETTING GERTIE'S IDA

A rumor circulating a couple of months ago hinted that Gertrude Stein's new novel, "Ida," was really about the Duchess of Windsor. Now that I have tottered through "Ida," I find I cannot categorically deny the rumor. It is certainly as much about the Duchess of Windsor as it is about anything or anybody else. If it is not about the Duchess of Windsor, what *is* it about? Don't look at me; I'm not your man.

"Ida" is Miss Stein's first novel in eleven years. "It is presented faithfully to you," says the amiable Mr. Bennett Cerf, "by a publisher who rarely has the faintest idea of what Miss Stein is talking about, but who admires her from the bottom of his heart for her courage and for her abounding love of humanity and freedom." This statement would seem to mark an interesting departure in editorial policy. Doubtless we shall soon be reading the works of authors who cannot tell a lie, are kind to their younger brothers, or have contributed heavily to the Salvation Army.

Out of her abounding love of humanity, Miss Stein gives us an elusive creature named Ida. The story of Ida is divided, like a football game, into two halves, called, for purposes of ready reference, First Half and Second Half. The printer and binder have ingeniously arranged to make Second Half follow First Half, so quite an effect of sequence and coherence is produced. It's never made quite clear whether Ida (who dominates both halves) is on her own or whether she is twins. On page 43 we have this: "Ida decided that she was just going to talk to herself. Anybody could stand around and listen but as for her she was just going to talk to herself. She no longer even needed a twin." This seems a forthright statement, but at other points the twin situation is not as lucid as one would wish. On page 52, however, Ida is definitely not a twin. Fifty-two is my favorite page.

Ida (or her twin) has certain quirks: she is very careful about Tuesday, she always hesitates before eating, and she rests a good deal during and between marriages. I should inform you that Ida is the marrying type. Among her various husbands is a man named Frank Arthur, and why not? We do not learn much about her marital habits, but we are told that "she was always good friends with all her husbands."

This goodness of Ida's also extends to other matters. "She was kind to politics while she was in Washington very kind. She told politics that it was very nice of them to have her be kind to them." No record exists of politics' reply.

Furthermore, there is a man in the book named Philip. "Philip was the kind that said everything out loud." This sentence about Philip appears on page 40, and he is never mentioned again. Philip is my favorite character.

I have a theory about Miss Stein's novel which—give me just a second—I should like to outline for you. My notion is that Miss Stein has set herself to solve, and has succeeded in solving, the most difficult problem in prose composition—to write something that will not arrest the attention in any way, manner, shape, or form. If you think this easy, try it. I know of no one except Miss Stein who can roll out this completely non-resistant prose, prose that puts you at once in a condition resembling the early stages of grippe—the eyes and legs heavy, the top of the skull wandering around in an uncertain and independent manner, the heart ponderously, tiredly beating. Take a sentence at random: "Ida instead of going on the way she was going went back the way she had come." Repeat it slowly once or twice and you will find that your head has fallen to one side and your eyelids are a little sandy. Try this: "Ida woke up. After a while she got up. Then she stood up. Then she ate something. After that she sat down. That was Ida."

See what I mean? Sleep tight.

FAULKNER, EXTRA-SPECIAL, DOUBLE-DISTILLED

At one point in "Absalom, Absalom!" William Faulkner makes Quentin Compson, who is telling the story, say to his auditor, "You can't understand it. You would have to be born there." This seems to me not merely one (or two) of the few comprehensible sentences in the entire novel, but also beyond a doubt the truest. At any rate, it is my particular Out. Not hailing from Mississippi (which Mr.

Faulkner, in his best Greek-tragedy mood, calls "a land primed for fatality"), I figure I'm not required to understand Mr. Faulkner's novels. I should like to state, therefore, in all humility, that I do not comprehend why "Absalom, Absalom!" was written, what the non-Mississippian is supposed to get out of it, or, indeed, what it is all about. Nor do I understand why Mr. Faulkner writes the way he does. And, having gone so far, I may as well break down and state my conviction that Mr. Faulkner's latest work is the most consistently boring novel by a reputable writer to come my way during the last decade. Duty also bids me report the opinion of the publishers, who see it as his major work, "his most important and ambitious contribution to American literature."

One may sum up both substance and style by saying that every person in "Absalom, Absalom!" comes to no good end, and they all take a hell of a time coming even that far. The story runs from 1807 to 1910, with the major action concentrated between 1833, when Thomas Sutpen appears in Jefferson, Mississippi, and 1869, when he is rather regretfully murdered by an old family retainer. Thomas Sutpen is a monomaniac, known familiarly to the other characters as The Demon. It is never quite clear what makes him so villainous, except that he has a habit of engaging in gouge-as-gouge-can fights with Negroes, and has the odd power of scaring ladies first into marrying him and then into conniption fits. However, he's the fellow you're supposed to shudder at, and if you understand Mr. Faulkner, you'll shudder. If you don't, I guess you just won't. The Demon's second wife, Ellen Coldfield, gives birth to two children, Henry and Judith, goes dotty, and dies after a while. Her younger sister, Rosa, is insulted by The Demon and also goes dotty, though it takes her much longer to die. The father of Rosa and Ellen goes nuts when the Civil War arrives, nails himself up in a garret, and perseveringly starves himself to death. Now, young Henry, upon finding out that his best friend, Charles Bon, engaged to be married to his sister Judith, is (a) his half-brother and (b) part Negro, also goes dotty in a complicated way, and finally shoots Charles dead. By the end of the story Henry has been reduced to straight, simple idiocy and is kept shut up in the attic. Judith, after some years passed in a vacant-eyed trance, passes out as a result of smallpox, a death so natural as to strike a rather jarring note. There is also Clytemnestra Sutpen, daughter of Thomas Sutpen (that's dat Ole Demon Sutpen) and a Negro slave. Clytie sets fire to herself and the idiot boy Henry, and so finishes her career in a fine blaze of pyromaniacal lunacy.

Then there are the Joneses. Wash Jones is a daft hanger-on of Ole Demon Sutpen. He has a granddaughter, Milly. Milly gives birth to a child (it's the Ole Demon's handiwork), Ole Demon insults her, Wash gets sore, shoots Milly, shoots the child, cuts Ole Demon in two with a scythe, and then commits suicide. The Joneses furnish the nearest thing to comic relief in the book. Now, if you'll think back a few lunatics or so, you will remember Charles Bon, preserved from incest and miscegenation by Henry Sutpen's fraternal bullet. Charles had an octoroon mistress, name and mental condition unrecorded, by whom he engendered the boy Charles Etienne. Charles Etienne, realizing that he is a few thirty-seconds Negro, promptly runs amuck. He dies rather dully, of smallpox, but not before he has begotten, with the assistance of a full-blooded Negress, a son Jim. Jim is the real McCoy, a legitimate idiot. (I mean one specifically so called by Mr. Faulkner.) At the end of the book, he is the only living descendant of the accursed Sutpens, which shows you what can happen to a family once they have committed themselves to Mr. Faulkner's tender care.

I think I've got them all in. There's a stray lunatic aunt here and there, but I'm no stickler for details. Come to think of it, there's the young man named Quentin Compson, whose grandfather had befriended Ole Demon Sutpen, and who tells the Sutpen saga to his college chum many years after all these murders, near-incests, fires, suicides, etc., occurred down on the Sutpen farm in Old Mississipp'. Neither Quentin nor his roommate carries on what you would call normal conversations, but as there is no evidence of either of them having married his grandmother, or roasted his grandfather over a slow fire (under the impression that the latter was merely a mulatto first cousin with a trace of chimpanzee blood), I think they should be accepted as Mr. Faulkner's concession to the gray, tawdry, non-Mississippian universe in which the rest of us poor folks live, if Mr. Faulkner can bring himself to call it living.

This cheerful little fable is filtered through the medium of a style peculiar to Mr. Faulkner. It seems peculiar to me, too. First, we have the Non-Stop or Life Sentence. The first two and a half pages of "Absalom, Absalom!" consist of seven sentences, composed of 123, 155, 9 (something wrong here), 146, 66, 93, and 135 words respectively.

Average: 104. To penetrate Mr. Faulkner's sentences is like hacking your way through a jungle. The path closes up at once behind you, and in no time at all you find yourself entangled in a luxuriant mass of modifiers, qualifications, relative clauses, parenthetical phrases, interjected matter, recapitulations, and other indications of a Great Style. All of Mr. Faulkner's shuddery inventions pale in horrendousness before the mere notion of parsing him.

After the Life Sentence comes the Far Fetch, or Hypertrope. Very few things in the book remain themselves. Each one reminds Mr. Faulkner of something else. "Her legs hung . . . clear of the floor with that air of impotent and static rage like children's feet." See it? No? Join me at the foot of the class, where you belong.

Then we have what may be called Anti-Narrative, a set of complex devices used to keep the story from being told. Mr. Faulkner is very clever at this. He gets quite an interesting effect, for example, by tearing the Sutpen chronicle into pieces, as if a mad child were to go to work on it with a pair of shears, and then having each of the jagged divisions narrated by a different personage: the author, Rosa, Quentin, Quentin's father, Quentin's grandfather. All these people do a neat job of mixing up the time sequences, delaying climaxes, confusing the reader, and otherwise enabling Mr. Faulkner to demonstrate that as a technician he has Joyce and Proust punch-drunk. I should add that everybody talks the same language, a kind of Dixie Gongorism, very formal, allusive, cryptic. Apparently the entire population of Jefferson, Mississippi, consists of rhetoricians who would blench at the sight of a simple declarative sentence. On the other hand, it is only fair to say that there are a score of pages (Rosa Coldfield's section of the narrative) full of remarkable prose poetry, beautiful in itself, if magnificently irrelevant.

Seriously, I do not know what to say of this book except that it seems to point to the final blowup of what was once a remarkable, if minor, talent. I imagine that many of my respected colleagues will see in it a tragic masterpiece, a great lament for the old dead South, a Sophoclean study of a doomed family. Perhaps they are right. For me, this is a penny dreadful tricked up in fancy language and given a specious depth by the expert manipulation of a series of eccentric technical tricks. The characters have no magnitude and no meaning because they have no more reality than a mince-pie nightmare. If we are to have tales of violence and sadism, let the violence and sadism be drawn from the behavior of grownups, let them be more than the melodramatic gestures of childish maniacs. A study of defeat can have great tragic weight, but only if the defeated are akin to us, which these mumbling, muttering, frozen-faced Sutpens surely are not. I fail to see why we must go into a spasm of ecstatic shivering just because Mr. Faulkner is a clever hand at fitting up a literary asylum for the feeble-minded. It takes more than these fake sepulchral voices, these synthetic incests, these Monk Lewis allusions, to scare ordinary sober citizens. Ole Demon Sutpen is a mechanical bogeyman, and the rest of his gang are no better. The whole affair reminds one more of "The Tavern" than of Greek tragedy, and I have the horrid suspicion that if enough people were to say boo the entire structure of "Absalom, Absalom!" would disappear in smoke. Does anyone care to say boo?

Frank Moore Colby

WHEN NATURE LOVERS WRITE BOOKS

Nature lovers have found their way into print with rather unusual frequency of late. The success of this kind of writing is a healthy sign. A people cannot be far removed from innocence when books of this sort are widely read and when even the daily newspapers drop wars and politics, as they sometimes do, for a wholly irrelevant editorial rhapsody on cock-robin or autumn leaves. The London papers, especially, are given to these rustic interludes. There are more "rambles" and "bird-notes" than you would ever have supposed, and, if reviewers are to be believed, they are all written in the most charming style. But reviewers are not to be believed. No one ought to take time for many of these books if there are passages of Thoreau which he has not yet learned by heart. These writers are serviceable only when they give information. As interpreters they are of no use. For this business we must still rely on the masters, and how few of them there are!

A clergyman goes a-fishing and comes home well browned and ten pounds fatter. So he sits down and writes a book full of trite compliments to nature interspersed with a good deal of self-congratulation. He lays claim to the most refined and exquisite emotion you ever heard of—not one particle of which he succeeds in passing along. Yet because it is a good sort of thing for a clergyman to do and shows a fine appetite for wholesome fare the critics are absurdly easy on him. "Such a subtle sympathy with nature in her varying moods," they say. How do they know he has it? Just because he swears he has. There is no question of the man's sincerity or of the worth of what he writes about, but unfortunately these two are not the only elements of good writing. Here is a beautiful object, and there a genuine admirer. Yet the net result of bringing them together may be merely twaddle.

It is a rare man who can be agreeably articulate in these matters. They are hardly more communicable in speech than music is.

Some of these books are full of a sort of outdoor snobbishness, an air of having an especially fine make of soul and being proud of it. The writer will pity people who do not penetrate this or that of nature's secrets or participate in certain intimate joys. And he will tell you what these things do for him—how they strengthen him and uplift him and keep his heart pure and his mind clear. It may be true, but there should be some other evidence than his word for it. It is indelicate to be forever harping on nature's partiality for you. You cannot fancy his enjoying a thing quietly and for itself, but taking notes on each emotion in order to write it up afterward ostentatiously. How much of it is delight in objective nature and how much is satisfaction with the trim little intellectual outfit he surveys her with? Yet if there is one lesson she is supposed to din into everyone who comes close enough it is humility.

In England there are signs that in certain highly respectable magazines and newspapers they have a staff correspondent whom they never let indoors—a literary bird dog for whom the house is no place. If they catch him in the office they shoo him out with the broom to flush some small game for the next number. I gather from one of them that "the winter wind, unlike the entrancing night breezes of summer, is one of the few sounds that please even more when listened to indoors than out.... It sighs in the chimney, it moans round the walls; it whistles sometimes, at others it roars." From another I have learned that as a result of the bad weather of the week before the birds were "thoroughly worn out and uncomfortable," and "went to bed an hour before their time," though some of the partridges may have sat up somewhat longer. Some say it is the Englishman's love of nature, and would have you think it spontaneous. It is nothing of the sort. It is a clear case of compulsion. The wretches hate what they write of in nine cases out of ten. You can tell that from their style, and it is a pity they should be so tormented. Why try and squeeze a great, wild, forest joy out of a little cockney heart?

You could follow Thackeray's fancy in a cab. Dickens, though the sense of locality was as strong in him as in a cat, used nature only to emphasize pathos or punctuate joy. To Bulwer all outdoors was only stage carpentry and paint. Once if a writer did not wish to do it he did not have to try; but there is no getting out of it in these days, and the rarest gift of the generations is aped by everyone who writes.

NOVELS AND HATS

Considering how writers set about their tasks, it may be unreasonable to expect any sort of lifelike consequence. A novel is not a product of imagination. Novelists do not invent or observe; they rearrange their literary memories. Probably it is no more reasonable to look for human nature in a novel than to look for Nature in a woman's hat. For each being a work of customary or crowd-derived inspiration, their value in depicting life is much the same. One matches human nature as already published; the other matches Nature as already worn on hats. So with a host of virilities and vitalities, love-storms, moral whirlwinds, calls of the wild—you never meet the novelist who first employed them. You see the thousand hats that followed the example but never the great, brave, strong, protagonistic and outrageous hat that set it.

The call of the wild as seen on women's hats some seasons past proved no wild fancies in the heads beneath them. It was a call to precedent. When you found on a hat some singular bit from wildlife, say a weasel sleeping on its native beads or biting its light blue omelette, it was not a sign of any personal wildness. It had occurred on many hats before. And so with the novels then in season. The call of the wild in novels at that time was not a call to any special wildness; it was the peaceful call of one Jack London to another.

The hat, however, has somewhat the advantage, for women do sometimes more utterly let themselves go, feel more of that first, fine, careless rapture, in a hat than the novelist does in the novel. And as to the rule that the style is the man, I believe it could be easily proved that the hat is more exactly the woman. A novel always seems a form of self-concealment. Yet a woman otherwise quite subdued may suddenly appear in a hat that is all ablaze with feeling—no doubt imprisoned passion's single mad escape—and you sometimes meet a hot, infuriate hat, hardly venturing to look at the rabid face beneath, yet find there a countenance of great serenity. The riot of emotion had passed off in the hat, leaving the soul at peace. This is not true of novelists, who, on the contrary, seen in the flesh, show personal diversities not to be guessed from their books.

THE LOEB CLASSICS

I have been reading a review of the Loeb Classics by Professor Gilbert Norwood of the chair of Greek, University College, Cardiff. He says it is a magnificent task splendidly executed, and that the company of scholars engaged in it are in "a fair way to revolutionize the study of ancient literature as profoundly and in much the same way as the motor has revolutionized transport." His paper, like almost every other one I have read on this subject, is, for the most part, a mere rhapsody on the marvels of Greek and Latin authors coupled with praise of the Loeb Classics for reviving an interest in them. In regard to the translations he does not say one word of discriminating criticism, and the only improvement he suggests is that translations of poetry should always be in verse.

This sort of writing about the Loeb Classics is the worst thing that could happen to them. The editors of the Loeb Classics are not in a fair way to "revolutionize" anything; they are making a beginning, and a very crude beginning, in the revival of interest in the classics. Sensible men among them are well aware of their failures and they also know that the chief obstacle to success is an even flow of unmeaning, undiscriminating praise. They have no encouragement for doing their best if their worst is equally admired.

Take this latest eulogist for example. He says Dr. A. S. Way's translation of Euripides "is uninspiring but close to the Greek," while Professor Gilbert Murray's "is often loose, but marvelously beautiful." Patience with Way's Euripides is almost a proof of illiteracy. I suppose no man outside a government bureau at Washington ever wrote worse English than Professor A. S. Way, and he wrote it out of sheer love of bad English, for page after page of it has not the slightest excuse in the Greek. Even among Greek scholars who have forgotten the capacities of the English language without yet appreciating the Greek, the Way's version is known as an atrocity. Professor Gilbert Murray's Euripides has so little to do with Euripides that all compliments paid to it belong to Professor Murray himself. To call his Euripides "marvelously beautiful" is to pronounce a judgment on a contemporary verse writer. With Professor Way's close translation and Professor Gilbert Murray's loose and beautiful one, Professor Norwood thinks the people who cannot read the Greek of Euripides "stand in excellent case." I cannot imagine why. Professor Way's method resulted in murder and Professor Gilbert Murray's in oblivion.

Another instance of this writer's apathy is his mildness toward Professor H. E. Butler's version of Quintilian. To be sure he does says that where Quintilian uses thirty-five words Professor Butler uses sixty-eight, but he excuses Professor Butler on the ground that he probably wanted to let other scholars know that no suggestion implied in any one of Quintilian's words had escaped him. That is an absurd supposition to anyone who will read a few pages of Professor Butler. Loquacity is a native quality in Professor Butler. He had rather use sixty-eight words than thirty-five, and he will say the same thing twice over in order to do so. This is shown on page after page, when the thought is simple and the way to brevity perfectly open. Professor Butler takes the longest way because he likes it. When he sees seven words by Quintilian, he says to himself, "Why does the old chap waste his opportunity? I can put the same idea in forty." It is a difference in temperament. Quintilian likes to pack things into small space, skip an explanation, leave a little to inference. Professor Butler hates that kind of thing—thinks it selfish, and secretive. He dislikes Quintilian for it and thwarts him when he can. If there is any man in the world that I should hate to resemble, said Professor Butler, when he began this version, it's Quintilian, and his whole text is a demonstration of this incompatibility. Not once does he let Quintilian have his own way about anything. There is no doubt that Quintilian becomes modern by this method. You would swear he was a contributor to the London *Spectator*. I confess I never liked Quintilian at college. I thought him a man of mean outlook and low morality with a vile habit of saying things I knew already, but I did give him credit for putting a platitude into a nutshell, and I should never have dreamed of this long merciless revenge.

Wolcott Gibbs

CRYING IN THE WILDERNESS

Facile is the descent from the editorial chair of a fashionable women's magazine to the psychoanalyst's grim confessional. This is the gospel, according to Moss Hart, whose "Lady in the Dark" has just moved into the Alvin Theatre. To an old magazine man it would doubtless appear that Liza Elliott was fortunate beyond the wildest dreams of anybody in that unsavory racket. She had a fancy office in which nobody threw cigarette butts on the floor or scrawled telephone numbers on the walls; there was a rich backer with no exasperating theories about how things ought to be run; there were no disgruntled contributors or, as far as I could see, anything so vulgar as a typewriter in the joint. In fact, about the only professional problem confronting this lucky girl was the choice of what cover to put on the Easter issue. Mr. Hart's play has been generally described as a fantasy. It is, indeed.

In spite of all these advantages, however, Miss Elliott wasn't happy. Her case history, as outlined to the sawbones at twenty bucks a throw, was full of frustrations. As a very little girl she was plain, in embarrassing contrast to her beautiful mother, and her school days were just one damn thing after another. They wouldn't let her be the Princess in the Commencement play, for instance, and then when the class elections came around she was chosen Best Student, a disgusting thing, of course, to happen to anybody. As those of you who are familiar with the black magic of Vienna will realize, such experiences as these can set up bothersome complexes, and by the time Mr. Hart's heroine got to be an editor she was as mixed up emotionally as Mrs. Ethan Frome. In the end, I am happy to say, Dr. Brooks fixed everything, and Miss Elliott was able to find peace with an advertising man called Charley Johnson. It is obvious that the author classifies this as a happy ending, and who am I to argue?

All this, I'm afraid, is a preliminary to saying that I wasn't altogether carried away by "Lady in the Dark." The plot of a musical play, as a

555

rule, is immune to rational criticism, but Mr. Hart clearly wishes his new piece to be taken seriously, as a dramatic work as well as a spectacle. On this basis, I can only report that Miss Elliott's wrestle with her subconscious, while spirited, would scarcely be likely to make any professional list of fascinating cases, and that, considered sheerly as a thing of beauty, the production at the Alvin may easily remind the captious of certain goings on at the Center Theatre, where giant turntables and similar miracles have also been used to astound the unwary.

Psychoanalysis, according to persistent rumor, has long been one of Mr. Hart's own best girls, beyond question or reproach, and this may account for something rather wide-eyed, reverent, and perhaps a little old-fashioned that crept into the scenes describing his heroine's conversations with her physician, as well as those dealing with her numerous suitors. It is harder to say why the musical sequences—the patient's fantasies and childhood memories—weren't altogether satisfactory either. Kurt Weill's tunes were pleasant, if not precisely memorable; Ira Gershwin's lyrics were always urbane, and often witty; the dances, supervised by Albertina Rasch, were brilliantly executed; and the costumes and settings, though stupendous, showed both imagination and taste. The total effect on me, however, was an almost perfect balance between rapture and fatigue. There were times when everything seemed wonderful, and there were others when I simply wished to see no more scenery split and dissolve, no more beautiful women rotate on turn-tables, no more ballets, each as pretty and expensive as a pure white yacht. I can't explain this peculiar reaction, except by saying that all this magnificence seemed exactly the sort of thing that could have been handled just as intelligently (and perhaps a little more magnificently) in Hollywood.

None of the above, of course, has anything to do with Gertrude Lawrence, who, in one carelessly chosen word, is superb, whether prone on her consultant's sofa, running over her symptoms, or merrily singing a fine, tough song called "The Saga of Jenny." Of the rest of the cast, I have only strength left to remark that Danny Kaye, Bert Lytell, Macdonald Carey, Margaret Dale, and Victor Mature (courtesy the Hal Roach Studio, Inc.) all deserve your respectful attention.

THE THEATRE IN FLUSHING

There is a sort of cock-eyed majesty in every project undertaken by Billy Rose, and the Aquacade is no exception. As far as I can see, it has everything—beauty, skill, size, humor, music, and, these chilly nights, a strong undertone of muted suffering. Of all the exhibits at the Fair, it is the one you are most likely to report to your grandson, though what he will be able to make out of your garbled and unlikely story I have no idea. There was a giant swimming pool anchored in a lake, you might tell him, and a grandstand to hold ten thousand people on the shore. These watched a hundred and seventy-seven young women (known as Aquafemmes, Aquagals, and Aquabelles, for our sense of humor in that dim yesterday may have been a little primitive) and seventy-seven young men (Aquadudes and Aquabeaux) swimming and diving and prancing in step. You could say that they were led by Johnny Weissmuller, a motion-picture star celebrated for impersonating apes, and Mr. Rose's fiancée, Miss Eleanor Holm, and that these two swam together in waltz time, an accomplishment both beautiful and unique.

None of these facts, however, would give him the faintest indication of what the Aquacade was really like. I'm afraid, in fact, that nobody who hasn't been to Flushing can hope to understand the strange balance of splendor and foolishness that Mr. Rose has achieved—the towers on the stage outlined pure and sharp against the sky, and the voice of God from somewhere telling everybody to buy Pabst Blue Ribbon beer and smoke Chesterfields (the man next to us borrowed a cigarette from Mr. Rose himself; it was a Lucky Strike), the perfect rhythm of the ballet and the gooseflesh on the childish limbs (it was 50° the night I went), the divers' bodies so lovely in the air and the distaste bordering on horror on every face confronted with the icy plunge.

In any case, I think you ought to go to Mr. Rose's unusual little party; a lot of water, I'm sure, will pass over Miss Holm before we shall see its like again. The only trend, incidentally, which I was able to note at the Aquacade is that the chorus girl of tomorrow will go in for a two-syllable Christian name, ending in "a." Lela, Lila, Glada, and Norma, they are called, Jona, Roma, Vela, and Willa.

Robert C. Benchley

LA PRESSE PERVERSE *

PARIS, AUGUST 7, 1929.

In reading French newspapers there is always one consolation: no matter how little of the meaning you are able to get, you aren't missing a thing. News is the last thing a French editor worries about. Even when he finds himself saddled with a real news-story, he doesn't know what to do with it, and will just as likely as not run it on page 7 among the *Petites Annonces.* He can take the story of an Atlantic flight or a cabinet crisis and undress it until it looks like something in the Special Westchester Section of the Sunday *Times.* There is always plenty to read in a French newspaper, but it doesn't make any difference whether you read it or not.

The attitude of the French press towards news is shown by the fact that most French papers run the latest dispatches on the third page under a vague departmental heading like *"Dernière Heure"* or *"Dernières Nouvelles."* The front page they save for their essays.

The left-hand column of the front page is usually given over to a red-hot story called something like: "Molière During the Middle Period of his Productivity." The right-hand column is probably a signed outburst by the owner of the paper urging the restoration of the Bourbons or calling attention to the drought in what the French persist in calling *"Tchécoslovaquie."* In the middle of the front page the eager reader may devour biographical sketches of the bicyclists who are engaging in the *"Tour de France"* and who are now just passing through Toulon. And inside, on page 3, all nestled together in little two-line dispatches, will be the brief announcements that China is on fire and that a tunnel has been found already built under the English Channel.

All summer *Le Matin* has been giving over the two right-hand

* *This review of the French newspapers of 1929 was published in* The New Yorker's *"Wayward Press" department over the signature Guy Fawkes.*

558

columns of its front page to a series called "My Fishing Trip in New-foundland." This has been illustrated copiously each day with photo-graphs taken by the author, reproduced by means of cuts such as only French newspaper-engravers can make, presumably etched on pieces of bread. The date line on the most recent installment was April 30. (I read the first two or three laboring under a slight misapprehension owing to the word for "to fish" being the same as the word for "to sin" and hoping that someone had gone to Newfoundland on a "cam-paign of sinning." You couldn't have told from the pictures whether it was sinning or fishing the author was engaged in.)

But no matter what page you look at in a French paper, you will find America mentioned. Even the front-page essays on Rousseau manage to slip in a paragraph or two taking a crack at Oncle Sam. The ratification of the *dettes* has, of course, been the chief topic of com-ment, and from *L'Humanité* to *L'Écho de Paris* the general attitude toward the United States is one of boiling rage. Practically the only general news-notes from America that French papers will play up are those dealing with torch-murders, flag-pole-sittings and the extreme heat. It was, therefore, with considerable surprise that we saw a head-line on the front page of *L'Écho de Paris* reading *"Un Grand Améri-cain,"* but it turned out to be a tribute to Theodore Roosevelt and a lament that America had strayed so far from his teachings.

As near as we could detect, there was no mention made in the French press of the recently disclosed fact that American tourists paid over twice as much money into France last year as France paid to the United States. Well, they can't be expected to print every-thing.

In one department, however, the newspapers here excel, and that is in the reporting of crime. They love it. Crimes of violence which American papers would hardly think worth a stick of type are written up by the French with a zest and thoroughness which make of each one a special case in criminology. This is not because crimes are less frequent in France than in America, for such papers as *Le Petit Marseillais,* after a perfunctory story on how the debts and the bicycle-tour are coming on, settle down each day to five or six solid pages of murder, arson, sex and robbery which apparently have been occupy-ing the time of the entire citizenry the day before.

Even the most modest of crimes is treated in the Edgar Wallace manner, and it makes fascinating reading. Instead of, as in American accounts, beginning with the names and addresses of the policemen who discovered the crime, your French re-write man gets into a dressing-gown, lights his pipe and lets himself go like this (in rough translation):

"Toward 21 o'clock on the night of August 2, in the dark which resulted from there being no moon, Mme. Marie Plissy was walking toward her little shop in the rue Fourteenth-of-October when she suddenly found herself beaten down on the neck, falling dead at almost the same time. One is mystified."

Or even in more tantalizing fashion, under the mysterious headline "The Amorous Refusals," we are led on like this by *Le Petit Journal:* "André Gerome, 24 years, electrician, had known, for about four years, when he was a subaltern in the 2nd regiment of infantry, a young girl, Claudia Poncet, who had, at that epoch, 15 years and lived at the home of her parents, 15 rue Saint-Hippolyte."

Well, anything might be going to happen, you must admit. So we read on: "On his liberation, the young officer wished to become engaged and rendered a visit to the parents of the young Claudia who refused to give their consent. In order not to be disagreeable to her parents, Mlle. Poncet wished to romp (probably not the meaning of *rompre,* but good enough) and accepted a later rendezvous."

The rest of the story is really too sordid, but suffice it to say that when a M. Grafouillère came to knock on the door, he found that Mlle. Claudia had ceased to live owing to having received three balls in the chest and neck.

This will give you some idea of how things are going in sunny France and if one hasn't time to read *all* the stories of sudden death and crime one may take that excellent paper, *L'Éclaireur de Nice et du Sud-Est,* and turn to page 3 where, under the general heading of *Nouvelles Diverses,* one finds, in summary, that at Aix an infant of five years drowns itself in a basin, at Lisieux a grandmother is killed with a hatchet for her money, that at Les Baux two lovers are shot by a jealous, and that in Orange a little boy sets fire to the mayor (possibly a slipshod translation, but that's what it looks like).

Of all French papers *Le Temps* seems to be the dullest, having a makeup such as would be effected by spreading two pages of the *Congressional Record* out side by side and doubling the length of their columns. This unexciting layout is not enhanced in the least by a department which fills the right-hand column under the dreary heading: *"La Vie à Londres."* There are no accounts of *crimes passionnels* in *Le Temps* and not even that concession to fresh air which most French newspapers make under the title *"La Vie Sportive."* If we were to recommend a paper *not* to buy for general reading it would be *Le Temps,* followed closely by *Le Figaro.* Compared with them our own New York *Times* is a tabloid. (Incidentally, our own New York *Times,* even ten days late, comes with all the excitement of the monthly installments of "The Hound of the Baskervilles" when it was running serially in the *Strand Magazine.* We are sorry for anything we ever said disrespectfully of the New York *Times.*) Day in and day out *Le Matin* and *Le Quotidien* give the best imitation of real newspapers, although even they would deceive nobody. *Le Quotidien,* in the issue which has just come hot from the presses, bears a two-column scarehead on the front page biting out the following terse announcement, so that he who runs may read: *"La France Se Flattait Naguère de Posséder le Système Électoral le plus Large qui eût Jamais Existé. Va-t-elle Aujourd'hui Rester le Seul Pays où les Femmes ne Votent pas?"* Not only do French headlines not tell you anything. They must ask questions.

We can not bring this scholarly summary of French journalism to a close, however, without commending the theatrical newspaper *Comœdia* as being the best of its kind we have ever seen. It appears daily, and, although it, too, devotes its front page to gentlemen's essays on classical subjects and the reproduction of a painting of some old master, its inside pages are as handy a guide to what is going on in the theatre world of Paris as newspaper skill could devise. Every theatre is listed, with address, telephone number, name of current attraction and the names of the cast. If it were not for this department we should never have known that a cinema called *"Le Chanteur de Jazz"* with *"la grande vedette du film parlant Al Jolson"* is playing at the Aubert-Palace, or that at the Casino de Paris one is able to see *"Les 16 Smart Boys."*

Edgar Allan Poe

WILLIAM ELLERY CHANNING *

In speaking of Mr. William Ellery Channing, who has just published a very neat little volume of poems, we feel the necessity of employing the indefinite rather than the definite article. He is *a*, and by no means *the*, William Ellery Channing. He is only *the son* of the great essayist deceased. He is just such a person, in despite of his *clarum et venerabile nomen*, as Pindar would have designated by the significant term τις. It may be said in his favor that nobody ever heard of him. Like an honest woman, he has always succeeded in keeping himself from being made the subject of gossip. His book contains about sixty-three things, which he calls poems, and which he no doubt seriously supposes so to be. They are full of all kinds of mistakes, of which the most important is that of their having been printed at all. They are not precisely English—nor will we insult a great nation by calling them Kickapoo; perhaps they are Channingese. We may convey some general idea of them by two foreign terms not in common use—the Italian *pavoneggiarsi*, "to strut like a peacock," and the German word for "sky-rocketing," *schwarmerei*. They are more preposterous, in a word, than any poems except those of the author of "Sam Patch"; for we presume we are right (are we not?) in taking it for granted that the author of "Sam Patch" is the very worst of all the wretched poets that ever existed upon earth.

In spite, however, of the customary phrase about a man's "making a fool of himself," we doubt if any one was ever a fool of his own free will and accord. A poet, therefore, should not always be taken too strictly to task. He should be treated with leniency, and, even when damned, should be damned with respect. Nobility of descent, too, should be allowed its privileges not more in social life than in letters. The son of a great author cannot be handled too tenderly by the critical

* *This book review has been cut. Mr. Poe took William Ellery Channing, Jr., apart with great thoroughness.*

Jack Ketch. Mr. Channing must be hung, that's true. He must be hung *in terrorem*—and for this there is no help under the sun; but then we shall do him all manner of justice, and observe every species of decorum, and be especially careful of his feelings, and hang him gingerly and gracefully, with a silken cord, as the Spaniards hang their grandees of the blue blood, their nobles of the *sangre azula*.

To be serious, then; as we always wish to be if possible. Mr. Channing (whom we suppose to be a *very* young man, since we are precluded from supposing him a *very* old one), appears to have been inoculated, at the same moment, with *virus* from Tennyson and from Carlyle. And here we do not wish to be misunderstood. For Tennyson, as for a man imbued with the richest and rarest poetic impulses, we have an admiration—a reverence unbounded. His "Morte D'Arthur," his "Locksley Hall," his "Sleeping Beauty," his "Lady of Shalott," his "Lotos Eaters," his "Ænone," and many other poems, are not surpassed, in all that gives to Poetry its distinctive value, by the compositions of any one living or dead. And his leading error—that error which renders him unpopular—a point, to be sure, of no particular importance—that very error, we say, is founded in truth—in a keen perception of the elements of poetic beauty. We allude to his quaintness—to what the world chooses to term his affectation. No true poet —no critic whose approbation is worth even a copy of the volume we now hold in our hand—will deny that he feels impressed, sometimes even to tears, by many of those very affectations which he is impelled by the prejudice of his education, or by the cant of his reason, to condemn. He should thus be led to examine the extent of the one, and to be wary of the deductions of the other. In fact, the profound intuition of Lord Bacon has supplied, in one of his immortal apothegms, the whole philosophy of the point at issue. "There is no exquisite beauty," he truly says, "without some *strangeness* in its proportions." We maintain, then, that Tennyson errs, not in his occasional quaintness, but in its continual and obtrusive excess. And, in accusing Mr. Channing of having been inoculated with *virus* from Tennyson, we merely mean to say that he has adopted and exaggerated that noble poet's characteristic defect, having mistaken it for his principal merit.

Mr. Tennyson is quaint only; he is never, as some have supposed him, obscure—except, indeed, to the uneducated, whom he does not address. Mr. Carlyle, on the other hand, is obscure only; he is seldom, as some have imagined him, quaint. So far he is right; for although quaintness, employed by a man of judgment and genius, may be made auxiliary to a *poem,* whose true thesis is beauty, and beauty alone, it is grossly, and even ridiculously, out of place in a work of prose. But in his obscurity it is scarcely necessary to say that he is wrong. Either a man intends to be understood, or he does not. If he write a book which he intends *not* to be understood, we shall be very happy indeed not to understand it; but if he write a book which he means to be understood, and, in this book, be at all possible pains to prevent us from understanding it, we can only say that he is an ass—and this, to be brief, is our private opinion of Mr. Carlyle, which we now take the liberty of making public.

It seems that having deduced, from Tennyson and Carlyle, an opinion of the sublimity of everything odd, and of the profundity of everything meaningless, Mr. Channing has conceived the idea of setting up for himself as a poet of *unusual* depth, and *very* remarkable powers of mind. His airs and graces, in consequence, have a highly picturesque effect, and the Boston critics, who have a notion that poets are porpoises, (for they are always talking about their running in "schools,") cannot make up their minds as to what particular school he must belong. *We* say the Bobby Button school, by all means. He clearly belongs to that. And should nobody ever have heard of the Bobby Button school, that is a point of no material importance. We will answer for it, as it is one of our own. Bobby Button is a gentleman with whom, for a long time, we have had the honor of an intimate acquaintance. His personal appearance is striking. He has quite a big head. His eyes protrude and have all the air of saucers. His chin retreats. His mouth is depressed at the corners. He wears a perpetual frown of contemplation. His words are slow, emphatic, few, and oracular. His "thes," "ands," and "buts," have more meaning than other men's polysyllables. His nods would have put Burleigh's to the blush. His whole aspect, indeed, conveys the idea of a gentleman modest to a fault, and painfully overburthened with intellect. We insist, however, upon calling Mr. Channing's school of poetry the Bobby Button school, rather because Mr. Channing's poetry is strongly suggestive of Bobby Button, than because Mr. Button himself ever dallied, to any very great extent, with the Muses. With the exception, indeed, of a *very* fine "Sonnet to a Pig"—or rather the fragment of a sonnet, for he proceeded no farther than the words "*O* piggy wiggy," with the *O* italicized for emphasis—with the exception of this, we say, we are not aware of his having produced anything worthy of that stupendous genius which is certainly *in* him, and only wants, like the starling of Sterne, "to get out."

The best passage in the book before us, is to be found at page 121, and we quote it, as a matter of simple justice, in full:

> Dear friend, in this fair atmosphere again,
> Far from the noisy echoes of the main,
> Amid the world-old mountains, and the hills
> From whose strange grouping a fine power distills
> The soothing and the calm, I seek repose,
> The city's noise forgot and hard stern woes.
> As thou once said'st, the rarest sons of earth
> Have in the dust of cities shown their worth,
> Where long collision with the human curse
> Has of great glory been the frequent nurse,
> *And only those who in sad cities dwell*
> *Are of the green trees fully sensible.*
> *To them the silver bells of tinkling streams*
> *Seem brighter than an angel's laugh in dreams.*

The four lines italicized are highly meritorious, and the whole extract is so far decent and intelligible, that we experienced a feeling of surprise upon meeting it amid the doggerel which surrounds it. Not less was our astonishment upon finding, at page 18, a fine thought so well embodied as the following:

> *Or see the early stars, a mild sweet train*
> *Come out to bury the diurnal sun.*

But, in the way of commendation, we have now done. We have carefully explored the whole volume in vain, for a single additional line worth even the most qualified applause.

Were we to quote specimens under the general head of "utter and irredeemable nonsense," we should quote nine-tenths of the book. Such nonsense, we mean, as the following, from page 11:

> I hear thy solemn anthem fall,
> Of richest song upon my ear,
> That clothes thee in thy golden pall
> As this wide sun flows on the mere.

Now let us translate this: He hears (Mr. Channing,) a solemn anthem, of richest song, fall upon his ear, and this anthem clothes the individual who sings it in that individual's golden pall, in the same manner that, or at the time when, the wide sun flows on the mere—which is all very delightful, no doubt.

At page 37, he informs us that,

> ————It is not living,
> To a soul believing,
> To change each noble joy,
> Which our strength employs,
> For a state half rotten
> And a life of toys,

And that it is

> Better to be forgotten
> Than lose equipoise.

And we dare say it is, if one could only understand what kind of equipoise is intended. It is better to be forgotten, for instance, than to lose one's equipoise on the top of a shot tower.

Occupying the whole of page 88, he has the six lines which follow, and we will present any one (the author not excepted,) with a copy of the volume, if any one will tell us what they are all about:

> He came and waved a little silver wand,
>   He dropped the veil that hid a statue fair,
> He drew a circle with that pearly hand,
>   His grace confin'd that beauty in the air,
> Those limbs so gentle now at rest from flight,
> Those quiet eyes now musing on the night.

At page 102, he has the following:

> Dry leaves with yellow ferns, they are
> Fit wreath of Autumn, while a star
> Still, bright, and pure, our frosty air
>   Shivers in twinkling points
>   Of thin celestial hair
> And thus one side of Heaven anoints.

This we think we can explain. Let us see. Dry leaves, mixed with yellow ferns, are a wreath fit for autumn at the time when our frosty air shivers a still, bright, and pure star with twinkling points of thin celestial hair, and with this hair, or hair plaster, anoints one side of the sky. Yes—this is it—no doubt.

At page 123, we have these lines:

> My sweet girl is lying still
> In her lovely atmosphere;
> The gentle hopes her blue veins fill
> With pure silver warm and clear.
>
> O see her hair, O mark her breast!
> Would it not, *O!* comfort thee,
> If thou couldst nightly go to rest
> By that virgin chastity?

Yes; we think, upon the whole, it would. The eight lines are entitled a "Song," and we should like very much to hear Mr. Channing sing it.

Pages 36, 37, 38, 39, 40, and 41, are filled with short "Thoughts" in what Mr. C. supposes to be the manner of Jean Paul. One of them runs thus:

> How shall I live? In earnestness.
> What shall I do? Work earnestly.
> What shall I give? A willingness.
> What shall I gain? Tranquility.
> But do you mean a quietness
> In which I act and no man bless?
> Flash out in action infinite and free,
> Action conjoined with deep tranquility,
> Resting upon the soul's true utterance,
> And life shall flow as merry as a dance.

All our readers will be happy to hear, we are sure, that Mr. C is going "to flash out." Elsewhere at page 97, he expresses very similar sentiments:

> My empire is myself and I defy
> The external; yes, I rule the whole or die.

It will be observed here, that Mr. Channing's empire is himself, (a small kingdom, however,) that he intends to defy "the external," whatever that is—perhaps he means the infernals—and that, in short, he is going to rule the whole or die; all which is very proper, indeed, and nothing more than we have to expect from Mr. C.

Again, at page 146, he is rather fierce than otherwise. He says:

> We surely were not meant to ride the sea,
> Skimming the wave in that so prisoned small,
> Reposing our infinite faculties utterly.
> Boom like a roaring sunlit waterfall.
> Humming to infinite abysms: speak loud, speak free!

Here Mr. Channing not only intends to "speak loud and free" himself, but advises every body else to do likewise. For his own part, he says, he is going to *"boom"*—"to hum and to boom"—to "hum like a roaring waterfall," and "boom to an infinite abysm." What, in the name of Belzebub, *is* to become of us all? ...

And this remarkable little volume is, after all, by William Ellery Channing.... There are many people in the world silly enough to be deceived by appearances. There are individuals so crude in intellect—so *green,* (if we may be permitted to employ a word which answers our purpose much better than any other in the language,) so green, we say, as to imagine, in the absence of any indication to the contrary, that a volume bearing upon its title-page the name of William Ellery Channing, must necessarily be the posthumous work of that truly illustrious author, the *sole* William Ellery Channing of whom any body in the world ever heard. There are a vast number of uninformed young persons prowling about our book-shops, who will be raw enough to buy, and even to read half through this pretty little book, (God preserve and forgive them!) mistaking it for the composition of another. But what then? Are not books made, as well as razors, to sell? The poet's name *is* William Ellery Channing —is it *not?* And if a man has not a right to the use of his own name, to the use of what has he a right? And could the poet have reconciled it to his conscience to have injured the sale of his own volume by any uncalled-for announcement upon the title-page, or in a preface, to the effect that he is not his father, but only his father's very intelligent son? ...

Persis Greely Anderson

LENGTHY SYMPHONY

The opus rises to fortissimo
  While I, once more, resign myself to fate,
Hemmed in quite hopelessly by row on row
  Of music lovers, hushed, insatiate.
I know it is a sacrilege to sigh—
  The end is nearing, in all likelihood—
But one affrighted piccolo and I
  See no way out of this enchanted wood.

Phyllis McGinley

PUBLIC JOURNAL

VERSES INSPIRED BY A DAY SPENT IN COMMUNION WITH THE BRIGHT
YOUNG MEN OF ENGLISH VERSE

Christopher Isherwood, Stephen Spender,
Auden and L. MacNeice—
I can't come along on an all-night bender,
But I'll have a quick one with you.

It is four in the afternoon. Time still for a poem,
A poem not topical, wholly, or romantic, or metaphysic,
But fetched from the grab-bag of my mind and gaudy with
Symbol, slogan, quotation, and even music.
And many a Marxian maxim and many allusions
To a daft system and a world-disorder.
I will mention machines and the eight hour day and
Czecho-Slovakia and the invaded border.

I will speak of love and I will do it slyly,
Unloosing the sacred girdle with a tired air,
Taking particular pains to notice the elastic garters
And the literal underwear.

I will put learning into my poem, for I acquired learning
At Cambridge or Oxford, it does not matter which.
But I'll freshen it up with slang which I got by ear,
Though it may sound a little off pitch.
And I'll be casual with rhymes for that is the trend,
Fashionable as the black hat of Anthony Eden.
I may put them at the middle of the stanza instead of the end,
For really amazing effect.
Or perhaps I'll find that assonance heightens the meaning better.
Yes, definitely, I prefer the latter.

Well, it will be sport, writing my private hates
And my personal credo.
I must bring in how I went to Spain on a holiday,
And how cold it was in Toledo.
There was a bootblack, too, in Madrid,
Who gave my shoes a burnish.
He told me something important which I cannot repeat,
For though I understand Spain, I do not understand Spanish.

I'll recall autumn weather in Birmingham,
Drearier than Boston.
And the pump-attendant there who sold me stormy petrol
For my thirsting Austin.

I will put tarts into my poem, and tenement people,
The poor but not the meek;
And pieces of popular songs for a hint of nostalgia,
And bits of Greek.

I shall be tough and ardent and angry-eyed,
Aware that the world is dying, gasping, its face grown pallid;
But quick to embalm it in language as an aspic
Enfolds the chicken salad.

Now it is five o'clock. The poem is finished
Like Poland, like the upper classes, like Sunday's roast.
I must straighten my waistcoat and see that it goes straight out
By the evening post.

For what is left for us? Only
The stanza a day,
And the American royalties, and an inherited income,
To keep the wolf at bay.

George Jean Nathan

BACK TO METHUSELAH

I surely advance no stunning morsel of news when I intimate to you that it has for some time now been the generous conviction of his many admirers that something ought to be done—by way of preserving the reputation he has antecedently established for himself— to make Mr. George Bernard Shaw shut up. To those of us who have been so greatly and so often soundly entertained by him for many years, the immediate institution and subsidy of an aesthetic Ku Klux with his muffling as its sole purpose would be a fond and gratifying thing. For, crossing the line of seventy some five or six years ago, the erstwhile Grand Old Boy of English drama and letters has, to the grief of the loving and yet judicious, made pretty much of a damned fool of himself. As damned fool is the exact phrase, I see no need for a more literary and genteel circumlocution. And not only has he made this damned fool of himself, but, in addition, he has turned out to be a very lamentable bore.

Any man, whether in his later or earlier years, is privileged to make something of a fool of himself if only he accompanies the act with a palliative dose of consoling humor or wit or with a persuasive and even slightly substantiating mocking philosophy. Any màn is not only privileged to make a fool of himself, indeed, but, as human nature goes, is apparently pretty well by the Fates bound. Yet when a man of Shaw's previous humor, wit, intelligence and very considerable dialectical skill makes a monkey of himself and no longer displays the humor, wit, intelligence and dialectical skill to make his public not only swallow the fact but like it, it is high time that some kind friend took him gently by the ear, led him back home to mama and begged her, in his best interests, to keep a close eye on him and not let him out at night anymore. The trouble with Shaw is that, metaphorically, he has been going out at night when his venerable years and enfeebled powers have made it more or less obvious that he should have had his glass of hot milk by nine o'clock and been put safely to bed in his long woolen underwear. Yet what has he done? What he has done, careless of his literary, dramatic, critical and disputatious health, has been to persist in frisking anciently about under the young stars and the inhospitable winds of the new springtime, with forced antic gayety croaking a song of the early Nineteen-Hundreds and with strained jocularity mimicking the noises of yon tree-top cuckoo. Where certain other quondam distinguished valetudinarians have, like the M. Maeterlinck, run off with a young girl, Shaw, being a vegetarian, has run off with an old joke.

Consider some of our erstwhile hero's septuagenarian monkey-shines. He has had his photograph taken in a state approximating the altogether. He has descended to a talking picture of himself wherein he has clownishly turned himself this way and that, instructing the onlookers to observe the rich beauty of his profile. He has made radio speeches in the language of Mr. Rube Goldberg's comic-strip "balloons." He has entered into Shakespearean discussions with prize-fighters, has played tag for the cameras on the Riviera with movie pantaloons, and has clambered laboriously atop a cannon in Moscow and cracked cheap vaudeville wheezes. He has engaged in sober philosophical discourse with one of the Four Marx Brothers and has given out interviews so silly that American newspaper editors, disbelieving that anything so juvenile could emanate from a mouth once so intelligent, have cabled to England for verification. He has taken up with the British *haute monde* and proudly posed for photographs with his bedizened hostesses. He has anticked for reporters at Malvern, performing circus-ring stunts with an umbrella. He has vainly insisted upon his youthfulness by going out in the rain bare-head and by being ostentatiously disgusted with persons who have sense enough to go in when it rains. He has made speeches on German railway platforms, on his return from a trip to Russia, so obviously manufactured for their publicity value that everyone has snickered at his performances. He has, in short, done just about everything that a dignified and still partly intelligent man could not think of doing. And, what is worse and what is our more immediate and relevant business, he has grown quite as dull and quite as stupid and quite as tiresome in his literary and dramatic enterprises as in his extra-literary and extra-dramatic.

In "The Apple Cart," we had a premonitory indication that a multiple, or brain, sclerosis had begun to attack Shaw. And now, in "Too True To Be Good," his latest substitute for playwriting, the doctor has told us the worst. I believe that I do not exaggerate when I say that, were any other name in the whole world of drama or literature attached to the play as author, no theatrical producer, white or black, would hesitate for a moment in throwing it forthwith into the trash-basket. Aside from one or two moderately fresh and faintly amusing flashes of paradox, it amounts in sum not only to a weary reiteration of all the antique Shavian opinions but to a restatement of various other opinions on the post-war dégringolade, the post-war spiritual uncertainty, the futility of carnage, etc., as stale and obvious as an old gin breath. It is dull, dull, dull, perhaps the dullest play, indeed, that a playwright of sometime high position has ever contributed to the theatre. And, being that dull, it carries with it a shade of sadness that its author, long so close to the admiring humor of most of us, has not at length the sagacity and wisdom to call it a day and, in some quiet corner of England, does not for the rest of his years sun himself peacefully and satisfiedly in the warm after-glow of his earlier career.

Dorothy Parker

THE HIGHLY RECURRENT MR. HAMILTON *

In advertising "Caste," the latest fantasy of that dreamer of dreams, Mr. Cosmo Hamilton, the publishers state not only that it is "a superb love story," but that it is "a biting social satire." In either of which cases, I am the entire Hanneford family, including the nice white horsie.

It is but fair to remark that this is my virgin try at any of the works of Mr. Hamilton; and perhaps it is necessary to eat seven before acquiring the taste. Until today, I walked square-shouldered among my fellows, looked them in the composite eye, and said in unshaken tones: "Anyway, there are two things I have never done. I never resisted an officer, and I never read anything by Cosmo Hamilton." Today only the first half of that ringing boast is true. I made, as usual, the wrong selection.

"Caste" is concerned with a Big Theme. Until this book, Mr. Hamilton, they tell me, has been frittering away his time in writing of that trifle, sex. Now he has lifted himself by his own spat-straps, so to say, and cracked the race question wide open. He has dared to tell, as only he can tell it, of the love of a fair young flower of the most exclusive New York society for a—put your head down a moment, while I whisper—for a Jew. Deliberately, the author has made things as difficult as possible for himself, for his J-w is none of your stereotyped Shylocks or Fagins. Mr. Hamilton's J-w is what those who announce benevolently that they number some of them among their best friends would call "a good J-w." Though of the Chosen People, he is a gentleman; also, he is young, beautiful, romantic, cultured, a genius of the pianoforte, the toast of London and the Continent, and you never see him lying drunk in a gutter. Indeed, cries the author, crazed with liberalism, "He might have been a

* *These two book reviews by Dorothy Parker were published in* The New Yorker *over the signature Constant Reader.*

575

Frenchman who had been educated at Harrow or Winchester." But neither you nor Mr. Hamilton can get around the fact that he is a J-w.

The full horror of the thing sweeps over you in that gripping scene where *Erskine Dalbeattie Farquhar,* the elegant father of the fair flower, demands of *Lord Warminster,* the fair flower's elegant uncle, the name of this Semite.

" 'It's Lorbenstein,' said Warminster, whose memory was good.

" 'Lorbenstein!'

"Farquhar shuddered, and a chill ran down his spine."

Well, from then on, hell rips loose. The United States rises and protests, practically in a body, against the proposed marriage of the fair flower and her J-w. The Old World stands up for young *Lorbenstein* something pretty, but America won't hear of the thing. The fair flower has "a mass of letters from her numerous friends, and in every one of them...she has been begged to scratch her engagement and play the game by her set." Secretaries of Societies protest, members of the Ku Klux Klan protest, rival social leaders protest, bishops and strangers (the redundancy is Mr. Hamilton's) from all over America protest, I protest, thou protestest, he, she, or it protests, we protest, you protest, they protest. It is easy to see that things cannot go on at that rate; some one, and it looks like the author, must give way under the strain.

So the book ends with *Max Lorbenstein,* gentleman if J-w, Going Away, leaving "the young and lovely girl holding a few brave and beautiful words of renunciation and sacrifice in a shaking hand."

But before that, there are all sorts of elegances to be read through. One sees the reason for the popularity of Mr. Hamilton's opera; their writer is, beyond question, the wish-fulfillment king. His characters live high and wide and handsome. Nothing is too good for them; theirs is an atmosphere of see-what-the-boys-in-the-back-room-will-have lavishness. Consider, for example, *Erskine Dalbeattie Farquhar's* instructions to his butler, on the night of a quiet little dinner for fifty:

"I want you to tell the orchestra to pause after their fourth selection. I telephoned to the leader this afternoon to give him a list of tunes. At the moment when you serve the champagne, and for God's sake don't ice it as you did one night in the winter, the pipers will march in. I want you to tell them to go four times round the table, disappear, have dinner, and then form up on both sides of the staircase when the ladies leave the room."

Consider, further, that butler's highly trained reply: "Thank you, Sir. I have remembered the formula."

It is all that grand. Old brandy and sumptuous fabrics, loveless marriages and extra-mural affections, dinner-tables with "the civilized number of wineglasses to each place"—these and kindred luxuries troop through the pages of "Caste."

And all are described in Mr. Hamilton's inimitable, please God, style. My second favorite passage in the book is the glimpse of *Erskine Dalbeattie Farquhar's* nobly renounced lady-friend, "the woman who had acquired the art of gorgeous silences," although given to playing "several of the Chopin Preludes with an artist's touch." But my favorite, oh, my true favorite, is the chummily recurrent phrase, "the *hoi palloi.*" Oh, Mr. Hamilton, Mr. Hamilton! Is that what you learned on the cricket field of Eton?

RE-ENTER MARGOT ASQUITH

"Daddy, what's an optimist?" said Pat to Mike while they were walking down the street together one day.

"One who thought that Margot Asquith wasn't going to write any more," replied the absent-minded professor, as he wound up the cat and put the clock out.

That gifted entertainer, the Countess of Oxford and Asquith, author of "The Autobiography of Margot Asquith" (four volumes, neatly boxed, suitable for throwing purposes), reverts to tripe in a new book deftly entitled "Lay Sermons." It is a little dandy if I have ever seen one, and I certainly have.

I think it must be pleasanter to be Margot Asquith than to be any other living human being; and this is no matter of snap judgment on my part, for I have given long and envious thought to the desirability of being Charles A. Levine. But the lady seems to have even more self-assurance than has the argumentative birdman. Her perfect confidence in herself is a thing to which monuments should be erected; hers is a poise that ought to be on display in the British Museum. The affair between Margot Asquith and Margot Asquith will live as one of the prettiest love stories in all literature.

In this book of essays, which has all the depth and glitter of a worn dime, the Countess walks right up to such subjects as Health, Human Nature, Fame, Character, Marriage, Politics, and Opportunities. A rather large order, you might say, but it leaves the lady with unturned hair. Successively, she knocks down and drags out each topic. And there is something vastly stirring in the way in which, no matter where she takes off from, she brings the discourse back to Margot Asquith. Such singleness of purpose is met but infrequently.

When she does get around to less personal matters, it turns out that her conclusions are soothingly far from startling. A compilation of her sentiments, suitably engraved upon a nice, big calendar, would make an ideal Christmas gift for your pastor, your dentist, or Junior's music teacher. Here, for instance, are a few ingots lifted from her golden treasury: "The artistic temperament has been known to land people in every kind of dilemma."..."Pleasure will always make a stronger appeal than Wisdom."..."It is only the fine natures that profit by Experience."..."It is better to be a pioneer than a passenger, and best of all to try and create."..."It is not only what you See but what you Feel that kindles appreciation and gives life to Beauty."... "Quite apart from the question of sex, some of the greatest rascals have been loved."..."I think it is a duty women owe not only to themselves, but to every one else, to dress well."

The Thames, I hear, remains as damp as ever in the face of these observations.

Through the pages of "Lay Sermons" walk the great. I don't say that Margot Asquith actually permits us to rub elbows with them ourselves, but she willingly shows us her own elbow, which has been, so to say, honed on the mighty. "I remember President Wilson saying to me"; "John Addington Symonds once said to me"; "The Master of Balliol told me"—thus does she introduce her anecdotes. And you know those anecdotes that begin that way; me, I find them more efficacious than sheep-counting, rain on a tin roof, or alanol tablets. Just begin a story with such a phrase as "I remember Disraeli —poor old Dizzy!—once saying to me, in answer to my poke in the eye," and you will find me and Morpheus off in a corner, necking.

Margot Asquith's is, I am sure, a naïve and an annoying (those two adjectives must ever be synonyms to me) and an unimportant book, yet somehow, grudge it though I do, there is a disarming quality to it and to its author. (There I go, getting tender about things, again;

's no wonder men forget me.) Perhaps it is because the lady's cock-
ureness implies a certain sort of desperate gallantry; perhaps it is
ecause there is a little—oh, entirely unconscious, please, Your Grace—
vistfulness in the recurrent references to the dear dead days of "The
ouls," in the tales of the hunting-field when the high gentry were
vont to exclaim, "You ride with such audacity, Miss Tennant!" I
uppose that wistfulness is a fighting word to the Countess, but there
t stands. She is, from her book, no master mind, God wot; but she
s, also from her book, a game woman, gamer, I think, than she knows.
always have to cry a little bit about courage.

However (and how good it feels to get back to the nice, firm ground
gain), "Lay Sermons" is a naïve and an annoying and an unimportant
ook. The author says, "I am not sure that my ultimate choice for
he name of this modest work is altogether happy." Happier I think
t would have been if, instead of the word "Sermons," she had selected
he word "Off."

it's no wonder men forget me.) Perhaps it is because the lady's acid-ness implies a certain sort of desperate gallantry; perhaps it is because there is a little—oh, earthly unconscious, please, Your Grace—wistfulness in the recurrent references to the dear dead days of "The Souls," in the tales of the hunting-field when the high gentry were wont to exclaim, "You ride with such audacity, Miss Tennant." I suppose that wistfulness is a fighting word to the Countess, but there it stands. She is from her book, no matter mind, God wot; but she is also from her book, a game woman, again, I think, than she knows. I always have to cry a little bit about courage.

However (and how good it feels to get back to the nice, firm ground again), "Lay Sermons" is a naïve and an annoying and an unimportant book. The author says, "I am not sure that my ultimate choice for the name of this modest work is altogether happy." Happier, I think it would have been if, instead of the word "Sermons", she had selected the word "Oh."

THE REPORTERS AT WORK

In the preface to this book we gave reasons for abandoning funny newspaper stories. We probably would have given up the search for them earlier in the game if it hadn't been for a Frank Sullivan story from the World *which we had on hand. It was headed DECKHANDS IN RESCUE PARTY, and began this way:*

Philip Lamb, twenty-five, a deckhand on the tug *Thomas Howard,* moored at North First Street, Brooklyn, was boarding the tug yesterday when he slipped and fell into the river.

"Ahoy!" he cried.

Then he decided he had better start swimming, both to keep warm and afloat.

"Ahoy!" he cried.

"Ahoy!" cried a deckhand on the *Thomas Howard.*

"Ahoy!" cried Mr. Lamb.

"Awhere?" cried the deckhand.

"Ahere," informed Philip. "Ahoy ahere."

"Oh," said the deckhand, "down THERE. . . ."

It took us a long time to find out that we just couldn't locate an unlimited quantity of such news stories.

The profile of Timenterprise, by Wolcott Gibbs, is placed in this section rather than under Parody for arbitrary reasons;

*it is definitely a parody, and a superb one, but it is also humor
in reporting.*

*For the sake of the record it should be stated that "The Talk
of the Town" pieces are often the work of two men—a reporter
and a rewrite man, each as guilty as the other. In all news
reports that are funny, imagination in fact-gathering is as
important as the actual writing of the story.*

*There are two pieces in this section on the subject of birds
and bird people. For some wholly mysterious reason birds
began crowding into our book early. They came in like flies
into a kitchen, and they kept on coming. It was an unexpected plague. We soon found ourselves with an embarrassing
number of bird pieces, and had to start discarding good things
for no other reason than that they pertained to birds and we
didn't want the book to be preponderantly ornithological.
Is there something about birds that attracts humorists, or vice
versa?*

Wolcott Gibbs

TIME ... FORTUNE ... LIFE ... LUCE

Sad-eyed last month was nimble, middle-sized *Life*-President Clair Maxwell as he told newshawks of the sale of the fifty-three-year-old gagmag to *Time*. For celebrated name alone, price: $85,000.

Said he: "*Life* ... introduced to the world the drawings ... of such men as Charles Dana Gibson, the verses of ... James Whitcomb Riley and Oliver Herford, such writers as John Kendrick Bangs. ... Be-

PROFILES
TIME ... FORTUNE ... LIFE ... LUCE

HENRY ROBINSON LUCE
For Cigarettes, $45,000?
(See FACTS, FIGURES)

ginning next month the magazine *Life* will embark on a new venture entirely unrelated to the old."

How unrelated to the world of the Gibson Girl is this new venture might have been gathered at the time from a prospectus issued by enormous, Apollo-faced C. D. Jackson, of Time, Inc.

"*Life,*" wrote he, "will show us the Man-of-the-Week...his body clothed, and, if possible, nude." It will expose "the loves, scandals, and personal affairs of the plain and fancy citizen...and write around them a light, good-tempered 'colyumnist' review of these once-private lives."

29,000 die-hard subscribers to *Life,** long accustomed to he-she jokes, many ignorant of King of England's once-private life (*Time,* July 25 *et seq.*), will be comforted for the balance of their subscription periods by familiar, innocent jocosities of *Judge.* First issue of new publication went out last week to 250,000 readers, carried advertisements suggesting an annual revenue of $1,500,000, pictured Russian peasants in the nude, the love life of the Black Widow spider, referred inevitably to Mrs. Ernest Simpson.

Behind this latest, most incomprehensible Timenterprise looms, as usual, ambitious, gimlet-eyed, Baby Tycoon Henry Robinson Luce, co-founder of *Time,* promulgator of *Fortune,* potent in associated radio & cinema ventures.

"High-Buttoned ... Brilliant"

Headman Luce was born in Tengchowfu, China, on April 3, 1898, the son of Henry Winters & Elizabeth Middleton Luce, Presbyterian missionaries. Very unlike the novels of Pearl Buck were his early days. Under brows too beetling for a baby, young Luce grew up inside the compound, played with his two sisters, lisped first Chinese, dreamed much of the Occident. At 14, weary of poverty, already respecting wealth & power, he sailed alone for England, entered school at St. Albans. Restless again, he came to the United States, enrolled at Hotchkiss, met up & coming young Brooklynite Briton Hadden. Both even then were troubled with an itch to harass the public. Intoned Luce years later: "We reached the conclusion that most people were not well informed & that something should be done...."

First publication to inform fellowman was *Hotchkiss Weekly Record;* next *Yale Daily News,* which they turned into a tabloid; fought

* Peak of *Life* circulation (1921): 250,000.

to double hours of military training, fought alumni who wished to change tune of Yale song from *Die Wacht am Rhein*. Traditionally unshaven, wearing high-buttoned Brooks jackets, soft white collars, cordovan shoes, no garters, Luce & Hadden were Big Men on a campus then depleted of other, older Big Men by the war. Luce, pale, intense, nervous, was Skull & Bones, Alpha Delta Phi, Phi Beta Kappa, member of the Student Council, editor of the *News;* wrote sad poems, read the *New Republic,* studied political philosophy. As successful, less earnest, more convivial, Hadden collected china dogs, made jokes.* In 1920 the senior class voted Hadden Most Likely to Succeed, Luce Most Brilliant. Most Brilliant he, Luce sloped off to Christ Church, Oxford, there to study European conditions, take field trips into the churning Balkans.

Best Advice: Don't

Twenty months after commencement, in the city room of Paperkiller Frank Munsey's *Baltimore News,* met again Luce, Hadden. Newshawks by day, at night they wrangled over policies of the magazine they had been planning since Hotchkiss. Boasted the final prospectus: *"Time* will be free from cheap sensationalism ... windy bias."

In May, 1922, began the long struggle to raise money to start *Time.* Skeptical at the outset proved Newton D. Baker, Nicholas Murray Butler, Herbert Bayard Swope, William Lyon Phelps. Pooh-poohed *Review of Reviews* Owner Charles Lanier: "My best advice ... don't do it." From studious, pint-sized Henry Seidel Canby, later editor of Lamont-backed *Saturday Review of Literature,* came only encouraging voice in this threnody.

Undismayed Luce & Hadden took the first of many offices in an old brownstone house at 9 East 17th Street, furnished it with a filing cabinet, four second-hand desks, a big brass bowl for cigarette stubs, sought backers.†

---

* Once, watching Luce going past, laden with cares & responsibilities, Hadden chuckled, upspoke: "Look out, Harry. You'll drop the college."

† In return for $50 cash, original investors were given two shares 6% Preferred Stock with a par value of $25, one share Class A Common Stock without par value. 3,440 Preferred, 1,720 Class A Common were so sold.

170 shares of Class A Common, 8,000 shares of Class B Common, also without par value, not entitled to dividends until Preferred Shares had been retired, were issued to Briton Hadden, Henry R. Luce, who gave one-third to asso-

JPMorganapoleon H. P. Davison, Yale classmate of Luce, Hadden, great & good friend of both, in June contributed $4,000. Next to succumb: Mrs. David S. Ingalls, sister of Classmate William Hale Harkness; amount, $10,000. From Brother Bill, $5,000. Biggest early angel, Mrs. William Hale Harkness, mother of Brother Bill & Mrs. Ingalls, invested $20,000. Other original stockholders: Robert A. Chambers, Ward Cheney, F. Trubee Davison, E. Roland Harriman, Dwight W. Morrow, Harvey S. Firestone, Jr., Seymour H. Knox, William V. Griffin. By November Luce & Hadden had raised $86,000, decided to go to work on fellowman.

"Snaggle-Toothed . . . Pig-Faced"

Puny in spite of these preparations, prosy in spite of the contributions of Yale poets Archibald MacLeish & John Farrar, was the first issue of *Time* on March 3, 1923. Magazine went to 9,000 subscribers; readers learned that Uncle Joe Cannon had retired at 86, that there was a famine in Russia, that Thornton Wilder friend Tunney had defeated Greb.

Yet to suggest itself as a rational method of communication, of infuriating readers into buying the magazine, was strange inverted Timestyle. It was months before Hadden's impish contempt for his

ciates, divided remainder equally.

In 1925, authorized capital of Time, Inc., was increased to 19,000 shares; of which 8,000 were Preferred, 3,000 Class A; as before, 8,000 Class B.

In June, 1930 (if you are still following this), the Preferred Stock was retired in full & dividends were initiated for both Common Stocks. Corporation at this time had 2,400 shares Class A, 7,900 Class B outstanding.

By the spring of 1931 *Time* had begun to march, shares were nominally quoted at $1,000. Best financial minds advised splitting stock on basis of twenty shares for one. Outstanding after clever maneuver: 206,400 shares Common.

In 1933, outlook still gorgeous, each share of stock was reclassified into 1/10th share of $6.50 Dividend Cumulative Convertible Preferred Stock ($6.50 div. cum. con. pfd. stk.) and one share of New Common Stock. New div. cum. con. pfd. stk. was convertible into a share and a half of New Common Stock, then selling around $40 a share, now quoted at over $200.

Present number of shares outstanding, 238,000; paper value of shares, $47,000,000; conservative estimate of Luce holding, 102,300 shares; paper value, $20,460,000; conservative estimate of Luce income from *Time* stock (shares earned $9.74 in 1935, paid so far in 1936, $6.50; anticipated dividend for full year, $8), $818,400; reported Luce income from other investments, $100,000; reported Luce bagatelle as editor of Time, Inc., $45,000; reported total Lucemolument, $963,400.

Boy!

readers,* his impatience with the English language, crystallized into gibberish. By the end of the first year, however, Timeditors were calling people able, potent, nimble; "Tycoon," most successful Timepithet, had been coined by Editor Laird Shields Goldsborough; so fascinated Hadden with "beady-eyed" that for months nobody was anything else. Timeworthy were deemed such designations as "Tomtom" Heflin, "Body-lover" Macfadden.

"Great word! Great word!" would crow Hadden, coming upon "snaggle-toothed," "pig-faced." Appearing already were such maddening coagulations as "cinemaddict," "radiorator." Appearing also were first gratuitous invasions of privacy. Always mentioned as William Randolph Hearst's "great & good friend" was Cinemactress Marion Davies, stressed was the bastardy of Ramsay MacDonald, the "cozy hospitality" of Mae West. Backward ran sentences until reeled the mind.

By March, 1924, the circulation had doubled, has risen since then 40,000 a year, reaches now the gratifying peak of 640,000, is still growing. From four meagre pages in first issue, *Time* advertising has now come to eclipse that in *Satevepost*. Published *Time* in first six months of 1936, 1,590 pages; *Satevepost,* 1,480.

No Slugabed, He ...

Strongly contrasted from the outset of their venture were Hadden, Luce. Hadden, handsome, black-haired, eccentric, irritated his partner by playing baseball with the office boys, by making jokes, by lack of respect for autocratic business. Conformist Luce disapproved of heavy drinking, played hard, sensible game of tennis, said once: "I have no use for a man who lies in bed after nine o'clock in the morning," walked to work every morning, reproved a writer who asked for a desk for lack of "log-cabin spirit."

In 1925, when *Time* moved its offices to Cleveland, bored, rebellious was Editor Hadden; Luce, busy & social, lunched with local bigwigs, addressed Chamber of Commerce, subscribed to Symphony Orchestra, had neat house in the suburbs. Dismayed was Luce when Hadden met him on return from Europe with premature plans to move the magazine back to New York. In 1929, dying of a streptococcus infec-

* Still framed at *Time* is Hadden's scrawled dictum: "Let Subscriber Goodkind mend his ways!"

tion, Hadden still opposed certain details of success-formula of *Fortune,* new, beloved Lucenterprise.

Oats, Hogs, Cheese ...

In January, 1930, first issue of *Fortune* was mailed to 30,000 subscribers, cost as now $1 a copy, contained articles on branch banking, hogs, glassblowing, how to live in Chicago on $25,000 a year. Latest issue (Nov., 1936) went to 130,000 subscribers, contained articles on bacon, tires, the New Deal, weighed as much as a good-sized flounder.*

Although in 1935 *Fortune* made a net profit of $500,000, vaguely dissatisfied was Editor Luce. Anxious to find & express "the technological significance of industry," he has been handicapped by the fact that his writers are often hostile to Big Business, prone to insert sneers, slithering insults. In an article on Bernard Baruch, the banker was described as calling President Hoover "old cheese-face." Protested Tycoon Baruch that he had said no such thing. Shotup of this was that Luce, embarrassed, printed a retraction; now often removes toovivid phrasing from writers' copy.

¶ Typical perhaps of Luce methods is *Fortune* system of getting material. Writers in first draft put down wild gossip, any figures that occur to them. This is sent to victim, who indignantly corrects the errors, inadvertently supplies facts he might otherwise have withheld.

¶ *March of Time* in approximately its present form was first broadcast on March 6, 1931, paid the Columbia System for privilege, dropped from the air in February, 1932, with Luce attacking radio's "blatant claim to be a medium of education." Said he: "Should *Time* or any other business feel obliged to be the philanthropist of the air; to continue to pay for radio advertising it doesn't want in order to provide radio with something worthwhile?" So popular, so valuable to the studio was *March of Time* that it was restored in September of the same year, with Columbia donating its time & facilities. Since then *March of Time* has been sponsored by Remington-Rand typewriter company, by Wrigley's gum, by its own cinema *March of Time,* has made 400 broadcasts.† Apparently reconciled to philanthropy is Luce,

---

* Two pounds, nine ounces.

† By some devious necromancy, statisticians have calculated that *March of Time* ranks just behind *Amos & Andy* as most popular of all radio programs; reaches between 8,000,000 and 9,000,000 newshungry addicts.

because time for latest version will be bought & paid for by his organization.

¶ No active connection now has Luce with the moving-picture edition of *March of Time,* which was first shown on February 1, 1935, appears thirteen times a year in over 6,000 theatres, has so far failed to make money, to repay $900,000 investment. Even less connection has he with *Time's* only other unprofitable venture. Fifty-year-old *Architectural Forum,* acquired in 1932, loses still between $30,000 and $50,000 a year, circulates to 31,000.

¶ *Letters,* five-cent fortnightly collection of *Time's* correspondence with its indefatigable readers, was started in 1931, goes to 30,000, makes a little money.

¶ For a time, Luce was on Board of Directors of Paramount Pictures. Hoped to learn something of cinema, heard nothing discussed but banking, resigned sadly.

Fascinating Facts ... Dreamy Figures ...

Net profits of Time, Inc., for the past nine years:

1927	3,860
1928	125,787
1929	325,412
1930	818,936
1931	847,447
1932	613,727*
1933	1,009,628
1934	1,773,094
1935	$2,249,823†

In 1935 gross revenue of *Time-Fortune* was $8,621,170, of which the newsmagazine brought in approximately $6,000,000. Outside investments netted $562,295. For rent, salaries, production & distribution, other expenses went $6,594,076. Other deductions: $41,397. Allowance for federal income tax: $298,169.

Time's books, according to Chicago Statisticians Gerwig & Gerwig, show total assets of $6,755,451. Liabilities, $3,101,584. These figures,

* Hmm.

† Exceeded only by Curtis Publishing Co. (*Satevepost*): $5,329,900; Crowell Publishing Co. (*Collier's*): $2,399,600.

conventionally allowing $1 for name, prestige of *Time,* come far from reflecting actual prosperity of Luce, his enterprises. Sitting pretty are the boys.

Luce ... Marches On!

Transmogrified by this success are the offices, personnel of *Time-Fortune.* Last reliable report: *Time,* 308 employees; *Fortune,* 103; Cinemarch, 58; Radiomarch, 10; *Architectural Forum,* 40; *Life,* 47. In New York; total, 566. In Chicago, mailing, editorial, mechanical employees, 216. Grand total Timemployees on God's earth, 782. Average weekly recompense for informing fellowman, $45.67802.

From first single office, Timen have come to bulge to bursting six floors of spiked, shiny Chrysler Building, occupy 150 rooms, eat daily, many at famed Cloud Club, over 1,000 eggs, 500 cups of coffee, much bicarbonate of soda. Other offices: Cinemarch, 10th Avenue at 54th Street; Radiomarch, Columbia Broadcasting Building.

Ornamented with Yale, Harvard, Princeton diplomas, stuffed fish, terrestrial globes are offices of Luce & other headmen; bleak, uncarpeted the writer's dingy lair.

¶ Heir apparent to mantle of Luce is dapper, tennis-playing, $35,000-a-year Roy Larsen, nimble in Radio- & Cinemarch, vice-president & second largest stockholder in Time, Inc. Stock income: $120,000.

¶ Looming behind him is burly, able, tumbledown Yaleman Ralph McAllister Ingersoll, former Fortuneditor, now general manager of all Timenterprises, descendant of 400-famed Ward McAllister. Littered his desk with pills, unguents, Kleenex, Socialite Ingersoll is *Time's* No. 1 hypochondriac, introduced ant palaces for study & emulation of employees, writes copious memoranda about filing systems, other trivia, seldom misses a Yale football game. His salary: $30,000; income from stock: $40,000.

¶ Early in life Timeditor John Stuart Martin lost his left arm in an accident. Unhandicapped he, resentful of sympathy, Martin played par golf at Princeton, is a crack shot with a rifle or shotgun, holds a telephone with no hands, using shoulder & chin, chews paperclips. First cousin of Cofounder Hadden, joined in second marriage to daughter of Cunard Tycoon Sir Ashley Sparks, Timartin is managing editor of newsmagazine, has been nimble in Cinemarch, other Timenterprises, makes $25,000 a year salary, gets from stock $60,000.

¶ $20,000 salary, $20,000 from stock gets shyest, least-known of all Time-editors, Harvardman John S. Billings, Jr., now under Luce in charge of revamped *Life,* once Washington correspondent for the Brooklyn *Eagle,* once National Affairs Editor for *Time.* Yclept "most important man in shop" by Colleague Martin, Billings, brother of famed muralist Henry Billings, is naïve, solemn, absent-minded, once printed same story twice, wanted to print, as news, story of van Gogh's self-mutilation, drives to office in car with liveried chauffeur, likes Jones Beach.
¶ Fortuneditor Eric Hodgins is thin-haired, orbicular, no Big Three graduate. Formerly on *Redbook,* boy & girl informing *Youth's Companion,* Hodgins inherited Pill-Swallower Ingersoll's editorial job two years ago when latter was called to greater glory, higher usefulness, still writes much of content of magazine, is paid $15,000; from stock only $8,000.
¶ Doomed to strict anonymity are *Time-Fortune* staff writers, but generally known in spite of this are former *Times* Bookritic John Chamberlain, Meistersinger Archibald MacLeish. Both out of sympathy with domineering business, both irked by stylistic restrictions, thorns to Luce as well as jewels they. Reward for lack of fame: Chamberlain, $10,000; MacLeish, $15,000; each, two months' vacation.

Brisk beyond belief are carryings-on these days in Luce's chromium tower. *Time,* marching on more militantly than ever, is a shambles on Sundays & Mondays, when week's news is teletyped to Chicago printing plant; *Fortune,* energetic, dignified, its offices smelling comfortably of cookies, is ever astir with such stupefying projects as sending the entire staff to Japan; new whoopsheet *Life* so deep in organization that staff breakfasts are held to choose from 6,000 submitted photographs the Nude of the Week; so harried perpetually all editors that even interoffice memoranda are couched in familiar Timestyle,* that an appointment to lunch with Editor Luce must be made three weeks in advance.

Caught up also in the whirlwind of progress are *Time, Fortune's* 19 maiden checkers. Bryn Mawr, Wellesley, Vassar graduates they, each is assigned to a staff writer, checks every word he writes, works hard & late, is barred by magazine's anti-feminine policy from editorial advancement.

---

* Sample Luce memorandum: "Let *Time's* editors next week put thought on the Japanese beetle. H. R. L."

Cold, Baggy, Temperate . . .

At work today, Luce is efficient, humorless, revered by colleagues; arrives always at 9:15, leaves at 6, carrying armfuls of work, talks jerkily, carefully, avoiding visitor's eye; stutters in conversation, never in speechmaking. In early days kept standing at Luce desk like butlers were writers while he praised or blamed; now most business is done by time-saving memoranda called "Luce's bulls." Prone he to wave aside pleasantries, social preliminaries, to get at once to the matter in hand. Once to interviewer who said, "I hope I'm not disturbing you," snapped Luce, "Well, you are." To ladies full of gentle misinformation he is brusque, contradictory, hostile; says that his only hobby is "conversing with somebody who knows something," argues still that "names make news," that he would not hesitate to print a scandal involving his best friend.

Because of his Chinese birth, constantly besieged is Luce by visiting Orientals; he is polite, forbearing, seethes secretly. Lunch, usually in a private room at the Cloud Club, is eaten quickly, little attention paid to the food, much to business. He drinks not at all at midday, sparingly at all times, takes sometimes champagne at dinner, an occasional cocktail at parties. Embarrassed perhaps by reputation for unusual abstemiousness, he confesses proudly that he smokes too much.

Serious, ambitious Yale standards are still reflected in much of his conduct; in indiscriminate admiration for bustling success, in strong regard for conventional morality; in honest passion for accuracy; physically, in conservative, baggy clothes, white shirts with buttoned-down collars, solid-color ties. A budding joiner, in New York, Luce belongs to the Yale, Coffee House, Racquet & Tennis, Union, & Cloud Clubs; owns a box at the Metropolitan; is listed in *Who's Who* & *Social Register*.

Colder, more certain, more dignified than in the early days of the magazine, his prose style has grown less ebullient, resembles pontifical *Fortune* rather than chattering *Time*. Before some important body he makes now at least one speech a year, partly as a form of self-discipline, partly because he feels that his position as head of a national institution demands it. His interests wider, he likes to travel, meet & observe the Great. Five or six times in Europe, he has observed many Great & Near Great. Of a twenty-minute conversation with King Edward, then Prince of Wales, says only "Very interesting." Returning from such trips, he always provides staff members with 10 & 12-page memoranda carefully explaining conditions.

Orated recently of conditions in this country: "Without the aristocratic principle no society can endure.... What slowly deadened our aristocratic sense was the expanding frontier, but more the expanding machine.... But the aristocratic principle persisted in the United States in our fetish of comparative success.... We got a plutocracy without any common sense of dignity and obligation. Money became more and more the only mark of success, but still we insisted that the rich man was no better than the poor man—and the rich man accepted the verdict. And so let me make it plain, the triumph of the mass mind is nowhere more apparent than in the frustration of the upper classes." Also remarked in conversation: "Trouble is—great anti-social development—is the automobile trailer. Greatest failure of this country is that it hasn't provided good homes for its people. Trailer shows that."

Milestones

Good-naturedly amused by Luce tycoon ambitions was Lila Hotz, of Chicago, whom he married there on Dec. 22, 1923. In 1935, the father of two boys, Luce was divorced by her in Reno on Oct. 5. Married in Old Greenwich, Conn., without attendants, on Nov. 23, 1935, were Luce, Novelist-Playwright Clare Boothe Brokaw, described once by Anglo-aesthete Cecil Beaton as "most drenchingly beautiful," former wife of elderly Pantycoon George Tuttle Brokaw.

Two days before ceremony, "Abide with Me," by new, beautiful Mrs. Luce, was produced at the Ritz Theatre. Play dealt with young woman married to sadistic drunkard, was unfavorably reviewed by all newspaper critics.*

In a quandary was Bridegroom Luce when *Time's* own critic submitted a review suggesting play had some merit. Said he: "Show isn't that good.... Go back.... Write what you thought." Seven times, however, struggled the writer before achieving an acceptable compromise between criticism, tact.

---

* Of it said Richard Watts, blue-shirted, moon-faced *Tribune* dramappraiser: "One almost forgave 'Abide with Me' its faults when its lovely playwright, who must have been crouched in the wings for a sprinter's start as the final curtain mercifully descended, heard a cry of 'author,' which was not audible in my vicinity, and arrived onstage to accept the audience's applause just as the actors, who had a head-start on her, were properly lined up and smoothed out to receive their customary adulation."

A Million Rooms, a Thousand Baths...

Long accustomed to being entertained, entertaining, is Mrs. Luce, intimate of Mr. & Mrs. A. Coster Schermerhorn, Bernard M. Baruch, Jock Whitney, glistening stage & literary stars. Many were invited last summer to 30-acre estate in Stamford to play tennis, croquet, swim; many more will be when Mrs. Luce has finished her new play, "The Women," * when *Life's* problems, budding policies have been settled by Luce.

Many, too, will come to 7,000-acre, $100,000 Luce plantation, near Charleston, S. C.; will sleep there in four streamlined, prefabricated guest cottages. Given to first Mrs. Luce in divorce settlement, along with $500,000 in cash & securities, was French Manoir at Gladstone, N. J., where Luce once planned to raise Black Angus cows, to become gentleman farmer.

Described too modestly by him to Newyorkereporter as "smallest apartment in River House," † Luce duplex at 435 East 52nd Street contains 15 rooms, 5 baths, a lavatory; was leased furnished from Mrs. Bodrero Macy for $7,300 annually, contains many valuable French, English, Italian antiques, looks north and east on the river. In décor, Mrs. Luce prefers the modern; evasive is Luce. Says he: "Just like things convenient & sensible." Says also: "Whatever furniture or houses we buy in the future will be my wife's buying, not mine."

Whither, Whither?

Accused by many of Fascist leanings, of soaring journalistic ambition, much & conflicting is the evidence on Luce political faith, future plans. By tradition a Tory, in 1928 he voted for Alfred E. Smith, in 1932 for Herbert Hoover, this year for Alfred M. Landon. Long at outs with William Randolph Hearst, it was rumored that a visit last spring to California included a truce with ruthless, shifting publisher. Close friend for years of Thomas Lamont, Henry P. Davison, the late Dwight Morrow, it has been hinted that an official connection with the House of Morgan in the future is not impossible. Vehemently denies this Luce, denies any personal political ambition, admits only that he would like eventually to own a daily newspaper in New York.

---

* Among backers are sad, ramshackle George S. Kaufman, high-domed fur-bearing Moss Hart.

† Smallest apartment in River House has six rooms, one bath.

Most persistent, most fantastic rumor, however, declares that Yale-man Luce already has a wistful eye on the White House. Reported this recently Chicago's *Ringmaster,* added: "A legally-minded friend ...told him that his Chinese birth made him ineligible. Luce dashed to another lawyer to check. Relief! He was born of American parents and properly registered at the Consulate."

Whatever the facts in that matter, indicative of Luce consciousness of budding greatness, of responsibility to whole nation, was his report to *Time's* Board of Directors on March 19, 1936. Declaimed he: "The expansion of your company has brought it to a point beyond which it will cease to be even a big Small Business and become a small Big Business.... The problem of public relations also arises. *Time,* the Weekly Newsmagazine, has been, and still is, its own adequate apologist. Ditto, *Fortune.* But with a motion-picture journal, a nightly radio broadcast, and with four magazines, the public interpretation of your company's alleged viewpoint or viewpoints must be taken with great seriousness." Certainly to be taken with seriousness is Luce at thirty-eight, his fellowman already informed up to his ears, the shadow of his enterprises long across the land, his future plans impossible to imagine, staggering to contemplate. Where it all will end, knows God!

Joseph Mitchell

TANYA

At one time or another I have talked with several of the lovely young women who hope to become the Sally Rand of the New York World's Fair of 1939. Of them all, Florence Cubitt is my favorite. She was the Queen of the Nudists at the California Pacific International Exposition at San Diego in 1936. The nudists—twenty girls and five bearded men—were segregated behind a fence in a big field, and the customers paid forty cents to go in and watch from a distance while they played games. Her Exposition name was Tanya Cubitt, she told me, because "Tanya sounds more sexy than Florence." I met her on St. Patrick's Day in 1936, and I spent several hours of a rainy afternoon listening to her talk in her room at the Hotel New Yorker.

Miss Cubitt was sent here to get some publicity for the San Diego Exposition. The officials of the San Diego fair, which was supposed to "tell the story of mankind's restless urge toward achievement," also said they would ban "all but the highest type of concession," but when customers stayed away by the million, they decided that Miss Cubitt's nudist concession was of an extraordinarily high type. More than one American exposition has been saved from bankruptcy by uninhibited young women.

The newspaper for which I work sent me up to interview Miss Cubitt the day after she arrived in New York. A photographer went along with me. I saved all my notes, and I want to tell you about Miss Cubitt because I think she will be one of the sensations of the Midway at Mr. Whalen's Fair.

We were met at the door of Miss Cubitt's room by one of the Exposition's press agents, a brisk young man named Jack Adams. We went in and sat down, and he said the Queen—he called her the Queen every time he referred to her—would be out in a minute. I had a bad cold that day and did not particularly like the assignment. I liked it even less when Mr. Adams began telling me about the Queen. He said she did not approve of the girls in the New York night-club shows because she felt they besmirched the cause of nudism. He said she ate uncooked carrots, took an orange-juice bath about once a week, and lived almost entirely off raw herbs.

He was telling about the Queen's dietary habits when she came in. She was naked. It was the first time a woman I had been sent to interview ever came into the room naked, and I was shocked. I say she was naked. Actually, she had a blue G-string on, but I have never seen anything look so naked in my life as she did when she walked into that room. She didn't even have any shoes on. She was a tall girl with a cheerful, baby face. She had long, golden hair and hazel eyes. The photographer was bending over his camera case, screwing a bulb into his flashpan, when she came in. As soon as he saw her, he abruptly stood erect.

"My God!" he said.

Mr. Adams introduced the Queen, and she shook hands with me and smiled. Then she shook hands with the photographer.

"Pleased to meet you," said the photographer.

"Likewise," said Miss Cubitt, smiling.

She went over and sat down in one of the hotel's overstuffed chairs and said she hoped we wouldn't mind if she didn't put anything on, and we shook our heads in unison. The telephone rang and Mr. Adams answered it. When he got through with the telephone, he said he would have to beat it, that he had an appointment with an advertising agency, and he said goodbye. The rain was beating against the windows, and when Mr. Adams got to the door, Miss Cubitt yelled, "You better wear your rubbers." The photographer was still standing in the middle of the floor with his flashpan in his hand, staring open-mouthed at the young woman. I didn't know how to begin the interview.

"Well, Miss Cubitt," I said, tentatively, "Mr. Adams just told me you eat a lot of raw carrots."

"Why," she said, sitting upright in the overstuffed chair, "I never ate a raw carrot in my life. I eat like anybody else. My mother cooks me great, big, old steaks and French-fried potatoes. That's what I eat. In the nudist colony, the men nudists eat a lot of that stuff. The men nudists are a bunch of nuts. Why, they eat peas right out of the pod. They squeeze the juice out of vegetables and drink it, and they don't eat salt. Also, they have long beards. They don't have any ambition. They just want to be nudists all their lives. I want to be a dancer, myself. I'm going to come to the New York World's Fair with my dance, and I bet it will make me a reputation."

I saw that the young woman was articulate, and that I wouldn't have to ask a lot of questions. When I said I had a bad cold, she said, "You poor man," and telephoned room service to send up whiskey. At the same time she ordered some sandwiches, some corned-beef sandwiches, saying, "I'm so hungry I could eat the flowers off the plate." While she was holding the telephone in her hand, waiting for room service to answer, she said she was only nineteen years old and that she had eight sisters, four of whom had been working with her in the nudist colony. Their names, she told me, were Ruthie, Bobbie, Lucille, and Diane. She said her mother was glad they were working in the colony.

"It keeps us out in the open," said Miss Cubitt. "It doesn't keep us out late at night, and we have a healthy atmosphere to work in. My girl friends think we have orgies and all, but I never had an orgy yet. Sometimes when the sun is hot, nudism is hard work."

She was a pretty girl. Her skin was ivory-colored and she had freckles on her cheeks, like Myrna Loy. In fact, she looked a little like Myrna Loy. She was obviously healthy, and she said she played a lot of tennis and handball. She said she sometimes posed for artists. "Once one of them told me I looked like a Madonna," she said, "and I said, 'O.K.'" I think she was the least inhibited person I ever saw. She reminded me of Reri, the Polynesian girl Florenz Ziegfeld brought to New York in 1931. Reri's feet were always dirty, because she insisted on walking about the theatre barefooted, and she used to sit in her dressing room at the "Follies" reading a movie magazine and wearing nothing but a pair of men's trunks.

"Mr. Adams told me you don't approve of the dancers in night clubs here," I said when she sat down again, "because you feel they besmirch the cause of nudism."

Miss Cubitt giggled.

"Well," she said, "you can put that in the paper if you want to, but I went to a night club last night and I thought the girls were real sweet. I would like to get a job in one. I sure do like New York. I've had lobsters every meal since I got here, and last night I had some real French champagne."

After the photographer had been introduced to the Queen, he had slumped into a chair and had remained there, staring. Now he roused himself and said he wanted to make some shots in a hurry, because he had to leave and cover the St. Patrick's Day parade. The young woman enjoyed posing and seemed to be sorry when the photographer finished, although he made about five times as many pictures as we needed. A few minutes after he left, a waiter, bringing the whiskey and the corned-beef sandwiches, knocked on the door. The waiter was either extremely sophisticated or had waited on the Queen before, because he did not seem to notice that she was not wearing anything. His eyes were respectfully averted, but he acted as if all the young women he waited on were nudists. When he had arranged his plates and glasses on a table, he handed Miss Cubitt the check. She signed it, and he bowed and left.

While we were eating the sandwiches, she told me of the dance she was working on, saying she called it the Tiger Lily dance. Why she called it that was a secret, she said.

"A World's Fair," the Queen remarked, "is a good place for a girl to make a reputation. When you get a reputation, you are fixed. Look at Sally Rand. What's she got I haven't got? I've seen her, and she's no world-beater. Look at Rosita Royce and her butterfly dance. Look at Toto La Verne and her swan dance. They're all World's Fair girls. If I can put my Tiger Lily over at the World's Fair, I'll be fixed."

I warned her that she might live to regret a World's Fair reputation, and mentioned the career of Mrs. Frieda Spyropolous, the Syrian girl whose dance as Little Egypt at the World's Columbian Exposition in 1893 attracted more attention than the seventy-ton telescope or any of the other educational exhibits. I told her how this Little Egypt had married the respectable Mr. Andrew Spyropolous, a Greek restaurant proprietor, not long after the Columbian Exposition closed, expecting to settle down to a peaceful way of life, and how the scandalous behavior of the hundreds of other Little Egypts who began doing her dance in low places all over the country had caused her acute anguish the rest of her life.

"Oh, I won't regret it," said the Queen, chewing on her sandwich. "I won't do anything unless it's artistic. Why, out at San Diego they even wanted me to do a Lady Godiva on a big white horse. I didn't do it because my boy friend made me mad. He said to go ahead and be Lady Godiva. He said he would sure pay forty cents to see me do it, because it had been years and years since he'd seen a horse."

Miss Cubitt giggled.

After we finished the sandwiches, we sat at a window and looked at the drizzle. I pointed out a few skyscrapers, but they didn't interest her. She wanted to talk about her career.

"It's swell being a nudist," she said, "but I wouldn't want to make it my life's work. I think the whole world should go nudist in the summer. You save so much on clothes. But then I don't know. I was in a real nudist colony once, and there were a lot of big, fat men there, and some women that must have weighed a ton. No kidding, you sure do see some terrible shapes in a nudist colony. Out at San Diego, we go on duty in the colony at noon and work until nine. It's like going back to your childhood—all you do is lie in the sun and play games. It's kind of silly, too. Sometimes me and my sisters get to laughing when we figure that already more than two million people have paid forty cents to see us girls running around naked. At the colony, we are a good distance from the customers, and they stand up there at the fence and strain their eyes. Sometimes I say to Ruthie, 'Ruthie, one of those psychologists would have a picnic down here.' "

By the time I got ready to go, my cold had vanished. Miss Cubitt went to the door with me. We were standing in the hall, shaking hands, when an elderly couple, a man and a woman, came out of a nearby room and started down the hall to the elevator. When they saw Miss Cubitt, their chins dropped. When they walked past us, they turned and stared. They did not appear to disapprove. They just seemed to be startled. Miss Cubitt giggled. She backed into her room.

"I guess I better say goodbye now," she said. "See you at the World's Fair."

Alva Johnston

HOW TO BECOME A GREAT WRITER*

Everybody sooner or later turns out to be a writer. Get deep enough into anybody's confidence, and you find that he has manuscripts. Psychoanalysts build a false science on the theory that millions of people are maladjusted lovers; a better knowledge of the world would teach that they are maladjusted writers.

David Binney Putnam launched himself on a serious literary career by wearing overalls, growing a beard and setting out to get the life stories of derelicts; the first derelict he met was a writer who took out a notebook and insisted on having young Putnam's life story.

Harold Ross, editor of The New Yorker, finding himself sick of New York City's 7,300,000 writers, tried to hunt a spot where there were no writers. He and Harpo Marx drove a car far into the Rockies. En route Harpo turned out to be a secret writer. The car broke down. The editor followed a trail leading to a cabin in a lonely mountain valley. In the cabin he found a writer writing a novel.

All this shows that, as Ed Howe put it, the people are smart. They are on the right trail. Writing is the shortest cut to affluence except inheriting big money. Today is the harvesttime for writers, and tomorrow's prospect is still better. A sure-hit writer can get $5000 a week and upwards in Hollywood. A good radio-script man or woman is worth four figures a week. Magazine editors and book publishers go out in posses after any promising writer. Writing is the royal road to statemanship; there is an enormous demand on the part of public men in Washington and elsewhere for artists in the oration-writing department of belles-lettres. Television holds a promise of becoming a writers' paradise; if it is a success it will require legions of writers to feed the television studios with scripts.

The paradox of the literary situation is that, while everybody is a writer, there is a shortage of writers for the thousand-a-week spots

* *This* Saturday Evening Post *article has been cut.*

601

and the five-thousand-a-week spots. According to Pandro Berman. head of the RKO picture studio. Hollywood can't get one tenth of the good writers it needs. His solution of the problem is for the universities to stop concentrating on the second-rate professions, which are already overcrowded, and to devote themselves to turning out big-money master writers, who are needed by the thousands. Law, medicine, engineering and the sciences have proved themselves to be excellent stopgaps and steppingstones for writers, but the demand of the time is for direct literary training which will enable young men and women to assume the thousand-a-week burdens immediately on graduation.

The main difficulty with Berman's suggestion is that of organizing the courses. Nobody seems to have worked out a satisfactory method of training writers to write. Colleges are good on punctuation marks, but not on what to put between them. Famous writers seem to have left few hints that are useful to beginners. Ring Lardner said it was a matter of selecting pencils of the right colors. Anthony Trollope said it was a matter of attaching the writer's pants to the chair with beeswax. Goethe attributed his output to a chair in which it was impossible to get into a restful position. In the vast literature about Dr. Samuel Johnson, only one practical rule of writing is to be found, and Doctor Johnson had that from an old schoolmaster; the rule being that, if you think any sentence you write is particularly good, strike it out. Dickens picked up his technique by accident. As a Parliamentary shorthand reporter during the decadence of parliamentary oratory, he learned the comic effect of presenting trivialities in ornate and sounding prose.

The subject has to be simplified before the universities can turn out prose masters on belt conveyors. A new approach to the problem would be to take the greatest living writer and make a thorough analysis of the factors which caused his greatness. Because of differences of opinion as to who is the greatest living writer, it is necessary to adopt arbitrary tests to identify him.

These tests are: 1. The size of the writer's public. 2. His success in establishing a character in the consciousness of the world. 3. The probability of his being read by posterity.

Judged by these tests, Edgar Rice Burroughs is first and the rest nowhere.

No other literary creation of this century has a following like Tarzan. Another character with a world-wide public is Mickey Mouse, but he belongs to a different art. The only other recent works of imagination in this class are Charlie McCarthy and The Lone Ranger, but their vogue is confined to the English-speaking peoples and they are still novelties rather than assured immortals.

Twenty-five million copies of the Tarzan books have been sold. Tarzan has established his durability; the first book on the ape boy came out a quarter of a century ago, and he is today more popular than ever. A writer's foreign following has been described as a contemporary posterity; Tarzan books have been translated into fifty-six languages and dialects. Hundreds of baseball players, football players, wrestlers, fighters and other athletes are nicknamed Tarzan. Extralarge schoolboys are called Tarzan in admiration, and undersized ones are called Tarzan in derision. Sherlock Holmes, Peter Pan, Pollyanna and Babbitt are perhaps the only literary creations of the last fifty years whose names are rooted in the English language as strongly as Tarzan; and Tarzan is a household word on every continent and on the larger islands from Iceland to Java.

Tarzan is a pillar of the American fiscal system. Through his author, his motion-picture company, his cartoon-strip syndicate, his radio sponsors and his various other concessionaires, the African ape boy contributes enough in taxes to pay the salaries of most of the United States senators.

Burroughs is clearly the man to tell the 130,000,000 American writers how to write. His life story ought to be the supreme textbook. The main rules for literary training that can be gathered from the experiences of Burroughs are:

1. Be a disappointed man.
2. Achieve no success at anything you touch.
3. Lead an unbearably drab and uninteresting life.
4. Hate civilization.
5. Learn no grammar.
6. Read little.
7. Write nothing.
8. Have an ordinary mind and commonplace tastes, approximating those of the great reading public.
9. Avoid subjects that you know about.

Burroughs had been an ill-paid employee and an unsuccessful small businessman for fifteen years before he wrote a word of fiction. The great difficulty in basing a college training on his rules is that of compressing into four years all the dullness, wretchedness and futility which it took Burroughs fifteen years to assimilate.

Burroughs started at twenty as a cattle drover and then became an employee on a gold dredge in Oregon. For a time he was a railroad policeman in Salt Lake City. He put in stretches as an accountant, as a clerk and as a peddler. His most important position was that of head of the stenographic department of Sears-Roebuck, in Chicago. A docile employee, he was never fired. An inveterate reader of help-wanted ads, he was constantly obtaining new positions not quite equal to his old ones. Added to that, he was always ready to join his own pennilessness to the pennilessness of some other man, and to found a partnership on any naïve dream of avarice.

Combining their resources of no capital, no experience and no contacts, Burroughs and a partner founded an advertising agency, which failed.

Having no experience with salesmanship beyond that of being repulsed by housewives when he tried to sell sets of Stoddard's Lectures, Burroughs wrote a correspondence course in salesmanship. After studying by correspondence for a few weeks, his students were to be graduated into field work. Small stocks of aluminum pots and pans were sent to them with instructions to sell them from door to door and remit the money to the home office.

Burroughs and his partner thought there were millions in it. They regarded themselves as aluminum kings about to corner the pot-an-pan trade with the help of peddlers who would pay tuition fees for the privilege of peddling. But the students all quit when they got to the field-work stage. Some failed to send back either the money or the pots and pans.

The Burroughs family had been rich when Edgar was a boy, but had lost its money. His allowance at prep school had been $150 a month. During his entire business career he never earned as much as his prep-school allowance. Twice he was compelled to pawn his family heirlooms in order to buy food for his wife and children. His failure as a businessman was so complete that he was reduced to earning a living by writing hints on how to become a successful businessman.

The businessman's bible three decades ago was *System, the Magazine of Efficiency*. It was a pioneer in introducing charts and graphs. Many businessmen worshiped charts and graphs as religious symbols. It was their belief that, if they stared long enough at these mystic curves and angles, red ink would turn into black.

A new department was introduced by the magazine. On payment of fifty dollars a year, a businessman could write to the magazine as often as he liked, and receive detailed advice on his business problems. Burroughs was hired to give the detailed advice. There was also a detailed-advice department for bankers, which was handled by a youth of twenty-one years. Burroughs sat at his desk from morning until night, writing counsel to merchant princes and captains. He used words that rumbled with portentous business wisdom, but were too vague to enable any industrial baron to act on them. Burroughs had a conscience, and it was always his fear that, if his advice ever became understandable, it would land his clients in the bankruptcy courts. With his letters he would enclose some of the awe-inspiring hieroglyphics now known as "barometrics."

Burroughs' advice never brought a complaint, and he may have been as good as anybody else in this field. Nothing is definitely known on the subject today except that the more the charts and graphs flourish, the faster business decays.

Burroughs' first contact with literature came in 1911 through his connection with Alcola, a cure for alcoholism. Alcola cured alcoholism all right, but the Federal Pure Food and Drug people took the position that there were worse things than alcoholism, and forbade the sale of Alcola.

One of Burroughs' duties in the Alcola firm was that of putting advertisements in the pulp fiction magazines. He bought the magazines in order to make sure that his ads were printed. He detested fiction, but when he looked at the ads some of the reading matter entered his field of vision. His reaction was approximately that of Dean Swift, who, under similar circumstances, exclaimed, "No man alive ever writ such damned stuff."

His next thought was that, if this was literature, any man could be a man of letters if he would abandon his mind to it. He wrote a novel. Thomas Newell Metcalf, editor of the *All-Story Magazine,* accepted it and sent Burroughs a check for $400. It was published as a serial in *All-Story* in 1912, under the title of "Under the Moon of Mars."

Metcalf wanted to make a Sir Walter Scott out of Burroughs. He induced him to spend months of research on the Wars of the Roses. The result was a novel entitled "The Outlaw of Torn." Metcalf rejected it.

Burroughs saw the folly of research. He had located his first novel on Mars because nobody knew the local color of that planet or the psychology of the Martians, and nobody could check up on him. A similar motive influenced him partly in writing his first Tarzan book, "Tarzan of the Apes." He created a new race of apes, bigger than gorillas, and placed them in an unknown part of Africa. He knew that nobody could trip him up on the psychology, customs and language of his own private anthropoids.

For African local color he read Stanley's "In Darkest Africa." He got his flora all right, but he made a blunder in his fauna. One of his important characters was Sabor, the tiger. There are no tigers in Africa. Letters from readers were printed in *All-Story* on this point. A man in Johannesburg confounded the critics, however, by writing that everybody in Africa referred to leopards as tigers. Nevertheless, Burroughs later changed Sabor to a lioness. He got a check for $700 from *All-Story* for "Tarzan of the Apes."

Burroughs had by this time retired from his last business, that of selling a pencil sharpener, and was devoting all his time to writing. His business career had, by its dreary futility, been a genuine literary apprenticeship. During his last few years in commercial pursuits, life had become almost intolerable to him.

He was too poverty-stricken to pay for any of the tired businessman's relaxations, but he hit upon a free method of making himself feel better. When he went to bed he would lie awake, telling himself stories. His dislike of civilization caused him frequently to pick localities in distant parts of the solar system. Every night he had his one crowded hour of glorious life. Creating noble characters and diabolical monsters, he made them fight in cockpits in the center of the earth or in distant astronomical regions. The duller the day at the office the weirder his nightly adventures. His waking nightmares became long-drawn-out action serials.

Psychiatrists consider these reverie addicts borderline cases. If Burroughs' family had known of his mental state, they would have called in a medical man, who would have probably insisted on having his teeth out, according to the fashionable method of treating such patients in 1911. Twenty years later, Burroughs would have been advised to save up his money for a few years and go to a psychoanalyst, who would have cured him of an incipient $10,000,000 affliction. A raise of twenty-five dollars a month in 1911, according to Burroughs' estimate, would have made him happy and caused him to put in nights of sound, refreshing slumber, instead of constructing penny-dreadful deliriums for himself.

Burroughs had given away serials to himself for five years or more before he learned that he could sell them. He had become a master of the slaughterhouse branches of fiction. It is clear from reading the Tarzan and other Burroughs books that he devoted little of his twilight sleep to tea-table and boy-meets-girl imbroglios.

Five years of dark and bloody mysteries gave his pen a high professionalism in pyramiding climaxes and piling up horror; but he was an awkward novice when the structure of his novel required him to introduce scenes of society life or hearts-and-flowers passages. Burroughs is great when Tarzan has a half nelson on a lion or a gorilla, but he has no talent for drawing-room hubble-bubble or boudoir hanky-panky. There is a trace of Homer in him, but not any Noel Coward.

In "Tarzan of the Apes" the reader can put his finger on the passages where Burroughs is the dream-disciplined artist and on the passages where he is the self-conscious amateur. He wanted to endow his ape-reared infant with a magnificent heredity. He was under the impression that the way to have a glorious moral, mental and physical inheritance was to be a scion of the British aristocracy. So Tarzan's parents were Lord and Lady Greystoke, the flower of the old nobility. Burroughs created them out of condescending sawdust.

It is obvious that Burroughs in his nightly trances had wasted no time messing around with lords and ladies. The Burroughs noblemen cause the reader to turn instinctively to P. G. Wodehouse for a sympathetic picture of the British aristocracy. But when the real Burroughs gets to work on his wild boy, his colossal anthropoids, his giant carnivora and his cannibals, it is not difficult to see why 3,000,000 copies of "Tarzan of the Apes" have been sold and why Tarzan is the best-known literary character of the twentieth century.

Burroughs says that his ordinariness explains his success. When he wrote his first novel for *All-Story,* he used the nom de plume of Normal Bean, meaning common head. By accident the editor changed it to Norman Bean. Burroughs was unwilling to use his own name at the time because he thought it would hurt his standing in the unsuccessful business world. He believes today that his novels are in demand because the things that interest him are bound to interest the ordinary people, who are abundant. Undoubtedly a certain galloping commonplaceness is one of his assets, but he has others. He did not win his world public solely through mediocrity. There are pages of his books which have the authentic flash and sting of storytelling genius.

One brilliant passage is that in which the half-grown Tarzan identifies himself as the being who is reflected in a pool of water. Tarzan had already had reason to suspect that he was not a trueborn ape. Gazing at himself in the waters, he discovers what a poor relation of the higher anthropoids he really is. Burroughs is in a high literary vein when he describes the boy's chagrin in comparing his parody of a countenance with the pretentious physiognomies of his playmates. Instead of nostrils that spread half across his face, he had a despicable imitation of an organ of smell. He had trifling bits of ivory where competent tusks should have been. Self-pity overwhelmed him when he discovered that his eyes were an insipid gray instead of being big, black and bloodshot. On realizing that he was hairless like a snake, he plastered himself from head to foot with mud.

Tarzan had already suspected that he was not a true ape, because he had discovered in a deserted cabin a number of kindergarten books with pictures of animals. He had begun to fear that he resembled the apes less than he resembled another animal, whose picture was always printed with what appeared to be three little bugs—*B, O* and *Y.* The painful conviction was forced upon him that he was a *B-O-Y.*

Using these three bugs as a clue, Tarzan works out the secret of all the twenty-six bugs in the alphabet. He learns written English without knowing how to pronounce it. Burroughs' handling of Tarzan's self-education is better than the cipher sequences in "The Gold Bug" or "The Dancing Men."

Tarzan's discovery that he is a member of the human species later lands him in a beautiful ethical dilemma. Having killed an African tribesman, Tarzan is about to help himself. Certain doubts assail him. His bringing up had taught him that eating a member of one's own species was not done. He has eaten raw gorilla, but the gorilla does not belong to his set. Tarzan now knows himself to be a man, and he recognizes the dead African as a man. On the other hand, Tarzan is hungry, and his political sympathies are all with the apes. It is a pretty case of conscience, and Burroughs does justice to it. In the end Tarzan takes the high ethical stand and never refreshes himself with an African.

One sequence in "Tarzan of the Apes" will bear comparison with the much-admired passage in "Gulliver's Travels" in which the Lilliputians, in an official report on the effects removed from Gulliver's pockets, suggest that his watch is his god because of the frequency with which he consults it. Tarzan sees Kulonga, son of a savage chief, cook a wild boar and eat it. Tarzan knows fire only as Ara, the lightning. He cannot understand why anybody would spoil raw meat by plunging it into fire. He concludes that Kulonga is a friend of the god of lightning and is sharing the wild boar with him. There is occasionally a touch of poetry in Burroughs, as in describing Tarzan's grass-woven lasso as "his long arm of many grasses."

Another source of the author's strength is his strong grip of character. Not only Tarzan but the apes and animals are highly individualized beings who seldom step out of character. Burroughs edits the Tarzan movies and newspaper strips to see that no liberties are taken with the Tarzan psychology. In one movie scene, for example, Tarzan threw his head back and laughed long and boisterously. "Strike it out," ordered Burroughs. Tarzan, in spite of his violent activity, is as reserved and contemplative as Hamlet. Nothing could be farther from his personality than brainless uproariousness.

One of the handsome passages in "Tarzan of the Apes" is the ape-bred boy's first encounter with white womanhood. Tarzan rescued the heroine, a glamorous but educated American girl, from the clutches of a mate-hunting giant ape. The bronzed and sun-baked Tarzan, accustomed to seeing none but ape women and blacks, was conscious of a sudden prejudice in her favor, in spite of her white body. He wanted her to know that he was favorably disposed toward her. His good will took the form of pawing and nuzzling. She slapped him. Tarzan was astonished. He had assumed that, when a member of a species showed a nice spirit toward another member of the same species, that spirit would be reciprocated. He could not understand why she was returning evil for good.

Burroughs was told that Kipling liked Tarzan and supposed that Tarzan was patterned after Mowgli of "The Jungle Book." According to Burroughs, Tarzan is a literary descendant, not of Mowgli but of Romulus and Remus, who got such a raising from a she-wolf that they founded Rome. Burroughs credits himself with only one stroke of genius—the naming of Tarzan. The impact of those two syllables on the eardrum is, in his opinion, largely responsible for the world success of the Tarzan books. This is one of the few literary secrets of Burroughs that is communicable. In christening his characters he works with syllables as some composers work with musical notes. He tests one sound against another until, after trying perhaps hundreds of combinations, he has a name that rings like a fire bell.

The early life of Burroughs was more interesting than his business career, but it furnishes few hints toward becoming a great writer. His father, who had been a major in the Civil War, grew rich in the distilling business. Later he became a manufacturer of electrical batteries. He had a habit of reading aloud, which partly caused young Edgar's aversion to literature. When, for example, his father read "Dombey and Son," Edgar hated Dombey and had the impression that Dombey and Dickens were one and the same person. When he learned the difference, it was too late for him to overcome his ingrained prejudice against Dickens. He has also cherished a lifelong dislike for Shakespeare, but is big enough to state that he assumes it to be his fault rather than the poet's.

Burroughs' escape from grammar was a lucky accident. He was sent first to a private school in Chicago which held that the teaching of English grammar was nonsense and that students should absorb grammar through Latin and Greek. Edgar absorbed no Latin and Greek. He was then sent to Phillips Andover, which, assuming that all freshmen were thoroughly drilled in grammar, ignored that subject. Phillips Andover quickly waived on young Burroughs, and he was sent to military academy, which paid no attention to grammar. Edgar thus became an uninhibited writer, free from the anxieties about moods and tenses which kill spontaneity. Burroughs doesn't know whether he is grammatical or not, and cares less. He always writes or dictates at top speed in order to get his thoughts on paper while they are fresh and hot. No grammar-scared writer can do that. Burroughs never makes corrections unless he finds an inconsistency in his development of plot.

The battery business led the elder Burroughs to become interested in an electrical horseless carriage. Edgar demonstrated it at the World's Fair, in 1893. The only time he ever felt that he amounted to something was when he drove a nine-seater horseless surrey about the fairgrounds, starting runaways every hundred feet or so.

In his youth Burroughs had a craving for glory. He preferred the military variety because his father had been a soldier. After graduating from the Michigan Military Academy he joined its faculty as a cavalry instructor. After the Sino-Japanese War of 1894-5, China, which had been defeated because her armament consisted largely of drums and dragon banners, started to reorganize her army. Burroughs sought a commission in the Chinese army, but failed. Later he obtained a commission in the Nicaraguan army, but his family interfered. At the age of twenty he enlisted in the Seventh Cavalry and was sent to Arizona against Geronimo. Instead of cavalry charges, however, the campaign consisted mainly of ditch-digging. Wires were pulled, and, because Burroughs had enlisted while under age, he was discharged. In 1898 he volunteered for the Rough Riders, but received a polite letter of regret from Theodore Roosevelt.

During his brief Regular Army service, Burroughs had committed two grave infractions of the military code. On sentry duty, he was required to shoot to kill if anyone disregarded his warning of "Halt, or I fire." His warning was twice disregarded, but Burroughs did not shoot. In each case he wrongfully saved the life of a drunken member of his own outfit. He escaped disgrace, his unsoldierly conduct never becoming known.

From the Army Burroughs went directly into cow handling, and then into gold dredging. Years later, after establishing himself as a writer about imaginary worlds and countries, he wrote "The Bandit of Hell's Bend," based on his Western experience. This was a violation of his custom of not writing things personally known to him; but Alexander Grosset, of the publishing house of Grosset & Dunlap, pronounced "The Bandit of Hell's Bend" the greatest Western ever written.

The old craving for glory was roused in Burroughs only once after the Spanish-American War. He happened to see the regal state in which the president of the Oregon Short Line traveled. He took the only railroad job he could get. In hot pursuit of glory, Burroughs chased bums out of boxcars in the Salt Lake City railroad yards for six months. But the idea of becoming a railroad president—last of his high ambitions—faded, and he drifted into the business career which punished him until he took refuge in literature.

The first Tarzan story did not immediately make Burroughs rich. The idea of bringing it out in book form was rejected by publishing houses, one reason being that they felt that the title, "Tarzan of the Apes," would shock refined people. Burroughs wrote a sequel, "The Return of Tarzan." It was declined by the Munsey publications, without the knowledge of Bob Davis, editor-in-chief of that organization.

Davis was furious when the Tarzan sequel was printed in a rival magazine. The famous editor took Burroughs under his wing and insisted on publishing everything he wrote. Even Davis, however, did not see the future of Tarzan. He induced Burroughs to cause the original Tarzan to assume his title of Lord Greystoke and take his seat in the House of Lords, while the series was carried on with the son of Tarzan. This caused confusion, and Burroughs finally went back to Tarzan the First. According to rigid rules of biology, the African wild boy is now a grandfather.

In less than a year after his first work was published, Burroughs was a big pulp name and a ten-cents-a-word writer. As his literary labor consisted largely of transcribing from memory the old phantasmagorias with which he soothed himself during his business life, his production was large. He was making more than $20,000 a year before his first book was published. On his banner day he wrote 9100 words— $910 worth.

Big money did not immediately soften Burroughs' hatred of modern life. His great aim was to escape from civilization, and, as soon as he had money, he went to Southern California. In 1919, after he had become wealthy, Burroughs bought the 600-acre Harrison Gray Otis ranch in the San Fernando Valley and founded the town of Tarzana, about half an hour's auto ride from Hollywood. He delighted to ride, stetson on head, gun across saddle, over his hills and through his valleys and his canyons.

He started to ranch on a large scale with pedigreed animals. It was necessary to write furiously to support the ranch. Scarcity of wells and springs was the trouble. Water had to be brought in from the outside. After some experience with water rates, he found it would be cheaper to take his cattle to a soda fountain. The ranch was turned over to the El Caballero Golf Club, which failed. After running it as a public golf course for a while, Burroughs sold out.

Burroughs had been writing four years before a publishing house would take a chance on printing his novels in book form. The late J. H. Tennant, editor of the *New York Evening World,* had read "Tarzan of the Apes" in *All-Story* and bought the right to print it in his newspaper. Other papers followed suit, and Tarzan fans became an important bloc in the community. A. C. McClurg & Co., one of the many publishers which had previously rejected "Tarzan of the Apes," began publishing the Tarzan books and then other Burroughs novels. Millions of boys took to leaping from limb to limb and from tree to tree. The nation resounded with the Tarzan yell and the snapping of collarbones.

Today Burroughs has forty-nine books in print. The sales have exceeded 30,000,000 copies. The Tarzan books are still in great demand in nearly every part of the world except Germany. In 1925 Burroughs was taking more royalties out of Germany than any foreign author, but in that year a German writer printed a book entitled "Tarzan the German Devourer." During the World War, Burroughs had, in "Tarzan the Untamed," caused Tarzan to do his bit by capturing German officers and feeding them to lions. The sensitive Teutons boycotted Burroughs after 1925.

Tarzan is a radio star today. The Tarzan comic strip is printed in about 150 American newspapers and forty foreign ones, including journals in Java and Ceylon. Tarzan has been a great money-maker in the movies for more than twenty years. Johnny Weissmuller is the ninth actor to play the part in the films.

Tarzan's importance in the films increased greatly in 1932, when the late Irving Thalberg took charge of his career. Thalberg and Burroughs agreed that Tarzan pictures should be great spectacles and should come out once a year, like a circus. Thalberg's first two pictures cost more than a million each, and the third, "Tarzan Escapes," cost more than a million and a half. After Thalberg's death, the Metro-Goldwyn-Mayer Company dropped Tarzan as too expensive. But the final audit showed that "Tarzan Escapes" had grossed more than $2,000,000, and the series was resumed.

The expensiveness of the Tarzan films lies partly in the nature of things and partly in the maniacal perfectionism of Hollywood. In the last picture, "Tarzan Finds a Son," the producers wanted an effect of steam rising from a lake. They ransacked the country for steamy lakes and at last found the one they wanted in Florida. The lake refused to steam for them. They found that it would steam only on certain days and then only for about fifteen minutes in the morning. It took the location company seven days to get the pictures they wanted.

Most of the Tarzan scenes are taken out of doors. Bad weather causes losses running into hundreds of thousands of dollars in salaries of actors, technical men and mobs of extras. But the greatest expense is that of getting animals to perform. In making the last picture a lion cost the company tens of thousands of dollars by refusing to chase a small boy. The lion would either walk or lie down or lope off in the wrong direction. When he finally took after the boy, the boy forgot to run. The pay roll ran wild for ten days before the scene could be shot. Flamingos, zebras and other live items of African background, after hours had been consumed in maneuvering them into their places, walked off the set just before the cameras started.

It took weeks to teach the big elephant, Queenie, to limp when she was supposed to have been shot in the foot. In the meantime the baby elephant, Bea, was limping sympathetically, and it took weeks to break her of the habit. A herd of hippopotamuses broke out of their stockade in Sherwood Lake and ate up $25,000 worth of horticulture in the neighborhood. Fresh ostrich eggs, which were used by Tarzan's mate in making omelets, cost twenty-five dollars each.

M-G-M spared no expense on the Tarzan yell. Miles of sound track of human, animal and instruments sounds were tested in collecting the ingredients of an unearthly howl. The cry of a mother camel robbed of her young was used until still more mournful sounds were found. A combination of five different sound tracks is used today for the Tarzan yell. These are: 1. Sound track of Weissmuller yelling, amplified. 2. Track of hyena howl, run backward and volume diminished. 3. Soprano note sung by Lorraine Bridges, recorded on sound track at reduced speed; then re-recorded at varying speeds to give a "flutter" in sound. 4. Growl of dog, recorded very faintly. 5. Raspy note of violin G-string, recorded very faintly. In the experimental stage the five sound tracks were played over five different loud-speakers. From time to time the speed of each sound track was varied and the volume amplified or diminished.

When the orchestration of the yell was perfected, the five loud-speakers were played simultaneously and the blended sounds recorded on the master sound track. By constant practice Weissmuller is now able to let loose an almost perfect imitation of the sound track.

Sanderson Vanderbilt

OWL MAN

Somehow or other, Miss Emily Nathan, publicity manager for the Audubon Society, got the idea that a barn owl sleeps every night with Mr. Irving Kassoy at his apartment in the Bronx at 817 Faile Street. Maybe it was because a *stuffed* barn owl is perched on the bureau in Mr. Kassoy's bedroom and he knows where there *is* a live barn owl. Miss Nathan, with other things on her mind, didn't catch the distinction. At all events she got word to me that Mr. Kassoy had an owl sleeping with him and that I could have an interview with Mr. Kassoy. "Besides," said Miss Nathan, "the National Association of Audubon Societies gets all its owl reports from Mr. Kassoy."

I met Mr. Kassoy at six that evening at the Audubon Society's headquarters, at Fifty-seventh Street and Broadway, after he had completed his day's work. He is a slim little fellow of thirty-two, very pale and somewhat bald. His chin is pointed and his skin is drawn taut from his cheeks up to his wide forehead. You couldn't help noticing his grave eyes because of the thick glasses he wears. Even to one not knowing the nature of his hobby, Mr. Kassoy's general appearance would be hauntingly suggestive of owls.

Mr. Kassoy was sitting there in the anteroom of the Audubon offices telling Miss Nathan about the difference in behavior between male and female owls. As soon as I came in, Miss Nathan broke the bad news to me that Mr. Kassoy's barn owl did not roost in Mr. Kassoy's bedroom, after all. Even if it did, it had occurred to Miss Nathan, it would be unlikely that an owl would stay home after dark to be visited. It occurred to me that I ought to have thought of that myself. Mr. Kassoy immediately moderated my dismay by saying that he could take me to the home of a barn owl resident in New York City if I cared to make a rather strenuous trip, and I impulsively accepted his invitation. With very little more conversation we started off, after saying good night to Miss Nathan.

Crossing town on Fifty-ninth Street, Mr. Kassoy told me that when he is not checking up on owls, he works as a jewelry salesman in midtown Manhattan. Then he went on eagerly to give me a brief introduction to the owl situation in the city. He said there might very likely be a pair of screech owls living right over there in Central Park and that the short-eared owl, the saw-whet owl, the great horned owl, and two or three other owls are seen around there occasionally on their way through town during migration seasons. But his interest was primarily in the barn owl, he said, because that's the kind that lives here all year round. As he talked, it developed that he was interested, actually, in only one barn owl, because, as far as he can find out, only one barn owl now lives in New York.

"Pelham Bay Park is the only place in the city where you can definitely go to see a barn owl when you want to see one," said Mr. Kassoy, picking his phrases with scientific care. "And, as a matter of fact, there's only one of the birds up there now. I've looked everywhere for more of them—last May there was a pair in a church over in Flushing, and a few years ago (you'd hardly believe it, would you?) there were some in a factory up on East 138th Street—but the only barn owl I know of now is in Pelham Bay Park. I suppose you can't print this, but a man who is familiar with barn owls can always tell where they are by the droppings outside the place they're nesting in. I mean, he knows it's a barn owl and not a pigeon or some other kind of bird. Barn owls generally live in church belfries. I've been looking at a lot of belfries but I haven't covered them all as yet. There are so many churches in New York."

We went into the subway at Bloomingdale's and got on an uptown local. It was crowded, and Mr. Kassoy shouted above the roar that he had first heard of barn owls living in Pelham Bay Park in 1932. A pair of them had built a nest in a ventilator over the library of the old Huntington mansion, erected by the railroad magnate and now used by the Parks Department as a sort of warehouse. The next spring the female laid six eggs, and five of them hatched. It was then that Mr. Kassoy began to develop what he described as his monomania. Owl study isn't very exciting when there are no young birds, because the adults won't stay on their nests to be observed. All you get is a glimpse of them at dusk darting forth in search of food. But when there are babies, the female stands guard over them all night long while the father bird brings in the food. You can observe them then to beat the band, it seems.

Mr. Kassoy first of all got permission and some keys from the Parks Department to visit the Huntington mansion at all hours. Then he set a birdhouse against the interior opening of the ventilator. The owls seemed to like the birdhouse, and even stayed right on when Mr. Kassoy installed in it a little electric light operated by a dry-cell battery. Finally, he rigged up a piece of glass so that when it was dark outside and the light was turned on inside the cage, Mr. Kassoy could see the owls but the owls couldn't see Mr. Kassoy.

Three of that first batch of baby owls waddled through the ventilator, fell two stories to the ground, and died. The two others grew up and flew away. Mr. Kassoy never saw them again. The parents stayed on and Mr. Kassoy observed them every night. Then, in March, 1934, Mr. Kassoy found the female dead on the nest. *That's* the one, stuffed and mounted, in his bedroom. The male had a new mate in ten days. "A commentary on the possible abundance of the barn owl in New York," Mr. Kassoy said as the train pulled into Ninety-sixth Street.

Well, the new female deposited four eggs and three of them hatched out, and Mr. Kassoy put up a little platform outside the ventilator to protect the young from the fate of their predecessors. "When they were only eighteen days old," said Mr. Kassoy, pushing a straphanger's *Evening Journal* out of his face, "the barn owl's ancient enemy, the crow, chased the mother out over Eastchester Bay, where some herring gulls took up after her, pounced on her, and apparently finished her off."

Within a fortnight, he went on, the widower had a new companion, and *that's* the owl over which Mr. Kassoy now keeps lonely vigil in Pelham Bay Park and the one he was now taking me to see. She would have nothing to do with rearing her predecessor's offspring, he said, and kept disappearing from time to time. While the father owl labored to bring up his half-orphans, she'd go away for as long as a fortnight at a stretch. Finally, when the youngsters grew up, she settled down and hatched out five of her own. They came along pretty late in the season.

It snowed heavily in January and February of 1935, but Mr. Kassoy floundered from the end of the subway line through the drifts in the park to the Huntington mansion two or three nights a week. Some of the young owls died of starvation and the others went away. Finally the male vanished, and since that time Mr. Kassoy has had only the movements of the lone female to observe.

"There was every indication during March of 1935 that she was seeking a new mate," Mr. Kassoy shouted down the neck of a bouncing matron in front of him. "But she was not successful, and in April she disappeared. I thought it was all over then, but she came back in June. Last spring it was the same thing—she went away for a long while but came back. No mates, so far as I could learn."

At the Hunts Point station we got out of the subway to pick up a flashlight at Mr. Kassoy's home. By this time we were both referring to the long series of bird tenants at the Huntington mansion as "female number one," "female number two," and "female number three." As we climbed the stairs to the street, I asked Mr. Kassoy if he had some pet name, like Lizzie or Iphigenia, for the last female barn owl whose life he had studied during the last two and a half years.

"Why should I?" he asked gravely. "The bird doesn't know me."

We walked up four flights to the apartment where Mr. Kassoy lives with his parents. Down the long hallway I could see them at dinner, but we just went into Mr. Kassoy's little bedroom, where the only ornaments were that stuffed owl on the bureau and a mounted duck on the bookcase. Mr. Kassoy told me he had been born in Russia and was brought to the Bronx when he was a few weeks old. He is unmarried. He asked me if I had had dinner, and when I told him I had, he said he'd had a late lunch and didn't want any. Then he called to his parents, "I'm going out," and we started downstairs.

We went back to the subway and continued on our way to Pelham Bay Park. The train was almost empty that far uptown, and the only person in the car with us was an extremely pretty girl who sat directly opposite. Mr. Kassoy was telling me about "the guttural, vibrant quality of the barn owl's call just before copulation" when the train ground to a halt and his voice suddenly became painfully audible. The young woman looked up and studied Mr. Kassoy intently. After appraising his shiny blue suit, his pink shirt, and his sweat-stained felt hat, she unexpectedly smiled directly at his earnest, wan face. Mr. Kassoy was looking in her direction, but I don't think he even saw her. He began to tell me about the winter night he tried to keep his owls from starving.

"It was in 1935, when the male disappeared, and we were having a heavy snow that night," he explained. "The next morning I said, 'Well, the barn owls are having a tough time up there, but I guess they'll weather it.' The next night it snowed again and there was a gale, so that evening I took two pounds of raw beefsteak up there. It was a Saturday night, and there was about a foot of snow on the ground. I had quite a time breaking a track through, and when I got there the keeper had locked up his home. (I have to go there to get the keys to the mansion.) It was midnight by that time. I couldn't get in, so I scattered the meat around outside."

Generally speaking, however, Mr. Kassoy does not like to feed his owl, because of a strange gastronomic process peculiar to the birds. Barn owls live mostly on mice and rats, which they swallow whole. Their digestive juices get to working on the mess and peel the meat from the skeleton sort of like boiling a soup bone. On the way home, the owl's insides roll up the bones, along with the fur, into a black pellet about the size of a horse chestnut. It would seem more conducive to pleasant living if the owl got rid of this somewhere outdoors, but it doesn't. It waits until it reaches its nest and then disgorges the pellet. Nasty as it sounds, the habit is a godsend to Mr. Kassoy, for it has afforded him his principal contact with his owl since the last batch of young went away, nearly two years ago. By opening up the pellets and examining the little rodents' skulls inside them, Mr. Kassoy can tell just how well his owl has been eating. He also can determine, from the consistency of the pellet, whether the owl has been home recently or whether she is out on one of her periodic wandering sprees. He seldom sees his owl any more, but feels that the pellets keep him on quite intimate terms with her.

The train reached the end of the line and we got off. Mr. Kassoy wanted to get some cigarettes, so we went into a neighborhood bar and grill. The bartender came forward with a smile. Mr. Kassoy asked him if he sold cigarettes and the man pointed to a vending machine. "You know," Mr. Kassoy told me, as he poked his coins into the device, "no one ever made a study of barn owls' behavior on the nest before."

We headed off cross-country through Pelham Bay Park. Mr. Kassoy flicked his flashlight on and off, but not to find our path. He kept flashing it up into the trees, hoping, he told me, to spot the sparkle of an owl's eye. There didn't seem to be any around. Then we stood still while Mr. Kassoy whistled low and mournfully. He said if there were any screech owls in the vicinity, they'd answer that. The only thing we heard was the rumble of our subway train, far behind us, starting back toward Manhattan.

"I wish you could hear a barn owl," Mr. Kassoy said, leading the way confidently through the darkness. "It's sort of a long, drawn-out, rasping scream. In fact, I wouldn't be surprised if it gave rise to the banshee legends in Ireland."

"You wouldn't?" I inquired, absently, as I stumbled through the underbrush.

"No," he replied, "but it's just an unsubstantiated theory of mine, so maybe you'd better not mention it."

After half a dozen more unanswered calls for screech owls, we saw a light through the trees. It came from the park caretaker's cottage, where Mr. Kassoy always has to stop to pick up the keys to the Huntington mansion. Mr. Kassoy told me that the caretaker, Mr. Devine, thinks the mansion is haunted and that anyone who'd sit up alone in it all night long looking for owls is mad.

The keys were in a little box on Mr. Devine's back porch. Mr. Kassoy called a cheery greeting to the caretaker, who was sitting in the living room in his shirtsleeves. Mr. Devine replied with a curt "Hello." Then we continued toward the mansion.

It was a gloomy place, all right. At one end of the library, Mr. Kassoy's light picked out a huge tree—an elm, I think he said it was— which, he said, in season, has such thick foliage that it's almost as dark as night underneath it on a summer afternoon. The building itself was covered with ivy, which rustled in the chilly evening air. Up near the eaves, Mr. Kassoy's flash spotted the little ventilation opening through which passes the only known barn owl in New York City.

We stood around in the courtyard for a while, looking for owls but not seeing any, and then Mr. Kassoy led the way around to the carriage entrance. "Gosh, I love this place!" he said as he fumbled with the lock. "After four years of coming up here nights alone and all the things I've seen here and all—I love it, you know."

The Parks Department keeps seeds in the old library, and the place smelled moist and warm. I found myself tiptoeing. Suddenly, Mr.

Kassoy opened the door to a stairway and flashed his light quickly upward. "Hmm, that's funny," he said. "Generally, there's a rat on these stairs. Runs up ahead of me every night." Two flights up we came to a trapdoor. Mr. Kassoy had a key for that, too. That brought us to the eaves and the ventilator. Mr. Kassoy fiddled around with some batteries in one corner and pretty soon a pale light appeared near the floor. It was in the barn owl's nest—a plain box with an open top, pushed up against the entrance afforded by the ventilator.

Removing one of the boards, Mr. Kassoy bent tenderly over the cubby-hole, which was foul. He picked up a buff-colored feather and told me it had been part of his barn owl's plumage.

Then Mr. Kassoy began inspecting the pellets left in the nest since his last visit. Nearly every one of them contained two rat skulls. A few of the pellets were old and dry, but presently Mr. Kassoy came upon a fresh one and he became visibly excited. "That was left just today," he said. "The owl was here last night!"

Sitting there in the faint light from the cage, I suggested to Mr. Kassoy that time must pass slowly during an all-night, solitary watch over the nest. But he said no, it didn't, and that Saturday nights were particular treats, because then he could sleep the next day.

"I remember one time, though," he went on. "It was about two o'clock on a Sunday morning. It was so quiet up here I could hear my watch ticking in my pocket. Suddenly, someone slammed the door downstairs. I knew I was the only one with a key to the place and that I had locked the door. And I knew whoever it was down there had no business in the house.

"Well, I never knew before that it really could happen, but my hair actually stood out on the sides of my head. Then I heard footsteps in the hall downstairs, and then they started coming upstairs. I heard them coming right up that stairway to the trapdoor. Just then, though, one of the owls flew in to feed the young and I had to make a note of that in my records. So I forgot all about the footsteps."

Mr. Kassoy paused—for dramatic effect, I suspected. He said no more. "What about the intruder?" I finally asked.

"I don't know," said Mr. Kassoy. "After I'd made my notes, I didn't hear the footsteps any more."

On the way back to the subway, I asked Mr. Kassoy where his owl went at night. He admitted, sadly, that he wasn't sure. "She generally starts out over Eastchester Bay," he said. One time Mr. Kassoy went over to the other side of the bay every evening for a week, hoping to catch a glimpse of the bird arriving there. After seven fruitless evenings, he returned to the nest and checked up on the pellets. His owl hadn't been home once during the whole week. She stayed away a month that time.

E. J. Kahn, Jr.

AT HOME WITH THE PALEYS

I am pretty sore at the William S. Paleys. They will be surprised to hear this, if they do, because they don't know me and I don't know them. I do know, of course, that Mr. Paley is the president of the Columbia Broadcasting System and that Mrs. Paley is a member of café society in good repute. Unless *Vogue* and *Harper's Bazaar* have been misinforming me, she is even a friend of Elsa Maxwell's. I am not a friend of Elsa Maxwell's, and the reason I am sore at the Paleys is that a while ago I went to call on them, in their own home, and they were out. I had seen in the papers that on a certain afternoon it would be possible for anyone—anyone with six dollars, that is—to visit half a dozen charming hostesses in their own salons. The money, I read, would go to the Neighborhood Playhouse Scholarship Fund, and it seemed like a worthy cause. I sent in my six dollars and received a nice printed card of admission—to six houses, I thought expectantly, full of gay people, sparkling repartee, and tall, tinkling glasses. Lily Pons and Elizabeth Arden were on the list, but I preferred to call upon the Paleys. I wanted to see Mr. Paley standing hostlike in the background, muttering about Martians while his wife passed the *pâté de foie gras*, looking just like a picture out of El Morocco. When I got there, the only thing I found that reminded me at all of El Morocco was a large carpet made of zebra skins, running up a staircase. There was not a sign of Mr. Paley, Mrs. Paley, Elsa Maxwell, or the Countess di Zoppola.

As a matter of fact, when my cab pulled up at the house I thought for a moment I was at the wrong address. Beekman Place is a section I rarely get to, and there wasn't a limousine parked within twenty yards of the door my driver pointed to, but the number 29 was unmistakably on it, so I went in, across a tarpaulin that had been thrown over the front steps to protect the Paley threshold from such humble feet as mine. The door was open, and when I went in there was no sound of carefree banter, no gentle hum of conversation. Not even an exploding flash bulb. There were simply two bored ladies sitting at a table in the entrance, in neither of whose faces I recognized those lovely characteristics that have endeared Mrs. Paley to many a roto-gravure reader like myself. "This *is* Mrs. Paley's, isn't it?" I asked for reassurance.

"Yes," said one of the ladies, looking at me peculiarly. "Have you a card?"

I produced it and they examined it critically, checked it with a list in front of them, and then handed it back to me. They had more or less the attitude of women selling doughnuts at a charity bazaar—women who had had no particular desire to make the doughnuts in the first place and knew they tasted like old cloth.

One of the ladies said, with no great enthusiasm, "I guess you'll want to see the rooms down here," and let me peer briefly into what appeared to be a reception room and a dining room. Then she led me to the foot of the zebra-striped stairs. I stood there for a moment, waiting for something to happen, and she said, "Well, don't you want to go up?" I nodded, and she called "June, coming up!" and went back to her table.

June was a girl in a reddish-brown dress, with a tassel on her hat. Neither of us could think of anything to say when we met on the second-floor landing, beside a large potted plant, so I took out a cigarette. "Oh, you can't do that," she said apologetically. "We aren't allowed to smoke here." Then she led me into the living room, a chamber containing a number of fragile knickknacks and, in one corner, a pair of orchids growing in a pot. There were a lot of modern paintings, too. In this and the other rooms, I saw and admired works by Cézanne, Matisse, Derain, Picasso, Degas, Gauguin, and Cecil Beaton. Beaton's were photographs, mostly of Mrs. Paley, and all signed with his name in prominent red letters. One stood near a sketch of Mrs. Paley—by Picasso, I think, or maybe by Matisse. In both portraits she was shown with her chin resting in her hand, and June drew my attention to the coincidence. "Notice that same lethargic, contented look," she said. It was the only information anyone there offered me about my absent hostess's character.

"Where is Mrs. Paley?" I asked.

"She's away somewhere," said June matter-of-factly. "She spends most of her time in the country."

Then June led me into the library, where my hopes rose at the sight of a table laden with bottles of whiskey and soda water. June didn't say anything about them, though, and I noticed that they were all unopened. I guess they were meant to stay that way.

"Well," said June, "that's that. . . . Polly, coming up!"

I recognized my cue and climbed another flight. Polly was an amiable, harassed-looking brunette with a corsage of wilting gardenias. She greeted me with "My God, what I'd give for a cigarette!"

I suggested that we go outside and have one, but she wouldn't do it. "I have to stay here till someone comes to relieve me," she said. "It's not that we don't trust people, but you know, they might burn holes in the furniture. My mother always used to worry about me burning holes in her furniture."

I nodded sympathetically. "You're a friend of the Paleys, I suppose?"

"Lord, no. Never saw the place before. I just came down from Elizabeth Arden's and they stuck me up here," she said.

Polly then showed me the ingenious devices by which the Paley art is lighted. For instance, should Mr. Paley be in his bedroom and want to meditate upon a Matisse, all he has to do is throw a switch and flash! there's a Matisse, all nicely and directly illuminated. The wiring system in the house is so contrived that almost every painting has its own tiny spotlight concealed in a molding or an end table. God knows what would happen if the Paleys decided to redecorate. Mr. Paley also has three telephones to play with at his bedside, which I daresay is more than Mr. Lohr of N.B.C. has. The most distinguishing feature of Mrs. Paley's bedroom is her bed. It's a tremendous four-poster affair with a silvery canopy and mirrored posts. It looks as if a queen might have died in it.

In Mrs. Paley's bedroom there is also a growing camellia plant and other flora that at first sight appear to be growing right out of the top of a table. The pots are built in. But her dressing room and bath are the killer-dillers. They are all done in mirrors, and when you sit at the dressing table, as I did at Polly's invitation, you see yourself not only from all sides but from above as well. I don't know how Mrs. Paley feels in the morning, but I'd hate to wake up and have to look down at the top of my own head. Mr. Paley's bathroom has no more than an ordinary quota of mirrors, but it has a radio in it—the only one I saw in the house.

There was still another flight of stairs leading up from the third floor, but Polly barred the way. "I'd like to let you go up," she said, "but the children are there. I keep hearing them shuffling around; makes me nervous."

It was nice to know there was a Paley in the house, but since it was evident that I wasn't going to get to see even a little one, I started downward. When I reached June again, she had two strangers in tow: a young man whom I took to be an interior decorator, and a young lady who looked as if she had just stepped out of the nearest branch of the Y.W.C.A. She was probably an applicant for one of those Neighborhood Playhouse scholarships, and I could see my six dollars making it possible for her to play Desdemona, with a slight lisp. It was a discouraging thought, but still these were fellow-visitors, and I joined them for a moment in the library. The girl had just made a remark about some white upholstered chairs and a matching couch, I gathered.

"They come from Russia, I think," she was saying.

"Not Russia!" exclaimed the young man in a voice of horror. "Nothing good comes from Russia."

"Well, I was told they come from Russia," said the girl stubbornly.

"Maybe they come from Georgia," said the young man hopefully.

I went outside then to have a cigarette, and I didn't go back. If I ever call on the Paleys again, they had better be home.

John McNulty

ATHEIST HIT BY TRUCK

This drunk came down the "L" stairs, and at the bottom he made a wrong turn. This led him into the gutter instead of onto the sidewalk, and a truck hit him and knocked him down.

It is a busy corner there at Forty-second Street and Second Avenue, in front of the Shanty, and there's a hack line there. Naturally, a little crowd and a cop gathered around the drunk and some hackies were in the crowd.

The cop was fairly young. After he hauled the guy up and sat him on the bottom step of the "L" stairs, he saw there wasn't much wrong with him. His pants were torn and maybe his knee was twisted slightly —maybe cut.

The cop got out his notebook and began asking questions and writing the answers down. Between questions he had to prop the man up. Fellow gave his name—Wilson, Martin, some noncommittal name —and his address. Everybody around was interested in these facts.

The blind man in the newspaper hut under the stairs felt a little put out because nobody was telling him what was going on, and he could hear beguiling fragments of it. "What happen? What happen?" the blind man kept asking, but the event wasn't deemed sensational enough for anybody to run and tell him, at least until afterward.

"What religion are yuh?" the policeman asked the man, who propped himself up this time and blurted out, "Atheist! I'm an atheist!"

For some reason, a lot of people laughed.

"Jeez, he's an atheist!" one of the hackies said. He shouted to a comrade who was still sitting behind the wheel of a parked cab at the corner, "Feller says he's an atheist!"

"Wuddaya laughing at?" the cop asked, addressing himself to the crowd generally. "Says he's an atheist, so he's an atheist. Wuddaya laughing at?" He wrote something in the book.

Another policeman, from over by Whelan's drugstore, where there was a picket line, strolled up. He was an older cop, more lines in his face, bigger belly, less humps around his hips, because the equipment —twisters, mace, and all that stuff—fitted on him better after all these years. "Wuzzamadder with 'im?" he asked his colleague.

"This here truck hit him. He isn't hurt bad. Says he's an atheist."

"I *am* an atheist!" the man yelled.

The crowd laughed again.

"Did you put that down—atheist?" the older cop asked.

"Yuh, I put it in where it says 'religion.'"

"Rubbid out. Rubbid out. Put in Cat'lic. He looks like a Cat'lic to me. He's got an Irish name? Anyway, rubbid out. When he sobers up, he'll be sorry he said that atheist business. Put in Cat'lic. We gotta send him to Bellevue just for safety's sake." The young cop started for the drugstore to put in a call.

"Never mind safety's sake. I'm an atheist, I'm telling you," the drunk said, loud as he could.

"Cuddid out, cuddid out," the older cop said. Then he leaned over like a lecturer or somebody. "An' another thing—if you wouldn't go round sayin' you're an atheist, maybe you wouldn't be gettin' hit by trucks."

The crowd sensed a great moral lesson and didn't laugh.

"Jeez! The guy says he's an atheist," the hackie said again.

A little later the Bellevue ambulance came.

"I yam a natheist," the man kept muttering as they put him into the ambulance.

A. J. Liebling

IN MULBERRY STREET*

In the middle of any New York block there is likely to be one store that remains open and discreetly lighted all night. This is the undertaker's. The undertaker or an assistant is always in attendance, waiting for something to turn up. Undertakers are sociable men; they welcome company during their unavoidable periods of idleness. High school boys study for their State Regents' examinations in undertakers' offices on hot June nights. The door is always open, the electric fan soothing, the whole environment more conducive to reflective scholarship than the crowded apartment where the boy lives. Policemen going off duty sometimes drop in for a visit with the undertaker before climbing into the subway for the long trip home to another part of the city.

There is no merchandise in the front part of an undertaker's store. Usually there are a few comfortable chairs for bereaved relatives, and policemen sit in these chairs. During the day, the undertaker acts as a referee in the disputes of children. Housewives tell him their troubles; priests appeal to him to head church committees. Ten to one he becomes the biggest man in the neighborhood, like my friend Mayor Angelo Rizzo of Mulberry Street. Some New York streets have Mayors, but they are not elected. A man lives on a street until the mayoralty grows over him, like a patina. To Mayor Rizzo Elizabeth Street, although but two blocks east of Mulberry, is an alien place. For the feast of San Gennaro, who is the Mulberry Street Saint, Mayor Rizzo usually heads at least three committees and festoons his shop-front with electric lights. A celebration on Elizabeth Street leaves him unmoved. "Just one of them Sicilian saints," he says.

Once Mayor Rizzo told me was hard put to keep track of his constituents' baths. "I think I will have to get a secretary," he said, as he

* Chapter I of A. J. Liebling's "Back Where I Came From." In the book it was titled "Beginning with the Undertaker."

improved the taste of a casket salesman's gift cigar with a swig of iced barbera wine. He sat in front of 178 Mulberry Street, enthroned upon one of the elegant portable chairs which he is prepared to furnish in any number for correct funerals. "They should call this cigar a La Palooka," he remarked on the side.

"Mrs. Aranciata is getting crazy because she don't remember whether Jimmy has been to Cooney Island twenty-two times or twenty-three times. So she come to me and said I should tell the kid not to go no more, because maybe that will make it an even number of times and he will get rheumatism. So I said to her, 'But suppose he has been only twenty-two times? Then by keeping him home you will be preventing him getting on the odd number again, and the rheumatism will be your fault.'

" 'Oh, Madonna mia,' she says, 'and what will I do?'

"So I says, 'Why don't you forget all about it and purtend this is a new year. Start all over again and when he goes to Cooney tell me, and I will keep track of it on a piece of paper.' So she is delighted and the next thing I know she tells all her friends and now I got about fourteen women coming in wanting me to keep score how many times the family goes swimming.

"It is like when I feed one cat spaghetti a couple of winters ago and in a week I got a waiting line of 598 cats, including a lot of Sicilian cats from Elizabeth Street."

"But what difference does it make how many times you go swimming—at Coney or any place else?" I asked.

"What difference does it make?" shouted Mr. Rizzo. "Do you mean to tell me that you, an educated man, do not know that salt water baths are only good for you if you go an odd number of times? Any old woman on Mulberry Street knows that much."

To prove his point Mayor Rizzo called the cop on the beat.

"You are an Italian," said His Honor. "Which is it lucky to take baths, an odd number or an even number?"

"Odd number," answered the officer promptly. "My mother-in-law, she keeps count on her fingers. She would never go in the water two times, or four times, in an afternoon, but always three times or five times."

The argument became a little involved here. Some of the folklore hydrotherapists held that each immersion counts as a bath, and if you go in the drink an odd number of times at each visit to the beach, your health will not suffer.

Others maintain that you must keep track of the total number of days' bathing, and be sure to wind up the season on an odd.

"I remember when I was a kid an old lady from Calabria made me go in fifty-one times one summer," said Al Gallichio, the restaurant man.

An antique and gracious lady waddling past with a bag of zucchini, was invoked as a superior authority.

"Pardon me, madame," said Mayor Rizzo, "but I would wish to request a word with you."

"Voluntarily," she replied.

"When you are accustomed to go bathing, which is the more auspicious, to go an even or an uneven number of times?"

"Childish," said the dame. "It makes no difference. But once you have begun to go you must go at least fifteen times, else your bones rot. It is for that reason I have not gone to the sea, this year, because I might not be able to afford fifteen visits."

She was an exception, because the odd-and-even belief, in one or other of its two forms, is prevalent all the way from Bleecker Street down to Park Row.

"It is very important this year," said the Mayor, "because we got no public bath in the neighborhood. There used to be a bathhouse on Center Market Place where the fellow would let you take a shower for a nickel. Of course, even the old-timers do not count whether a shower is odd or even. But now the Broome St. Tamanacle Church has bought the building. A lot of these old houses have no bathtubs even, so the nearest place the people can get a bath is Allen Street and they figure they might just as well go out to Cooney.

"Do I believe in this odd-and-even business?" he said. "Well, I tell you. I went swimming off the Battery just once, which is an odd number, and a kid pushed my head under and nearly drowned me, so I figured if I went back that would be an even number and even worse luck and I probably would remain drowned, so now I do all my swimming in a bathtub."

The Talk of the Town *

SUITS FOR JIMMY

October 20, 1928

Seven new suits are now under construction for Mayor Walker. For this important work, Jeann Friedman, tailor to His Honor, has moved his shop from Thirty-fourth Street up to Forty-sixth Street, opposite the Ritz. Here, behind heavily panelled walls, we found a squad of men on their haunches, stitching away at the royal garments.

Mr. Friedman, who knows our unflagging interest in the Mayor's appearance, telephoned last week, inviting us to inspect the new raiment, and when we called received us personally in his reception room and let us finger the executive swatches. One series is called the Hyde Park Ensemble. Another the Biarritz Casino. Both are new departures, featuring jackets of plain cloth, with pants of a slightly different hue, vigorously striped—like the Bush Terminal Building. Five of the new suits now under the needle are of the Hyde Park (different-color-pants) type. Two are of the standard (pants-match-coat) variety. At the moment the Mayor is in an autumnal mood and leans toward brown. Among the ensembles there will be one reddish brown, two oak leaf (or Broadway) browns, one blue, one gray.

The Biarritz group is a sports group. (There is always a suspicion in Mr. Friedman's mind that the Mayor may be going south.) As a group it has not been recommended to His Honor's attention yet. "Just now am I just studying them," said Mr. Friedman. "These combination effects, only for an outstanding man they are, different from other people." And he showed us exactly how the Biarritz Casino garment works—coat of dark gray, knickers of thatched-roof motif, flannels of light gray stripes—"for lolling."

To fend off cold winds, three topcoats of pure cashmere are also being built for Mr. Walker. He already owns two fur coats, one black,

* *The following nine short news stories are from The Talk of the Town department in The New Yorker.*

one brown, and will be able to get through the winter inside of these, Mr. Friedman thinks. The brown is worth ten thousand dollars, on account of a very fine collar that a fellow brought the Mayor from Russia.

About seventy suits comprise the Walker wardrobe. Many have been around the house for years. Ten of them hang in the tailor shop all the time. No room at home. "He leaves things laying around," Mr. Friedman confided, pulling out a dandy cocoa-colored specimen, said to be a favorite. The Mayor spends three thousand dollars a year on this kind of equipment, and enjoys every cent of it.

Life has opened up like a flower for Jeann Friedman since becoming tailor to Mr. Walker. Fifteen years ago he made a suit for a friend of Jimmie's, and the snappy effect so took the Walker fancy that Jeann has done the tailoring ever since. Other tailors try with siren notes and custom effects to lure the Mayor away, but Jeann makes the Walker pants twenty inches at the knee, eighteen and a half inches at the bottom, no break at the instep; makes the Walker lapels sit up where they belong; and Jeann now has a nice shop with ashtrays in the reception room and a view of the Ritz. Also he has attracted attention in the trade. A writer for a fashion magazine interviewed him and quoted him as saying: "It is not so much a matter of a designing system, but accomplishment which comes through the trained, artistic eye visualizing the finished product according to the individuality of the customer." Jeann sits among his ashtrays and reads that statement over and over.

ISADORA'S BROTHER
December 7, 1929

Raymond Duncan is in town with the idea of starting a branch of his academy here. He serves tea every afternoon in his studio in West Seventy-fifth Street, surrounded by his fabrics, his poems, his shepherdess, and his disciples. Reclining on a couch, he talks with you about the future, which he believes must be prepared for by throwing off the past and learning to perform the simple motions of life, such as digging and making sandals. His poems are five dollars, his "Eternal Beauty" is two dollars, and his fabrics run from four dollars on up. The couch is very hard.

The little brother of Isadora is getting on in years, and looks more ike a witch than a shepherd. His long gray locks are held back by a ibbon, his tunic flows classically from his shoulders, and his chubby little arms that have woven so many yards of piece goods look rather labby and old. After years of tending donkeys and goats on the Acropolis with Penelope, organizing refugees, rebuilding a city in Albania, weaving rugs, digging holes, dyeing linen, writing poems, and administering academies and temples of arts, always clinging ight to the immortal and somewhat elusive spirit of his inspired sister, he is still hopeful. He hasn't had on a pair of pants in nineteen years, man and boy.

While we were reclining with him, doing our best to look like a goatherd despite our sack suit, a lady entered the room and asked him "if it would brutalize him if she suggested a cup of tea." "My dear Julia," he replied, "the whole world is trying to brutalize me."

Brute that we were, we drank the tea, bought a small doily, and departed, our sandals clinking merrily along the pave.

TEA PARTY

October 24, 1931

Simon & Schuster gave a tea last week called the "Believe-It-or-Not" party, the occasion being the publication of a new book by that name. The idea was to get up a party which would be like the book—that is: incredible but true—and it was a success. About a hundred and fifty people, mostly literary figures, moved about with teacups and fountain pens, drinking tea and autographing books. Gene Tunney was there and he autographed a book for Sir Hubert Wilkins, who was autographing a book for Count Felix von Luckner. Tunney wore a brown suit, with soft tan shirt and dark red tie, secured by a small gold pin. Count von Luckner wore a blue suit and a hard shiny collar. Both looked debonair but unreal.

Everybody had to sign a huge book at the door. It contains the oddest collection of names in the world and is probably worth a great deal of money. Count von Luckner was the third person to arrive. His signature, "Felix Count Luckner," was fourteen inches long and two inches high. A Mr. Joe Rosenblatt signed right under him, taking up only the same amount of space as the word "Count." Ely Culbertson signed right after we did. Sidney Lenz arrived eight signatures later. The two, as you know, have for months been challenging each other to a contract-bridge game. To everybody's surprise, the game was not played at the party. Some people thought they wouldn't even speak, but they signed each other's book and the news spread quickly through the crowd. Then Eddie Cantor signed Culbertson's book and Tunney signed Lenz' and Lenz signed Major James Doolittle's. A Mr. Sam Weisenhouse signed ours and asked us if Hendrik Van Loon had arrived yet. It was all very crowded and now and again you signed somebody's book or somebody signed yours by accident, due to jostling. Somebody said one book was signed "Count von Wilkins," due to jostling, but we didn't see it. The Count and the Sir talked together for a long time, and we edged up to hear what was being said. Count von Luckner was saying: "Our two countries should never have fought." We were introduced *to* Tunney and *as* Tunney. A strange woman in a green hat, mistaking us for somebody else, said: "Where was you?" We said: "To the taxidermist's" and she went around telling people we were Ring Lardner. Sir Hubert thereupon came over and praised us for "The Outline of Science."

Simon & Schuster's is a lot of bright, ivory-colored rooms joined together, containing pictures of Thomas Mott Powys and Will Durante, Simon & Schuster authors. People moved from room to room, passing sandwich tables, passing Tunney, passing a radio to which one couple was dancing, passing a ping-pong table at which two women, wearing fur coats, were playing. At the end of three hours, we hadn't met Ripley, the so-called guest of honor. We hadn't met One Long Hop, the Chinaman who was named after Lindbergh's flight, either. He was there. We asked a young lady how to find Ripley. "He's got spats," she said. A man who looked like Coolidge arrived. Believe it or not, it wasn't Coolidge.

———————

GTDE STEIN
November 24, 1934

Miss Stein was seven or eight minutes late for her autographing at Brentano's last week and about fifty people were waiting restlessly for her when she solidly arrived with Alice B. Toklas pertly in tow. On a table were arranged solid stacks of Miss Stein's books and next to the table was a big desk at which she sat solidly down. She was calm, quick, and smiling throughout the ordeal. Of course, it wasn't as exciting as the immortal Hugh Walpole-Gene

Tunney autographing, but it had its moments. As soon as she sat down, Miss Stein looked up expectantly and people began pushing toward the desk, carrying books. Clerks fluttered about selling the pushers whatever book of Miss Stein's they might want: the books ran in price from ninety-five cents (the Modern Library edition of "Three Lives") to $3.50. At an autographing, you are supposed to write down on a card your name, or Aunt Lisbeth's name, or the name of whomever you are buying the book for, and hand the book and the card to the autographer. This speeds things up, because people standing in front of an author and meeting the author's eyes are likely to get timid and dry-throated and say "Zassfrank Dooselinch" or what sounds like "Zassfrank Dooselinch" to the author. Miss Stein doesn't like people to be incoherent about names.

She signed two hundred and seventy-five books in all, and her signing time was a little under an hour and a half. She wrote with a big pen, vigorously. We bought one of her books and got in line behind a man named Twifflefinks, Moited Twifflefinks (he hadn't written his name on a card). That was straightened out after a while—Miss Stein is always gracious and patient. We just handed our book to her, and she glanced at us with her keen, humorous eyes and, seeing that we didn't have a name, simply put her own name on the flyleaf, and the date. She signs herself always Gtde Stein. Now and again somebody (once it was a girl of twelve) would slip her an autograph book or a blank sheet of paper, but she would push these away and say "No," and these autograph-hunters would retreat in humiliation. There are ethics in autographing: you can't just walk into a bookstore out of the street and get an author to sign his name for you. You have to buy or bring one of the author's books.

One confused man somehow found himself standing in front of Miss Stein without a book, so he shouted at a clerk, " 'Three Saints'! 'Three Saints'!" he said. "Give me a 'Three Saints'!" The right title is "Four Saints." A clerk corrected the gentleman coldly. Miss Stein just laughed. She doesn't get peeved about things like that. Behind us was a lady named Mielziner. Miss Stein, hearing the name, looked up and asked about Leo Mielziner, Jr. "Leo Mielziner is Kenneth MacKenna," said the lady. Miss Stein took that in her stride. Now and again someone would ask the hovering Toklas to sign a book, and she always did. Somebody asked Miss Stein what had been her greatest thrill in America. She said her airplane trip to Chicago.

A friend of ours who heard the great lady lecture a few days after the autographing said it was very interesting and seemed to make sense. Our friend, however, copied down a few sentences that Miss Stein said and showed them to us. Our favorite was "When the inside had become so solidly inside that all the outside could be outside and the inside inside." The lady who listened said that when you hear Gtde talk that way, you can see what she means, or think you can. People who hear her always like her as a person. After her lectures she will answer any questions—if they are sensible. Once she waved her hand and said pooh at a woman who asked her what she thought of the effect of psychology on literature. She then said that psychology hasn't any effect on literature. She told some other questioner that she doesn't believe much in the subconscious. "It's subconscious because it's inarticulate," she said.

This is probably all we're going to tell you about Miss Stein.

UNDER THE LINDENS

June 27, 1936

The open-air Promenade Café, in the sunken plaza of Rockefeller Center, opened Wednesday evening, June 17th. A tropical disturbance, which had been moving northeastward, was centered about four hundred miles south of Cape Race when the first diners arrived. All afternoon the southeasterly breeze had been freshening, and at sundown it hauled into the south and increased to a velocity of 25. At nine o'clock, with the glass hovering around 29.9 and with our lady on our arm, we entered the café, where one of the captains took us in tow, skirted some cedar hedges, and led us to a fountain-side table right abeam of Prometheus's groin. By this time the restaurant was beginning to roll a bit, and some of the smaller tables were trying to shorten sail. Tablecloths whipped in the wind, umbrellas tugged at their moorings, and the eight linden trees bent to the gale while their wire rigging sang. In the west, right above our heads, the enormous waterspouts shot noisily into the air, were caught by the downdraft from the R.C.A. Building, and sprayed out in a fine mist over the decks. It was difficult to hear anything above the roar. A waiter came up, his hair in his mouth.

"What'll you have?" he yelled.

"Two Martinis and some oilskins!" we called back, and he was off, bending low. As he departed, the fog shut down, and we couldn't see our own partner but could feel her knee against ours under the table. Steep seas were making up in the basin of the fountain, and a cross-current from the jets of Prometheus churned up a nasty chop. Over to the eastward near Al Donahue and his orchestra, a silver platter came adrift and went down with a deafening crash. The fog lifted. Some mint from the fruit cup of the people at the next table blew across our nostrils in a fine green dust. Ladies in thin evening clothes clutched at their back hair, while their men shifted the dinner service around crazily, in an attempt to batten down the meal. A singer from the Music Hall fought her way to the microphone and sang "Let Yourself Go." Even then we didn't realize how hard the wind was blowing till we looked down at our butter plate and noticed that the hard roll was rocking slowly back and forth, back and forth.

In the north we could see tier on tier of the common people lined up behind the hedges on Fiftieth Street, gazing down into the cave of the winds at us. Spotlights burned down from the roof of the British Building, so that one's shoulders threw one's food into deep shadow. At about half past nine, an unseen right-minded mechanical wizard turned Prometheus off, and the noise abated but not the wind. A cigarette girl, dressed in a cutaway and wearing a monocle, tacked back and forth across our bow, and once, when we looked up from our hearts of lettuce with fines herbes et fines Lucky Strike ashes, we saw the wind tear the glass right out of her eye. At eight minutes after eleven, a man's straw hat went by, bottom up, in the green, angry waters of the fountain. Toward midnight, it became apparent that the worst of the blow was over, and guests made things as snug as possible and settled down to enjoy the dancing and the food. Spots went out, the dark came, the lindens rustled, and violin music drifted out over the garden. The precision dance of the Rockettes, on the platform with the waving trees throwing leaf shadows on them, was a surprisingly beautiful and almost unearthly sight—the Rockettes, who had heretofore been merely puppets seen indoors at a distance of a quarter of a mile, now suddenly translated into living girls dancing in the clean bright night in a big wind. We saw them again, later, in the British bar, at even closer range, and were surprised at their faces, which were earnest rather than gay.

The Promenade Café, we learn on inquiry, serves table d'hôte lunches from $1 up, table d'hôte dinners from $1.50 up. Also à la carte for lunch and dinner. It is open for cocktails in the afternoon, and for supper at night. The dance platform remains throughout the summer for dancing. There is no cover charge at any time. There is an indoor section on the north side called the English Grill, which has a bar, and an indoor section on the south side called the Restaurant Français, which hasn't. On calm nights, with Prometheus idling, or shut off entirely, we should think it would be a rather pleasant spot.

THE JAPANESE ARMY

March 5, 1938

The Japanese army is listed in the Manhattan telephone directory, on page 494—"Japanese Army, 1775 Broadway, CIrcle 7-4466." We didn't find this out until last week, but the minute we did we dropped everything and hurried around to investigate. We found the Japanese army firmly entrenched just off Columbus Circle, on the sixth floor of the General Motors Building. It occupies a modest office suite and has no sentry or receptionist. When we entered (without knocking), we found ourself looking across a waist-high partition and gate into a biggish room in which a half-dozen Japanese, all in mufti, were engaged in some sort of clerical work. One of them, a short, dark gent with horn-rimmed glasses and hair parted in the middle, got up and came toward us, stopping on the other side of the gate. We introduced ourself and right off, without subterfuge, asked him why the Japanese army had a New York office. "You go do this up?" he said. We said yes, we'd like to write a piece about it. "No true," he said in rather a heated tone. "You think we only army with office? Hah, you not know all armies have office in New York? Go, go learn others, then have purpose do this up." He thereupon turned from us and went into the inner office, followed by all his colleagues.

This sudden retreat left us in complete command of the field but uncertain as to whether or not the interview was at an end. We held our gains, observing what we could of the Japanese army's New York equipment. It wasn't much—just books, filing cabinets, a safe, and a couple of things which we took to be Japanese multigraphing machines. For a moment we caught excited mumbling from the inner office, then this stopped and there was complete Oriental quiet. We were almost on the point of going away when we noticed that the inner office door was ajar and that a man was peeking at us. We motioned to him to come out, and he did, somewhat hesitantly. This was another army man, tall and slender, with thin hair and no eyebrows. Deciding to try a different gambit with him, we asked if we might see the general. "No general," he said, smiling and showing pale gums. "One lieuten' colonel, two major." We asked if we could see the lieutenant colonel, whereupon he withdrew again to the inner office. He returned in a moment with the news that the lieutenant colonel was "bissy with friend." So were both the majors. "All time bissy with friend," he said, with another pale smile that hardly seemed to include us as a friend. Why, we asked, getting back to the original point, did the Japanese army have an office in New York? "You know," he said slowly, "the purchases. We inspect." All of them? we asked. "All." Where? "Here." To whom was the New York office of the Japanese army responsible, the Japanese consulate? He shook his head, arching what could have been his eyebrows. The embassy? "No." The Emperor? "No.... Yes." With that, the second Japanese army man who ever came into our life grinned, backed away, and disappeared into the inner office. Again all was quiet as a Japanese flower garden, so we left.

We snooped around the General Motors Building a bit and learned that the Japanese army has been a tenant for about seven years. It's the irritated opinion of several of the building employees that the army can speak perfectly good English if it wants to. Nobody, not even the postman or the superintendent, has been in the inner office.

WIND AND WATER

February 10, 1940

Too many buildings in this city were erected without the slightest regard for devils. The Chinese manage things better. In China, when a building is to go up, a geomancer is called in to pass on the site. A geomancer is a practitioner of *fung sui*—a doctor of the wind and the water. He corresponds roughly to our architect, except that he has a better grasp of the situation.

This much you know if you read Carl Crow's book, "Four Hundred Million Customers." Mr. Crow made the statement that geomantically the Empire State Building is in a very dangerous condition, while the Hotel New Yorker is fine, and this eventually got us started to Chinatown, where we found an old retired geomancer named Loo Chan, whose father practiced extensively in China and who himself once had hopes of practicing here. A good building, he says, must be designed to repel and confound evil spirits. Demons avoid pagodas, national banks and trust companies, and running water. They are stupid and fly always in a straight line. Therefore it is possible to plan your building accordingly. Take, for example, the New Yorker Hotel. An evil spirit, flying at the New Yorker Hotel at a low altitude, would crash into surrounding buildings and become baffled. If it flew at a high altitude, it would be met by the house spirit of the New Yorker, which, from its perch on a setback, would grapple with the demon. You never hear of anybody in the New Yorker Hotel getting boils, or scurvy, do you? Well?

The Empire State Building, on the contrary, violates every principle of *fung sui*. It is the butt of all the wandering devils in midtown Manhattan. From about the thirtieth story up, it rises perpendicularly, a vast unprotected expanse, no surrounding obstructions, no pagodas, no running water—except the occasional flow in the lonely lavatories. No place for the house spirit to perch until you get clear to the top. You notice that all that middle section of the building is vacant, don't you? Well?

Since learning about geomancy, we study every building we pass with an eye to its vulnerability. We have noticed that the Chinese Consulate (in fact, our geomancer pointed this out) is in a cozy spot in Radio City, strategically located behind a setback and enjoying the beneficent influence of St. Patrick's, a nearby pagoda. There is also a good deal of running water in the fountain. The Japanese Consulate is wide open. It is in the Salmon Tower and is in the path of devils working north from Lord & Taylor's. The Waldorf is well-nigh impregnable. It has St. Bartholomew's, the Chemical Bank & Trust Co., and a fire station, which makes a lot of noise and scares spirits off.

Loo Chan says there is no chance of a *fung-sui* practitioner making a living in New York (some years ago he went into the rice-cake business) because Chinese don't build buildings or bury their dead here. (Locating graves is really the principal task of the geomancer; a proper grave should be on a hill, near a stream and a pagoda—like Grant's tomb.) Residents of Chinatown are content with the narrow, winding streets of their district. Makes it tough for devils, and if the neighborhood engine company isn't kicking up a rumpus, you can always shoot off firecrackers. The Chinese revere the art of *fung sui* because of their desire to have everything on their side. They think this life is a peculiar one.

We are sorry to say that our own office building is badly planned. Spirits skirt around the Guaranty Trust Company and come in across a parking lot. There are continual distempers and fevers. We asked the receptionist the other day if she was ever troubled by devils getting off the elevator.

"You mean the ones that have been to art school?" she replied, sullenly.

We noticed she had a racking little cough.

PASTORAL SCENE

February 22, 1941

Next time a broker, toying wanly with his frayed cuffs, tells you a seat on the Stock Exchange recently sold for $27,000 and that the daily average of shares traded this January was 512,000, as compared to 4,300,000 in January, 1928, you might enter into the spirit of things by telling *him* how the amount of waste-paper swept up from the Exchange floor at the close of a day's trading stacks up against the amount swept up ten years ago. Current sweepings, consisting of brokers' orders, memorandums, and quotation slips, are only about two-thirds what they used to be: in 1931 they averaged twenty-one bags, or 1,500 pounds, a day; today they hover around thirteen bags, or 950 pounds. Moreover, the figures jotted on these scraps of paper are substantially lower than they were in the days when stockbrokers warned their sons against becoming college professors, poets, or harmonica players, and their daughters against marrying same.

We obtained this interesting wastepaper statistic, and a few sidelights that may be of value to some morbid historian, when we visited the Exchange last week. An official guide took us to the visitors' gallery, from which, around noon, we watched the following sluggish scene unfold itself. At Trading Post 6, a bald-headed broker was sitting down, reading a copy of *Time,* no doubt the "Business & Finance" section. At Post 2, another broker was working on the *Herald Tribune* crossword puzzle. At Post 4, where General Motors is traded, three members were talking; one was sitting, two standing. Our guide pointed to the left of Post 2, where U.S. Steel is traded, and said, "There's the steel crowd." The steel crowd consisted of four brokers and one Stock Exchange employee, all conversing without animation. Another crowd of four brokers stood about Post 10, where Bethlehem Steel is traded; under our very eyes one of them walked away from the others and wrote something on a pad. Our guide advised us to keep on watching him, because it looked as though the man was about to trade. "Yes," the guide said breathlessly a moment later, "he did trade, he did trade."

Around this time the annunciator board, which is used to call members from the floor to their phones and is equipped with a thousand numbers, had sixteen numbers up. In the old days, three or four hundred numbers showing was nothing unusual. Brokers' carnations have declined even more sensationally. Formerly about half the members sported them; the day we were there all buttonholes were bare. According to E. Burd Grubb, a governor of the Exchange, most brokers have given up lunch, along with the carnations. Mr. Grubb told us he stopped eating lunch a year and a half ago. "It's an easy way to save a dollar and a half," he said. He just has a bigger dinner when he gets home. A few of the more improvident, or hungrier, brokers have sandwiches sent in, or go to Walgreen's, or patronize a recently installed sandwich bar in the Luncheon Club. The smoking room is more popular than it used to be, since members go there increasingly to read, complain, do crossword puzzles, and talk deferentially about such profitable ventures as photography and stamp-collecting. Backgammon stakes in this room, once a quarter a point, are now generally a nickel.

We asked a broker about the horseplay and practical jokes which have long been an Exchange tradition and were told that the last prank occurred before the election, when a trader, having bought a carton of eggs from John Conklin, a broker who has a farm in New Jersey and peddles seventy dozen eggs a week to his colleagues, checked his carton in the cloakroom. Another member, apparently feeling Willkie was going to be elected, giddily removed the eggs, had them hard-boiled at a restaurant across the street, and returned them to the cloakroom. The owner's wife later tried to make some scrambled eggs, and the joke was judged a success. By the end of the year, however, no one felt humorous, and December 31st, formerly an occasion marked by revelry, song, two bands, paper hats and noise-makers, was celebrated gloomily with prolonged booing at the three-o'clock close. The man who told us this went on to say that no one has had the initiative to haze the two newest members; that the Stock Exchange theme song, "Wait Till the Sun Shines, Nellie," formerly rendered by all hands when something good happened in the market, hadn't been sung for months; that no one whistles at girls in the visitors' gallery any more; and that James Seligman, once one of the wittiest men on the floor, had given up conversation altogether. "You don't crack jokes at a funeral," our informant said.

YOUNG MAN IN THE BED

March 1, 1941

Having a healthy interest in both the drama and the human head, we called at four o'clock last Thursday afternoon on Victor Mature, who plays opposite, or almost opposite, Gertrude Lawrence in Moss Hart's psychoanalytical play, "Lady in the Dark." Although only twenty-six years old, Mr. Mature has been singled out by the Harvard *Lampoon* as "the actor least likely to succeed," has already made a fool of the Harvard *Lampoon,* has met socially in recent weeks various Paleys, Swopes, Hearsts, Vanderbilts, Harrimans, and other resourceful hosts and hostesses, and has been mentioned in the gossip columns as being alarmingly handsome. We found him in bed in a room at Essex House, discussing some sample suitings with a tailor and drinking Coca-Cola out of a bottle. He motioned the tailor to a chair in a corner and apologized to us for not being up, explaining that he had stayed out late the night before. "I used to have low moments and they were just low moments," he remarked abruptly, "but since this play, when I have low moments I worry about them. The other night I got to worrying about the face of the stage manager looking through the square hole in the wings and I couldn't concentrate and I knew my performance was stinking and later I couldn't get my mind off it and I thought 'Lord! Maybe there *is* something wrong with my complexes and stuff.'"

"Just lie back and say whatever comes into your mind," we suggested.

"I can't figure it out," he went on, putting his hands under his head. "I've got to find something to do with these afternoons. In Hollywood, since I got a break a year and a half ago, I've had a little house and a tennis court and a car and I had confidence and was happy just getting ahead and pushing. Now here in New York, for instance, I have

to get all these new suits because all the ones I had were the sports outfits which you wear out there exclusively, and these New York clothes
make me feel sharp. Too sharp, see? Mr. Hart and everybody have
been wonderful, and this is what I want, this is *it,* this is strictly the
good thing, and my God, meeting the Paleys and all those and so
forth—why, think of it, when I went to Hollywood in 1935, when I
was nineteen, I lived in a garage that was all charcoal inside and only
last week I'm at the Paleys', stumbling over Swopes and stuff."

"You lived in a garage that was all charcoal inside?" we asked
softly.

"It was only eight dollars a month," he said. "That's why—because
it had had a fire in it and was burned out, only not burned *down.* It
was fixed up like an apartment but it was really a garage and all the
wood inside was charred and came off black on your fingers. I got
to Hollywood from my home in Louisville, Kentucky, with eleven
cents left after I paid this eight dollars' rent and I wired Dad saying
I had eleven cents and he wired back saying that was six cents more
than he'd had when he came over from Austria and he couldn't speak
English, but *I* could. Dad used to grind scissors in Louisville and he
got into the refrigeration business later and made a good deal of
money, so he thought acting was unsound and wanted me to go into
his business. I was an only child. We never had any real quarrel or
anything and you ought to see them now—Dad and Mother. Boy, are
they proud! Mature's my real name, you see—same as theirs. I had a
tough time in Hollywood but it was constructive and did me good and
I'm glad Dad didn't send me any dough. The tough going gave me
an insight, which is strictly a good thing."

"It's what parents ought to do instead of mollycoddling," said the
tailor emphatically.

"There you are wrong, old man," said Mature. "You can't generalize.
Now, for me it was right, it was *it,* but for some other kid it would
not have been constructive. I was pushing, and the works were *proper*
and they still are, only—well, like I've just been reading six movie
magazines with features about me: 'Mature's opinion on love,' 'Mature's taste in dames.' I never gave any of them out, but it's O.K., it is
strictly the stuff, it is *it,* only I worry more now and I'm not as happy
with myself—O.K. but not *as* O.K. I watch my step. This way? That
way? Lord, sometimes I think maybe I'll talk to one of these psycho

guys, like Mr. Hart did. But nuts! I got to figure out something to do with these afternoons. I may walk in the Park a little. I may join the New York Athletic Club. I may take some courses at Columbia. But nuts!"

Geoffrey Hellman

BOY MEETS BULLFINCH*

Dr. Frank M. Chapman, who has been Curator of Ornithology at the American Museum of Natural History since 1908, has probably spent more time in the society of birds than any other man alive. For over sixty years he has patiently concealed himself in bushes and blinds all over North and South America in order to study at close range the habits of everything from the blue jay and the pelican to the vulture and the dusky-tailed ant tanager. He has reported his findings in some two hundred scientific papers, in *Bird-Lore,* an ornithological magazine which he founded in 1899 and edited for thirty-six years, and in fifteen books, which have sold, all told, over a quarter of a million copies. His "Handbook of Birds of Eastern North America," first published in 1895, still sells around 800 copies a year. Since going to work at the Museum in 1888, Dr. Chapman has helped build up its collection of bird specimens from about 10,000 to over 750,000 and to make its bird department the best in the world.

With the exception of a few species which he dislikes, like starlings and English sparrows, Chapman has a whole-souled admiration for birds. His approach to his subject is aesthetic and social rather than physiological, and he is more concerned with a bird's appearance, song, and way of life than with its underlying bone structure. His book "The Warblers of North America" for example, carefully classifies warblers into such groups as Warblers Which Have Loud, Whistled Songs; Warblers Which Have Not Loud, Whistled Songs; Warblers Which Have Songs of the Wee-Chee or Cher-Wee Type, with a Whistled Quality; Warblers Whose Songs Possess Pebbly, Twittering Notes or Which Suggest a Song of the Chipping Sparrow or Junco Type; and Warblers in Whose Songs There Is a Pronounced Zee Quality. This book contains plenty of the sort of prose which has made Dr. Chapman the most influential man since Audubon in interesting people in

* *This is the first half of a Profile from* The New Yorker, *March, 1939.*

birds, prose which in its way tells a good deal about Dr. Chapman himself:

All the sweetness and promise of spring seems stored in Parula's little sizzling gurgle; there is good cheer and sunshine in Yellow Warbler's lay; peace and rest in the quaint *zeeing* of the Black-throated Green.... If, however, you would see the [Yellow-Breasted] Chat satisfactorily, fight him with his own fire. Seat yourself in the thicket where as pursuer you are at the bird's mercy, and with pursed lips *squeak* gently but persistently. Soon there will be an answering *chut,* and with due patience and discretion you may induce this elusive creature to appear before you. I do not recall a more suspicious bird than the Chat.... The song of the Redstart can be readily recognized by those who know it but like so many Warblers' songs of what may be called the *weechy* type, loses all character when it is reduced to syllables.

Dr. Chapman's idea of a tremendous compliment is to compare a person to a bird, and he recently said of the late Lord Grey, bird-loving statesman, "Grey was the most charming host and companion, just like a bird." Dr. Chapman likes to think that birds are fond of him, too, and enjoys telling friends of the time an English wild eider duck permitted him to stroke her as she sat on her eggs. "She turned and pecked my finger gently, almost caressingly, I thought," he says. A good many birds have come to tolerate Dr. Chapman during his long career, and this pleases him immensely. One winter in Florida he spent the better part of three days forty-five feet up in a cypress tree, in a blind consisting of a green umbrella and a lot of Spanish moss, in order to observe herons and egrets. The birds in the vicinity kept their distance for a while, but toward the end of the third afternoon a spoonbill and two snowy egrets came and roosted in the same tree with him. Dr. Chapman, then a young man, felt he had arrived. "Surely," he later wrote in the first of several autobiographical books, "Camps and Cruises of an Ornithologist," "this was an honor these rarest of American birds have accorded few ornithologists." He did not allow the experience to turn his head, however, and went on to report in a matter-of-fact way that the adult egret says "Cuk-cuk-cuk," while young egrets say "Kek-kek-kek."

For the last thirty-five years, Dr. Chapman, along with most North American birds, has migrated South in the winter, usually going to Florida, South America, or Panama. In the spring he comes North again with the first robin. He is able to reproduce the songs of any number of birds by whistling and likes nothing better than to fool a bird into thinking he is another bird. By answering their songs in the woods, he has astonished many varieties of birds, who have come up within a few feet of him and looked at him closely. Since some of them sing only to attract mates, Dr. Chapman's replies have led to a certain amount of disappointment, misunderstanding, and bad feeling among birds. He often used to imitate an owl's cry while walking in the country, in order to get a flock of crows, who despise owls, to fly up and caw at him. He once played this trick when a real owl was around. Crows flew up and attacked the owl, which was quietly taking a nap. The owl was amazed. Dr. Chapman, who likes an owl as well as the next bird, has not done this since. He did, however, in the interests of science, play a rather elaborate trick not long ago on some blue jays. He wanted to see, at close range, the jays feed their young, and after spending several fruitless hours near a blue-jay nest, while concealed in a canvas affair painted to resemble tree bark and liberally draped with poison-ivy vines, he hit on the idea of wiring a mounted blue jay to a limb below the nest. He thought the parent jays, who were frightened away by his blind, would come back to evict the stranger loitering near their home. Instead, the mother at once returned and fed her young, apparently reassured by the mounted bird, whom she took for an old friend of the family's. Dr. Chapman next removed the dummy jay and replaced it with a mounted screech owl, which is a great enemy of the jay. The parent jays screamed in horror and attacked the owl, which they knocked over so that it hung upside down, still wired to the tree. Even in this position it continued to terrify the jays, and Dr. Chapman, who thought the thing had gone far enough, finally removed it.

Dr. Chapman has on several occasions occupied the nests of some of the larger birds himself. Some years ago, marooned by a storm on a small island in a Canadian lake, he moved three pelican eggs from one nest to another and climbed into the vacant nest, which was made of heaped-up sand and pebbles and was well above water level. He sat there in comparative snugness until the downpour was over, feeling exactly like a pelican. Another time, on a beach in the Bahamas, he passed several days in an unoccupied nest in the middle of a settlement of two thousand flamingos, making notes and taking photographs. The flamingos accepted Dr. Chapman as one of themselves and poked about right under his nose. "Seated on the deserted nest," he reported, "I myself seemed to have become a flamingo." For all this, Dr. Chapman realizes that he is actually neither a flamingo nor a pelican. He deplores the fact that there is no real communication between men and birds and that consequently he is unable to let certain birds know how much he enjoys their singing. "I often wish there were some way of assuring vireolanius that he is doing more than his duty," he once said.

Most of the time when he has not been directly fraternizing with birds, Dr. Chapman has spent classifying them, skinning them, writing about them, agitating to get them off women's hats, helping establish sanctuaries for them, and lecturing on them. He began to lecture in the eighteen-nineties in order to supplement the modest salary he was then getting as associate curator of the Museum's Department of Ornithology and Mammalogy. He made his first talk at the Ogontz School, a girls' institution near Philadelphia. Dr. Chapman, who in those days felt more at home in a cypress tree than on a lecture platform, pretended to himself that he was talking to a group of birds, and everything went smoothly. He soon became known as the most articulate ornithologist in the country and was invited to give lecture courses at places ranging all the way from the University of Indiana to the Lowell Institute in Boston. In 1901 he got a letter from the New York Farmers, an organization he had never heard of, asking him to speak on farm birds at their annual dinner. Dr. Chapman, then a rising young ornithologist of thirty-seven, was reluctant to waste an evening before a group of agriculturalists and rather offhandedly recommended another speaker, pleading a prior engagement. The next year the Farmers invited him again. Not wishing to be rude, he accepted and found himself at a dinner at the Metropolitan Club, surrounded by such farmers as J. P. Morgan, George F. Baker, Cleveland H. Dodge and Adrian Iselin. The New York Farmers turned out to be a group of part-time country gentlemen who met once a year to eat an enormous meal and discuss the problems of Long Island and Westchester estates. The private dining room where Dr. Chapman addressed them was embellished with moss, plants, a small log cabin, and dozens of mounted birds. Dr. Chapman was torn between pleasure at the company and dismay at the arrangement of the stuffed birds. "Without regard to haunt or habit, 100 or more of these specimens were distributed where they could be most easily attached or seemed to produce the best effect," he wrote in his autobiography. "It was a Habitat group such as never was seen before or since. There were Terns in the evergreens and Swallows on the forest floor, while birds of the Temperate and Tropic Zones met in a hitherto unheard-of association."

Dr. Chapman will be seventy-five in June. In recent years he has had to give up lecturing, but he still likes to talk about birds by the hour to friends and visitors at the Museum, and he is writing his sixteenth book about the subject with which he has been in love all his life. He was born in 1864 on his family's forty-acre farm in Englewood, N. J. The place was full of birds and he was conscious of the songs of wrens, bluebirds, and red-winged blackbirds from the start. He was the first birdman in the Chapman line. His father, a lawyer associated with Joseph H. Choate's firm, paid no particular attention to birds. Frank thinks he may have inherited from his grandfather the patience which has enabled him to set down long, detailed classifications of birds. His grandfather was Lebbeus Chapman, a banker who between July 1, 1846, and May 25, 1847, copied the entire Bible in longhand, averaging four hours a day at this work.

Dr. Chapman recalls seeing his first cardinal at the age of eight while visiting his grandparents in Georgia. This visit also brought him into contact with a European bullfinch, owned by a neighbor of his grandparents, which made a deep impression on him. He memorized the song of this bird and still whistles it occasionally. It takes twenty-three seconds, which is long for a birdcall. An uncle to whom he whistled the bullfinch song was so favorably affected that he gave Frank his first book about birds, Johnson's "Natural History," and later sent him some pelican feathers. These became the nucleus of a rather large accumulation of feathers. Frank got his mother's cook to give him wings of prairie hens, then common in butcher shops, and enlarged his collection of feathers by shooting robins, blue jays, Carolina parakeets, and cedar waxwings, and by trapping bobolinks. Today he wouldn't think of trapping a bobolink. He has followed the bobolink to its winter quarters in the Argentine and has pronounced it his favorite American bird. "I like it for its sweet song," he wrote in one of his books, "for its high character, for its habits, and for its extraordinary migrations." He feels different about ducks, and has been an active duck-shooter most of his life, pursuing this sport somewhat surreptitiously in later years out of deference to an anti-duck-shooting bloc in the Audubon Society.

Dr. Chapman graduated from Englewood Academy in 1880 and

then went to work for the American Exchange National Bank in New York. He had an independent income of around $2,000 a year, left to him by his father, and although he had no particular desire for more money, he thought he should find some sort of conventional career. He commuted every day and on the train fell in with a couple of Hackensack bird-lovers, who lent him ornithological books, showed him their collections of mounted birds, and introduced him to other birdmen. Dr. Chapman toiled faithfully at the bank, but his heart was in the woods and he frequently stimulated his colleagues by whistling bird songs as he worked. He became a faithful reader of *Forest & Stream* and in 1884 answered an appeal in this publication, issued by Dr. C. Hart Merriam, chairman of the committee on bird migration of the recently organized American Ornithologists' Union, calling for volunteers to observe and report on the seasonal movements of birds. In the line of duty, Dr. Chapman rose at dawn every morning from March 10th through May 23rd and went into the woods to shoot birds. He followed a route which got him to the West Englewood station at 7:30, where he checked the birds, changed from rough clothes to a double-breasted blue suit, and boarded the 7:39 train to business. In the evening he would pick up the birds at the station and usually shoot more specimens before dinner. After dinner he skinned the day's haul and took notes. During this period he turned up at the bank every day except May 15th, when he got so excited after getting a Brewster's warbler that he took the day off. His report was pronounced the best in the Atlantic Division and he was invited to join the Linnæan Society of New York, a natural-history group which specializes in birds. Through this organization he got to meet still more birdmen. In 1885 he was elected an associate member of the Ornithologists' Union. His passion for birds made him dissatisfied with his work at the bank but didn't interfere with his business progress, and in the fall of 1886 he was placed in charge of the city collecting department. He saw ahead long years of steady advancement and this discouraged him. He resigned at once. He had decided to become a full-time bird-man.

St. Clair McKelway and A. J. Liebling

WHO IS THIS KING OF GLORY? *

Father Divine has said on more than one occasion that he is God. On the walls of his various Heavens here and in other cities hang banners which state that

FATHER DIVINE IS GOD ALMIGHTY

and on the buses which take his followers on joyous excursions from the Harlem Heavens to the Heavens of Newark and Jersey City is the invariable, red-lettered inscription:

FATHER DIVINE
(God)

The effect of this bold claim, on the press and government of the city in which he makes his headquarters, has been remarkable. The papers, on the whole, have appeared to regard his works as miraculous. The city government has been singularly deferential in its attitude toward him. The two principal candidates for Mayor of New York called on him at one of the nightly meetings in his Harlem Heaven in 1933. "I came here tonight," said Mr. LaGuardia, "to ask Father Divine's help and counsel. Whatever he wants, I'll do it for him." Mr. O'Brien, appearing before the meeting a little earlier, had said, "Peace! Come what may, adversity, joy, or sorrow, you can meet it by reason of your leadership under Father Divine. Peace!" It looks sometimes as if a good many people besides Father Divine's followers think maybe he *is* God.

Father Divine would like everybody to believe that he was born mature, and only a few years ago, in Providence, which is neither in Rhode Island nor the sky, but right here (or over there), like the

---

* *This is part of a long portrait of Father Divine which was published in* The New Yorker *in June, 1936.*

pantheistic Deity or the Buddhists' eternal life. "Except a man be born again," Jesus told Nicodemus, "he cannot see the Kingdom of God." Father Divine not only sees the Kingdom of God every day, but leases it and lives in one of the main apartments himself. Naturally, he says, he had to be born again before that could be. He insists that he can't remember who he was or what he was like before that happened. "Can you remember back to before you were born?" he has asked skeptics who have questioned him on this point.

If you bear firmly in mind the fact that the Father is a short, dignified colored man with a bald head, the true story of his life is more impressive than his story of divine rebirth. It is a story of arduous struggle, onward and upward, from obscurity to national prominence, from rags to riches. In a mere forty years, he rose from hedge-clipper and grass-cutter to evangelist, from evangelist to The Messenger, from The Messenger to Major J. Devine, from Major J. Devine to the Rev. J. Divine, and from the Rev. J. Divine to Father Divine (God).

He is around sixty now, and the earliest records of his life are obscure. People who knew him when he was in his twenties think he came from Georgia, or Florida, or Virginia. They are not sure which. But in 1899, beyond all question, he was a man named George Baker and was earning an honest living in Baltimore, mostly by clipping hedges and mowing lawns. He had a scythe and a pair of pruning shears, and he would canvass the white residential districts in spring and summer, offering his services for fifty cents a day. He was frugal, and when winter came he had usually saved up enough money to loaf for a while. If his store of coins began to get too low, he would find odd jobs on the docks. He did not seem to be very ambitious.

On Sundays he taught in the Sunday school of the Rev. Mr. Henderson's Baptist Church on Eden Street. He was a serious-minded young fellow and worried a lot about God. He didn't feel, or claim to be, closer to God than any of the other members of the Rev. Mr. Henderson's colored congregation. He just taught his Sunday-school class, read his Bible, and went about his work during the week with his head full of large words and sounding phrases. At Wednesday-night prayer meetings in the church he sometimes made little speeches, as any member of the congregation had a right to do, and in these he almost always would get tangled up with some tremendous thought, such as "God is personified and materialized." He would grasp the thought firmly and wrestle with it. "God," he would say, "is not only personified and materialized. He is repersonified and rematerialized. He rematerializes and He rematerial*ates*. He rematerial*ates* and He is rematerial*izable*. He repersonificates and He repersoni*fitizes*." He would go on like that for a while, sweating, his eyes bulging a little, and then he would stop abruptly and resume his seat. People liked to hear him talk even then. There would be cries of "Amen, brother!" and "Brother, ain't it so!" between his words and sometimes between the syllables of his words. But he wasn't the superb orator then that he is now, and he never seemed to be quite sure what it was he was driving at.

* * *

Twenty years later, George Baker, who by a process of multiple birth had become The Messenger and then Major J. Devine, was born a fourth time, and then a fifth time, almost as soon as he established himself in Sayville, Long Island, in 1919. He became Rev. J. Divine, dropping the military title and adopting a vowel which gave the name a supernatural significance. Then almost immediately afterward he became Father Divine (God). He has been God ever since. A few weeks ago his disciples in Harlem stretched a streamer of black-and-gold silk across the throne of Heaven, the headquarters of the cult, on West 115th Street, with the blaring legend:

FATHER DIVINE IS DEAN OF THE UNIVERSE

But that is rank hyperbole. The promotion to Dean of the Universe is simply a gratuitous expression of the enthusiasm of his followers and does not represent a formal rebirth. Neither in the early years in Sayville nor in the later years in Harlem has Father Divine ever hinted that he considers himself to be anything more than God.

As God, after he had settled down in Sayville, he was modest and almost entirely without affectation. His white neighbors on Macon Street were never exactly friendly with him, but they didn't object to him particularly. It was not a pretentious street. The houses, set back from the curbs in comfortable, shady yards, were occupied mostly by people who worked in the village the year round. The summer colony was on the other side of the Merrick Road and the hotels and great estates were still further away. To his neighbors, Father Divine was known not as Major J. Devine, the name he had signed to the deed when he bought his house, but as the Rev. J. Divine, and he told them he was operating an employment agency. He seemed to be an exceptionally clean, upright, and dignified colored man, with soft doe eyes and gentle manners. The neighbors did not know until some years later that he was supposed to be God. They used to see him doing odd jobs around his yard in his spare time, pruning the shrubbery, cutting the grass, and tidying up the places where the former owner had allowed rubbish to accumulate. He was alone all day except for a cook. The twenty-odd men and women who lived with him were workers. Some of them were in New York except on Sundays; others left the house in the morning and returned in the evening. They were decent, orderly colored folk, and bothered nobody. They sang a good deal at night, especially on Sunday, but the singing was soft and they never kept it up much later than nine o'clock. Inside the house George Baker was called Father Divine, and all his followers were sure that he was God.

Once each week Father Divine walked to the office of the *Suffolk County News,* down the block from the Oystermen's Bank & Trust Company, and placed a classified advertisement offering reliable colored help for all work. Whenever a householder answered the advertisement, Father Divine would call in person, bearing a business card marked "Rev. J. Divine." He would remove his hat and, standing on the doorstep, would say, "I can guarantee and *re*guarantee the character and probity and uprighteousness of all my clients." People liked him, and within a year or so, working at a leisurely pace, he got jobs in and near Sayville for all of the early disciples. This relieved the communal purse of the cost of commuting, which had been a considerable strain.

These early followers of Father Divine had never had much to give him but their wages, and their wages were never high. They were poor people who labored on the outer fringe of domestic service. None of them was expert as cook or laundress. They worked mostly for families of three or four who could afford one servant and who paid not more than $10 or $12 a week. But now Father Divine began to attract from the kitchens and butlers' pantries of the summer hotels and big houses of Nassau and Suffolk Counties a new kind of disciple —colored people of some means, who earned sometimes as much as $100 a month, slept and ate in their employers' houses, and had bank accounts and insurance policies. To these people Father Divine seemed to be God in an even more wonderful degree than he had been to the early followers. As he became acquainted with the better class of colored folk in Sayville and neighboring towns, he began to invite them to Sunday dinners at his house; he preached to them after dinner, and never took up a collection. When the guests asked him candidly how he managed to give them free dinners, he would say cheerfully, "Father will provide," and his disciples would say, "It's wonderful! Ain't it wonderful? Sweet Father is God Almighty!" He enjoyed no sudden popularity. He attracted people to his house only by twos and threes. Some Sundays there were no outside guests at all; on others there might be three or four. For six or seven years Father Divine's progress was slow. It was not until the late nineteen-twenties that things began to boom.

The experiences of a butler-and-cook couple named Thomas and Verinda Brown, who worked for a substantial white family in Forest Hills and earned a joint salary of $150 a month, plus board and room, are typical of the experiences of scores of disciples who joined the cult of Father Divine about this time. Thomas and Verinda occupied prominent places in Father Divine's Heaven from 1930 until 1933. They were what Father Divine calls Angels, a title conferred upon any person who assigns all his property to Father Divine, hands over all the money he earns, and takes a new name. Verinda was called Rebecca Grace, and throughout one Sunday dinner in 1931 sat at the right hand of God. Thomas was called Onward Universe and for a while was one of God's favorite Angels. Now the two are Thomas and Verinda again and are back in Forest Hills, working for the same family they were with when they first met Father Divine. They no longer believe that he is God.

Verinda is a very tall, very healthy-looking middle-aged woman, the color of a fine mink coat. Her features are large and frank—a great nose, an enormous jaw, a mouth that opens and shuts decisively. Her natural expression is an expansive grin. Thomas is shorter, darker, less vivacious, a sort of understatement of Verinda. His eyes are drowsy and slow-moving. He is deliberate, methodical, and thoughtful by nature. Verinda comes from Barbados, Thomas from the Bahamas. Both have been in this country thirty years or more and they have been married ten. Both are excessively neat; Thomas is even something of a dude, and at one time owned sixteen suits of clothes, all of them in fair condition. Verinda is a fine cook and a capable children's nurse; as a butler and house man, Thomas is efficient and has a soothing manner. They are decent, honest people. They estimate that during the time they were Angels in Sayville they gave Father Divine, freely and of their own accord, something over $5,000, itemized as follows:

Savings withdrawn from the Railroad Coöperative Building & Loan Association	$ 700
Verinda's salary of $75 a month from April, 1930, to October, 1933	3,225
Gold coins	100
Seven Florida lots (estimated value)	350
Thomas's salary, averaging $75 a month, for six months in 1930	450
Thomas's earnings at odd jobs in Sayville during eighteen months of 1931-32	750
Fifteen suits of clothes relinquished by Thomas (estimated value)	85
Total	$5,660

The manner in which Verinda and Thomas became acquainted with Father Divine seemed to them for a long time afterward to be clearly miraculous. One day in the spring of 1929, after Father Divine's Sunday dinners had become quite an event for the colored population in and near Sayville without attracting attention in other quarters, a laundryman in Forest Hills made a mistake and left some strange clean clothes at the home in which Thomas and Verinda worked. Thomas knew that another family down the street patronized the same laundry, so he took the bundle to the servants' entrance of that house and introduced himself to the cook. He asked if by any chance the laundry bundles for the two houses had been transposed, and found that was just what had happened. The cook was a happy colored woman who said her name was Priscilla Paul. "After the Apostle," she explained. Thomas himself was a constant reader of the Bible and he and Priscilla exchanged, along with the laundry bundles, a few Biblical texts. They parted friends. "Peace! It's wonderful!" Priscilla said as Thomas started off, and Thomas still remembers how pleasant and reassuring it sounded. ("It's a catching phrase," he says now, in the depths of his agnosticism.)

That night Priscilla Paul came to see Verinda and Thomas in their kitchen. "Peace!" she said as she entered. "It's wonderful!" She invited them to come to the evening meal at her father's house in Sayville the next Sunday. She explained that she went to Sayville every Sunday herself and suggested they go with her on the bus. They accepted, and on Sunday were surprised but not displeased to find themselves at a sort of religious meeting. The dinner was very good. The fact that each plate, before it was passed to the eater, was blessed by the man Priscilla and all the other diners called "Father" rather appealed to Verinda and Thomas. Father Divine said nothing memorable in his sermon after dinner. He did not say he was God, or even intimate it, but his phrasemaking was glorious, and Thomas especially liked the Biblical sound of the things Father Divine said. Verinda thought Father Divine had the loveliest, softest eyes she had ever seen.

Verinda and Thomas had Sundays off after midday dinner, and they became regular visitors at Father Divine's house. They asked him if they shouldn't pay for the meals they had every Sunday— told him they'd be more than glad to, because they enjoyed themselves so much. But he would always wave them away with a cheerful smile and say, "Father will provide." It was wonderful. As they got to know the other disciples—a preoccupied and prim old fellow named Gabriel; an elderly woman named Susanna, who sang beautifully; and others named Ruth Rachel, Hozanna Love, Faith Sweetness, Frank Incense, Blessed Charity, and so on—they began to learn how much more wonderful it was than they had dreamed. Not only did the Father provide a dinner every week that must have cost $15 or $20; he worked other miracles besides. The loaves-and-fishes trick, to him, was just a routine. He was a healer, too. Everybody there, it seemed, had been cured of some physical or spiritual disorder. After dinner in the evenings, between songs like:

> Father Divine is the Perfect God,
> Perfect God,
> Perfect God ...

and

> I love to sing the praise of thee,
> Sweet Father Divine.
> I love to sing the praise of thee,
> Be practical all the time,

testimonials would be given by the Angels. This phase of the meeting was a sort of burnt-cork Buchmanism. Verinda and Thomas were perfectly healthy physically, but both had stern consciences and they managed to join in by telling about things they had done wrong, and explaining that, since they had come to know the Father, they didn't do wrong any more.

In the Father's sermons at this time there ran a refrain which had to do with "conscious mentality." He would say, "Relaxation of the conscious mentality is the super-mental relaxativeness of mankind." The Angels, who sat nearest to him at the big dinner table, had achieved this sublime state, it seemed. They had relaxed their conscious mentalities until they had been born again as Angels, they had got fine new names, and they didn't remember anything that had ever happened to them in the past. Verinda and Thomas thought the Angels, and everything about them, were enviable, and they began to try to relax their conscious mentalities. The way to do this, they were told, was to love the Father and think about him all the time.

The employers of Verinda and Thomas were puzzled, and somewhat unnerved, when, during this period, their splendid servants seemed to be going to pieces. Upon being reprimanded for breaking dishes or being slow with the cocktail things, Verinda and Thomas would explain mournfully that they were trying to relax their conscious mentalities. They seemed preoccupied, sad, and solemn, and they probably would have lost their jobs had they not been faithful servants for nine years past. Besides the worry over their conscious mentalities, they had anxieties which their employers did not understand. Thomas and Verinda had grown to love Father Divine. He had been so kind to them during those first months, and he had seemed to know everything, to feel everything, to be so confident when he said, over and over at the dinners, "Your Father is rich in all your needs and all your wants shall be supplied." Those ecstatic shouts of "Yes, Father, you are *so* wonderful!" and "Thank you, Father!" which came from the Angels were impressive and contagious. There was something keenly satisfying and delightful about the idea of putting one's trust in somebody as the Angels put their trust in Father Divine. Verinda and Thomas had begun to think of him as God. And now, just when they were loving him so, and were trying so hard to please him, he seemed not to notice them at all. They found themselves seated further and further away from him every Sunday. When he looked at them at all, it was as if he despised them. He was always talking these days about sacrifice and self-denial and consecration, building the words up till they seemed four times as big as they really were. "He who would enter into the Kingdom of God must have nothing he can call his own," he would say sometimes, candidly. He preached against life insurance, against all forms of insurance, and said that anybody who stood to benefit by an insurance policy was a murderer or an incendiarist at heart. "Look," he would say, "at the Snyder-Gray case. If Albert Snyder hadn't been insured, he would never have been killed. He was putting temptation in the way of the iniquitous. Live right and keep my commandments and you shall never die. It is so written. He who insures his life or his property is a man of little faith." He did not tell his followers that he had insured his house against fire with the Firemen's Insurance Company, the Glens Falls Insurance Company, and the National Liberty Insurance Company, but he had.

When Verinda and Thomas heard the speech against insurance they were delighted. It seemed to be addressed directly to them. They had small insurance policies of the kind that may be cashed in, and they applied for the money that Monday. When they got the cash the next week, Verinda bought a trunk for Thomas and Thomas bought a diamond ring for Verinda. Then they made a special night trip to Sayville to tell the Father about it, feeling sure that he would be pleased.

"Why didn't you ask me what to do with the money?" he demanded bluntly, and added in a more Godlike tone, "He that loveth father or mother, son or daughter, husband or wife, more than me is not worthy to enter the Kingdom of God." They were abashed. Verinda, quicker of tongue than Thomas, said she was so sorry and asked the Father's forgiveness. They had, she said after a silence, a joint account in the Railroad Coöperative Building & Loan Association that contained about $700. They would do anything Father wished with that, she said. Father Divine said, "Draw it out. Lay not up treasures on earth where moth and thief and mouse break in and steal, but lay it up in Heaven with your Father."

This they did. Father Divine got the $700 that Friday.

Then, for a while, Thomas and Verinda dwelt in a state of beatitude. They were told that they had achieved the rank of Angels and were permitted to choose new names for themselves. Verinda chose Rebecca Grace, after some advice from the other Angels. Thomas had already thought up Onward Universe for himself, and he adopted it forthwith. They remained Thomas and Verinda to their employers, but they explained one day that their old names were really just nicknames, that their real names now were Rebecca Grace and Onward Universe. "But you just keep calling us Thomas and Verinda," Thomas said to his master. "That will be perfectly all right."

Thomas and Verinda were happy now. They were moved back nearer the head of the table, and Father Divine beamed on them with heart-warming affection. As a matter of course, without being invited to do so by the Father, they began at once to turn over their wages to him every week, as all the other Angels did. Thomas took the deeds to his Florida lots out of his trunk and signed them over to the Father. When Verinda's mistress, the following year, gave her a bonus of $100 in gold, Verinda turned that over to the Father. For one Sunday, Verinda sat on the right hand of God, and Thomas, only a few seats away, found himself talking intimately with God during dinner. They never talked with the other Angels about the money they were giving to Father Divine because part of the gospel taught at Heaven was that true believers "relaxed all recollection of material transactions." This was a phrase which, with prefixes and suffixes, Father Divine built into something of impressive proportions.

Father Divine was a keen-eyed God. He noticed that Thomas had on a different suit nearly every time he came to Heaven, and one day he asked Thomas about that and learned that Thomas had sixteen suits. "Bring me fifteen of those suits," he told Thomas. "Look how the lilies of the field are clothed, and they spin not."

He was a jealous God, too. In Brooklyn he had always preached the gospel of celibacy to the followers who lived in the flat with him, and now, in Sayville, with about twenty Angels living with him and forty living with their employers, he preached the same gospel with even more determination. When the conscious mentality is really relaxed, he argued, all love except for the Father has to relax, too. Verinda and Thomas were a devoted couple and they slept at night in a double bed. They took the Father's preaching literally and seriously, and Thomas faced the same hardships as those third-century monks who used to exorcise themselves by inviting attractive women to come to the monastery and tempt them. As Gibbon said of the monks, outraged nature sometimes vindicated herself. Whenever that happened, Verinda and Thomas would appear before the Father ill at ease and heavy of conscience, and he, looking at them, would say, "I see you have sinned. You cannot hide from God. I am everywhere. I see all. I know all." And they would moan and cry, "Oh, Father! Yes, Father! Forgive us, Father! You are *so* wonderful, Father!"

A man of Thomas's abilities was needed in Heaven, and six months after Thomas became Onward Universe, he left his job and his Verinda, and came to live in the house on Macon Street. He was one of the principal Angels, and for a while used to hold long Biblical discussions with the Father on weekday evenings. He is handy with tools, and by day he worked around Heaven, putting up partitions where the Father wanted them, repairing the roof, and doing other useful chores. Evidently it was worth the loss of Thomas's salary to Father Divine to have Thomas around. When there was nothing for Thomas to do, he found odd jobs in the village and earned a little cash from time to time, which he turned over to the Father. Verinda kept her job in Forest Hills and came to Heaven only on Sundays, as in the past. She used to meet Thomas there, but never clandestinely, and when they spoke to one another it was just to say, "Peace! It's wonderful!" For a long time it seemed to them that they were happier than they had ever been before. Verinda remained a faithful follower of Father Divine until the fall of 1933. By that time she had become just one of sixty-odd Angels, she was beginning to have her doubts about the divinity of the Father, and she was tired of not having any spending money. Her employers in Forest Hills, who were fond of her, advised her to quit going to Father Divine's meetings, and finally she took their advice. Thomas stayed with Father Divine until last year, by which time he had been demoted to furnace man in the Harlem Heaven. Then one day he walked out, got his old job back, and his Verinda, and never returned.

A good many other Angel couples became estranged in the same way during the Sayville period. Some of them lived separately in Heaven itself and some lived separately outside, and all of them were lonely, their hearts were full of affection, and they didn't love anybody but God. He looked after everything. As he had done in Brooklyn with his early disciples, he now provided second-hand clothes for his Angels, skillfully altered and made over by Angel seamstresses. The Angels had no outside expenses to speak of. They had no doctors' bills to pay. Father Divine preached against doctors and dentists. "Father is the Doctor" became the refrain of one of the Heavenly songs. If a disciple was in the habit of going to a clinic for treatment of some disease, even the most contagious ones, Father Divine frowned upon him and told him not to be of little faith. Death, he said, could not come to a true believer. If it did come, it was a proof that the dead Angel had not been a true believer. At least one Angel died at the Sayville Heaven. This was a woman named Bowman. It was recorded at the time that she was a pauper, with no relatives to pay for her funeral, and she was buried in the town's potter's field.

How much money Father Divine was taking in during the winter of 1929-30 is anybody's guess. Figuring that sixty skilled and unskilled disciples earned an average of $15 a week apiece (some of them in those boom years were making $40 and $50), the total, aside from insurance policies and savings accounts which he took over, would have been $900 a week.

The Sunday dinners had become large affairs by the spring of 1930. Word of the strange preacher who seemed to be God, who gave free Sunday dinners, and who never took up a collection, had got back to Harlem. People began to go out to Sayville from Harlem to see for themselves and to eat the miraculous dinners. But they, like the new disciples, were not riffraff. The round-trip ticket from New York to Sayville cost $2.40 and it was cheaper for people who had to count the pennies to eat at home. Only the well-to-do class of Negroes came to Father Divine's Sunday dinners. Some of them became Angels. A few newspaper stories appeared, all of them marvelling at the hospitality of Father Divine, and after the publicity white people began to go to the Sunday dinners in Sayville. There was a Mrs. Withers, of Long Island City, for instance, who went through the customary initiation and eventually became an Angel named Sister Everjoy. She had been a Christian Scientist, had lost a child, and was vulnerable to any kind of new faith that came along. There was J. Maynard Matthews, an automobile dealer of Brookline, Massachusetts, who had tried Divine Science, Unity, and a number of swamis and yogis without having found what he wanted. He presented Father Divine with a Cadillac, abandoned his business, and became the Father's secretary. His name is John Lamb and he is one of the most important Angels in the movement. Other white followers arrived from all over the country, not in great numbers, but singly, one at a time—a widow from Charlotte, North Carolina; a doctor from Chicago; a young accountant from Kansas City. They were solitaries, marked by that peculiar, agonized look which profound faith seems to bring to people's eyes, and they were all looking for some new kind of life on earth.

By midsummer that year, the Sayville police on Sundays had to put no-parking signs up and down the block in which Heaven stood, to prevent hopeless traffic jams. Trucks and buses were bringing scores of Negroes out from Harlem every week. Father Divine's neighbors rented parking space in their front yards, thus combatting the nascent depression. Not more than seventy-five persons could be seated in Father Divine's dining-room, and he served the Sunday dinners to hundreds, in shifts, all day long and into the evening. A new technique of serving these meals was introduced about this time. The hungry visitors would sit down around the table and Father Divine would bless, first of all, the coffee and tea, and those drinks would be served. There would be an interval of thirty minutes or so, during which everybody was urged to have four or five cups apiece. Then, when the diners had reached a bloated condition, great platters of spaghetti, potatoes, Lima beans, and other starches would be blessed and served. Another half-hour would go by before the impressive hams, roasts, chickens, and turkeys would appear. Usually these dishes, having been blessed and offered to everybody, would leave the table almost intact, to be blessed and served again at successive meals for the rest of the day, and to turn up again on quiet week nights when the Angels sat down to dinner. Father Divine himself found the Heavenly meals unsatisfactory. He used to call on Verinda a little before noon on Sundays in her kitchen in Forest Hills and she would invite him to have a bite to eat. "I can't do that," he would say, drawing himself up to the table. "My Angels are waiting on me in Sayville, to bless their food," he would protest. Verinda would cook up some scrambled eggs, pancakes, sausage, fried potatoes, and coffee, and the Father would fall to, remarking that he might have a snack, at that, to strengthen him on his drive back to Sayville. "When I scrambled eggs for him," Verinda says now, "I always scrambled six."

As Father Divine's fame increased, so did the suspicions of many people outside his cult. Letters were sent to him containing cash, money orders, and checks, by investigators in the pay of the Sayville police authorities, who thought he might be open to prosecution on a federal charge of using the mails to defraud. In every case the enclosure was returned with a note that said, "Father will provide." The Suffolk County District Attorney planted two colored women from Harlem in Father Divine's Heaven in an effort to find out where his money came from, but at the end of two weeks they told him they hadn't been able to find out anything. This procedure was doomed from the start, for the reason that the two colored women were Harlem followers of Father Divine and were well on the way toward becoming Angels themselves. In the end, the Suffolk County authorities ceased trying to work up a criminal case against Father Divine. Nobody could with authority challenge his claim that his money came to him out of the sky. "Everything comes to him automatically because he's God," the Angels used to say, and it seemed to be the only possible explanation.

By fall of that year, there were so many Angels in Heaven that Father Divine had to expand. Property in his block had declined in value somewhat since the big meetings had begun, and he bought the house next door, at No. 64 Macon Street. It is a smaller house than the other one, and was used as a dormitory for female Angels. This left room in Heaven for an extra dining-room to accommodate the guests who came each Sunday in increasing numbers. Father Divine had by this time about a hundred and fifty Angels living with him. In the summer of 1931, he leased a house across the street for white Angels exclusively. About the same time he established what he called an Extension Heaven in Harlem, a flat of five or six rooms on Fifth Avenue at 128th Street. Some twenty Angels who worked in New York lived in the Extension Heaven just as the suburban Angels lived in the one at Sayville. The sexes were segregated, and one of Father Divine's principal Angels looked after the marketing, directed the household work, and collected the wages of all the Angels every payday.

By the fall of 1931, the police authorities in Sayville and the Suf-

folk County District Attorney had decided that Father Divine was a
public nuisance, and he was arrested on that charge on November
16th of that year. After a change of venue had been obtained, he
was brought to trial in Nassau County, before Justice Lewis J. Smith,
who turned out to be the man who contributed as much as anybody to the present greatness of Father Divine. The Justice, according to the opinion of the higher court which subsequently overruled
him, permitted prejudice to enter into the trial and charged the jury
in a manner that virtually demanded a verdict of guilty. Father Divine was convicted and Justice Smith fined him $500 and sentenced
him to one year in jail. Four days after Justice Smith pronounced
this sentence, he died. He had been a robust man and was only fifty-
five years old. His physicians said his death was caused by heart
failure. It was obvious to all of Father Divine's followers, and to
thousands of people, both white and colored, all over the country
who read about it in the newspapers, that Father Divine had struck
down the Justice. The appeal was handled brilliantly by James C.
Thomas, a Negro attorney who is a former Assistant United States
District Attorney. He donated his services because he believed the
issue to be one of racial prejudice. When the Appellate Division reversed the conviction in January, 1933, it was accepted as further evidence of the divinity of Father Divine. The Angels gave Mr. Thomas
no credit at all for the victory.

During the five weeks Father Divine had been held in jail without
bail, scores of new followers joined his cult. The Heavens in Sayville, and the branch in Harlem, had been efficiently maintained by a
few trusted Angels, who came to him often at the Nassau County
Jail for instruction and advice. He was ready now to expand still
further, and he selected Harlem as his new headquarters. Leaving a
few elderly Angels to look after his property in Sayville, he moved
to New York. By this time not fewer than three hundred Angels
were turning over to him everything they earned.

* * *

When Father Divine addresses his followers these days in Heaven,
a roomy, five-story structure at 20 West 115th Street, his demeanor is
marked by an alertness which suggests that he is an extremely nervous man. One of his favorite routines is that of leading a chant which
starts like this:

> One million blessings,
> Blessings flowing free,
> Blessings flowing free.
> There are so many blessings,
> Blessings flowing free for you.

Then it goes:

> One *billion* blessings,
> Blessings flowing free,
> Blessings flowing free,
> There are so many blessings,
> Blessings flowing free for you,

and so on—trillion, quadrillion, quintillion, and on up to what he calls septdecillion. He shouts the catch line of each verse and then, as he hums the chorus and the followers sing, his soft eyes begin to wander. They shift rapidly over the audience, they glance for an instant at the entrance door, at the exits, and once or twice during the singing of a verse he turns half about and looks sharply behind him. He seems agitated and apprehensive, and it is clear that there is more on his mind than the task of conducting a religious meeting. He has the detached, preoccupied manner of a bartender in the early days of prohibition who, while mixing a highball, was always wondering when the police would come in.

VERSE

It is grim business being a minor poet, so little is expected of you. Perhaps for this very reason the writers of non-serious verse give the reader such good measure—they give him poems which sometimes contain music, emotion, and humor, all at once. Even loaded with these noble burdens, the stuff gets called "light."

The editors here offer a few of the heaviest poems they could collect. Others will be found scattered through the book.

Don Marquis

THREE SONNETS TO A RED-HAIRED LADY

Suzanne, I bid you fling aside your comb
And down the wind let stream your burning hair!
My soul, perchance, through midnights of despair,
May see it, Sultry Kid, and flutter home!
Or is there danger in that flaming dome? ...
Suppose I fluttered moth-like, frying there
Unto a crackling, Susan! ... would you care,
My pink-beaned Venus crowned with fiery foam?

My Fifth Wife had a wad of hair herself;
She used to wash and wash and wash the stuff;
I canned her, Sue; I put her on the shelf;
I like clean hair, but still, enough's enough....
She'd get it dry the radiator way....
How these old griefs return! Ah, welladay!

I saw some bright flowers swaying in the park
And thought how like their life your red locks blow....
My Flame! My Sunrise and mine Afterglow!
My genial Hearthfire blazing through the dark!
My Gaudy Kid! Upon life's headlands, stark
And bleak, over the treacherous tides that flow,
A beacon light your Fiery Bean doth throw....
I steer by you and save my giddy bark.

How I should hate it, Lighthouse tall and slim,
If you should cut your hair and dim your fire!
My Seventh Wife did that; she doused her glim,
And dousing it, she damped my soul's desire—
I took a brick and shaved the rest away,
But still her memory stirs me.... Welladay!

When I grow older will you be my wife?
Not now, Suzanne...in twenty years or more.
Unless I change my mind, I'd like you for
A Bonfire in the Autumn of my Life.
But, no! You may be faded then with strife
Of living...marry another, I implore!
And raise me up your daughter to adore,
Red-Haired, with your own candent beauty rife.

My Fourteenth Wife had *unresponsive* hair,
As drab in tone, inert to touch, as clay;
She wore it in an ugly little knot;
She had a morbid interest in prayer,
Which vexed me so I had to have her shot....
She's with the angels now! Ah, welladay!

Angela Cypher

WOMAN OUT OF TAXI

Any woman
   When she's grown
And goes to parties
   All alone

Finds taxicabs
   Exert a spell
That segregate her
   Like a shell

Wherein detached
   From life she's whirled
Through this exciting
   Clamorous world.

Within a cab
   She grows compact,
A separate, keen,
   Dynamic fact,

Unentertained,
   Untouched, unspent,
Safe in her own
   Integument.

Out of the taxi
   She will come
From an emotional
   Vacuum,

Out of the darkness
Into the light,
As highly charged
As dynamite.

She draws her cloak
About her hips,
Twists her bracelet,
Bites her lips,

From head to toe
Grows tense and narrow,
Simple and dangerous
As an arrow

Aimed at a door
That may, by chance
Swing inward, brightly,
On romance.

Ogden Nash

CAT NAPS ARE TOO GOOD FOR CATS

Oh, early every afternoon
I like a temporary swoon.
I do not overeat at luncheon,
I do not broach the bowl or puncheon;
Yet the hour from two to three
Is always sleepy-time to me.

Bolt upright at my desk I sit,
My elbows digging into it,
My chin into my hands doth fit,
My careful fingers screen my eyes,
And all my work before me lies,
Which leads inquisitive passer-bys
Who glance my way and see me nod,
To think me wide awake, if odd.

I would not sell my daily swoon
For all the rubies in Rangoon.
What! sell my swoon? My lovely swoon?
Oh, many and many's the afternoon
I've scoured the woods with Daniel Boone,
And sipped a julep with Lorna Doone,
And Former Governor Ruby Laffoon.
I'll sell my soul before my swoon,
It's not for sale, my swoon's immune.

From two to three each afternoon
Mine are the Mountains of the Moon,
Mine a congenital silver spoon.
And I can lead a lost platoon

Or dive for pearls in a haunted lagoon,
Or guide a stratosphere balloon.
Oh, where the schooner schoons, I schoon,
I can talk lion, or baboon,
Or make a crooner cease to croon.
I like to swoon, for when I swoon
The universe is my macaroon.
Then blessings on thee, my afternoon torpor,
Thou makest a prince of a mental porpor.

"MY CHILD IS PHLEGMATIC..."

—ANXIOUS PARENT

Anxious Parent, I guess you have just never been around;
I guess you just don't know who are the happiest people anywhere to
be found;
I guess you just haven't ever been to the Beaux Arts or Kit Kat or
Cholly Knickerbocker or Old Guards Ball;
I guess you just haven't had any experience of life at all.
So you are worried, are you, because your child is turning out to be
phlegmatic?
Forgive me if I seem a trifle unsympathatic.
Why do you want your child to be a flashing, coruscating gem?
Don't you know the only peace the world can give lies not in flame
but in phlegm?
Don't you know that the people with souls of putty
Are the only people who are sitting prutty?
They never get all worked up at the drop of a pin or a feather or a hat,
They never go around saying bitterly to themselves: "Oh God, did I
really do, did I really say *that?*"
They never boil over when they read about stool pigeons getting girls
into reformatories by making treacherous advances;
They never get perfectly futilely harrowed about Sacco and Vanzetti
or Alice Adamses who don't have good times at dances;
They never blink an eyelash about colleges that are going to the dogs
because of football overemphasis;
They never almost die with indignation when some colored person is
lynched in Natchez or Memphis.

No, when they eat they digest their food, and when they go to bed
they get right to sleep
And four phlegmatic angels a stolid watch over them keep.
Oh to be phlegmatic, oh to be stolid, oh to be torpid, oh to be calm!
For it is only thus, Anxious Parent, that we can get through life with-
out a qualm.

THE SONG OF SONGS

Is anybody here in favor of a redistribution of wealth?
Because I think it ought to be redistributed, only not by force or by
stealth,
Because it is only when other people have it and you haven't that it
is evil,
So we had better try to correct the situation before it is made worse
by a revolution or an upheaval.
Let us not be like the Soviets and fall prey to any communistic
demagog.
No, surely we have more sense than a mujik and would yawn at
arguments that keep them agog;
And let us not be sheep like a Fascist audience
Who get played on by their leaders like concertinas or accaudience;
Let us rather correct in our own 100% American way the wrongs that
annoy and disgust us,
And correct them so the corrections will not offend the Constitution
and Mr. Hughes, our imposing Chief Justice;
Let us handle it in the manner of Washington and Jefferson and
Jackson
And keep very level-headed and Anglo-Saxon.
There are several things standing in the way of a natural distribution
of wealth, but if you want to know which is the chief thing, well,
I will tell you which:
The rich marry only the rich.
It is one of our national disasters
That, broadly speaking, Astors and Vanderbilts and Rockefellers and
Morgans never marry anybody but Morgans and Rockefellers and
Vanderbilts and Astors,

Whereas if they only bestowed their affections on somebody in a
lower crust,

Why money would be distributed over this broad land of ours like
dust,

So I think they may all be rich but honest,

But I think their matchmaking proclivities ought to be harnessed.

Yes, if money marrying money were prohibited,

How speedily and how painlessly it would be redistributed.

Yes, yes, the rich and the poor can settle and forget their differences
just as the Blue and the Gray have

As soon as we have a law saying that people can only marry people
who have a lot less money than they have,

And that will be the end of all your present and future Townsends
and Coughlins and Longs,

And that is why I call this piece the Song of Songs.

H. C. Bunner

BEHOLD THE DEEDS!

(Being the Plaint of Adolphe Culpepper Ferguson, Salesman of Fancy Notions, held in durance of his Landlady for a failure to connect on Saturday night.)

I.

I would that all men my hard case might know;
   How grievously I suffer for no sin:
I, Adolphe Culpepper Ferguson, for lo!
   I, of my landlady am lockéd in,
For being short on this sad Saturday,
Nor having shekels of silver wherewith to pay;
   She has turned and is departed with my key;
   Wherefore, not even as other boarders free,
     I sing (as prisoners to their dungeon stones
   When for ten days they expiate a spree):
     Behold the deeds that are done of Mrs. Jones!

II.

  One night and one day have I wept my woe;
   Nor wot I when the morrow doth begin,
If I shall have to write to Briggs & Co.,
   To pray them to advance the requisite tin
For ransom of their salesman, that he may
Go forth as other boarders go alway—
   As those I hear now flocking from their tea,
   Led by the daughter of my landlady
     Piano-ward. This day for all my moans,
   Dry bread and water have been servéd me.
     Behold the deeds that are done of Mrs. Jones!

III.

Miss Amabel Jones is musical, and so
    The heart of the young he-boardér doth win,
Playing "The Maiden's Prayer," *adagio*—
      That fetcheth him, as fetcheth the banco skin
The innocent rustic. For my part, I pray:
That Badarjewska maid may wait for aye
    Ere sits she with a lover, as did we
    Once sit together, Amabel! Can it be
      That all that arduous wooing not atones
For Saturday shortness of trade dollars three?
    Behold the deeds that are done of Mrs. Jones!

IV.

Yea! she forgets the arm was wont to go
    Around her waist. She wears a buckle whose pin
Galleth the crook of the young man's elbów;
      I forget not, for I that youth have been.
Smith was aforetime the Lothario gay.
Yet once, I mind me, Smith was forced to stay
    Close in his room. Not calm, as I, was he;
    But his noise brought no pleasaunce, verily.
      Small ease he gat of playing on the bones,
Or hammering on his stove-pipe, that I see.
    Behold the deeds that are done of Mrs. Jones!

V.

Thou, for whose fear the figurative crow
    I eat, accursed be thou and all thy kin!
Thee will I show up—yea, up will I shew
      Thy too thick buckwheats, and thy tea too thin.
Ay! here I dare thee, ready for the fray!
Thou dost *not* "keep a first-class house," I say!
    It does not with the advertisements agree.
    Thou lodgest a Briton with a puggaree,

And thou hast harboured Jacobses and Cohns,
Also a Mulligan. Thus denounce I thee!
   Behold the deeds that are done of Mrs. Jones!

ENVOY

Boarders! the worst I have not told to ye:
She hath stolen my trousers, that I may not flee
   Privily by the window. Hence these groans,
There is no fleeing in a *robe de nuit*.
   Behold the deeds that are done of Mrs. Jones!

Franklin P. Adams

TO A THESAURUS

O precious codex, volume, tome,
  Book, writing, compilation, work
Attend the while I pen a pome,
  A jest, a jape, a quip, a quirk.

For I would pen, engross, indite,
  Transcribe, set forth, compose, address,
Record, submit—yea, even write
  An ode, an elegy to bless—

To bless, set store by, celebrate,
  Approve, esteem, endow with soul,
Commend, acclaim, appreciate,
  Immortalize, laud, praise, extol.

Thy merit, goodness, value, worth,
  Expedience, utility—
O manna, honey, salt of earth,
  I sing, I chant, I worship thee!

How could I manage, live, exist,
  Obtain, produce, be real, prevail,
Be present in the flesh, subsist,
  Have place, become, breathe or inhale,

Without thy help, recruit, support,
  Opitulation, furtherance,
Assistance, rescue, aid, resort,
  Favor, sustention, and advance?

Alas! alack! and well-a-day!
  My case would then be dour and sad,
Likewise distressing, dismal, gray,
  Pathetic, mournful, dreary, bad.

* * *

Though I could keep this up all day,
  This lyric, elegiac song,
Meseems hath come the time to say
  Farewell! adieu! good-by! so long!

LINES TO THREE BOYS, 8, 6½, AND 2 YEARS OF AGE

Gentlemen, I love and like you,
Caring little for your IQ.

ADVICE TO YOUNG MEN

Never smash thy promise, lad;
  Never break thy word;
Never kiss a lady's lips,
  Lest thou seem absurd.

Be a rock the girls can trust;
  Never tell a lie;
Never come thou back again
  When they say good-by.

Never let them wonder, lad,
  If thou'lt be on time;
Pay thy debts with diamonds,
  Never with a rhyme.

Never be a wastrel, lad;
  Never fool a maid;
Make of honor a business,
  Make of truth a trade.

Do thou as I tell thee, lad;
  Be the best of men:
And girls won't write of thee in verse,
  Nor think of thee again.

Louis Untermeyer

A. E. HOUSMAN TURNS "GEORGEY PORGEY" INTO SHROPSHIRE LAD

Where lanes are bright with basil
And the blue Severn twirls,
Young Georgey ran to dazzle
And kiss the rose-lipt girls.

No love as light as Georgey's
Who gave his heart at will,
And there were rustic orgies
On many a moonlit hill.

But Spring's first tender buddings
Oft bear a bitter fruit;
And age prefers its puddings
To the unchaste salute.

Now when the dusk is humming
And girls come out to play,
Old Georgey sees them coming
And, oh—he runs away!

Clarence Day

SCENES FROM THE MESOZOIC

I

The parting injunctions
Of mothers and wives
Are one of those functions
That poison their lives.

II

The real objection to the nude,
   Apart of course from chill,
Is that it looks a trifle crude;
   It doesn't fill the bill.

The fact is we need some disguise,
At least in other people's eyes;
Though not so very long ago,
Tradition says, this wasn't so.

The well-dressed beast in ages gone
Had absolutely nothing on,
And yet—if one of the elect—
Achieved with ease the right effect.

III

In mesozoic days a war,
However short, went quite as far
As those du Pont equips, or Krupp.
Like us, they ate each other up.

IV

Soundless is her laughter grim
As he stumbles through the storm.
Fate, he knows, is trailing him,
And the back of his neck feels warm.

V

Farewell, my friends—farewell and hail!
I'm off to seek the Holy Grail.
   I cannot tell you why.
Remember, please, when I am gone,
'Twas Aspiration led me on.
Tiddlely-widdlely tootle-oo,
All I want is to stay with you,
   But here I go. Goodbye.

Irwin Edman

INTERMISSION, PLEASE!

What poet wrote these lovely lines?
What theme is this, from what sonata?
What king invented minus signs?
What's English for *persona grata*?

 The aria we now shall hear
 Is sung by basso, alto, tenor—?
 What actress first played "Chanticler"?
 What's *Lebensraum*? What's *Sprachenkenner*?

Whichever way I turn the dial,
Somebody's asking someone something,
Somebody's learning is on trial,
Someone is being proved a dumb thing.

 Where is the Yard? The Hook of Holland?
 The Taj Mahal? The Iron Lung?
 What college sings the Song of Roland?
 How do you tie a person's tongue?

The famous crowd the microphones
Primed with *bon mots* and information—
A movie star on postal zones,
A prince on pin-point carbonation.

 Name four, name six, name three, name two.
 Send the tinfoil, send in the bottle.
 Send in your question; we'll send you
 A full Greek text of Aristotle.

I listen as they quip and quiz
And get a joke or get an answer:
    What's the pluperfect tense of *Is?*
    Whose head was carried by what dancer?

And as the quizzes end I go
(Sometimes I last but half-way through them)
To study hard until I know
So much I needn't listen to them.

Stephen Vincent Benét

FOR CITY SPRING

Now grimy April comes again,
Maketh bloom the fire-escapes,
Maketh silvers in the rain,
Maketh winter coats and capes
Suddenly all worn and shabby
Like the fur of winter bears,
Maketh kittens, maketh baby,
Maketh kissing on the stairs.
Maketh bug crawl out of crack,
Maketh ticklings down the back
As if sunlight stroked the spine
To a hurdy-gurdy's whine
And the shower ran white wine.

April, April, sing cuckoo,
April, April, maketh new
Mouse and cockroach, man and wife,
Everything with blood and life;
Bloweth, groweth, flourisheth,
Danceth in a ragged skirt
On the very stoop of Death
And will take no mortal hurt.
Maketh dogs to whine and bound,
Maketh cats to caterwaul,
Maketh lovers, all around,
Whisper in the hall.

Oh, and when the night comes down
And the shrieking of the town
Settles to the steady roar
Of a long sea-beaten shore,

April hieth, April spieth
Everywhere a lover lieth,
Bringeth sweetness, bringeth fever,
Will not stop at "I would liever,"
Will not heed, "Now God a mercy!"
Turneth Moral topsy-versy,
Bringeth he and she to bed,
Bringeth ill to maidenhead,
Bringeth joyance in its stead.
By May, by May, she lieth sped,
Yet still we praise that crocus head,
April!

Carolyn Wells

FAMOUS BATHS AND BATHERS

The baths of Caracalla
Beat those in Walla Walla;
Their emblems and omens
Appealed to the Romans.

The baths of Diocletian
Were filled to repletion
With aediles and eunuchs
In togas and tunics.

Susanna, young fool,
Bathed in the pool;
The elders in the shrubbery
Kicked up a bobbery.

Diogenes, old chap,
Just turned on a tap;
(No, that couldn't be,
For he lived in B.C.)

Brave Sir Launcelot
Liked the water hot;
While the old Ettrick shephe'd
Preferred his quite tepid.

Marat, we know,
Used a bathtub, and so
Was put out of the way
By Charlotte Corday.

All of the Pitts
Always used Sitz;
The family tradition
Decreed this position.

But E. Humperdinck
Washed at the sink;
He said, "It saves time
And it takes off the grime."

Samuel Hoffenstein

POEMS IN PRAISE OF PRACTICALLY NOTHING

I

You buy some flowers for your table;
You tend them tenderly as you're able;
You fetch them water from hither and thither—
What thanks do you get for it all? They wither.

II

Only the wholesomest foods you eat;
You lave and you lave from your head to your feet;
The earth is not steadier on its axis
Than you in the matter of prophylaxis;
You go to bed early, and early you rise;
You scrub your teeth and you scour your eyes—
What thanks do you get for it all? Nephritis,
Pneumonia, appendicitis,
Renal calculus and gastritis.

III

You get a girl; and you say you love her;
You pan the comparative stars above her;
You roast the comparative roses below her;
You throw the bull that you'll never throw her—
What thanks do you get? The very first whozis
Who tips his mitt, with him she vamooses.

IV

You buy yourself a new suit of clothes;
The care you give it, God only knows;

The material, of course, is the very best yet;
You get it pressed and pressed and pressed yet;
You keep it free from specks so tiny—
What thanks do you get? The pants get shiny.

V

You practise every possible virtue;
You hurt not a soul, while others hurt you;
You fetch and carry like a market basket;
What thanks do you get for it? Me don't ask it!

VI

You leap out of bed; you start to get ready;
You dress and you dress till you feel unsteady;
Hours go by, and you're still busy
Putting on clothes, till your brain is dizzy.
Do you flinch, do you quit, do you go out naked?—
The least little button, you don't forsake it.
What thanks do you get? Well, for all this mess, yet
When night comes around you've got to undress yet.

———

LOVE SONG

The honey of the Hybla bees
Is not so sweet as kissing you;
Nor autumn wind in dying trees
So wistful is as missing you.

And when you are not mine to kiss,
My every thought is haunting you;
And when your mouth is mine, I miss
The wistfulness of wanting you.

David McCord

SONNETS TO BAEDEKER

I

My old companion on the beaten track,
Who brought me villages and bed and board,
Settled the day and laid me on my back
At inns whose tariff I could not afford;
Sweet *vade mecum* of the *Tuileries,
And audible in naves and barrel vaults,
Still smelling of an earlier Cheddar cheese,
Or blemished with red wines and English malts;
So I remember with what crafty charm
Of small italics and appropriate miles
Distinguished pages loosened a new swarm
Of ancient *Ninevehs* and distant *Niles,*
And played upon my mind as men at chess,
And sold me to AMERICAN EXPRESS.

II

Once it was Paris of *la Reine Pédauque,*
With *SACRÉ-CŒUR like loaves of a young yeast,
And people trading in a foreign talk
For seriatims of the *bouquiniste.*
O glory then upon the face of France:
Who painted what, and where the most is hung,
Such royal chambers of strange occupance
As burned to envy the guide's eager tongue.
Figures and dates assigned at *ST.-SULPICE,

And when the garlic boats ran down the *Seine;*
Recumbent *Abélard and Héloïse,*
The streets that saw a thousand Shelleys plain.
Fine view **(adm. gratis).** Was it Psyche?
Or Cook's own clients round the nerveless ****Nike?**

III

The Coast of Normandy, whose sands are quick,
But troubled by the rock **Mont St. Michel**
Where omelette, *langouste,* and heretic
Mix with the fragrant French monastic smell;
Cathedral towns, the rose-stained glass of **Chartres,**
Septentrional winds upon the mouth,
Vie in the blood with memories **Montmartre,*
The Château country lying to the S.
Travelers' cheques (*sigaro, pourboire, tip*)
Cashed to the least advantage of exchange,
Silver the Riviera as we trip
The marquised beaches or what you arrange;
Dining on balconies and running bills,
With sidelong glances toward the Spanish hills.

IV

They called him Ishmael. I call you Karl,
Who printed London on a Leipzig press,
And left delirious in simple snarl
What most obliges of her great noblesse.
Out of red covers wells the million sound
Of tram and lorry over Oxford Circ.,
And from the purlieus of the underground
The actual Londoners emerge to work.
Sweet catalogue, beyond the last inhab.
Who dwell in **Claridges* and Berkeley Sqs.,
Or blithe Americans by taxicab
Ascending thus her golden British stairs—
Open to **Simpson's* and a London play,
And let me read and eat my heart away.

V

Then up to **Bicester** and the English towns:
Hail *Royal George (Pl. a; B, 4) and how!
Green separate spots of separate renowns,
As where some stout Archbp. made his vow.
Perp. churches, sir, cathedrals, E. E. style,
Castles to open **Wed. 10-3**;
Or Roman ruins of a domicile,
And *Keeps*, 12th cent. (restored), for a small fee.
Number of miles to **Tottenham** and back
(*Cycle or motorbus, afoot or train*),
The kind of villages one used to sack,
And what the Duke said to the King of Spain;
Who died wherever, and God rest their bones,
And why the *Druids* left such funny stones.

VI

But chief, in the moist latitudes of Skye,
You burred the difficult names of Scottish breed:
Blairgowrie, Tomnahurich, Morven—aye,
Of glens and invers to the trouty *Tweed*.
The grandest moors upon the purpled airth,
A Celtic twilight, and Midlothian heart
Commingle sadly in the sound of 'Perth'
As strong rfmt. offered by a bart.
Good patient soul, you spelled the Gaelic word,
Say *usquebaugh* for whiskey, in the notes;
Selected curlew, gannets, the wild bird
That screams the cowried shore by **John o' Groats**;
And where *Auld Reekie* stands eternal guard
You led me to the city ***triple-starred.

Arthur Guiterman

ANTHOLOGISTICS

Since one anthologist put in his book
Sweet things by Morse, Bone, Potter, Bliss and Brook,
All subsequent anthologists, of course
Have quoted Bliss, Brook, Potter, Bone and Morse.
For, should some rash anthologist make free
To print selections, say, from you and me,
Omitting with a judgment all his own
The classic Brook, Morse, Potter, Bliss and Bone,
Contemptuous reviewers, passing by
Our verses, would unanimously cry,
"What manner of anthology is this
That leaves out Bone, Brook, Potter, Morse and Bliss!"

SEA-CHILL

When Mrs. John Masefield and her husband, the author of "I Must Go
Down to the Seas Again," arrived here on a liner, she said to a reporter,
"It was too uppy-downy, and Mr. Masefield was ill."—*News item.*

I must go down to the seas again, where the billows romp and reel,
So all I ask is a large ship that rides on an even keel,
And a mild breeze and a broad deck with a slight list to leeward,
And a clean chair in a snug nook and a nice, kind steward.

I must go down to the seas again, the sport of wind and tide,
As the gray wave and the green wave play leapfrog over the side.
And all I want is a glassy calm with a bone-dry scupper,
A good book and a warm rug and a light, plain supper.

I must go down to the seas again, though there I'm a total loss,
And can't say which is worst, the pitch, the plunge, the roll, the toss.
But all I ask is a safe retreat in a bar well tended,
And a soft berth and a smooth course till the long trip's ended.

Phyllis McGinley

ODE TO THE END OF SUMMER

Summer, adieu.
                  Adieu, gregarious season.
Goodbye, 'revoir, farewell.
Now day comes late; now chillier blows the breeze on
Forsaken beach and boarded-up hotel.
Now wild geese fly together in thin lines
And Tourist Homes take down their lettered signs.

It fades—this green, this lavish interval,
This time of flowers and fruits,
Of melon ripe along the orchard wall,
Of sun and sails and wrinkled linen suits;
Time when the world seems rather plus than minus
And pollen tickles the allergic sinus.

Now fugitives to farm and shore and highland
Cancel their brief escape.
The Ferris wheel is quiet at Coney Island
And quaintness trades no longer on the Cape;
While meek-eyed parents hasten down the ramps
To greet their offspring, terrible from camps.

Turn up the steam. The year is growing older.
The maple boughs are red.
Summer, farewell. Farewell the sunburnt shoulder,
Farewell the peasant kerchief on the head.
Farewell the thunderstorm, complete with lightning,
And the white shoe that ever needeth whitening.

Farewell, vacation friendships, sweet but tenuous.
Ditto to slacks and shorts.
Farewell, O strange compulsion to be strenuous

Which sends us forth to death on tennis courts.
Farewell, Mosquito, horror of our nights;
Clambakes, iced tea, and transatlantic flights.

The zinnia withers, mortal as the tulip.
Now from the dripping glass
I'll sip no more the amateur mint julep
Nor dine al fresco on the alien grass;
Nor scale the height nor breast the truculent billow
Nor lay my head on any weekend pillow.

Unstintingly I yield myself to Autumn
And Equinoctial sloth.
I hide my swim suit in the bureau's bottom
Nor fear the fury of the after-moth.
Forswearing porch and pool and beetled garden,
My heart shall rest, my arteries shall harden.

Welcome, kind Fall, and every month with "r" in
Whereto my mind is bent.
Come, sedentary season that I star in,
O fire-lit Winter of my deep content!
Amid the snow, the sleet, the blizzard's raw gust,
I shall be cozier than I was in August.

Safe from the picnic sleeps the unlittered dell.
The last Good Humor sounds its final bell,
And all is silence.
                    Summer, farewell, farewell.

SONG FROM NEW ROCHELLE

WITH A REFRAIN TO BE CHANTED SOLEMNLY BY A CHORUS CONSISTING
OF N. Y., N. H. & HARTFORD R. R. CONDUCTORS, PASSENGER
AGENTS, AND JOHN COOLIDGE

Monday's child is fair of face,
    And her chauffeur's a handsome fellow.
Tuesday's child is full of grace,
    So she gracefully hails a Yellow.

Wednesday's child has a red coupé
    With a little black horn she toots,
But I was born on a Saturday,
    And Saturday's child commutes!

CHORUS:

*No responsibility is assumed for errors in time tables, nor for incon-
venience or damage resulting from delayed trains or failure to make
connections.*

They that live on Washington Square
    May sleep as long as they please.
And they slumber deep and they slumber fair
    In the affluent seventies.
In Tudor City, the good and mild
    Lie late with a brow serene,
But I am only Saturday's child
    So I get the eight-sixteen.

CHORUS:

Buy tickets before boarding trains and avoid payment of extra charge.

The other girls go out to play
    In the fields of corn and clover.
And the other girls can always stay
    Until the party's over.
But just when the height is at its fun
    And the yodelers growing vocal,
I am the one who needs must run
    To catch the Stamford Local.
It's I that hostesses yearn to shelve;
    The bridge-table Blight am I.
(If Cinderella went home at twelve,
    She probably lived in Rye.)
Before the chorus has ceased to smile
    Or the maestro dropped his baton,
I am the lass in the middle aisle
    Who's trying to get her hat on.

O, gayety dwells
In the best hotels,
  But little to me it boots,
For I was born
On Saturday morn,
  And Saturday's child commutes.

CHORUS:

The schedules shown herein are subject to change without notice.

A HOBBY A DAY KEEPS THE DOLDRUMS AWAY

OR THE PROJECTS OF OLIVER AMES

This is Oliver's garden...
Here is the earth we watched him splinter
When spring was baying the tracks of winter
Here are the bountiful beds he laid out
The earliest day he could get his spade out.
These are his borders—you couldn't miss 'em—
Of ageratum and sweet alyssum.
These are the plots where he put his signs up,
Yonder his trellis to lure the vines up,
And here are the flowers he let go *their* ways
When "Fore" resounded along the fairways;
The blooms I reared in the sweat of my brow.
For it's *my* garden now.

This is Oliver's workshop...
Behold the nook where my hero planned to
Build whatever he set his hand to.
Observe his hammers and saws and wrenches,
His braces and bits, his drawers and benches.
These are his cupboards—a costly come-on.
This is the tool that he cut his thumb on,
And here is the table he almost finished
Before his masculine zeal diminished,

When he decided perhaps he might
Leave some of the laurels for Hepplewhite;
While here are the cobwebs that coil and cluster
For *my* broom and duster.

Sing hey for Oliver's playthings ...
For the wireless set that he cannot send with,
For the tropical fish that I contend with,
For the herbs I hang when he tires of cookery,
For the books I shelve in his unread bookery,
For the faithful hound of a doting master
That I take out to avoid disaster;
The trays and acids in which I traffic
When palls the interlude photographic;
The grain he buys for the snowbound starlings
That I distribute—they're all my darling's.
Each for the moment his one, his true love,
And mine to store when he takes a new love.

For Man proposes the Fuller Life,
But the debris's disposed of by his wife.

Bert Leston Taylor

THE PASSIONATE PROFESSOR

But bending low, I whisper only this:
"Love, it is night."
—Harry Thurston Peck.

Love, it is night. The orb of day
Has gone to hit the cosmic hay.
    Nocturnal voices now we hear.
    Come, heart's delight, the hour is near
When Passion's mandate we obey.

I would not, sweet, the fact convey
In any crude and obvious way:
    I merely whisper in your ear—
        "Love, it is night!"

Candor compels me, pet, to say
That years my fading charms betray.
    Tho' Love be blind, I grant it's clear
    I'm no Apollo Belvedere.
But after dark all cats are gray.
        Love, it is night!

Morris Bishop

A WORM-CHORUS

Rain, wind, and rain!
The heavens are of ashen hue,
They kiss with their celestial dew
Walks of cement, and flagstone too—
Rain, wind, and rain!

Spring, joy of Spring!
Let's break the prison where we're pent
And heed the Spring's admonishment
To bask upon the wet cement!
Spring, joy of Spring!

—Stay yet a while!
Ye know the song the old worms sing
Of them that went adventuring,
Their long abdomens mad with Spring;
Stay yet a while!

Oh, wise old worms!
For home they brought the rovers, dead,
Smit by a Herculean tread,
Their long abdomens all outspread!
Oh, wise old worms!

—Pooh, old worms' tales!
E'en were their drowsy mumbling sooth
(And old worms rarely speak the truth)
Death cannot daunt the heart of youth!
Faugh, old worms' tales!

Rain, wind, and rain!
The asphalt calls us, let us fly;
Forward! We urge with purpose high
Our long abdomens forth to die!
Rain, wind, and rain!

OZYMANDIAS REVISITED

I met a traveller from an antique land
Who said: Two vast and trunkless legs of stone
Stand in the desert. Near them on the sand,
Half sunk, a shatter'd visage lies, whose frown
And wrinkled lip and sneer of cold command
Tell that its sculptor well those passions read
Which yet survive, stamp'd on these lifeless things,
The hand that mock'd them and the heart that fed;
And on the pedestal these words appear:
"My name is Ozymandias, king of kings:
Look on my works, ye Mighty, and despair!"
Also the names of Emory P. Gray,
Mr. and Mrs. Dukes, and Oscar Baer
Of 17 West 4th St., Oyster Bay.

Dorothy Parker

LITTLE WORDS

When you are strayed, there is nor bloom nor leaf
  Nor singing sea at night, nor silver birds.
And I may only stare, and shape my grief
  In little words.

I cannot conjure loveliness, to drown
  The bitter woe that racks my chords apart.
The staggering pen that sets my sorrow down
  Feeds at my heart.

There is no mercy in the shifting year;
  No beauty wraps me tenderly about.
I turn to little words—so you, my dear,
  Can spell them out.

THE SEARCHED SOUL

When I consider, pro and con,
What things my love is built upon—
A curly mouth; a sinewed wrist;
A questioning brow; a pretty twist
Of words as old and tried as sin;
A pointed ear; a cloven chin;
Long, tapered limbs; and slanted eyes
Not cold nor kind nor darkly wise—
When I so ponder, here apart,
What shallow boons suffice my heart,
What dust-bound trivia capture me,
I marvel at my normalcy.

TOMBSTONE FOR AN ACTRESS

Her name, cut clear upon this marble cross,
  Shines, as it shone when she was still on earth;
While tenderly the mild, agreeable moss
  Obscures the figures of her date of birth.

Clarence H. Knapp

AIN'T THERE AT LEAST ONE GEN'LEMAN HERE?

A MODERN SOB BALLAD

I

A travelling man once entered
  Into a cabaret.
'Twas midnight and quite naturally
  The throng there all was gay.
He sat down to a table
  And ordered a Port wine.
Right near him was a party,
  Most of whom felt fine.
Now one of this fast comp'ny
  Was a youth too full of beer,
Who rose unsteady from his seat
  And said so all could hear:
"That dancing girl looks good to me,
  A kiss I'm going to steal."
The girl cried out as he drew near,
  Then made this sweet appeal:

REFRAIN

"Ain't there at least one gen'leman here,
  One who ain't full of whiskey or beer,
One who remembers his wife or his mother,
  One who will act just like a big brother?
Don't think 'cause I dance midst these lights and these lures,
  That my feelings ain't hurt as easy as yours.
And though dancing girls are sporty 'tis claimed,
  I've never done nothing of what I'm ashamed."

II

The travelling man rose from his seat,
  And picking up a chair,
He threat'ningly strode toward the youth
  So near that dancer fair.
Said he, "Miss, I heard your plea
  And I'll protect your name."
The drunken youth then did shrink back
  In terror and in shame.
The man glanced at the girl once more,
  The frown from his face fell.
He recognized to his surprise
  His boyhood's sweetheart, Nell.
He cried, "At last I've found you, Nell.
  We'll leave this place and wed."
She whispered, "Bert, I knew you'd come
  When those words I had said:

REFRAIN

" 'Ain't there at least one gen'leman here,
  One who ain't full of whiskey or beer,
One who remembers his wife or his mother,
  One who will act just like a big brother?
Don't think 'cause I dance midst these lights and these lures,
  That my feelings ain't hurt as easy as yours.
And though dancing girls are sporty 'tis claimed,
  I've never done nothing of what I'm ashamed.'"

E. B. White

HARPER TO MIFFLIN TO CHANCE

Among the authors who have recently gone to other publishers are H. G. Wells, who left Doubleday Doran for Macmillan; Charles Morgan, author of "The Fountain," who went to Macmillan from Knopf; Harold Bell Wright, who left Appleton's for Harper's; Aldous Huxley, who left Doubleday Doran for Harper's; Louis Bromfield, who left Stokes for Harper's; Tiffany Thayer, who left Claude Kendall for Liveright; and J. P. McEvoy, who went from Simon & Schuster to Houghton Mifflin.—*The Times*.

Come Harper, come Schuster, come Appleton all,
The winter is coming, and gone is the fall,
The authors are restless and pining to go
And Santa is poorly and we shall have snow!
  Come *on,* Harper!

Come Huxley, come Morgan, come Harold Bell Wright,
The dew's on the turnip—the publisher's blight;
Come Bromfield and Thayer, come all God's chillun,
Goodbye to Knopf, sir, and ho for Macmillan!
  Come *on,* Macmillan.

Ho ho! for the writers who pass in the night,
Hey hey! for Al Huxley and Harold Bell Wright,
For the moon on the crest of the new fallen snow
And the luster of Doubleday all in a row.
  Come *on,* Doubleday!

Come author, come poet, come scriveners bold,
The royalty's gone and the days grow cold,
So put on the imprint of Simon & Schuster
And sell a lot more than you formerly uster!
  Come *on,* Simon!

Come Appleton, Harper, come Mifflin and all!
To the top of the list, to the top of the wall!
Your authors are dressed in their last year's loyalty,
They'll kiss you goodbye for the first pretty royalty.
    Come *on,* Pater.

Kenneth Allan Robinson

THE MESECKS

(Respectfully Dedicated to the Meseck Towing Line)

Swaggering up the harbor,
  With Quarantine left behind you,
Your liner stops and tootles for help,
  And who comes out to find you?
Who comes out to help you
  But Mesecks all in a flock—
A fleet of little Mesecks,
Of hovering, anxious Mesecks,
Of scurrying tugboat Mesecks,
  To waggle you into dock.

Walter Meseck, and Bessie Meseck, and Meseck, Carrie T.,
Margaret, Madeline, William Meseck, and Meseck, Mary E.

I've never come up the harbor
  At the end of a six days' journey
But the Meseck names have taken my gaze
  Like unknown knights at a tourney.
Mary and Bessie and Carrie,
  Madeline, Walter, and Bill—
What are they like, those Mesecks,
Those veiled, mysterious Mesecks,
Those secret, glamorous Mesecks
  Whose navies are never still?

Walter Meseck, and Bessie Meseck, and Meseck, Carrie T.,
Margaret, Madeline, William Meseck, and Meseck, Mary E.

I never have met the Mesecks
  —Though I pray that they're hale and hearty—
And I'm never a guest at a dinner
  Or a large, superior party
But I hope that my host or hostess
  Will hail me before I go
With "Haven't you met the Mesecks?
Come here and meet the Mesecks,
Come here and meet *all* the Mesecks,
  They're *such* nice people to know:

Walter Meseck, and Bessie Meseck, and Meseck, Carrie T.,
Margaret, Madeline, William Meseck, and Meseck, Mary E."

Oliver Wendell Holmes

CACOËTHES SCRIBENDI

If all the trees in all the woods were men,
And each and every blade of grass a pen;
If every leaf on every shrub and tree
Turned to a sheet of foolscap; every sea
Were changed to ink, and all earth's living tribes
Had nothing else to do but act as scribes,
And for ten thousand ages, day and night,
The human race should write, and write, and write,
Till all the pens and paper were used up,
And the huge inkstand was an empty cup,
Still would the scribblers clustered round its brink
Call for more pens, more paper, and more ink.

REMINISCENCE

Humorists have wonderful memories, or think they have. They are constantly recording emotional fragments of their lives, as recalled in tranquillity—or in drink. As for the truth of what they put down on paper, it is questionable: we can assure the reader that the reminiscences on the following pages range from straight fact to the most barefaced lies. When grilled about the faithfulness of their memoirs, different humorists tell different stories. Clarence Day always insisted that his pieces about the Day family were true in every detail, and he believed this himself. James Thurber never used to claim that his memories were wholly factual, but he has by now almost persuaded himself that the Columbus, Ohio, of his childhood was as fantastic as he describes it. (It is easy to believe the Thurber household was an unusually active one, but surely the most tempestuous and busy spot in the whole place was the mind of little Jamie.) Bemelmans, we believe, states that his stories of the Hotel Splendide are fiction written in autobiographical form. The reader can reasonably accept this as true, at the same time realizing that in setting up a background for his plots, memory has served Mr. Bemelmans well.

Clarence Day

THE NOBLEST INSTRUMENT

Father had been away, reorganizing some old upstate railroad. He returned in an executive mood and proceeded to shake up our home. In spite of my failure as a singer, he was still bound to have us taught music. We boys were summoned before him and informed that we must at once learn to play on something. We might not appreciate it now, he said, but we should later on. "You, Clarence, will learn the violin. George, you the piano. Julian—well, Julian is too young yet. But you older boys must have lessons."

I was appalled at this order. At the age of ten it seemed a disaster to lose any more of my freedom. The days were already too short for our games after school; and now here was a chunk to come out of playtime three days every week. A chunk every day, we found afterward, because we had to practice.

George sat at the piano in the parlor, and faithfully learned to pound out his exercises. He had all the luck. He was not an inspired player, but at least he had some ear for music. He also had the advantage of playing on a good robust instrument, which he didn't have to be careful not to drop, and was in no danger of breaking. Furthermore, he did not have to tune it. A piano had some good points.

But I had to go through a blacker and more gruesome experience. It was bad enough to have to come in from the street and the sunlight and go down into our dark little basement where I took my lessons. But that was only the opening chill of the struggle that followed.

The whole thing was uncanny. The violin itself was a queer, fragile, cigar-boxy thing, that had to be handled most gingerly. Nothing sturdy about it. Why, a fellow was liable to crack it putting it into its case. And then my teacher, he was queer too. He had a queer pickled smell.

I dare say he wasn't queer at all really, but he seemed so to me, because he was different from the people I generally met. He was

probably worth a dozen of some of them, but I didn't know it. He
was one of the violins in the Philharmonic, and an excellent player,
a grave, middle-aged little man—who was obliged to give lessons.

He wore a black, wrinkled frock coat, and a discolored gold watch
chain. He had small, black-rimmed glasses; not tortoise-shell, but
thin rims of metal. His violin was dark, rich, and polished, and would
do anything for him.

Mine was balky and awkward, brand new, and of a light, common
color.

The violin is intended for persons with a passion for music. I
wasn't that kind of person. I liked to hear a band play a tune that
we could march up and down to, but try as I would, I could seldom
whistle such a tune afterward. My teacher didn't know this. He greeted
me as a possible genius.

He taught me how to hold the contraption, tucked under my chin.
I learned how to move my fingers here and there on its handle or
stem. I learned how to draw the bow across the strings, and thus
produce sounds. . . .

Does a mother recall the first cry of her baby, I wonder? I still
remember the strange cry at birth of that new violin.

My teacher, Herr M., looked as though he had suddenly taken a
large glass of vinegar. He sucked in his breath. His lips were drawn
back from his teeth, and his eyes tightly shut. Of course, he hadn't
expected my notes to be sweet at the start; but still, there was something unearthly about that first cry. He snatched the violin from me,
examined it, readjusted its pegs, and comforted it gently, by drawing
his own bow across it. It was only a new and not especially fine violin,
but the sounds it made for him were more natural—they were classi-
fiable sounds. They were not richly musical, but at least they had
been heard before on this earth.

He handed the instrument back to me with careful directions. I
tucked it up under my chin again and grasped the end tight. I held
my bow exactly as ordered. I looked up at him, waiting.

"Now," he said, nervously.

I slowly raised the bow, drew it downward. . . .

This time there were *two* dreadful cries in our little front basement.
One came from my new violin and one from the heart of Herr M.

Herr M. presently came to, and smiled bravely at me, and said if
I wanted to rest a moment he would permit it. He seemed to think

I might wish to lie down awhile and recover. I didn't feel any need
of lying down. All I wanted was to get through the lesson. But Herr
M. was shaken. He was by no means ready to let me proceed. He
looked around desperately, saw the music book, and said he would
now show me that. We sat down side by side on the window-seat,
with the book in his lap, while he pointed out the notes to me with
his finger, and told me their names.

After a bit, when he felt better, he took up his own violin, and instructed me to watch him and note how he handled the strings. And
then at last, he nerved himself to let me take my violin up again.
"Softly, my child, softly," he begged me, and stood facing the wall....

We got through the afternoon somehow, but it was a ghastly experience. Part of the time he was maddened by the mistakes I kept
making, and part of the time he was plain wretched. He covered his
eyes. He seemed ill. He looked often at his watch, even shook it as
though it had stopped; but he stayed the full hour.

That was Wednesday. What struggles he had with himself before
Friday, when my second lesson was due, I can only dimly imagine,
and of course I never even gave them a thought at the time. He came
back to recommence teaching me, but he had changed—he had hard-
ened. Instead of being cross, he was stern; and instead of sad, bitter.
He wasn't unkind to me, but we were no longer companions. He
talked to himself, under his breath; and sometimes he took bits of
paper, and did little sums on them, gloomily, and then tore them up.

During my third lesson I saw the tears come to his eyes. He went
up to Father and said he was sorry but he honestly felt sure I'd never
be able to play.

Father didn't like this at all. He said he felt sure I would. He dismissed Herr M. briefly—the poor man came stumbling back down
in two minutes. In that short space of time he had gallantly gone
upstairs in a glow, resolved upon sacrificing his earnings for the sake
of telling the truth. He returned with his earnings still running, but
with the look of a lost soul about him, as though he felt that his
nerves and his sanity were doomed to destruction. He was low in his
mind, and he talked to himself more than ever. Sometimes he spoke
harshly of America, sometimes of fate.

But he no longer struggled. He accepted this thing as his destiny. He
regarded me as an unfortunate something, outside the human species,

whom he must simply try to labor with as well as he could. It was a grotesque, indeed a hellish experience, but he felt he must bear it.

He wasn't the only one—he was at least not alone in his sufferings. Mother, though expecting the worst, had tried to be hopeful about it, but at the end of a week or two I heard her and Margaret talking it over. I was slaughtering a scale in the front basement, when Mother came down and stood outside the door in the kitchen hall and whispered, "Oh, Margaret!"

I watched them. Margaret was baking a cake. She screwed up her face, raised her arms, and brought them down with hands clenched.

"I don't know what we shall do, Margaret."

"The poor little feller," Margaret whispered. "He can't make the thing go."

This made me indignant. They were making me look like a lubber. I wished to feel always that I could make anything go. . . .

I now began to feel a determination to master this thing. History shows us many examples of the misplaced determinations of men—they are one of the darkest aspects of human life, they spread so much needless pain: but I knew little history. And I viewed what little I did know romantically—I should have seen in such episodes their heroism, not their futility. Any role that seemed heroic attracted me, no matter how senseless.

Not that I saw any chance for heroism in our front basement, of course. You had to have a battlefield or something. I saw only that I was appearing ridiculous. But that stung my pride. I hadn't wanted to learn anything whatever about fiddles or music, but since I was in for it, I'd do it, and show them I could. A boy will often put in enormous amounts of his time trying to prove he isn't as ridiculous as he thinks people think him.

Meanwhile Herr M. and I had discovered that I was nearsighted. On account of the violin's being an instrument that sticks out in front of one, I couldn't stand close enough to the music book to see the notes clearly. He didn't at first realize that I often made mistakes from that cause. When he and I finally comprehended that I had this defect, he had a sudden new hope that this might have been the whole trouble, and that when it was corrected I might play like a human being at last.

Neither of us ventured to take up this matter with Father. We knew that it would have been hard to convince him that my eyes were not perfect, I being a son of his and presumably made in his image; and we knew that he immediately would have felt we were trying to make trouble for him, and would have shown an amount of resentment which it was best to avoid. So Herr M. instead lent me his glasses. These did fairly well. They turned the dim grayness of the notes into a queer bright distortion, but the main thing was they did make them brighter, so that I now saw more of them. How well I remember those little glasses. Poor, dingy old things. Herr M. was nervous about lending them to me; he feared that I'd drop them. It would have been safer if they had been spectacles: but no, they were pince-nez; and I had to learn to balance them across my nose as well as I could. I couldn't wear them up near my eyes because my nose was too thin there; I had to put them about half-way down where there was enough flesh to hold them. I also had to tilt my head back, for the music-stand was a little too tall for me. Herr M. sometimes mounted me on a stool, warning me not to step off. Then when I was all set, and when he without his glasses was blind, I would smash my way into the scales again.

All during the long winter months I worked away at this job. I gave no thought, of course, to the family. But they did to me. Our house was heated by a furnace, which had big warm air pipes; these ran up through the walls with wide outlets into each room, and sound traveled easily and ringingly through their roomy, tin passages. My violin could be heard in every part of the house. No one could settle down to anything while I was practicing. If visitors came they soon left. Mother couldn't even sing to the baby. She would wait, watching the clock, until my long hour of scale-work was over, and then come downstairs and shriek at me that my time was up. She would find me sawing away with my forehead wet, and my hair wet and stringy, and even my clothes slowly getting damp from my exertions. She would feel my collar, which was done for, and say I must change it. "Oh, Mother! Please!"—for I was in a hurry now to run out and play. But she wasn't being fussy about my collar, I can see, looking back; she was using it merely as a barometer or gauge of my pores. She thought I had better dry myself before going out in the snow.

It was a hard winter for Mother. I believe she also had fears for the baby. She sometimes pleaded with Father; but no one could ever tell Father anything. He continued to stand like a rock against stopping my lessons.

Schopenhauer, in his rules for debating, shows how to win a weak case by insidiously transferring an argument from its right field, and discussing it instead from some irrelevant but impregnable angle. Father knew nothing of Schopenhauer, and was never insidious, but, nevertheless, he had certain natural gifts for debate. In the first place his voice was powerful and stormy, and he let it out at full strength, and kept on letting it out with a vigor that stunned his opponents. As a second gift, he was convinced at all times that his opponents were wrong. Hence, even if they did win a point or two, it did them no good, for he dragged the issue to some other ground then, where he and Truth could prevail. When Mother said it surely was plain enough that I had no ear, what was his reply? Why, he said that the violin was the noblest instrument invented by man. Having silenced her with this solid premise he declared that it followed that any boy was lucky to be given the privilege of learning to play it. No boy should expect to learn it immediately. It required persistence. Everything, he had found, required persistence. The motto was, Never give up.

All his life, he declared, he had persevered in spite of discouragement, and he meant to keep on persevering, and he meant me to, too. He said that none of us realized what he had had to go through. If he had been the kind that gave up at the very first obstacle, where would he have been now—where would any of the family have been? The answer was, apparently, that we'd either have been in a very bad way, poking round for crusts in the gutter, or else nonexistent. We might have never even been born if Father had not persevered.

Placed beside this record of Father's vast trials overcome, the little difficulty of my learning to play the violin seemed a trifle. I faithfully spurred myself on again, to work at the puzzle. Even my teacher seemed impressed with these views on persistence. Though older than Father, he had certainly not made as much money, and he bowed to the experience of a practical man who was a success. If he, Herr M., had been a success he would not have had to teach boys; and sitting in this black pit in which his need of money had placed him, he saw more than ever that he must learn the ways of this world. He listened with all his heart, as to a god, when Father shook his forefinger, and told him how to climb to the heights where financial rewards were achieved. The idea he got was that perseverance was sure to lead to great wealth.

Consequently our front basement continued to be the home of lost causes.

Of course, I kept begging Herr M. to let me learn just one tune. Even though I seldom could whistle them, still I liked tunes; and I knew that, in my hours of practicing, a tune would be a comfort. That is, for myself. Here again I never gave a thought to the effect upon others.

Herr M., after many misgivings, to which I respectfully listened—though they were not spoken to me, they were muttered to himself, pessimistically—hunted through a worn old book of selections, and after much doubtful fumbling chose as simple a thing as he could find for me—for me and the neighbors.

It was spring now, and windows were open. That tune became famous.

What would the musician who had tenderly composed this air, years before, have felt if he had foreseen what an end it would have, on Madison Avenue; and how, before death, it would be execrated by that once peaceful neighborhood. I engraved it on their hearts; not in its true form but in my own eerie versions. It was the only tune I knew. Consequently I played and replayed it.

Even horrors when repeated grow old and lose part of their sting. But those I produced were, unluckily, never the same. To be sure, this tune kept its general structure the same, even in my sweating hands. There was always the place where I climbed unsteadily up to its peak, and that difficult spot where it wavered, or staggered, and stuck; and then a sudden jerk of resumption—I came out strong on that. Every afternoon when I got to that difficult spot, the neighbors dropped whatever they were doing to wait for that jerk, shrinking from the moment, and yet feverishly impatient for it to come.

But what made the tune and their anguish so different each day? I'll explain. The strings of a violin are wound at the end around pegs, and each peg must be screwed in and tightened till the string sounds just right. Herr M. left my violin properly tuned when he went. But suppose a string broke, or that somehow I jarred a peg loose. Its string then became slack and soundless. I had to re-tighten it. Not having an ear, I was highly uncertain about this.

Our neighbors never knew at what degree of tautness I'd put such a string. I didn't myself. I just screwed her up tight enough to make a strong reliable sound. Neither they nor I could tell which string would thus appear in a new role each day, nor foresee the profound transformations this would produce in that tune.

All that spring this unhappy and ill-destined melody floated out through my window, and writhed in the air for one hour daily, in sunshine or storm. All that spring our neighbors and I daily toiled to its peak, and staggered over its hump, so to speak, and fell wailing through space.

Things now began to be said to Mother which drove her to act. She explained to Father that the end had come at last. Absolutely. "This awful nightmare cannot go on," she said.

Father pooh-poohed her.

She cried. She told him what it was doing to her. He said that she was excited, and that her descriptions of the sounds I made were exaggerated and hysterical—must be. She was always too vehement, he shouted. She must learn to be calm.

"But you're downtown, *you* don't have to hear it!"

Father remained wholly skeptical.

She endeavored to shame him. She told him what awful things the neighbors were saying about him, because of the noise I was making, for which he was responsible.

He couldn't be made to look at it that way. If there really were any unpleasantness then I was responsible. He had provided me with a good teacher and a good violin—so he reasoned. In short, he had done his best, and no father could have done more. If I made hideous sounds after all that, the fault must be mine. He said that Mother should be stricter with me, if necessary, and make me try harder.

This was the last straw. I couldn't try harder. When Mother told me his verdict I said nothing, but my body rebelled. Self-discipline had its limits—and I wanted to be out: it was spring. I skimped my hours of practice when I heard the fellows playing outside. I came home late for lessons—even forgot them. Little by little they stopped.

Father was outraged. His final argument, I remember, was that my violin had cost twenty-five dollars; if I didn't learn it the money would be wasted, and he couldn't afford it. But it was put to him that my younger brother, Julian, could learn it instead, later on. Then summer came, anyhow, and we went for three months to the seashore; and in the confusion of this Father was defeated and I was set free.

In the autumn little Julian was led away one afternoon, and imprisoned in the front basement in my place. I don't remember how long they kept him down there, but it was several years. He had an ear, however, and I believe he learned to play fairly well. This would have made a happy ending for Herr M. after all; but it was some other teacher, a younger man, who was engaged to teach Julian. Father said Herr M. was a failure.

Joseph Mitchell

THE DOWNFALL OF FASCISM IN
BLACK ANKLE COUNTY

Every time I see Mussolini shooting off his mouth in a newsreel or Göring goose-stepping in a rotogravure, I am reminded of Mr. Catfish Giddy and my first encounter with Fascism. In 1923, when I was in the ninth grade in Stonewall, North Carolina, Mr. Giddy and Mr. Spuddy Ransom organized a branch of the Knights of the Ku Klux Klan, or the Invisible Empire, which spread terror through Black Ankle County for several months. All the kids in town had seen "The Birth of a Nation," and they were fascinated by the white robes and hoods worn by the local Klansmen, and by the fiery crosses they burned at midnight on Saturdays in the vacant lot beside the Atlantic Coast Line depot. On Tuesday and Friday, the Klan's meeting nights, the kids would hide in the patch of Jerusalem-oak weeds in the rear of the Planters Bank & Trust Company and watch the Klansmen go up the back stairs to their meeting hall above the bank. Sometimes they reappeared in a few minutes, dressed in flowing white robes, and drove off mysteriously. I spent so many nights hiding in the weed patch that I failed my final examinations in geometry, history, French, and Bible, and was not promoted, which I did not mind, as I had already spent two years in the ninth grade and felt at home there.

Now, when I look back on that period and reflect on the qualities of Mr. Giddy, Mr. Ransom, and their followers, I wonder why the people of Black Ankle County, particularly the people of Stonewall, stood for the Ku Klux Klan as long as they did. Traditionally, the people of Stonewall are sturdy and self-reliant. In fact, the town was named General Stonewall Jackson, North Carolina, when it was founded right after the Civil War; later the name was shortened to Stonewall. There was certainly nothing frightening about Mr. Giddy, the Führer of the local Klan. His full name was J. Raymond Giddy, but he had a mustache on his plump face which he treated with beeswax and which stuck out sharply on both sides, and consequently he was almost always referred to as Mr. Catfish Giddy, even in the columns of the weekly *Stonewall News*. He was rather proud of the nickname. He used to say, "I may not be the richest man in Black Ankle County, but I sure am the ugliest; you can't take that away from me." Mr. Giddy was a frustrated big businessman. Before he got interested in the Klan, he had organized the Stonewall Boosters and a Stonewall Chamber of Commerce, both of which died after a few meetings. He was always making speeches about big business, but he was never much of a big businessman himself. At the time he and Mr. Ransom organized the Klan he was a travelling salesman for a chewing-tobacco concern. When he returned from a trip he would never brag about how many boxes of cut plug he had sold. Instead, he would brag that the cut plug manufactured in North Carolina in one year, if laid end to end, would damn near reach to Egypt, or Australia, or the moon, or some other distant place.

"In the manufacture of chewing tobacco, my friends," he would boast, "the Tarheel State leads the whole civilized world."

He was the town orator and the town drunk. In his cups, he would walk up and down Main Street, singing. He had a bass voice and his favorite songs were "Old Uncle Bud," new verses for which he would make up as he went along, and a song about Lydia Pinkham's vegetable compound and its effect on the human race, a song he had learned when he was a young man attending a business college in Atlanta. The high-school boys and girls, drinking Coca-Colas in the Stonewall Drug Company, would run to the door and stare and giggle when Mr. Giddy got drunk and marched up Main Street. "Old Uncle Bud," he would sing, "is the jelly-roll king. Got a hump on his back from shaking that thing." At that time, the shimmy, introduced by some tent-show girls at the Black Ankle County Fair, was popular in Stonewall, and the young people called it the "jelly roll."

Mr. Ransom was far more frightening than Mr. Giddy. He was a gaunt, wild-eyed farmer. He was a religious fanatic, always screaming about wickedness. Even when he was dressed in his Ku Klux Klan outfit, he could easily be identified because he walked with a peculiar, hobbledehoy gait. He was a deacon in the Stonewall Jackson Baptist Church, the church I went to, and he used to ring the bell before services until he got a little too impassioned one Sunday morning and pulled the rope so hard the bell came unscrewed and fell out of the oft, landing on his left shoulder. After that accident he always walked as if his next step would be his last. Like Mr. Giddy, he had a nickname. He was christened John Knox Ransom, but he was called Mr. Spuddy because he habitually argued that the Southern farmer should quit planting cotton and tobacco and plant Irish potatoes. "Something you can eat," he would argue, smacking his palms together for emphasis. "Goodness gracious, my friends, if you can't sell your crop, you can put it on the table and eat it." One winter he tried to live on Irish potatoes and got so thin his belt wouldn't hold his pants up. His worried wife would urge him to eat some meat to get his strength back, and he would shout, "Is a mule strong? Does a mule eat meat?" His wife, who was a sensible woman, would ask meekly, "Does a mule eat Irish potatoes?"

I don't think Mr. Giddy, the drunken drummer, and Mr. Ransom, the fanatical deacon, thought very highly of each other until Mr. Giddy returned from a selling trip in the winter of 1923 with some booklets about the Klan he had picked up in Atlanta. Mr. Giddy discreetly distributed the booklets among some of the loafers in Stonewall, and Mr. Ransom got one. After reading it, he decided that the best way to fight wickedness, the best way to drive corn-whiskey distillers, gipsy mule traders, loose women, profane men, and Holy Roller preachers out of Black Ankle County was to organize the Klan there.

He and Mr. Giddy got together, hired the hall over the bank, painted the windows black for the sake of secrecy, and enrolled seventeen men in the Klan. They included a tobacco auctioneer, an undertaker, a grocery clerk, an indolent house painter, and a number of farmers. The farmers were all like Mr. Ransom in that they spent less time in their fields than they did around the pot-bellied stove of the Stonewall Hardware & General Merchandise Company, arguing about religion and politics. Most of the men joined the Klan because it gave them an excuse to get away from their wives at night and because it seemed to them to have even more mystery and ceremony than the Masons or the Woodmen of the World. The undertaker and Mr. Ransom were the only "respectable" men in it; most of the others, according to the rather rigid standards of Stonewall, were either "common" or "sorry." Some were both—the house painter, for example. I once heard him summed up by an old woman in Stonewall, who said, "He's common. Fishes in the summer and hunts in the winter, and when it rains he sits by the stove and plays checkers. He sure is one sorry man."

The fathers of some of my friends joined the Klan and gradually I learned many of the Klan secrets. I learned that the initiation fee was ten dollars and that the robe and hood cost six-fifty. A friend of mine swiped his father's Klan books. One was called "The Platform of the Invisible Empire." I persuaded him to let me have it in exchange for Zane Grey's "Riders of the Purple Sage." I still have it. On the cover is this declaration: "The Ku Klux Klan stands on a platform of 100-per-cent Americanism, white supremacy in the South, deportation of aliens, purity of womanhood, and eradication of the chain store." In the book are a number of denunciations of Catholics, Jews, Negroes, and labor unions. The kids in Stonewall spied on the Klan much as kids now play G-men and gangsters; it was a game. We were frightened by the Klansmen, but not too frightened to hide in the weed patch and watch them come and go. I remember one kid, lying beside me in the weeds, pointing to a robed figure and hoarsely whispering, "There goes Pa."

Mules are used almost exclusively instead of horses in the tobacco and cotton fields of Black Ankle County, and during the first weeks of the Klan's existence in Stonewall the members rode plough mules on their night rides about the countryside. They preferred to ride cross-country, and they could not use automobiles because they would quickly bog down in the sticky mud of the fields, the black mud which gives the county its name. The mules were supplied by Mr. Ransom and by other members who were farmers. That lasted until Mr. Giddy and Mr. Ransom, as the leaders, sent to Atlanta for some white horse robes. They draped the robes over their mules one dark night and rode out to a sawmill in a swamp to keep a rendezvous with their followers. When they galloped up on their shrouded steeds the mules of the other Klansmen got frightened; they let out angry neighs, reared back on their heels, and stampeded into the swamp with their riders. One Klansman was thrown from his mule and suffered a broken leg and three fractured ribs. After that the Klansmen gave up cross-country riding. They stuck to the highways and used automobiles. Fat Mr. Giddy undoubtedly felt out of place on the sharp back of a plough mule, anyway.

The Klansmen began their terrorism by burning fiery crosses, huge crosses made of fence rails sprinkled with kerosene, in the yards of all the Negro churches in the lower part of the county. Then they kidnapped an aged, irritable blacksmith who was celebrated for his profanity. They covered him with tar. They sprinkled chicken feathers over the tar. Then they tossed him into Bearcat Millpond. I have heard that the old blacksmith crawled out of the millpond with ten brand-new oaths. A few nights later the Klansmen went after a mentally defective woman who used to wander about the county with her fatherless children, sleeping in tobacco barns and haylofts. They flogged her, clipped her hair close to her scalp, and branded a "K" on her head. Next day a rural policeman found the bleeding, frantic woman on a ditch bank beside a country road and took her to a hospital. Later she was sent to an asylum. One night, a few weeks later, they broke into a chain grocery in Stonewall, the A. & P., and wrecked it. The same night they went to a Negro café in the Back Alley, the Negro section of Stonewall, and smashed a big, loud Edison phonograph, which the proprietor of the café had mortgaged her home to buy. Then they began threatening a quiet, lonesome Jew who lived above his dry-goods store on Main Street. Some of the members of the Klan had charge accounts, long unpaid, at his store. At the post office one night, waiting around for the evening mail to be sorted, I heard Mr. Giddy talking about him. He said, "He sits up there all night long, reading books. No telling what he's plotting." The dry-goods merchant went to the hardware store one morning at a time when some of the Klan members were sitting around the stove and bought a double-barrelled shotgun and three boxes of twelve-gauge shells. He was not threatened any more.

Late that spring it was rumored in Stonewall that the Klan had decided to do something about the corn-whiskey-distilling situation. The biggest distiller was Mr. Sledge MacKellar; he employed four men at his copper still in Pocahontas Swamp. We knew he was immune from the Klan because he was Mr. Giddy's personal bootlegger, because he was fabulously expert with a shotgun, and because he had publicly served notice on the Klan. Mr. MacKellar came out of the swamp one afternoon and said he was prepared for "the Bed-Sheets." By that time Klansmen were called "the Bed-Sheets." He said, "I'm a Democrat and I got my rights. The first time one of them Bed-Sheets sticks his head in my front gate, I'm going to take his head right off. I got a shotgun and I got it loaded and I'm just aching to pull the trigger."

We knew the distillers the Klan had in mind were the Kidney boys, and we were not surprised when we heard that a date had been set on which they were to be tarred and feathered. The Kidney boys were three drunken Irish brothers who lived in a house about two and a half miles out from Stonewall and operated a still in Big Cherokee Swamp, behind their house. Their names were Patrick, Pinky, and Francis. They drank about half the whiskey they manufactured. When they came to town that week for supplies, the clerks in the stores kidded them. "I hear the Bed-Sheets are going to call on you boys for a pot of tea Friday night," one clerk said.

The Kidney boys had a hired man, an aged Negro named Uncle Bowleg, who later worked for a relative of mine. One time Uncle Bowleg told me how the Kidney boys brought about the downfall of the Invisible Empire in Black Ankle County. There were three entrances to the Kidney house—a front door, a back door, and a side door. When they heard the Klan was planning a call on Friday night, the brothers rented three dynamite outfits from a man who made his living blasting out tree stumps. They swapped him a gallon of charcoal-cured corn whiskey for the use of the outfits. They buried three great charges of dynamite in the yard, under the three paths leading to the entrances of the house. Wires led from the buried dynamite to batteries, to which switches were attached. The Kidney boys placed the batteries in the house, beneath three windows where they could sit and watch for approaching Klansmen. They planned to throw a switch the moment the Klansmen walked up one of the paths.

That night the Kidney boys turned off all the lights and took places at the windows with the dynamite batteries and switches in their laps. Uncle Bowleg was in the house with them. The Kidneys soon got tired of staring out into the yard, waiting for Klansmen, and ordered Uncle Bowleg to fetch them a jug of whiskey and a pitcher of water. Uncle Bowleg said he was kept busy running from one Kidney to another with the whiskey. The whiskey made them happy and they began to talk, speculating on how much noise their blasts would make. "We'll blow those Bed-Sheets to Kingdom Come," said Pinky.

About ten o'clock, when the moon was high, Francis Kidney, who was guarding the side door, decided he could wait no longer. The whiskey had given him an irresistible desire to throw the switch on his battery.

"Get ready!" he shouted suddenly. "I just can't wait no longer. I'm going to test this dynamite. The Bed-Sheets won't come in by the side door, anyway."

He threw the switch and there was a blast that shook the entire lower half of Black Ankle County. It caused people to leap out of their beds. We heard the blast in my home, and I remember that my grandmother said she thought that Judgment Day or the Second Coming was at hand.

Uncle Bowleg said the blast tore up a massive longleaf pine tree in the yard of the Kidney house and threw it into the highway. Uncle Bowleg was so frightened he jumped under a bed and hid. The Kidneys ran to the front porch and looked at the great tree lying in the highway. It pleased them. They laughed and slapped each other's shoulders. They came in and poured themselves some drinks. Then Patrick and Pinky took their places again, but Francis had thrown his switch, so he lost interest and went to sleep in his chair. In about half an hour, Patrick Kidney, who was guarding the rear door, heard a rustle out in back of the house. He knew it was the wind rustling the leaves on the chinquapin bushes, but all he wanted was an excuse to throw his switch.

"I think I hear them coming!" he shouted to Pinky, who was sitting at the front door with his hand on his switch. "Get ready. I'm going to let go."

Pinky needed some excitement, too. "Throw the switch!" he yelled.

Patrick threw his switch. The blast rattled Pinky and he threw his switch, too. The blasts were almost simultaneous. The slats fell out of the bed under which Uncle Bowleg was hiding and bruised him all over. A big framed picture of the mother of the Kidney brothers fell off the wall and hit Francis on the head. The legs dropped off the kitchen range and it fell apart. The entire back porch was torn loose from the house. The blast blew up the chicken house and a barrel in which the two hounds slept. All the chickens were killed, except an old rooster, and he never crowed again. Next morning there were six dead hens on the roof of the house and dead hens and ducks were scattered all over the yard. The South Carolina line runs near the rear of the Kidney house, and Uncle Bowleg swears that the hounds landed in South Carolina and were so shocked and outraged they never crossed back into North Carolina again. The mule's stall fell in.

"The roof fell down on that old mule," Uncle Bowleg told me later, "and he pounced out into the yard with the roof on his back like a saddle and galloped two miles before he felt safe enough to slow down and look around. And there was a rocking chair on the back porch and the dynamite set it to rocking. Next morning it was still rocking."

When the noise died down that night, and when things stopped falling apart, the Kidney brothers looked at each other. They were shamefaced. Suddenly they felt frightened. Without their dynamite, they felt naked and defenceless. "If the Bed-Sheets come now, we're sure done for," Francis said. His mother's picture was raising a bump on his head. All of a sudden the Kidney boys ran out of the house and made a dash for Big Cherokee Swamp, with Uncle Bowleg following. Early next morning Uncle Bowleg got hungry and went back to the house for something to eat but the Kidney boys stayed in the swamp until noon.

As a matter of fact, they would have been just as safe in their wrecked house as they were in the swamp, because the Ku Klux Klan never did show up. The Klan had postponed its scheduled call because Mr. Giddy had arrived at the hall over the bank too drunk to take any interest in Klan matters. However, while the Kidneys were still snoring in the swamp, Mr. Ransom, who hadn't been able to get any sleep because of the three strange blasts, drove into Stonewall in his Ford and picked up Mr. Giddy. Mr. Ransom was sleepy and irritable and Mr. Giddy had a bad hangover, and they were not a happy pair. They drove out to the Kidney house to see what had happened during the night. When they arrived, Uncle Bowleg was sitting in the rocking chair on the front porch, eating a plate of corn bread and molasses. Mr. Giddy and Mr. Ransom walked into the yard and looked into the three gaping holes. Uncle Bowleg watched them like a hawk.

"Spuddy," said Mr. Giddy as he peered into the hole out of which the longleaf pine had come, "that sure is a damned big hole. I sure am glad I wasn't around when those holes were dug."

"Catfish," said Mr. Ransom in a frightened voice, "somebody might of got murdered last night. It's a good thing the Klan didn't ride last night."

Uncle Bowleg said they both stared into the holes and shuddered. Then they got into the Ford and drove away rapidly. During the day all the members of the Invisible Empire took occasion to drive by the Kidney house. They also shuddered when they saw the dynamite pits.

Late that afternoon Mr. Giddy showed up on Main Street. He was drunk again. He walked down Main Street, but he didn't sing. He stopped each person he met and said, "Friend, I have resigned." "Resigned from what, Mr. Catfish?" people asked. "Don't make no difference what I resigned from," he answered. "I just want you to know I resigned." The Ku Klux Klan never held another meeting in Stonewall. In a week or two the black paint was scraped off the windows in the hall above the bank and a "For Rent" sign was hung out. One woman ripped up her husband's Klan robe and made a pillowcase out of the cloth. Others heard about it and did the same. Mrs. Catfish Giddy ripped up her husband's robe and told her friends he was so fat she found enough material in it for two pillowcases, an apron, and a tablecloth.

Last summer I went back to Stonewall for a visit. North Carolina is a local-option state and Black Ankle is a dry county, and I wondered if the Kidneys were still making whiskey. One afternoon I drove by the Kidney house. The gaping dynamite pits were still in the yard. Pinky Kidney was sitting on the front porch in a rocking chair, smoking his pipe, and I stopped and had a talk with him.

"The mosquitoes breed in those holes," he said, motioning toward the dynamite pits with the stem of his pipe. "We been aiming to fill them up, but we keep so busy 'stilling whiskey down in the swamp that we just never get around to it."

Richard Lockridge

WHAT DID YOU DO, GRANDFATHER?

Recent editorial speculations about the next war and all the trouble it is going to make for everybody got me to thinking about the last war and all the trouble I made for the United States Navy. The next war I expect to spend with the rest of the civilian population, being blown into small pieces, but during the other war I was, in a manner of speaking, a combatant. Or, if that is too strong a word, I was at least a member of the U.S.N.R.F., which meant United States Naval Reserve Force and was usually interpreted by its members, and others, as meaning "You shall never reach France."

I was nineteen when I got into it, and barely twenty when the Navy, with a sigh of relief which could be heard all over the Brooklyn Navy Yard, got me out. I went in for a variety of reasons, none of any particular interest. I got out, I have always felt, because the Navy decided it couldn't take the responsibility any longer. The final straw, so far as the Navy was concerned, was when I very nearly did die for my country, or at any rate for the coal bunkers of the U. S. S. North Dakota.

My naval career up to the time I actually got aboard ship was not particularly remarkable. All through the training period, which took me from Kansas City to Chicago, and from Chicago to Newport, and from Newport to Hampton Roads, things were moderately quiet. I learned the manual of arms at Newport well enough; I even got to be a color guard. I learned how to get the smallest-size issue leggings, bleach them as near white as possible, and wear my trousers bagging out over them, and I learned, too, that you had to stitch your white hats round and round until the brim stood up stiffly. These things were "seagoing." I also, during long hours in the sail loft, learned to tie a number of knots and to make a serviceable if not particularly neat eye splice. I also, being adaptable in certain ways, learned a great deal about keeping out of work.

The Navy puzzled me somewhat, of course, as it puzzled everybody. It patently regarded me as a contributor of brawn—my weight went up to a hundred and thirty, thanks to the regular hours and beans for breakfast—and it firmly declined to take any chances on the quality of my brainwork. I had wanted to be a radio operator; heaven knows why, and the Navy merely ignored that. It let me take, and pass, an examination for submarine listener, which was probably one of the worst jobs it offered but at least sounded more interesting than chipping paint, and then moved my whole company hurriedly away so it wouldn't have to send me to Pelham for training. I have never understood why, later, it asked all who wanted to become signalmen to step forward and then picked for training all those who *hadn't* stepped forward. And I doubt whether there was any malicious connection between the fact that the smell of paint always made me ill and the fact that never once, during the nine months of my enlistment, did I miss a painting detail. I gained considerable art in dodging through those months and toward the end I even got out of swabbing decks. But when there was painting, particularly in one of the lower and more airless compartments, they always caught me.

But these were items in the common fate, and I didn't stand out until I got aboard the North Dakota. She was one of the older ships —she was junked not long after the war—and when I went aboard with a draft she was in the yard in Brooklyn having new engines put in. She remained there, as it happened, until after the armistice; the finishing touches were put on and she was ready for service, as I recall it, November 12, 1918. This kept her crew safe from the ordinary dangers of war, although it subjected them pretty steadily to the dangers of New York City, all of which they enjoyed very much indeed.

Even aboard ship my misadventures were minor until almost the end, and merely aroused a general suspicion of my ability to take care of myself without definitely confirming it. There was, for example, the time I almost got both legs taken off by a dummy powder bag which was being hurled through a dummy gun breech by what the petty officer in charge obviously regarded as a dummy gun crew. I had just wandered behind the breech, which was set up on a bracket screwed into the deck, for some reason. Everybody yelled a warning when the bag, which weighed a couple of hundred pounds, came hurtling through from the other side, and I had time to jump straight up in the air. Things like that might, I think, have happened to any-body.

So, certainly, might the rather unfortunate contretemps in No. 3 turret in the middle of one night. I was on watch there, with nothing to watch, of course, except a telephone. At fifteen-minute intervals somebody would call through the telephone and you were supposed to answer. He'd say "No. 3 turret?" and you'd answer "Aye, aye, sir" or something of the kind. The telephone was a small hand-set device and I yelled into it every time I was asked to. The conversations puzzled me a little. "No. 3 turret?" "Aye, aye, sir." "No. 3 turret?" "Aye, aye, sir." "No. 3 *turret!*" "Aye, aye, sir." It was after this had happened three times that a chief petty officer, an ensign of my sec-tion, the officer of the deck, and a couple of seamen poked their heads up into my cranny, where I was reading a book. They were indignant and worried. It turned out there was a button to press on the tele-phone before your voice became audible through it, and the whole ship had thought that somebody had stolen No. 3 turret and me.

There was also the time I went to sleep while standing up, again on watch, at the head of the crew gangplank and almost fell off onto the dock, being saved only at the last minute by a Marine who was also guarding. There was the time when somebody grabbed me just as I was about to be blown off the deck by a little wind we had off the coast of Maine on the shakedown cruise. None of these things was any-thing much in itself, but all of them together sort of made the Navy begin to wonder. The Navy quit wondering the day we coaled ship.

That was after the shakedown cruise, and about three weeks after the armistice. All of us who were in for the duration had immediately put in applications for discharge from active service as soon as we were given the forms, and we hoped to get out right away. We went on the cruise first, however, and it wasn't until we came back that they posted a list of names of those who were, two days later, to be allowed to go home. All of us crowded around, and whenever one of us read his name he jumped up in the air and yelled. I read the list over twice before I was finally convinced that my name wasn't there and that I was going to stay on the North Dakota.

The elation of the lucky ones was calmed a bit when they found out that before they went home they were going to help the rest of us coal ship. They felt the Navy had pulled rather a mean trick on them, as in fact it had. Nobody who has never coaled ship can imagine how mean a trick, as we all found out when the barges were brought alongside and we were sent into them to fill great canvas bags with coal dust. We started right after breakfast and didn't stop until evening. They sent down sandwiches at noon so we wouldn't lose any time. The sandwiches gritted between our teeth and stuck on the coal dust in our throats.

We finished the job, finally, and the barges were empty and riding light when I provided the drama in a dull day. We formed lines, roughly, and began to jump from the barges to the five-inch-gun ports, from which we could clamber to the North Dakota's deck. It wasn't much of a jump and the barge I happened to be on was bobbing only slightly. Subsequent events cleared my mind of the precise details, but perhaps my foot slipped. Perhaps I merely stopped to think matters over in mid-jump. Anyhow, I missed the port.

I missed the port and fell, like the blackened stick of a skyrocket, straight down between the ship and the barge. There was about a yard separating them at the waterline, and I didn't graze either one. I hit the water and kept on going down and not expecting ever to come up again. For what it is worth, my evidence is that you don't remember your past life and aren't particularly scared. You just think the whole thing is preposterous and decide it is happening to somebody else. "This can't be happening to me," you tell yourself, particularly if you know that what is happening is pretty serious. What was happening to me was serious, all right. I couldn't swim, but that wasn't the point—the point was that the chances were at least even that the barge would bob in and rub affectionately against the ship again, as it had been doing off and on. And that I would be in between. Or I might come up under the barge and just stay there.

I began clawing instinctively as soon as I hit water, and after a while I quit going down. Then I even began going up again, and a couple of hours later, while I was still wondering who this was happening to, somebody grabbed my hand. A boatswain's mate dragged me out then, excitedly, and the next moment the barge nuzzled gently up against the side of the ship. Everybody looked at me with astonishment and, after the first surprise wore off, disapproval. The whole deck force lined up and looked.

The next day there was a special supplementary list posted of those who were to go home. It read: "Lockridge, Richard, S2c." I thought this was a trifle pointed, but I was glad enough to go.

Lee Strout White

FAREWELL, MY LOVELY!

I see by the new Sears Roebuck catalogue that it is still possible to buy an axle for a 1909 Model T Ford, but I am not deceived. The great days have faded, the end is in sight. Only one page in the current catalogue is devoted to parts and accessories for the Model T; yet everyone remembers springtimes when the Ford gadget section was larger than men's clothing, almost as large as household furnishings. The last Model T was built in 1927, and the car is fading from what scholars call the American scene—which is an understatement, because to a few million people who grew up with it, the old Ford practically *was* the American scene.

It was the miracle God had wrought. And it was patently the sort of thing that could only happen once. Mechanically uncanny, it was like nothing that had ever come to the world before. Flourishing industries rose and fell with it. As a vehicle, it was hard-working, commonplace, heroic; and it often seemed to transmit those qualities to the persons who rode in it. My own generation identifies it with Youth, with its gaudy, irretrievable excitements; before it fades into the mist, I would like to pay it the tribute of the sigh that is not a sob, and set down random entries in a shape somewhat less cumbersome than a Sears Roebuck catalogue.

The Model T was distinguished from all other makes of cars by the fact that its transmission was of a type known as planetary—which was half metaphysics, half sheer friction. Engineers accepted the word "planetary" in its epicyclic sense, but I was always conscious that it also meant "wandering," "erratic." Because of the peculiar nature of this planetary element, there was always, in Model T, a certain dull rapport between engine and wheels, and even when the car was in a state known as neutral, it trembled with a deep imperative and tended to inch forward. There was never a moment when the bands were not faintly egging the machine on. In this respect it was like a horse, rolling the bit on its tongue, and country people brought to it the same technique they used with draft animals.

Its most remarkable quality was its rate of acceleration. In its palmy days the Model T could take off faster than anything on the road. The reason was simple. To get under way, you simply hooked the third finger of the right hand around a lever on the steering column, pulled down hard, and shoved your left foot forcibly against the low-speed pedal. These were simple, positive motions; the car responded by lunging forward with a roar. After a few seconds of this turmoil, you took your toe off the pedal, eased up a mite on the throttle, and the car, possessed of only two forward speeds, catapulted directly into high with a series of ugly jerks and was off on its glorious errand. The abruptness of this departure was never equalled in other cars of the period. The human leg was (and still is) incapable of letting in a clutch with anything like the forthright abandon that used to send Model T on its way. Letting in a clutch is a negative, hesitant motion, depending on delicate nervous control; pushing down the Ford pedal was a simple, country motion—an expansive act, which came as natural as kicking an old door to make it budge.

The driver of the old Model T was a man enthroned. The car, with top up, stood seven feet high. The driver sat on top of the gas tank, brooding it with his own body. When he wanted gasoline, he alighted, along with everything else in the front seat; the seat was pulled off, the metal cap unscrewed, and a wooden stick thrust down to sound the liquid in the well. There were always a couple of these sounding sticks kicking around in the ratty sub-cushion regions of a flivver. Refueling was more of a social function then, because the driver had to unbend, whether he wanted to or not. Directly in front of the driver was the windshield—high, uncompromisingly erect. Nobody talked about air resistance, and the four cylinders pushed the car through the atmosphere with a simple disregard of physical law.

There was this about a Model T: the purchaser never regarded his purchase as a complete, finished product. When you bought a Ford, you figured you had a start—a vibrant, spirited framework to which could be screwed an almost limitless assortment of decorative and functional hardware. Driving away from the agency, hugging the new wheel between your knees, you were already full of creative worry. A Ford was born naked as a baby, and a flourishing industry grew up out of correcting its rare deficiencies and combatting its fascinating diseases. Those were the great days of lily-painting. I have been looking at some old Sears Roebuck catalogues, and they bring everything back so clear.

First you bought a Ruby Safety Reflector for the rear, so that your posterior would glow in another car's brilliance. Then you invested thirty-nine cents in some radiator Moto Wings, a popular ornament which gave the Pegasus touch to the machine and did something godlike to the owner. For nine cents you bought a fan-belt guide to keep the belt from slipping off the pulley.

You bought a radiator compound to stop leaks. This was as much a part of everybody's equipment as aspirin tablets are of a medicine cabinet. You bought special oil to prevent chattering, a clamp-on dash light, a patching outfit, a tool box which you bolted to the running board, a sun visor, a steering-column brace to keep the column rigid, and a set of emergency containers for gas, oil, and water—three thin, disc-like cans which reposed in a case on the running board during long, important journeys—red for gas, gray for water, green for oil. It was only a beginning. After the car was about a year old, steps were taken to check the alarming disintegration. (Model T was full of tumors, but they were benign.) A set of anti-rattlers (98c) was a popular panacea. You hooked them on to the gas and spark rods, to the brake pull rod, and to the steering-rod connections. Hood silencers, of black rubber, were applied to the fluttering hood. Shock-absorbers and snubbers gave "complete relaxation." Some people bought rubber pedal pads, to fit over the standard metal pedals. (I didn't like these, I remember.) Persons of a suspicious or pugnacious turn of mind bought a rear-view mirror; but most Model T owners weren't worried by what was coming from behind because they would soon enough see it out in front. They rode in a state of cheerful catalepsy. Quite a large mutinous clique among Ford owners went over to a foot accelerator (you could buy one and screw it to the floor board), but there was a certain madness in these people, because the Model T, just as she stood, had a choice of three foot pedals to push, and there were plenty of moments when both feet were occupied in the routine performance of duty and when the only way to speed up the engine was with the hand throttle.

Gadget bred gadget. Owners not only bought ready-made gadgets, they invented gadgets to meet special needs. I myself drove my car directly from the agency to the blacksmith's, and had the smith affix two enormous iron brackets to the port running board to support an army trunk.

People who owned closed models builded along different lines: they bought ball grip handles for opening doors, window anti-rattlers, and deluxe flower vases of the cut-glass anti-splash type. People with delicate sensibilities garnished their car with a device called the Donna Lee Automobile Disseminator—a porous vase guaranteed, according to Sears, to fill the car with a "faint clean odor of lavender." The gap between open cars and closed cars was not as great then as it is now: for $11.95, Sears Roebuck converted your touring car into a sedan and you went forth renewed. One agreeable quality of the old Fords was that they had no bumpers, and their fenders softened and wilted with the years and permitted the driver to squeeze in and out of tight places.

Tires were 30 x 3½, cost about twelve dollars, and punctured readily. Everybody carried a Jiffy patching set, with a nutmeg grater to roughen the tube before the goo was spread on. Everybody was capable of putting on a patch, expected to have to, and did have to.

During my association with Model T's, self-starters were not a prevalent accessory. They were expensive and under suspicion. Your car came equipped with a serviceable crank, and the first thing you learned was how to Get Results. It was a special trick, and until you learned it (usually from another Ford owner, but sometimes by a period of appalling experimentation) you might as well have been winding up an awning. The trick was to leave the ignition switch off, proceed to the animal's head, pull the choke (which was a little wire protruding through the radiator), and give the crank two or three nonchalant upward lifts. Then, whistling as though thinking about something else, you would saunter back to the driver's cabin, turn the ignition on, return to the crank, and this time, catching it on the down stroke, give it a quick spin with plenty of That. If this procedure was followed, the engine almost always responded—first with a few scattered explosions, then with a tumultuous gunfire, which you checked by racing around to the driver's seat and retarding the throttle. Often, if the emergency brake hadn't been pulled all the way back, the car advanced on you the instant the first explosion occurred and you would hold it back by leaning your weight against it. I can still feel my old

Ford nuzzling me at the curb, as though looking for an apple in my pocket.

In zero weather, ordinary cranking became an impossibility, except for giants. The oil thickened, and it became necessary to jack up the rear wheels, which, for some planetary reason, eased the throw.

The lore and legend that governed the Ford were boundless. Owners had their own theories about everything; they discussed mutual problems in that wise, infinitely resourceful way old women discuss rheumatism. Exact knowledge was pretty scarce, and often proved less effective than superstition. Dropping a camphor ball into the gas tank was a popular expedient; it seemed to have a tonic effect on both man and machine. There wasn't much to base exact knowledge on. The Ford driver flew blind. He didn't know the temperature of his engine, the speed of his car, the amount of his fuel, or the pressure of his oil (the old Ford lubricated itself by what was amiably described as the "splash system"). A speedometer cost money and was an extra, like a windshield-wiper. The dashboard of the early models was bare save for an ignition key; later models, grown effete, boasted an ammeter which pulsated alarmingly with the throbbing of the car. Under the dash was a box of coils, with vibrators which you adjusted, or thought you adjusted. Whatever the driver learned of his motor, he learned not through instruments but through sudden developments. I remember that the timer was one of the vital organs about which there was ample doctrine. When everything else had been checked, you "had a look" at the timer. It was an extravagantly odd little device, simple in construction, mysterious in function. It contained a roller, held by a spring, and there were four contact points on the inside of the case against which, many people believed, the roller rolled. I have had a timer apart on a sick Ford many times, but I never really knew what I was up to—I was just showing off before God. There were almost as many schools of thought as there were timers. Some people, when things went wrong, just clenched their teeth and gave the timer a smart crack with a wrench. Other people opened it up and blew on it. There was a school that held that the timer needed large amounts of oil; they fixed it by frequent baptism. And there was a school that was positive it was meant to run dry as a bone; these people were continually taking it off and wiping it. I remember once spitting into a timer; not in anger, but in a spirit of research. You see, the Model T driver moved in the realm of meta-physics. He believed his car could be hexed.

One reason the Ford anatomy was never reduced to an exact science was that, having "fixed" it, the owner couldn't honestly claim that the treatment had brought about the cure. There were too many authen-ticated cases of Fords fixing themselves—restored naturally to health after a short rest. Farmers soon discovered this, and it fitted nicely with their draft-horse philosophy: "Let 'er cool off and she'll snap into it again."

A Ford owner had Number One Bearing constantly in mind. This bearing, being at the front end of the motor, was the one that always burned out, because the oil didn't reach it when the car was climbing hills. (That's what I was always told, anyway.) The oil used to re-cede and leave Number One dry as a clam flat; you had to watch that bearing like a hawk. It was like a weak heart—you could hear it start knocking, and that was when you stopped and let her cool off. Try as you would to keep the oil supply right, in the end Number One always went out. "Number One Bearing burned out on me and I had to have her replaced," you would say, wisely; and your companions always had a lot to tell about how to protect and pamper Number One to keep her alive.

Sprinkled not too liberally among the millions of amateur witch doctors who drove Fords and applied their own abominable cures were the heaven-sent mechanics who could really make the car talk. These professionals turned up in undreamed-of spots. One time, on the banks of the Columbia River in Washington, I heard the rear end go out of my Model T when I was trying to whip it up a steep incline onto the deck of a ferry. Something snapped; the car slid backward into the mud. It seemed to me like the end of the trail. But the captain of the ferry, observing the withered remnant, spoke up.

"What's got her?" he asked.

"I guess it's the rear end," I replied, listlessly. The captain leaned over the rail and stared. Then I saw that there was a hunger in his eyes that set him off from other men.

"Tell you what," he said, carelessly, trying to cover up his eager-ness, "let's pull the son of a bitch up onto the boat, and I'll help you fix her while we're going back and forth on the river."

We did just this. All that day I plied between the towns of Pasco and Kennewick, while the skipper (who had once worked in a Ford garage) directed the amazing work of resetting the bones of my car.

Springtime in the heyday of the Model T was a delirious season. Owning a car was still a major excitement, roads were still wonderful and bad. The Fords were obviously conceived in madness: any car which was capable of going from forward into reverse without any perceptible mechanical hiatus was bound to be a mighty challenging thing to the human imagination. Boys used to veer them off the highway into a level pasture and run wild with them, as though they were cutting up with a girl.

Most everybody used the reverse pedal quite as much as the regular foot brake—it distributed the wear over the bands and wore them all down evenly. That was the big trick, to wear all the bands down evenly, so that the final chattering would be total and the whole unit scream for renewal.

The days were golden, the nights were dim and strange. I still recall with trembling those loud, nocturnal crises when you drew up to a signpost and raced the engine so the lights would be bright enough to read destinations by. I have never been really planetary since. I suppose it's time to say goodbye. Farewell, my lovely!

Ruth McKenney

THE SOCK HUNT

I suppose, what with the passing years and the girls he's met since, that young Mr. Randolph Churchill, the scion of the London Churchills, does not remember me. Still, looking back on it all, I should think he would. I certainly do. Precisely as I can never, for so long as I walk this earth, forget the time I fell down at my high-school senior prom, right smack in front of the orchestra with my best beau sprawled beside me, so can I never put aside the memory of young Mr. Churchill. My flesh still crawls. Not that Mr. Churchill is anything to make a girl's flesh crawl. Not at all. In a certain way, like the men in the breakfast-food ads, he is quite handsome.

Mr. Churchill and I met in a purely professional capacity. It was the late fall of 1930. He was touring America, speaking before literary clubs, Rotary Clubs, university clubs, and the like on a variety of light topics, including "Fate of an Empire" and "Why I Am a Conservative." He was then nineteen, and I was the daisy-eyed star reporter on the *Ohio State Lantern,* a newspaper published daily, except Saturday and Sunday, by the students of journalism at Ohio State University.

Young Mr. Churchill arrived in Columbus, Ohio, on the flood tide of a lot of awe-struck advance notices. He was to address a local men's dinner club which for pure hauteur would make the Union Club look sick any day. All the speeches before this tony oufit were dead secret; no reporters allowed. Furthermore, celebrities who appeared before these hallowed few were never interviewed by the Columbus press. The editors of the papers were all members of the club, and that was that.

Well, my mouth watered to interview Mr. Churchill. I had never seen a real Englishman in the flesh, for one thing. For another thing, my deadly rival on the *Lantern* staff, a chap of considerable energy and no ethics, had publicly stated that he considered the feat of obtaining an interview with Mr. Churchill too great even for his remarkable talents. After this, nothing could hold me. I marched forward with determination to my doom.

I arrived at the hotel lobby at 4:35 P.M. and briskly set about finding out Mr. Churchill's room number. Then, with success almost in the hollow of my hand, I collapsed on a lobby lounge with an attack of acute panic. This lasted until 5:22 P.M., when a man insulted me. At least he came directly over to my lounge and said, in a chummy tone, "Waiting for somebody?"

This drove me to Mr. Churchill. I fled from my insulter and arrived at the forbidding door of Mr. Churchill's hotel room, still unnerved. I knocked valiantly. I had mapped out my strategy well in advance. When Mr. Churchill asked, "Who's there?" I intended to reply, "Maid, with towels." Then, when he opened the door, I planned to stick my foot in the crack and ask him a lot of questions very fast. I think a scene such as this had been in a newspaper film about that time.

Anyway, Mr. Churchill ruined my pretty plans by replying, to the knock, "Come in." I hesitated, getting a burning sensation in my throat. I was nineteen and lived with my grandmother, who would have been absolutely horrified at the thought of any young woman traipsing into a man's hotel room alone.

"Come IN!" roared Mr. Churchill from behind the door. He sounded rather angry. I kept telling myself that after I got out of school and got a real job on a newspaper, I would look back on this moment and laugh. As it turned out, however, in spite of a lot of jobs on newspapers, genuine daily ones, the mere thought of that frightful moment, with Mr. Churchill bellowing "Come IN" on one side of the door and me trembling on the other, has never brought even the sickliest of smiles to my face. It still makes my hair prickle.

Finally I opened the door very timidly indeed, and beheld Mr. Churchill, surely the blondest young man in the world, seated at a desk, writing. He wore a smoking jacket over his dinner trousers, black vest, and starched shirt front. His bare feet were stuck in floppy leather slippers. Mr. Churchill looked so very public-school English he was faintly incredible. Maybe he's grown out of that now, but in 1930 he was certainly breath of Empire. You could—or at least I could—just see him wolfing down supper off in the tropics, dressed to the teeth in tails and white tie. Mr. Churchill's eyes were a china blue and his smoking jacket was the same, overlaid, however, with old rose and gold.

I stood by the door for several seconds while Mr. Churchill continued to scratch away at his desk. Now, a cynical old interviewer of ripened years, I fear that Mr. Churchill was attempting to impress me. But on that trying evening I felt that I had intruded on the literary labors of a young genius. Finally Mr. Churchill lifted his blue eyes to mine.

"Ah," he said, leaping gallantly to his feet, "a lady! I beg your pardon. Pray do forgive me."

My mouth sagged. Mr. Churchill drew up a chair beside his desk and, with a cozy gesture, beckoned me over. I went.

"Pray excuse me," said Mr. Churchill. "I must finish this wireless message." On his desk lay eleven or twelve Western Union blanks covered with writing.

"What?" I said. The reason I said this was that I could not understand very much of what he said. His accent, which I had so longed to hear, a real, bona-fide Oxford accent, was so broad that unfortunately he might as well have spoken French. I can get every other word a Frenchman says, too, which is fairly good, considering I studied French in the Ohio public schools for only eight years.

Young Mr. Churchill now turned to me and said in a fierce tone, "What would you say if you wanted to tell your manager you did not want ladies to give you flowers at lectures?" At least that is what I thought he said. It was so difficult for me to decipher Mr. Churchill's accent, and the question seemed so entirely improbable, that, after agonized reflection, I simply shook my head.

Mr. Churchill didn't note my silence. He apparently hit on just the right words, for he signed his name with a flourish I am sure no American operator ever spelled out, and turned briskly to me, saying, "Now, what may I do for you?"

I explained haltingly that I was a newspaper reporter. Mr. Churchill didn't ask, so I didn't find it necessary to tell him that the paper I was interviewing him for was only, alas, the university daily. I simply trotted out all my carefully prepared questions. I asked him about Ramsay MacDonald and Hoover and Briand and a few other such people. Mr. Churchill roundly denounced them all, for different reasons. MacDonald was too far left, and even Mr. Hoover was pretty much of a Socialist. I asked him about the future of English youth, and Mr. Churchill said that if only a few more young people of his class would awaken to their responsibility, the future of England was safe. I was slightly shaken at Mr. Churchill's firm Tory opinions. He seemed quite young to be so fierce.

However, I drew a breath and started off on the English public-school system. Just at this point Mr. Churchill created a diversion.

In an ordinary speaking voice, as distinguished from the voice in which he denounced Mr. Hoover or Mr. MacDonald, he said, "Would you care for a drink?"

This unnerved me again. I could explain the interview to Grandma and my conscience, but drinking with a total stranger in his hotel room certainly seemed excessive. In those days, most college students —at least at my school—still thought drinking, no matter where, was pretty darned daring. Mr. Churchill, however, had already unearthed from his suitcase a bottle of what he assured me was fine Scotch, straight from England.

I was no judge. Up to that very moment I had never tasted anything in alcoholic beverages except a variety of bootleg liquor called "New Straitsville corn," because it was distilled in some abandoned mines near New Straitsville, Ohio. New Straitsville corn burned your throat and made you sick. Also, it hurt so to choke down New Straitsville corn that you were acutely conscious of every drink. It was the suave, sneaking quality of Mr. Churchill's fine liquor which undid me. You hardly knew you were drinking it, until afterward.

Mr. Churchill and I soon forgot serious topics. I asked him whether he really enjoyed lecturing about "Fate of an Empire." He said he did not, and also that he hated America and couldn't wait to get home. After a while Mr. Churchill thought we ought to eat something.

"I say," he said, "how about a spot of food, what?" He really talked just like that.

"O.K.," I said. "Let me order, though. They can't understand you over the phone. You talk so funny."

Mr. Churchill glowered. He said I was the one who had a peculiar accent.

"You talk through your nose," he said, with truth, "and you pronounce all your 'r's. They aren't supposed to be pronounced."

"That's what you think," I said, feeling hilarious, "Old Mushmouth."

For some reason, Mr. Churchill thought that was very funny. " 'Mushmouth!' " he shouted joyously, amid peals of real upper-class

English laughter, very high-pitched, like a whinny. " 'Mushmouth'! Deah me, I must remembaw that."

We ate lamb chops, a lot of them. "Tell them to send up a bally lot of them!" Mr. Churchill roared while I telephoned. "I want six lamb chops all for myself. After all, I must lecture on the 'Fate of an Empire.' "

While we were gnawing on lamb-chop bones we traded opinions on moving pictures. Mr. Churchill was a fan, and so was I. It turned out we both adored Vilma Banky. Suddenly Mr. Churchill said, "What about my lecture?"

"Well," I said, "what about it?"

"I won't do it," Mr. Churchill said. "Let the Empire go rot for tonight. Let's go to the cinema. You and I."

For a moment I was sorely tempted. Then I pictured the fearful scandal. The lecturer disappears. The town's leading citizens are left waiting. Among the leading citizens was the publisher of the Columbus *Dispatch*. I was the campus correspondent for the Columbus *Dispatch,* and I lived—in a very meagre way, to be sure, but still I lived—on the weekly wages the *Dispatch* paid me. In my fancy I saw the publisher of the *Dispatch* discovering that his most minor employee had practically kidnapped young Mr. Churchill.

"No," I said firmly. "You have to make that speech."

Mr. Churchill sighed. "Well, then," he said, "I have to put on my dinner jacket." He found that all right; also his white scarf and his black overcoat and his two patent-leather pumps. But alas, as the hour approached nine, he could find only one black sock. The club was to send a committee at nine, to escort Mr. Churchill to the lecture hall.

"What shall I do?" Mr. Churchill inquired frantically. "I can't lecture with only one sock." I rose from the dinner table, still gnawing a bone, and cast a quick look over the room.

"Be calm," I said. "They'll never notice."

"Oh, yes they will," Mr. Churchill said. "Besides, I won't go unless we find that sock. And I only have one black pair with me. The rest of them are in Pittsburgh."

"Wear another color," I said lightly. "What happened to the socks you had on this afternoon?"

"Tan socks," Mr. Churchill shouted, "with a dinner coat?"

I observed Mr. Churchill's frenzy with a motherly eye. "There, there," I said. "Relax. I'll find it."

Mr. Churchill sat down, putting a childish faith in me. I failed. I trotted around in circles, afraid to look in his luggage—for after all, that would hardly be proper—and unable to spot a stray black sock in the immediate surroundings.

Suddenly Mr. Churchill shouted, "I bet it's under the bed. I unpacked my things on the bed, and maybe it fell off on the floor." He threw himself down beside his bed and stuck his head under the springs.

"I can't see it," he said dismally, sounding muffled. "You have a look from the other side."

I obligingly sprawled out under the wall side of the bed, and peered around, coughing in the dust. At this moment precisely, there was a knock on the door.

"Come in!" bellowed Mr. Churchill, before he thought. I gave a faint scream, and too late Mr. Churchill considered the informality of his position. He tried to get up, too suddenly, and bumped his head severely on the bed slats. He relapsed, groaning, just as the committee of super-leading citizens walked in.

Fortunately, I do not now remember the names of those three well-starched, beautifully tailored citizens who marched in on that sock-hunting expedition. It would be frightful to be haunted all my life by their names as well as their faces.

"Mr. Churchill?" said the first leading citizen, in a tone of pained surprise.

Young Mr. Churchill showed the heritage of generations of gentlemen. Still reclining on the floor, he turned his head, nodded an acknowledgment, and said in a loud, belligerent voice, "I'm looking for my lost black sock." The second leading citizen went directly to the bureau and picked up the lost black sock.

"Your sock, sir," he said. Mr. Churchill rose, bowed slightly, and said, "I thank you very much." Then he shouted to me, "Get up! We've found it."

I hesitated. I wanted to stay under that bed and just die there peacefully, without ever having to rise and face those three leading citizens. I did get up, though, feeling the way you do in dreams when you have no clothes on at a gala performance of "Aïda" in the Metropolitan. I suppose, from the expression on the faces of the three leading citizens, that they had not realized until the moment my face slowly emerged from behind the bed that there was a young lady in the room. Each leading citizen did a combination gasp and snort.

"She's coming to hear my lecture," Mr. Churchill announced as he put on his sock. The purple staining my cheeks now rose to my hairline.

"I couldn't," I said weakly. "I couldn't indeed. It's private. They don't allow women in."

"Nevertheless," said Mr. Churchill briskly, "I don't speak unless you come."

The three leading citizens looked so grim I thought I should really faint, although I never had in my whole life. Mr. Churchill and I and the committee now left the room and boarded the elevator. All the way down, Mr. Churchill maintained his position. I was to come or he wouldn't speak. The three leading citizens took turns saying, "But that is impossible, Mr. Churchill. The rules of the club do not permit ladies."

As we got off the elevator, one of the leading citizens, a tall, white-haired man with a large stomach, managed to fall in step with me while the two other leading citizens took Mr. Churchill by the arms.

"Now," said my sudden escort, "you go away fast, and stop bothering Mr. Churchill."

"Me?" I said in honest astonishment. "I never bothered him."

The leading citizen did not stop to argue. "Go away," he hissed, giving me a slight push into the lobby. I went. I was never so glad to leave any place in my life. I wrote my interview that night, and it was a big success. My rival, Ernest, was a picture of jealous confusion when he read it next day. But even the sweet rewards of college fame and my colleagues' envy did not erase the memory of that hideous moment when I was caught, red-handed, looking for Mr. Churchill's sock. It is comparatively easy to recover from honest sorrows, but I wake up in the dead of night at least twice a year and my heart fills with agony, remembering that unspeakable moment when, like a rising moon, my face slowly appeared from behind Mr. Churchill's bed, to confound the three leading citizens of Columbus, Ohio.

Life can hold no further terrors for me.

M. R. A.

MEMOIRS OF A MASTER

There were always servants in my father's house, and now there are servants in mine. This morning, from a vantage point in the upstairs hall of my house in the city, I counted five. We have a cook, a chambermaid-and-waitress, a nurse, a laundress, and a furnace man. There are times when amity and peace brood over the home, when the servants remain with us and I begin to have a bowing acquaintance with some of them. There are other periods when the arrivals and departures are frequent and dramatic, and the house takes on the momentous character of the North Beach Airport.

Whenever a new servant is due to arrive, my wife and I always prepare the room for her with our own hands—with a sort of loving suspicion, as you might make a nest for a litter of lion cubs. I have just this minute come from the top floor, where we are fixing up a room for an incoming cook. Her name is said to be Gloria. It sounds implausible; but to me, an old master, nothing is impossible, not even a cook named Gloria. Nothing is even remotely unlikely. I await Gloria with head held high. The encounter with Gloria's bedroom suite, however, has exhausted me; and as I sit here on my study couch, I feel a great wave of fatigue engulf me—the peculiar weariness that afflicts a man who has always had everything done for him. I call it *Meisterschmerz*. I realize that I am not getting any younger and that the day may come when I shall no longer have the physical stamina to be waited on hand and foot by a corps of well-trained domestics.

When bachelors enjoy a reverie, I understand that all the girls of their past float before their eyes in rings of smoke from their pipe. My benedictine smoke dreams are full, not of past loves but of former servants. I dream of Alma, Estelle, Mrs. Farrell, Sylvia, Susan, Anna (who chose a brief interlude with us to have gallstones), Gaston and Eugénie, Elaine the beautiful, Zelda, Otto and Mildred, Mrs. Farnsworth, Joan, Claire. I like to sit here now and dream about them, count them over, like beads in a rosary, and think of all the bright, fierce times I have had with them, sharing their sorrows and their joys, their sickness and their health, taking their phone calls, filling in for them on their days out, driving them to distant churches in remote country districts. They have had some magnificent sicknesses, these old friends of mine, vivid bits of malaise, and truly distinguished indispositions. Every name calls up some bright recollection of bygone days.

Sylvia, for example. Sylvia to me means Christmas, and Christmas in turn means pneumonia. Someone in my family is always sick at Christmas, and when it isn't I, it is quite apt to be a servant. The year we had Sylvia, it was she. Sylvia had been looking a bit stringy for several days before the twenty-fifth, and we could feel something coming on. We nursed her along and refused to let her do any work, but her fever began on the twenty-fourth, with the early-afternoon carol singing, and rose steadily with the dusk. At last her conversation faded out and she just mumbled something and went to bed. I wasn't feeling any too fit myself, so at six o'clock my wife took first Sylvia's temperature and then mine. Sylvia had me by four and two-tenths degrees, and it was decided that *she* would be the one to go to the hospital. Our doctor verified this and mentioned pneumonia. I simply picked up the phone and said those magic words which I had read so many times on the cover of the directory: "I want an ambulance."

To my astonishment, an ambulance soon appeared in the street below. Police arrived with it, and the living room soon smelled pleasantly of balsam wreaths and Irishmen. The children, of course, adored having police on Christmas Eve—it gave a gala touch to the holiday—but the whole business presented special problems to us parents because all the gifts were hidden in Sylvia's room, and we had the devil's own time keeping the youngsters from running in and out with the cops.

None of us could think of Sylvia's last name, not even Sylvia; but I gave "Cassidy" to the ambulance doctor, and he bundled her downstairs to the waiting car, and away she went through the merry streets, myself following along afoot (with my lowgrade fever) like one of the Magi, to attend to the admittance problem—which is part of the servant problem. I shall never forget the hospital's reception of Sylvia.

To begin with, the place was jammed—the holiday rush—and the pneumonia ward was full to bursting. Sylvia was rolled into a downstairs corridor and parked there for about half an hour, while sisters of mercy flitted about conjuring up an extra bed. Finally it was arranged, and I accompanied Sylvia up to the ward to tuck her in and wish her a last Merry Christmas, although the poor girl was barely conscious by this time of what was going on. It was after nine o'clock, and the corridor was lit only by a small red night light. Just as our little procession groped its way into the ward, with its dim forms of sickness and the smell of calamity, we were welcomed by a woman's delirious scream.

"Sylvia!" the voice cried, in unwordly pain. "Seeelvyah!" And then a short, rapid "Sylvia, Sylvia, Sylvia," ending with a mournful wolf note, "Seeeeeeelvyah!"

It was the cry of a female who must have had a Sylvia in her family, or in her past, or both. But it was too much for my Sylvia. I think she imagined herself crossed over into purgatory. "Dear God!" I heard her mumble. "Dear God, get me out of here!" Feeling definitely pneumonic myself, and damn sorry for Sylvia and for the world in general, I trudged shakily home and spent the rest of the holy night putting together a child's fire truck, which had arrived from a department store that must have known of our domestic quandary, for they sent the thing in knockdown form—a mass of wheels, axles, bolts, screws, nuts, bars, and cotter pins.

Well, that was all a long while ago. Sylvia pulled through all right, but took a place in the country, where the air would be better for her. I thought, in those days, that I knew what sickness was; but I tell you now that nobody knows what sickness is till he's had an upstairs maid with gallstones. Anna had been with us only six days when her seizure came. In fact, I had never actually seen Anna— her paths and mine never crossed—and I knew her only by hearsay and by the sound of her typewriter tap-tapping on the floor above me. She was an elderly sort, my wife said, with eyes set too near together, like Franklin D. Roosevelt's. I inquired about the presence of the typewriter and my wife explained that Anna had taken up typing, hoping to improve herself. I couldn't very well object, because I had been up to the same trick myself for some years.

Anna, it turned out, was more than a typist—she was a Christian Scientist as well, and she waited grimly through three hours of torture before letting out the yell that began our acquaintanceship. The yell came at four o'clock in the morning, and my wife and I sprang out of bed and instinctively rushed up one flight to see what was the matter.

"Mister," groaned Anna, recognizing me instantly as a friend, "please get me some morphine—it's my gallbladder!"

"Call the doctor!" said my wife. "And," she added peremptorily, "you better get dressed, you may have to go somewhere and you might as well be ready."

As I pattered downstairs, I remember trying to decide between my blue unfinished worsted (whose pockets contained everything necessary for a gallstone operation, such as money, fountain pen, and keys) and my brown tweed, which seemed a more workaday proposition but needed servicing. I knew the day would come and go before I slept again, and I figured I might as well be dressed correctly.

When the doctor arrived, I was fully attired in the blue, and ready for anything. He seemed suspicious of Anna's familiarity with morphine, but admitted that her gallbladder might be on the blink and said we'd better get in touch with her relatives. Now, the relatives of domestics are an even more mysterious band of people than domestics themselves. I knew from experience that sometimes they didn't even have names. I also knew that they never had telephones, although they sometimes lived in the same building with a telephone. However, we grilled Anna on the subject of relatives, after the doctor had relieved her, and eventually, by an elaborate bit of telephoning through third parties, we dug up a beauty—a niece, Anna said she was. We asked her to come as soon as possible. She turned out to be one of the most beautiful women I have ever seen in my life. She arrived about nine that morning, with a fourteen-month-old child in rather bad repair. I let her in, and she immediately handed the baby to me. "Would you mind?" she said. "I have a terrible hangover and can hardly stand up. Isn't it a shame about Bumpo?"

"About who?" I asked.

"Bumpo," she said. "That's what we call my Aunt Anna."

"Oh, I didn't know," I replied. "Yes, it's a dreadful thing, with much pain. I'm sorry *you* don't feel good, either," I added courteously.

"I'll be all right as soon as I get a drink," she said. "I was on a bender last night after the show. I have a walk-on part in the 'Scandals,' you know. Have you seen it?"

"No, but I will," I replied.

Together we marched upstairs. The baby was heavy and soggy, a rather spiritless child. With him in my lap, I made a quick phone call to the office and told them that it didn't look as though I'd be in till afternoon.

I sometimes think that that morning, as I stood around pacifying the grand-nephew of a stricken domestic named Bumpo, my career as a master reached a minor pinnacle, achieved something like nobility. It didn't last, though. Anna had been gone hardly an hour when my wife and I found ourselves engaged in the cheap, vulgar trick of reading the diary which she left behind her. We discovered it on her bureau. Our intentions were honorable enough at first—we were simply thumbing through it hoping to come across her niece's address, which in the confusion she had neglected to leave us. Gradually, however, we became absorbed; Anna's story began to grip us and sweep us along. Written in ink, in a fine, close hand, the diary covered a period of about two years and chronicled her goings and comings in two previous places. For the most part it was a rather dreary recital of a cheerless life. "The madam out this afternoon." "Getting colder." "Robert Taylor was at the Strand yesterday but didn't get to go." We waded, fascinated, through page after page of this commonplace stuff, and suddenly, as though we had been hit across the eyes with a board, we came upon the following terse item: "Phoned Milwaukee police today."

That was all there was to it. Nothing led up to it. Nothing led away it. It stood there all alone a tiny purple chapter in a gray little book. We still don't know what it was all about, and we still dream about it sometimes.

Anna had her stones out in good shape and soon grew fit again. We volunteered to pay for the operation, but she refused financial help. Although we held the situation open for her, she never came back to us—which rather disappointed me, as I wanted to get to know her well enough to call her Bumpo. She is probably even now tapping away at her portable machine somewhere—a one-act play, perhaps, or a friendly note to the Department of Justice.

The presence in my house of a group of persons with whom I have merely a contractual relationship is a constant source of wonder to me. Left to my own devices, I believe I would never employ a domestic but would do my own work, which would take me about twenty minutes a day. However, all matters pertaining to the operation of the home are settled agreeably and competently for me by my wife, who dearly loves complexity and whose instinctive solution of any dilemma like marriage is to get about four or five other people embroiled in it. Although the picturesque and lurid rôle of householder saps my strength and keeps me impoverished, I must admit it gives life a sort of carnival aspect, almost as though there were an elephant swaying in the dining room. And then, once in a lifetime, some thoroughly indispensable and noble person walks casually into one's home, like Antoinette Ferraro, who proceeds to become a member of the family, blood or no blood. Antoinette has been fooling around our house for thirteen or fourteen years, and we would as lief part with her as with our own children. There is no danger of any separation, however. I am perfectly sure that when I draw my last breath, Antoinette will still be somewhere about the premises, performing some grotesquely irrelevant act, like ironing a dog's blanket.

Her name is really Antonietta, and I suspect that I had better not go on with these memoirs without taking her up in some detail, as she is the core of our domestic apple. Without her we should perish; and *with* her (such is the pressure of her outside obligations) we very nearly do. The other night, as my wife and I were sitting by Antoinette's side in the crowded auditorium of a trade school, watching her legitimate son Pietro graduate with honors in my blue serge suit, I had a chance to study the beatific face of this remarkable woman and brood about my good fortune in having encountered her in this world. She was born, I believe, in northern Italy, and speaks an impartial blend of Italian, French, and English. The only form of an English verb which appeals to her, however, is the present participle. In fact, she speaks almost entirely in participles, joining them by French conjunctions, to which she is loyal. If you ask if she'd be good enough to boil you an egg, her reply is simply, *"Oui,* I'm boiling." Once, on New Year's, she got a little tight on some mulled wine of her own concoction, and when we inquired of her next day if she had reached the Sixth Avenue "L" safely the night before, she blinked her long lashes shyly and said, "Oh, *oui*. Hah! I'm so running! Oh, my!"

Although she ostensibly works full time for us, and gets paid for it, this is merely a mutual conceit on our parts, for she has a full, absorbing life of her own—an apartment full of birds and plants, a son on whom she pours the steady stream of her affection, two boarders for whom she prepares two meals a day, and a thoroughbred Cairn bitch, which (like Antoinette herself) is forever being taken advantage of by an inferior male. The last time this animal had puppies, Antoinette brought one over, tenderly, for us to see. It was something of a monster, with chow characteristics and a set of inflamed bowels. When we offered our condolences on the continuance of the bitch's bitter destiny, Antoinette sighed. *"Ah, oui,"* she said, dreamily. "Wazz that night on the roof."

I marvel that we go on paying Antoinette anything. It takes her two hours and a half to dust one side of a wooden candlestick, and even then she forgets to put it back on the mantelpiece and our Boston terrier carries it to the cellar and worries it in the coalbin. All we gain from the arrangement is Antoinette's rich account of the little adventure, including a perfect imitation of the dog. "He so hoppy," she will explain, "holding in mouth, like beeg cigar, *mais* never dropping. Oh, he barking, he jomping..."

It doesn't sound reasonable, I know, that we should pay anyone to sit around our house and imitate a dog, but we do, nevertheless. One morning she showed up, ready for work, accompanied by a sick bird in a gilded cage, her bitch (again pregnant), and her own family wash, which she always seems to do on our time. "Antoinette," said my wife, exasperated, "I honestly don't see how you expect to do anything for *us* today." Antoinette fluttered her wonderful lashes. "Is all right," she announced, "I'm doing." She never leaves any opening for you at the end of a sentence.

She is a magnificent cook, easily the best we ever encountered, but, because our hours interfere with the proper functioning of her own domestic establishment, she has given up cooking for us and prepares food now only for our dog, kneading raw meat and carrots with kindly red hands and adding a few drops of "colliver oily" as cautiously and precisely as a gourmet fussing over a salad dressing. There have been times when I have looked into the dog's dish with unfeigned envy, for the instant Antoinette's hand touches food, it becomes mysteriously delectable. When I think of her risotto, the tears come to my eyes.

I suppose our affection for Antoinette is temperamental: she likes the same things we do, has the same standards, reacts the same in any situation. She drinks moderately and likes to see other people drink and have a good time; consequently, when you ask her to bring you some ice, she does it with gusto and a twinkle in the eye. We usually manage to sneak her a glass of wine at night, when the other more straitlaced members of the staff aren't looking. She smokes our brand of cigarettes, and is a chain smoker. She is fond of dogs, and indeed is the only domestic of my acquaintance whose first concern, when a dog is sick on the rug, is for the dog. I can't help liking that in her, even though I often have to clean the rug myself while she is comforting the animal. If you give her an old flannel shirt to launder, she lavishes all her love and skill upon it, and it comes back to you the same size as when it went to the tub. And then, Antoinette has that great Latin quality: she is a realist. Life is life, and it's the way it is. We had a manservant one time—a middle-aged Belgian who went hog wild one morning about ten o'clock, kicked pots and pans all over the pantry, and wound up by taking off all his clothes and running naked up and down the laundry, hoping by this sudden noisy revel to engage Antoinette's fancy. Neither my wife nor I was home, and when we apologized later to Antoinette for this unexpected bit of goatishness, she chuckled reminiscently. "La, that old fellow," she snickered. "Is nothing."

This same old fellow who was nothing was my first experience with a manservant. His name was Gaston, and his career with us was brief but colorful. He was one half of a "couple," and nobody has had any experience of a domestic nature till he has employed a couple. I was against the idea, but my wife assured me that a couple would be more economical because then the man could tend the furnace. Unimpressed by this flimsy bit of logic, I went to a nursemaid then in our employ and asked her if she had ever worked in the same house with a couple. "Oh, sure, I like it," she replied. "It's fun to come down in the morning and see which one has the bruises."

I really held out for quite a while against a couple.

"But why?" asked my wife doggedly. "What earthly reason is against it?"

"Well," I said, "I'm not going to have any man pussyfooting around this house, bowing and scraping."

"What's wrong with a man?"

"Well, I don't know," I cried, "it's just sort of immoral, that's all."

"Immoral! What kind of crazy reason is that? It's no more immoral than having *you* around."

"You know what menservants do sometimes, don't you?" I asked.

"What do they do?"

"They steam open your letters. I saw one do it in the movies one time."

"Oh, my God," said my wife, and the talk ended. Gaston and Eugénie arrived the following Monday, in a cab.

They were, as I have said, Belgians. It seemed to me then, and still seems, an inspired bit of deviltry on my wife's part to engage a couple neither of whom could speak or understand English. I myself neither speak nor understand any other language. I can usually grasp Antoinette's meanings, because she puts in a liberal dash of English participles and nouns. Gaston and Eugénie spoke a mixture of French and Flemish, which gave even my bilingual wife a little trouble. In fact, until Gaston and I worked out a system of arm signals and small guttural cries, there was practically no communication between any of us in the home.

"He'll soon learn English," my wife assured me. And indeed the old fellow did make a stab at it. One evening, after a formal dinner party at which Gaston had officiated, we men stepped out into the garden for a smoke while the ladies withdrew, genteelly, to the living room upstairs. I was half through a cigarette when Gaston appeared in the garden, his bald streak shining in the moon, his gray curls festooned like tiny vines around his big, rascally ears. With his index finger pointing upward, he placed his heels neatly together, bowed, and said, *"Pardon, M'sieu. Café* oops."

"How's that, Gaston?" I said sheepishly, while my fascinated guests watched. *"Café* what?"

"Café oops, *M'sieu.* Oopstair."

"Ah, oui. Ah, oui, Gaston," I replied glibly, and led the gentlemen aloft to their coffee.

In the long roster of persons who have been attached at one period or another to our house, Gaston and Eugénie were far from being the most successful, but they were in many ways the most distinguished.

The head of the employment agency where my wife found them had been most enthusiastic—they were the "perfect servants" and had been trained in the household of a Washington diplomat, an ambassador, I believe. I think my wife was just a shade impressed by this. Anyway, she failed to foresee the unhealthy effect it would have on Gaston to go straight from serving an ambassador to serving a screwball like me. I was always rather sorry for the old boy, with his courtly manner and his bucktoothed little wife, who grinned and said yes even when she didn't understand what you said, which was always! The very first meeting between Gaston and myself was unpropitious and drab. I had a rotten cold on the Monday when he arrived, and spent the morning wrapped in an old button-up-the-front sweater in my third-floor study among some diseased house plants and empty picture frames. My wife left early in the morning, to be gone all day, and had given instructions to the breathless new couple to prepare for me, the unseen master, a lunch, explaining that I was unwell, in the chambers above, but would descend to the dining room for the noon meal.

"*M'sieu est* grippy," she said, in her best Flemish.

"*Oui, Madame,*" Gaston had replied respectfully.

At one o'clock, I heard stealthy footsteps outside the door, then a rap. "Yes?" I said. The door opened, and there he was—a faded, gray little man, beautifully if unsuitably attired in tails. There was something tragic about the appearance, in my dismal doorway on a Monday noon, of a Belgian husband in evening dress. Against the peeling plaster walls, he looked wrong, and I knew then and there that our adventure with a couple was ill-starred. His skin was a cigarette-ash gray, and his bow tie was not much less dingy. Having been instructed by my wife never to address me in French or Flemish, and being incapable of announcing lunch in any other tongue, he simply raised one arm in a long, eloquent sweep toward the stairs and the smell of meat balls, and departed.

Lunch turned out to be a considerably gayer occasion than I reckoned on. I was joined at table by my small son, Bertrand, and our Boston terrier, Palsy. The latter, far from being depressed by the sight of a tailcoat at noontide, was exhilarated. He took up a wing-back position near the woodbox and executed a brilliant series of line bucks through Gaston's skinny legs. Ordinarily, Bertrand would have welcomed a free-for-all of this sort with howls of encouragment, but to my amazement the little boy sat spellbound and quiet, his steady gaze never wavering from Gaston's contorted features, his grave demeanor in strange contrast to Palsy's clowning. There was something genuinely compelling in Gaston's hauteur, and throughout the meal Bertie spoke only in whispers. I kept blowing my nose and scolding Palsy, but there wasn't much use in it. Finally I said to Gaston, "I am sorry, Gaston, that the little dog attacks you foolishly. Soon he will get to know you."

"*M'sieu?*" queried Gaston, trembling with incomprehension.

"The little dog," I said, pointing. "I fear he is a great trouble to you."

Gaston considered this speech carefully, searching for meanings. Then his features composed into a hideous smile. Picking up a meat ball between thumb and forefinger, he bent stiffly from the waist and handed it to Palsy, dreaming, I do not doubt, of his life in Washington, among decent people.

When we fired Gaston and Eugénie for Gaston's vile interlude in the laundry, he put on quite a scene, at first refusing flatly to accept the dismissal. I stood by while my wife alternately discharged him in French and translated his protests to me in English. We were, he said (and his great, melodious voice dipped deep into the lower register and then swooped up again like some dark bird), making the supreme mistake of our lives, dispensing with the services of himself and his so talented wife. We countered. Liquor, we said, had unquestionably debased him. Eugénie, hearing the word "liquor," nodded violently in agreement: liquor had made Gaston gross, but we should not concern ourselves with such harmless derelictions. Gaston grew more and more surly. A discharge was out of the question, and he was willing to lay the whole unfortunate affair to our inexperience as master and mistress of a household. "He says we're inexperienced, darling," said my wife.

This, for some reason, made me mad, for I remembered Anna's gallstones and a thousand and one other nights. "By God, nobody's going to stand there and call me inexperienced!" I shouted. "You get out of here, you lecherous old scarecrow."

Half an hour later they were gone, but not before Gaston had got in the last word. He appeared on the second-floor landing with his trunk, set it down, and turned to salute us.

"*S'il faut partir, il faut partir. Pfui!*" And with a quick little push, he launched the trunk into the air and watched it go roaring down to the floor below, chipping off pieces of stair as it went. Thus departed the perfect servant.

My wife is not easily discouraged, and Gaston and Eugénie were followed closely by another wedded pair, Otto and Mildred. They were young Germans, but they spoke English clearly enough—it just came natural to them. Otto was the *Turnverein* type, big, blue-eyed, vain, and strong; well-being oozed from every pore. I always felt that he should wear shorts and a small rucksack when waiting on table. He loved moving heavy objects, because it showed off his strength, and he frequently went down cellar and threw boxes and crates around for no particular reason. When my Aunt Helen, who is a fairly fleshy old lady, returned to our house to convalesce after she'd had her appendix out, the problem came of getting her upstairs. "Dot's nudding," said Otto, appraising her quickly. And before any of us could stop him, he gathered Aunt Helen in his arms, scar tissue and all, and bounded up two flights of stairs with her. "So!" he said, plopping her down on the bed.

Otto loved to be in the same room with me. When he discovered I was a writing man, he determined to be of the greatest possible assistance to me, and was always busting into my study, clad in a zipper campus jacket and bearing a greasy clipping from the *Daily Mirror*. "Here's a tchoke for you," he would announce, handing me some unattractive oddity in the news, such as a cat mothering a baby robin. I had to give up trying to work at home during the time he was with us. I used to go to the reading room of the Public Library and sit with other escapists at long oak desks.

There is something about our household which invariably makes it seem like a comedown to servants after other houses they have been in. Gaston and Eugénie were gravely disappointed that our home wasn't an embassy. Otto was crushed when he found out I didn't own two Duesenbergs. The man he worked for just before he came to us had two Duesenbergs, and Otto kept throwing them in my face. Even had I allowed Otto to drive my old Hudson sedan, which I never did, I'm sure it wouldn't have filled the void in his life. I think it was the humdrum of our home that drove him into aviation as a sideline. He managed to combine the two vocations charmingly—

waiting on table here and spending his Thursday and Sunday after-noons off at an airfield in Flushing, taking flying lessons.

I asked him if it wasn't pretty expensive. "Na," he replied. "Ten dollars an hour, dot's all." His goggles, which he showed me one day, cost $27.50.

He progressed rapidly in the air. When he got so he could solo, he used to fly across the river and circle above our house, banking sharply at the prescribed altitude and showing off as much as he could without violating the Bureau of Air Commerce regulations. It was a perfect outlet for his Aryan spirits, but it was just one more straw for my tired old back. I got damned sick of hearing the drone of my em-ployee's plane over my rooftop, and I never got quite used to having my Friday-morning coffee poured by a man lately down from the skies. I felt earthbound, insignificant, and stuffy; and I began to compensate for this, unconsciously, in my attitude toward Otto.

"Well," I would say sourly, "I see you didn't break your neck yesterday." Otto would laugh—a loud, bold laugh.

"Na, I'm too schmart."

He *was* too smart, too. He left our household not as the result of any aerial mishap but because he couldn't get on with Bertrand's nurse, Katie, a pretty little Irish girl who called him Tarzan behind his back and was no more impressed by his gorgeous torso than I was.

I guess Otto's most notable quality was his readiness to answer all questions, at table. We first noticed this in him the day Aunt Helen went to the hospital for her appendectomy, which was very soon after Otto's arrival.

"I wish I knew how much the operation is going to cost," I re-marked to my wife at dinner.

"Fifty dollars," replied Otto, coming up on my left with a dish of broccoli.

I was delighted at this sign of alertness in him and soon discovered that his store of information covered every subject. If a guest, for example, filled in a dull pause at dinner by remarking that she had found a terribly nice little flower shop but she couldn't remember whether it was on Fifty-first Street or Fifty-second Street, Otto would pipe up, "Fifty-first." If you speculated as to what theatre a certain show was playing in, Otto would announce, "Broadhurst."

I never knew him to be right about anything, but he was an

enormous comfort just the same. There are lots of times when you like to get a quick answer, even though it means nothing.

Another thing I rather enjoyed about Otto was his identification with the world of crime. Otto hadn't been with us three days when a jeweller's wife was murdered in a small suburban apartment building by a lover in a state of pique.

"It's funny how dot feller got in her hallway," said Otto, taking a quick glance over my shoulder at the newspaper.

"What's so funny about it?" I replied. "He got in by pushing some-body else's bell and walking in when they clicked."

"Dot's what *you* think," said Otto. "But dot building ain't dot way. You godda be let in."

"How do you know so much about it?"

"I worked there."

It soon became clear that Otto had worked not only at the scene of that crime but at the scene of all crimes. While police wallowed in the darkness of an unsolved mystery, Otto and I walked in the light of exact knowledge. I consulted him whenever I was in doubt about any point, and always got a direct, clear answer.

Smoke dreams! How charmingly these dear people drift before me as I sit here with my pipe and my memories! I think back to the soft spring evening, ten years ago, when I was in the dining room lingering over coffee. The door opened and a young peasant woman entered, carrying a dustpan full of horse manure. It was some which she had discovered in front of the house, following the fitful passage through our street of a Borden's delivery wagon. The young woman, surprised to find me still in the dining room, blushed prettily, then carried her treasure out into the back garden and spread it tenderly on the exhausted little plot of soil which supported our privet bush.

The smoke curls in wreaths around my head. I see the thin, com-petent form of Mrs. Farrell, whom Antoinette always called Farola and who in turn called me Dearie. I think of Minnie, the Bahai, whose piety allowed her to partake of food only before sunrise and after sundown, and whose abstinence so weakened her that she used to run the egg-beater in the kitchen to drown out the noise of her lamentation. And of Mrs. Farnsworth, the aged eccentric, whom, in the course of a five-hundred-mile motor journey, I regaled with a dollar-and-a-quarter chicken dinner only to see her sweep the entire contents of her plate off into her purse, to take to the little dog that was the delight of her life.

I count them over, one by one. Today, however, I feel a great lethargy creep over me. Sometimes I wish I could relive all those strange and golden times; but there are other moments, when the radio is particularly loud in Francine's room and the *Meisterschmerz* is strong upon me, when I know that all I want is peace.

Wolcott Gibbs

RING OUT, WILD BELLS

When I finally got around to seeing Max Reinhardt's cinema version of "A Midsummer-Night's Dream," and saw a child called Mickey Rooney playing Puck, I remembered suddenly that long ago I had taken the same part.

Our production was given on the open-air stage at the Riverdale Country School, shortly before the war. The scenery was only the natural scenery of that suburban dell, and the cast was exclusively male, ranging in age from eleven to perhaps seventeen. While we had thus preserved the pure, Elizabethan note of the original, it must be admitted that our version had its drawbacks. The costumes were probably the worst things we had to bear, and even Penrod, tragically arrayed as Launcelot in his sister's stockings and his father's drawers, might have been embarrassed for us. Like Penrod, we were costumed by our parents, and like the Schofields, they seemed on the whole a little weak historically. Half of the ladies were inclined to favor the Elizabethan, and they had constructed rather bunchy ruffs and farthingales for their offspring; others, who had read as far as the stage directions and learned that the action took place in an Athenian wood, had produced something vaguely Athenian, usually beginning with a sheet. Only the fairies had a certain uniformity. For some reason their parents had all decided on cheesecloth, with here and there a little ill-advised trimming with tinsel.

My own costume was mysterious, but spectacular. As nearly as I have ever been able to figure things out, my mother found her inspiration for it in a Maxfield Parrish picture of a court jester. Beginning at the top, there was a cap with three stuffed horns; then, for the main part, a pair of tights that covered me to my wrists and ankles; and finally slippers with stuffed toes that curled up at the ends. The whole thing was made out of silk in alternate green and red stripes, and (unquestionably my poor mother's most demented stroke) it was covered from head to foot with a thousand tiny bells. Because all our costumes were obviously perishable, we never wore them in rehearsal, and naturally nobody knew that I was invested with these peculiar sound effects until I made my entrance at the beginning of the second act.

Our director was a man who had strong opinions about how Shakespeare should be played, and Puck was one of his favorite characters. It was his theory that Puck, being "the incarnation of mischief," never ought to be still a minute, so I had been coached to bound onto the stage, and once there to dance up and down, cocking my head and waving my arms.

"I want you to be a little whirlwind," this man said.

Even as I prepared to bound onto the stage, I had my own misgivings about those dangerously abundant gestures, and their probable effect on my bells. It was too late, however, to invent another technique for playing Puck, even if there had been room for anything but horror in my mind. I bounded onto the stage.

The effect, in its way, must have been superb. With every leap I rang like a thousand children's sleighs, my melodies foretelling God knows what worlds of merriment to the enchanted spectators. It was even worse when I came to the middle of the stage and went into my gestures. The other ringing had been loud but sporadic. This was persistent, varying only slightly in volume and pitch with the vehemence of my gestures. To a blind man, it must have sounded as though I had recklessly decided to accompany myself on a xylophone. A maturer actor would probably have made up his mind that an emergency existed, and abandoned his gestures as impracticable under the circumstances. I was thirteen, and incapable of innovations. I had been told by responsible authorities that gestures went with this part, and I continued to make them. I also continued to ring—a silvery music, festive and horrible.

If the bells were hard on my nerves, they were even worse for the rest of the cast, who were totally unprepared for my new interpretation. Puck's first remark is addressed to one of the fairies, and it is mercifully brief.

I said, "How now, spirit! Whither wander you?"

This unhappy child, already embarrassed by a public appearance in cheesecloth and tinsel, was also burdened with an opening speech of sixteen lines in verse. He began bravely:

> "Over hill, over dale,
>   Thorough bush, thorough brier,
> Over park, over pale,
>   Through flood, through fire..."

At the word "fire," my instructions were to bring my hands up from the ground in a long, wavery sweep, intended to represent fire. The bells pealed. To my startled ears, it sounded more as if they exploded. The fairy stopped in his lines and looked at me sharply. The jingling, however, had diminished; it was no more than as if a faint wind stirred my bells, and he went on:

> "I do wander every where,
>   Swifter than the moone's sphere..."

Here again I had another cue, for a sort of swoop and dip indicating the swiftness of the moone's sphere. Again the bells rang out, and again the performance stopped in its tracks. The fairy was clearly troubled by these interruptions. He had, however, a child's strange acceptance of the inscrutable, and was even able to regard my bells as a last-minute adult addition to the program, nerve-racking but not to be questioned. I'm sure it was only this that got him through that first speech.

My turn, when it came, was even worse. By this time the audience had succumbed to a helpless gaiety. Every time my bells rang, laughter swept the spectators, and this mounted and mingled with the bells until everything else was practically inaudible. I began my speech, another long one, and full of incomprehensible references to Titania's changeling.

"Louder!" said somebody in the wings. "You'll have to talk louder."

It was the director, and he seemed to be in a dangerous state.

"And for heaven's sake, stop that jingling!" he said.

I talked louder, and I tried to stop the jingling, but it was no use. By the time I got to the end of my speech, I was shouting and so was t' e audience. It appeared that I had very little control over the bells, which continued to jingle in spite of my passionate efforts to keep them quiet.

All this had a very bad effect on the fairy, who by this time had many symptoms of a complete nervous collapse. However, he began his next speech:

"Either I mistake your shape and making quite,
Or else you are that shrewd and knavish sprite
Call'd Robin Goodfellow: are you not he
That..."

At this point I forgot that the rules had been changed and I was supposed to leave out the gestures. There was a furious jingling, and the fairy gulped.

"Are you not he that, that..."

He looked miserably at the wings, and the director supplied the next line, but the tumult was too much for him. The unhappy child simply shook his head.

"Say anything!" shouted the director desperately. "Anything at all!"

The fairy only shut his eyes and shuddered.

"All right!" shouted the director. "All right, Puck. *You* begin *your* next speech."

By some miracle, I actually did remember my next lines, and had opened my mouth to begin on them when suddenly the fairy spoke. His voice was a high, thin monotone, and there seemed to be madness in it, but it was perfectly clear.

"Fourscore and seven years ago," he began, "our fathers brought forth on this continent a new nation, conceived..."

He said it right through to the end, and it was certainly the most successful speech ever made on that stage, and probably one of the most successful speeches ever made on any stage. I don't remember, if I ever knew, how the rest of us ever picked up the dull, normal thread of the play after that extraordinary performance, but we must have, because I know it went on. I only remember that in the next intermission the director cut off my bells with his penknife, and after that things quieted down and got dull.

H. L. Mencken

BRIEF GUST OF GLORY

When I was a boy in the Aurignacian Epoch of Baltimore, the favorite bivouac and chapel-of-ease of all healthy males of tender years was the neighborhood livery stable. I have since learned, by a reading in the social sciences, that the American livery-stables of that era were seminaries of iniquity, with a curriculum embracing cursing and swearing, gambling, cigarette-smoking, tobacco-chewing, the classical or Abraham Lincoln répertoire of lewd anecdotes, the design and execution of dirty pictures, and even the elements of seduction, burglary, and delirium tremens. It may have been true, for all I know, in the pathological small towns that all social scientists appear to hail from, but certainly it was not true in West Baltimore, a sedate and sequestered section of a great American seaport. I was a regular student at Reveille's stable in Stricker Street from the beginning of my seventh year to the end of my nonage, and a special student at Coblens's stable in Paca Street, off and on, for most of the same period, but so far as I can recall I never heard a word uttered in either of them, or beheld any human act, transaction, or phenomenon, that might not have been repeated before a bench of archbishops.

On the contrary, they were both schools of decorum, operated by proud and even haughty men, and staffed by blackamoors of a generally high tone. No palpably dipsomaniacal or larcenous coon could survive more than a few days in any such establishment. There were too many valuable horses and rigs on hand to be trusted to the former, and too many valuable carriage robes, buggy whips, hassocks, etc., to be exposed to the latter. My father's No. 1 whip, hung up by the snapper in Mr. Reveille's office, had a gold band around the handle engraved with the insigne of the Ancient Arabic Order of Nobles of the Mystic Shrine, and in Mr. Coblens's office, where my father commonly kept his No. 2 whip, there was also a buffalo robe that he set great store by, although I should add that its hair had pretty well played out, and that after his death I gave it freely to the poor.

Mr. Coblens was a man of erect bearing, reserved manner, and great dignity. He wore none of the loud checks associated with his vocation, but was always clad in plain colors, and not infrequently appeared in a black cutaway. His only concession to the public expectation was a gray derby, very high in the crown. If you can imagine a Jewish colonel of a swagger cavalry regiment, then you have got him to the life. My father had a high regard for him, and often paused to discuss horses with him—a subject about which he knew everything and my father next to nothing. Mr. Coblens seldom descended from his heights to speak to my brother or me. He knew us very well and would indicate by a vague flicker of his eyes that he was aware of our presence, but it was not often that he said anything.

His cousin Felix was a far more cordial fellow. Felix was a bachelor in those days, and apparently a somewhat gay one, for more than once I saw him set out of an afternoon in a buggy shining like a hundred-dollar coffin, with sometimes a blonde lady beside him and sometimes a brunette. My brother and I, boylike, regarded his ease and success at gallantry with great respect. He was, indeed, one of our heroes, and also one of our friends. He was never too busy to explain to us, with the use of living models paraded by his blackamoors, the points of a harness horse, and he also had illuminating ideas about buggy architecture. When I was eight years old and my brother six, my father gave us a pony named Frank, and it was Mr. Felix who taught us how to handle it—no mean art, I assure you, for Shetland ponies not only kick like mules but also bite like dogs, and no doubt would scratch like cats if they had claws. To this day I have a scar on my bosom, often passing for a war wound, that proves how effectively Frank could use his teeth.

In 1890 or thereabout my father traded two cases of leaf tobacco and a Swiss repeater watch for a gelding bearing the strange name (for a horse) of John. John was a trotter, and supposedly of some speed in harness, but my father could never get it out of him. The two did so badly together, indeed, that my father concluded that John must have rheumatism, and thereafter, for a year or so, the poor beast was the patient of a veterinarian who sent in large bottles of a fiery, suffocating liniment and even larger bills, but never did John any good. Mr. Felix, it appeared, had suspected all the while that the trouble was predominantly in the driver rather than in the horse, and eventually he volunteered to go out with my father some afternoon and make a scientific review of his driving. He returned downcast. "Your pa," he said to me the next time I dropped in, "is hopeless. It would take him two or three hundred years to learn to drive a cart horse, let alone a trotter. He holds the lines like a man dealing cards. If he ever got John to really stepping, he would fall out of the buggy and break his neck."

A few days later, as if reminded by conscience that he might have been hasty in dismissing his duty to the family, he amazed and delighted me by offering to give *me* a few lessons. It was a colossal opportunity to a boy of eleven, for Mr. Felix was an eminent figure in the trotting world of Baltimore and seldom condescended to pedagogy. I had, as I recall it, only four or five lessons, but when they were over, Mr. Felix was so complimentary that I developed on the spot a complacency which still survives after nearly fifty years, protecting me like an undershirt of concrete from the contumely of mankind. Indeed, he said flatly, and I believe he meant it, that I had in me the makings of a really smart harness driver. "By the time you begin to shave," he concluded, "you'll be showing 'em."

By that time, alas, I had turned from equestrology to chemistry, and a little while later I abandoned chemistry (to my sneaking regret on many a rainy day) for the kind of beautiful letters on tap in newspaper offices. But for two or three years I drove John every day, and so gradually improved and mellowed my technique. On summer afternoons, when my father and I were driving home to the country, and the clomp-clomp of a trotter's scissoring hooves began to sound behind us on the Pimlico Road, he would silently hand me the reins and settle back to be torn between parental pride and personal humiliation. I seemed to hear him groan now and then, but he never said anything. When John, who was really very fast, had left the other nag behind, and the brush was over, my father would quietly revive his cigar with a few sad puffs and resume the reins. He never complimented me: it would have been ruinous to his dignity as a harness driver. Despite the unction to my vanity that flowed out of these episodes, there was also melancholy in them, and they implanted in me a lifelong conviction that children, taking one day with another, must be damned pests.

It was not the Coblens stable, however, but the Reveille stable that was my chief haunt in boyhood. The Coblens stable was downtown near my father's place of business; the Reveille stable was only two blocks from our home on Hollins Street. My brother and I spent many happy hours there, watching the blackamoors currying and feeding the horses, plaiting their tails, excavating and blacking their hooves, dosing them with Glauber's salts and condition powders, and treating their lampas (pronounced "lampers") with red-hot pokers. This last was a horrifying spectacle, for lampas is an overgrowth of tissue behind the upper incisor teeth, and burning it out involved thrusting the poker into the poor horse's gaping mouth. But I learned before long that horses have very little sense of pain, if indeed any at all; and years afterward I saw one, with a leg cut off by a trolley car, munching the grass between the cobblestones as it lay on a Baltimore street, waiting for a cop to shoot it.

Mr. Reveille was a Frenchman who seemed venerable and even ancient to my brother and me, for he wore a straggling beard and always had on a black coat. He had two grown sons, both stout and hearty fellows, but, like their father, very dignified. There was a period when both the trotter John and our pony Frank were quartered in the Reveille stable, along with two buggies, a pony cart, and several other rigs, so my brother and I had plenty of excuse for hanging about. The Reveilles always welcomed us gravely, and let us warm up, in winter, in their tiny office, which was so filled with robes that there was scarcely room for the stove, always verging on white-hot. We admired especially the rack of whips, which included some virtuoso pieces by the Baltimore master craftsmen of the time. A good whip might cost as much as $25. We figured that the whole lot must be worth at least $1,000, and toyed for a while with a plan to break in some dark night, smouch them all, sell them to the cattle-herders at the Calverton stockyards, and go West with the proceeds to fight the Indians. What the herders would do with puny buggy whips we never paused to figure out. In the end, we abandoned the scheme as probably unlawful.

The colored brethren who pontificated at Reveille's have all faded, with the flight of the years, into a brown smudge—all, that is, save Old Jim. Jim was the carriage-washer, and a fellow of vast size and unparalleled amiability. He was coal-black and built like a battleship, and when he got into his hip-high rubber boots and put on his long rubber apron he had the imposing presence of an emperor in Hell. Jim's atelier was a skylighted space at the rear of the carriage house, paved with cobblestones and always flowing with water. He got to work at six in the morning, and was sometimes still going hard at nine at night. He had the care of fifty or more buggies, and of perhaps as many other vehicles, and he kept them clean and shining. His hardest time came on Sunday morning, when he had to wash and polish all the buggies in preparation for the pleasure jaunts of the afternoon. For this business he brought out his newest sponges and cleanest chamois skins. Also, he put on a black derby, never worn on weekdays.

In the intervals of his washing and polishing, Jim took out rigs to the homes of clients of the stable, and thereby sometimes acquired quiet brannigans, for it was the custom to reward him not with money but with drinks. My father kept a special jug for the purpose. It was shared by the iceman, but Jim got most of it, for in view of his great bulk he was given a much larger drink than the iceman. He always downed it at a gulp, and after it was down he would blink his eyes, rub his belly, and say "Ah-h-h-h-h!" This ritual was a Baltimore custom of the time, practiced by most of the nobility and gentry and imitated by serving folk. Sometimes Jim also got a cigar. He would light it at once and stalk back to Reveille's smoking it at an angle of forty-five degrees. Smoking was forbidden to the faculty at the stable and when he reached there he would choke it carefully and deposit it on a high ledge in the brick wall. Some of its other members had sharp eyes for likely stumps and the cigar was out of their reach there, but not out of his.

My brother and I greatly admired Jim, and delighted in watching him at work. He had a way of spinning buggy wheels that was really magnificent, and he worked with larger sponges and broader chamois skins than any other carriage-washer in West Baltimore. The buggies of those days all had carpets, and when there was nothing else to do he would get out a dozen or so of them and beat them. Sometimes he would find a nickel or a dime under one of them. It always went into his pocket, for it was the theory among the colored proletariat of Baltimore in those days that whatever a white person lost or mislaid he really didn't want. If he wanted it, he would ask for it, and probably raise hell about it. Jim's income from this source was not large, for he found a great many more pins than nickels. He always laid them aside and then threw them into the manure pit, for a pin in the frog of a horse's hoof might bring on calamity.

One day my brother and I were astonished to find Jim missing; it seemed almost as strange as finding Mr. Reveille missing, or the stable itself. His *locum tenens,* a short, spotty colored man named Browny, ordinarily a hostler, told us the sad news. Jim's youngest son, a youth of sixteen, had been blown up by an explosion in a one-horse soda-pop factory up a nearby alley, and Jim was off for the day, arranging for the interment of the few fragments that had been recovered. We had never heard of this son, but we were full of sympathy, and when Jim returned we tried to tell him so in the shy manner of boys. He replied that it was God's deliberate act and will, and that he did not repine. The son, he added judicially, was not really bad, at least as sons went in an age of moral chaos, but nevertheless there was some worry in him, for now and then, like any other high-spirited colored boy, he got into trouble with the cops, and when that wasn't going on he wasted his substance on trashy yallah gals. Now he was far, far away, riding some cloud or rainbow, and hence safe from the hangman forever. He had even escaped, by the unusual manner of his death, the body-snatchers.

Two or three days later we saw a brisk-looking white man in a short yellow overcoat talking to Jim, and the day following, Jim again disappeared. We heard from Browny that the brisk-looking man was a lawyer and that the talk had been of damages. Another talk, he said, was proceeding downtown. Jim was gone a week, and then suddenly reappeared, but not to resume work. He showed up one morning in a stovepipe hat and a long-tailed black coat, carrying an ebony cane with a bone head in the shape of a horse with widely distended nostrils tinted red, and green gems for eyes. His right-hand coat pocket was bulging with at least a quarter's worth of peanuts, and he invited all his old colleagues to thrust in their paws and help themselves. In his other coat pocket he had half a dozen apples for horses he especially liked, including our pony Frank but not the trotter John, and in the hand unburdened by the cane he carried a two-pound bag of lump sugar. In all four pockets of his white waistcoat were rows of five-cent cigars, standing up like cartridges in a belt. He offered the cigars freely and recommended them as the best in West Baltimore.

He even offered one to Mr. Peter Reveille. His hip pockets were stuffed with chewing tobacco.

Such was Jim in the full tide of his bereavement. Mr. Peter Reveille told us that the lawyer had offered Jim $250, but that he had stuck out for $300, and got it. He let it be known that he had demanded the money in one-dollar bills, but where he kept them we didn't know until later. Some of the hostlers were of the opinion that he had sneaked into the stable loft by night and hidden them in the hay, and for a week or so a vain search for them went on. Browny insisted that they were in Jim's stovepipe hat. He knew, as all of us knew, that policemen always kept their valuables in their helmets; ergo, why not Jim? But this theory blew up when Jim dropped in, a week or so later, without his hat and complaining that two bad niggers from Boot Alley had knocked it off with clubs and run away with it. The hat was gone, but Jim continued in funds for a long while afterward— indeed, for fully a month. He visited the stable almost daily, and never failed to distribute cigars, peanuts, and chewing tobacco, with sugar and apples for the horses. He appeared, at different times, in no less than five hats, and was often mildly in liquor. But he never brought any liquor on the premises, and so the Reveilles, who had a large experience with the darker races, tolerated him patiently.

They knew that he would be back in his long boots and rubber apron soon or late, and he was. One morning early they found him at work, somewhat trembly and with a cut over his left eye, but otherwise as he had been in the days before wealth corrupted him. He had not been seen during the preceding week, and for a while his final adventures were unknown, for neither then nor thereafter did he ever mention them. But the other colored men gradually assembled and disgorged the story, and the cop on the beat helped out with a fact or two. It was really very simple. Jim, a decent widower, had been ganged and undone by the massed yallah gals of three alleys. They had all tackled him singly and failed, but when they tackled him in a body he succumbed.

The ensuing party raged for four days and four nights, with continuous music by banjos, mouth organs, and bones. It began in a little saloon that was the G.H.Q. of one of the alleys, but gradually spread over the whole block, and ended at last in a loft over an empty stable. There was no hint whatever of carnality; the thing was purely alcoholic. After the first few hours each of the yallah gals sent for her regular fellow, and beginning with the second day, all sorts of gate-crashers barged in. Thereafter there was a flow in and a flow out. Every hour or two some guest would collapse and roll home, and another would make the gate. Only Jim himself and a yallah gal named Mildred survived for more than forty-eight hours. Mildred, on the last day, was in the first stages of *mania à potu,* and the cop on the beat, looking in, ordered her off the job, but Jim was still going strong.

Alas, he didn't go long, for a little while later the saloonkeeper's son Otto came in to say that time was called on the party. Otto and his brother Hermann had been hauling booze for it for four days and four nights, and both were badly used up. Hermann, in fact, had had to be put to bed. But it wasn't fatigue that made Otto call time; it was the fact that Jim's last dollar bill had been devoured. The father of Otto and Hermann was known to be a determined man, with the cops always on his side, so no one questioned the fiat. One by one, they simply faded away, leaving only Jim. He rolled himself in his long-tailed coat and lay down to a prodigal's dreams. He slept all the rest of that day and all of the ensuing night to 5 A.M. Then he shuffled off to Reveille's stable and resumed his station in life.

It was not until long afterward that my brother and I learned where Jim had kept his fortune while it oozed away. Mr. Reveille, worming the story out of the blackamoors, told my father, who told it to a neighbor, Mr. Glaser, whose boy Harold, lurking about, overheard the telling and brought it to us. The money had been in the care and custody of the saloonkeeper all the while. He doled it out to Jim dollar by dollar, marking the score on a blackboard behind his bar. He charged Jim a dollar a day "interest" for keeping it. When the final orgies began, he charged a dollar for every day and a dollar for every night.

The Glaser boy reported that, in telling about this "interest," my father swore in a hair-raising manner. He had, in fact, little use for saloonkeepers. He would often say that while he knew and respected some upright men among them, only too many were disgraces to a humane and even noble profession.

William Saroyan

THE SUMMER OF THE BEAUTIFUL
WHITE HORSE

One day back there in the good old days when I was nine and the
world was full of every imaginable kind of magnificence, and life was
still a delightful and mysterious dream, my cousin Mourad, who was
considered crazy by everybody who knew him except me, came to my
house at four in the morning and woke me up by tapping on the
window of my room.

Aram, he said.

I jumped out of bed and looked out the window.

I couldn't believe what I saw.

It wasn't morning yet, but it was summer and with daybreak not
many minutes around the corner of the world it was light enough for
me to know I wasn't dreaming.

My cousin Mourad was sitting on a beautiful white horse.

I stuck my head out of the window and rubbed my eyes.

Yes, he said in Armenian. It's a horse. You're not dreaming. Make
it quick if you want to ride.

I knew my cousin Mourad enjoyed being alive more than anybody
else who had ever fallen into the world by mistake, but this was more
than even I could believe.

In the first place, my earliest memories had been memories of
horses and my first longings had been longings to ride.

This was the wonderful part.

In the second place, we were poor.

This was the part that wouldn't permit me to believe what I saw.

We were poor. We had no money. Our whole tribe was poverty-
stricken. Every branch of the Garoghlanian family was living in the
most amazing and comical poverty in the world. Nobody could understand where we ever got money enough to keep us with food in our
bellies, not even the old men of the family. Most important of all,

though, we were famous for our honesty. We had been famous for our honesty for something like eleven centuries, even when we had been the wealthiest family in what we liked to think was the world. We were proud first, honest next, and after that we believed in right and wrong. None of us would take advantage of anybody in the world, let alone steal.

Consequently, even though I could *see* the horse, so magnificent; even though I could *smell* it, so lovely; even though I could *hear* it breathing, so exciting; I couldn't *believe* the horse had anything to do with my cousin Mourad or with me or with any of the other members of our family, asleep or awake, because I *knew* my cousin Mourad couldn't have *bought* the horse, and if he couldn't have bought it he must have *stolen* it, and I refused to believe he had stolen it.

No member of the Garoghlanian family could be a thief.

I stared first at my cousin and then at the horse. There was a pious stillness and humor in each of them which on the one hand delighted me and on the other frightened me.

Mourad, I said, where did you steal this horse?

Leap out of the window, he said, if you want to ride.

It was true, then. He *had* stolen the horse. There was no question about it. He had come to invite me to ride or not, as I chose.

Well, it seemed to me stealing a horse for a ride was not the same thing as stealing something else, such as money. For all I knew, maybe it wasn't stealing at all. If you were crazy about horses the way my cousin Mourad and I were, it wasn't stealing. It wouldn't become stealing until we offered to sell the horse, which of course I knew we would never do.

Let me put on some clothes, I said.

All right, he said, but hurry.

I leaped into my clothes.

I jumped down to the yard from the window and leaped up onto the horse behind my cousin Mourad.

That year we lived at the edge of town, on Walnut Avenue. Behind our house was the country: vineyards, orchards, irrigation ditches, and country roads. In less than three minutes we were on Olive Avenue, and then the horse began to trot. The air was new and lovely to breathe. The feel of the horse running was wonderful. My cousin Mourad who was considered one of the craziest members of our family began to sing. I mean, he began to roar.

Every family has a crazy streak in it somewhere, and my cousin Mourad was considered the natural descendant of the crazy streak in our tribe. Before him was our uncle Khosrove, an enormous man with a powerful head of black hair and the largest mustache in the San Joaquin Valley, a man so furious in temper, so irritable, so impatient that he stopped anyone from talking by roaring, *It is no harm; pay no attention to it.*

That was all, no matter what anybody happened to be talking about. Once it was his own son Arak running eight blocks to the barber shop where his father was having his mustache trimmed to tell him their house was on fire. This man Khosrove sat up in the chair and roared, It is no harm; pay no attention to it. The barber said, But the boy says your house is on fire. So Khosrove roared, Enough, it is no harm, I say.

My cousin Mourad was considered the natural descendant of this man, although Mourad's father was Zorab, who was practical and nothing else. That's how it was in our tribe. A man could be the father of his son's flesh, but that did not mean that he was also the father of his spirit. The distribution of the various kinds of spirit of our tribe had been from the beginning capricious and vagrant.

We rode and my cousin Mourad sang. For all anybody knew we were still in the old country where, at least according to some of our neighbors, we belonged. We let the horse run as long as it felt like running.

At last my cousin Mourad said, Get down. I want to ride alone.

Will you let me ride alone? I said.

That is up to the horse, my cousin said. Get down.

The *horse* will let me ride, I said.

We shall see, he said. Don't forget that I have a way with a horse.

Well, I said, any way you have with a horse, I have also.

For the sake of your safety, he said, let us hope so. Get down.

All right, I said, but remember you've got to let me try to ride alone.

I got down and my cousin Mourad kicked his heels into the horse and shouted, *Vazire,* run. The horse stood on its hind legs, snorted, and burst into a fury of speed that was the loveliest thing I had ever seen. My cousin Mourad raced the horse across a field of dry grass to an irrigation ditch, crossed the ditch on the horse, and five minutes later returned, dripping wet.

The sun was coming up.

Now it's my turn to ride, I said.

My cousin Mourad got off the horse.

Ride, he said.

I leaped to the back of the horse and for a moment knew the awfulest fear imaginable. The horse did not move.

Kick into his muscles, my cousin Mourad said. What are you waiting for? We've got to take him back before everybody in the world is up and about.

I kicked into the muscles of the horse. Once again it reared and snorted. Then it began to run. I didn't know what to do. Instead of running across the field to the irrigation ditch the horse ran down the road to the vineyard of Dikran Halabian where it began to leap over vines. The horse leaped over seven vines before I fell. Then it continued running.

My cousin Mourad came running down the road.

I'm not worried about you, he shouted. We've got to get that horse. You go this way and I'll go this way. If you come upon him, be kindly. I'll be near.

I continued down the road and my cousin Mourad went across the field toward the irrigation ditch.

It took him half an hour to find the horse and bring him back.

All right, he said, jump on. The whole world is awake now.

What will we do? I said.

Well, he said, we'll either take him back or hide him until tomorrow morning.

He didn't sound worried and I knew he'd hide him and not take him back. Not for a while, at any rate.

Where will we hide him? I said.

I know a place, he said.

How long ago did you steal this horse? I said.

It suddenly dawned on me that he had been taking these early morning rides for some time and had come for me this morning only because he knew how much I longed to ride.

Who said anything about stealing a horse? he said.

Anyhow, I said, how long ago did you begin riding every morning?

Not until this morning, he said.

Are you telling the truth? I said.

Of course not, he said, but if we are found out, that's what you're to say. I don't want both of us to be liars. All you know is that we started riding this morning.

All right, I said.

He walked the horse quietly to the barn of a deserted vineyard which at one time had been the pride of a farmer named Fetvajian. There were some oats and dry alfalfa in the barn.

We began walking home.

It wasn't easy, he said, to get the horse to behave so nicely. At first it wanted to run wild, but, as I've told you, I have a way with a horse. I can get it to want to do anything *I* want it to do. Horses understand me.

How do you do it? I said.

I have an understanding with a horse, he said.

Yes, but what sort of an understanding? I said.

A simple and honest one, he said.

Well, I said, I wish I knew how to reach an understanding like that with a horse.

You're still a small boy, he said. When you get to be thirteen you'll know how to do it.

I went home and ate a hearty breakfast.

That afternoon my uncle Khosrove came to our house for coffee and cigarettes. He sat in the parlor, sipping and smoking and remembering the old country. Then another visitor arrived, a farmer named John Byro, an Assyrian who, out of loneliness, had learned to speak Armenian. My mother brought the lonely visitor coffee and tobacco and he rolled a cigarette and sipped and smoked, and then at last, sighing sadly, he said, My white horse which was stolen last month is still gone. I cannot understand it.

My uncle Khosrove became very irritated and shouted, It's no harm. What is the loss of a horse? Haven't we all lost the homeland? What is this crying over a horse?

That may be all right for you, a city dweller, to say, John Byro said, but what of my surrey? What good is a surrey without a horse?

Pay no attention to it, my uncle Khosrove roared.

I walked ten miles to get here, John Byro said.

You have legs, my uncle Khosrove shouted.

My left leg pains me, the farmer said.

Pay no attention to it, my uncle Khosrove roared.

That horse cost me sixty dollars, the farmer said.

I spit on money, my uncle Khosrove said.

He got up and stalked out of the house, slamming the screen door.
My mother explained.

He has a gentle heart, she said. It is simply that he is homesick
and such a large man.

The farmer went away and I ran over to my cousin Mourad's house.

He was sitting under a peach tree, trying to repair the hurt wing
of a young robin which could not fly. He was talking to the bird.

What is it? he said.

The farmer, John Byro, I said. He visited our house. He wants his
horse. You've had it a month. I want you to promise not to take it
back until I learn to ride.

It will take you *a year* to learn to ride, my cousin Mourad said.

We could keep the horse a year, I said.

My cousin Mourad leaped to his feet.

What? he roared. Are you inviting a member of the Garoghlanian
family to steal? The horse must go back to its true owner.

When? I said.

In six months at the latest, he said.

He threw the bird into the air. The bird tried hard, almost fell
twice, but at last flew away, high and straight.

Early every morning for two weeks my cousin Mourad and I took
the horse out of the barn of the deserted vineyard where we were
hiding it and rode it, and every morning the horse, when it was my
turn to ride alone, leaped over grape vines and small trees and threw
me and ran away. Nevertheless, I hoped in time to learn to ride the
way my cousin Mourad rode.

One morning on the way to Fetvajian's deserted vineyard we ran
into the farmer John Byro who was on his way to town.

Let me do the talking, my cousin Mourad said. I have a way with
farmers.

Good morning, John Byro, my cousin Mourad said to the farmer.

The farmer studied the horse eagerly.

Good morning, sons of my friends, he said. What is the name of
your horse?

My Heart, my cousin Mourad said in Armenian.

A lovely name, John Byro said, for a lovely horse. I could swear
it is the horse that was stolen from me many weeks ago. May I look
into its mouth?

Of course, Mourad said.

The farmer looked into the mouth of the horse.

Tooth for tooth, he said. I would swear it *is* my horse if I didn't know your parents. The fame of your family for honesty is well known to me. Yet the horse is the twin of my horse. A suspicious man would believe his eyes instead of his heart. Good day, my young friends.

Good day, John Byro, my cousin Mourad said.

Early the following morning we took the horse to John Byro's vineyard and put it in the barn. The dogs followed us around without making a sound.

The dogs, I whispered to my cousin Mourad. I thought they would bark.

They would at somebody else, he said. I have a way with dogs.

My cousin Mourad put his arms around the horse, pressed his nose into the horse's nose, patted it, and then we went away.

That afternoon John Byro came to our house in his surrey and showed my mother the horse that had been stolen and returned.

I do not know what to think, he said. The horse is stronger than ever. Better-tempered, too. I thank God.

My uncle Khosrove, who was in the parlor, became irritated and shouted, Quiet, man, quiet. Your horse has been returned. Pay no attention to it.

James Thurber

THE NIGHT THE BED FELL

I suppose that the high-water mark of my youth in Columbus, Ohio, was the night the bed fell on my father. It makes a better recitation (unless, as some friends of mine have said, one has heard it five or six times) than it does a piece of writing, for it is almost necessary to throw furniture around, shake doors, and bark like a dog, to lend the proper atmosphere and verisimilitude to what is admittedly a somewhat incredible tale. Still, it did take place.

It happened, then, that my father had decided to sleep in the attic one night, to be away where he could think. My mother opposed the notion strongly because, she said, the old wooden bed up there was unsafe: it was wobbly and the heavy headboard would crash down on father's head in case the bed fell, and kill him. There was no dissuading him, however, and at a quarter past ten he closed the attic door behind him and went up the narrow twisting stairs. We later heard ominous creakings as he crawled into bed. Grandfather, who usually slept in the attic bed when he was with us, had disappeared some days before. (On these occasions he was usually gone six or eight days and returned growling and out of temper, with the news that the federal Union was run by a passel of blockheads and that the Army of the Potomac didn't have any more chance than a fiddler's bitch.)

We had visiting us at this time a nervous first cousin of mine named Briggs Beall, who believed that he was likely to cease breathing when he was asleep. It was his feeling that if he were not awakened every hour during the night, he might die of suffocation. He had been accustomed to setting an alarm clock to ring at intervals until morning, but I persuaded him to abandon this. He slept in my room and I told him that I was such a light sleeper that if anybody quit breathing in the same room with me, I would wake instantly. He tested me the first night—which I had suspected he would—by holding his breath after my regular breathing had convinced him I was asleep. I was not asleep, however, and called to him. This seemed to allay his fears a little, but he took the precaution of putting a glass of spirits of camphor on a little table at the head of his bed. In case I didn't arouse him until he was almost gone, he said, he would sniff the camphor, a powerful reviver. Briggs was not the only member of his family who had his crotchets. Old Aunt Melissa Beall (who could whistle like a man, with two fingers in her mouth) suffered under the premonition that she was destined to die on South High Street, because she had been born on South High Street and married on South High Street. Then there was Aunt Sarah Shoaf, who never went to bed at night without the fear that a burglar was going to get in and blow chloroform under her door through a tube. To avert this calamity—for she was in greater dread of anesthetics than of losing her household goods—she always piled her money, silverware, and other valuables in a neat stack just outside her bedroom, with a note reading: "This is all I have. Please take it and do not use your chloroform, as this is all I have." Aunt Gracie Shoaf also had a burglar phobia, but she met it with more fortitude. She was confident that burglars had been getting into her house every night for forty years. The fact that she never missed anything was to her no proof to the contrary. She always claimed that she scared them off before they could take anything, by throwing shoes down the hallway. When she went to bed she piled, where she could get at them handily, all the shoes there were about her house. Five minutes after she had turned off the light, she would sit up in bed and say "Hark!" Her husband, who had learned to ignore the whole situation as long ago as 1903, would either be sound asleep or pretend to be sound asleep. In either case he would not respond to her tugging and pulling, so that presently she would arise, tiptoe to the door, open it slightly and heave a shoe down the hall in one direction and its mate down the hall in the other direction. Some nights she threw them all, some nights only a couple of pair.

But I am straying from the remarkable incidents that took place during the night that the bed fell on father. By midnight we were all in bed. The layout of the rooms and the disposition of their occupants is important to an understanding of what later occurred. In the front room upstairs (just under father's attic bedroom) were my mother and my brother Herman, who sometimes sang in his sleep,

usually "Marching Through Georgia" or "Onward, Christian Soldiers." Briggs Beall and myself were in a room adjoining this one.
My brother Roy was in a room across the hall from ours. Our bull
terrier, Rex, slept in the hall.

My bed was an army cot, one of those affairs which are made wide
enough to sleep on comfortably only by putting up, flat with the
middle section, the two sides which ordinarily hang down like the
sideboards of a drop-leaf table. When these sides are up, it is perilous
to roll too far toward the edge, for then the cot is likely to tip completely over, bringing the whole bed down on top of one with a tremendous banging crash. This, in fact, is precisely what happened,
about two o'clock in the morning. (It was my mother who, in recalling the scene later, first referred to it as "the night the bed fell on your
father.")

Always a deep sleeper, slow to arouse (I had lied to Briggs), I was
at first unconscious of what had happened when the iron cot rolled
me onto the floor and toppled over on me. It left me still warmly
bundled up and unhurt, for the bed rested above me like a canopy.
Hence I did not wake up, only reached the edge of consciousness and
went back. The racket, however, instantly awakened my mother, in
the next room, who came to the immediate conclusion that her worst
dread was realized: the big wooden bed upstairs had fallen on father.
She therefore screamed, "Let's go to your poor father!" It was this
shout, rather than the noise of my cot falling, that awakened my
brother Herman, in the same room with her. He thought that mother
had become, for no apparent reason, hysterical. "You're all right,
mamma!" he shouted, trying to calm her. They exchanged shout for
shout for perhaps ten seconds: "Let's go to your poor father!" and
"You're all right!" That woke up Briggs. By this time I was conscious
of what was going on, in a vague way, but did not yet realize that I
was under my bed instead of on it. Briggs, awakening in the midst of
loud shouts of fear and apprehension, came to the quick conclusion
that he was suffocating and that we were all trying to "bring him
out." With a low moan, he grasped the glass of camphor at the head
of his bed and instead of sniffing it poured it over himself. The room
reeked of camphor. "Ugf, ahfg!" choked Briggs, like a drowning man,
for he had almost succeeded in stopping his breath under the deluge
of pungent spirits. He leaped out of bed and groped toward the open
window, but he came up against one that was closed. With his hand,

he beat out the glass, and I could hear it crash and tinkle in the alley-way below. It was at this juncture that I, in trying to get up, had the uncanny sensation of feeling my bed above me! Foggy with sleep, I now suspected, in my turn, that the whole uproar was being made in a frantic endeavor to extricate me from what must be an unheard-of and perilous situation. "Get me out of this!" I bawled. "Get me out!" I think I had the nightmarish belief that I was entombed in a mine. "Gugh!" gasped Briggs, floundering in his camphor.

By this time my mother, still shouting, pursued by Herman, still shouting, was trying to open the door to the attic, in order to go up and get my father's body out of the wreckage. The door was stuck, however, and wouldn't yield. Her frantic pulls on it only added to the general banging and confusion. Roy and the dog were now up, the one shouting questions, the other barking.

Father, farthest away and soundest sleeper of all, had by this time been awakened by the battering on the attic door. He decided that the house was on fire. "I'm coming, I'm coming!" he wailed in a slow, sleepy voice—it took him many minutes to regain full consciousness. My mother, still believing he was caught under the bed, detected in his "I'm coming!" the mournful, resigned note of one who is prepar-ing to meet his Maker. "He's dying!" she shouted.

"I'm all right!" Briggs yelled, to reassure her. "I'm all right!" He still believed that it was his own closeness to death that was worry-ing mother. I found at last the light switch in my room, unlocked the door, and Briggs and I joined the others at the attic door. The dog, who never did like Briggs, jumped for him—assuming that he was the culprit in whatever was going on—and Roy had to throw Rex and hold him. We could hear father crawling out of bed upstairs. Roy pulled the attic door open, with a mighty jerk, and father came down the stairs, sleepy and irritable but safe and sound. My mother began to weep when she saw him. Rex began to howl. "What in the name of God is going on here?" asked father.

The situation was finally put together like a gigantic jigsaw puzzle. Father caught a cold from prowling around in his bare feet but there were no other bad results. "I'm glad," said mother, who always looked on the bright side of things, "that your grandfather wasn't here."

Ludwig Bemelmans

THE BALLET VISITS
THE SPLENDIDE'S MAGICIAN

The management of the Hotel Splendide, the luxurious establishment where I once worked as a busboy, a waiter, and eventually as an assistant maître d'hôtel in the banquet department, kept on file the addresses of a number of men who were magicians, fortune-tellers, or experts with cards. One of these entertainers frequently appeared at the end of the small dinner parties which were given in the private suites of the Splendide in the boom days, before the depression put an end to such pastimes and at last brought about the demise of the Splendide itself. Our entertainers had acclimated their acts to the elegance of the hotel, and the magicians, for example, instead of conjuring a simple white rabbit from their hats, cooked therein a soufflé Alaska or brought out a prize puppy with a rhinestone collar. When young girls were present, the magician pulled from their noses and out of corsages Cartier clips, bracelets, and brooches, which were presented to them with the compliments of the host.

Among the best and most talented of our performers was Professor Maurice Gorylescu, a magician who did some palmistry on the side. He came to the hotel as often as two or three times a week. After coffee had been served, he would enter the private dining room, get people to write any number they wanted to on small bits of paper, and hold the paper to their foreheads. Then he would guess the numbers they had written down and add them up. The total would correspond to a sum he found on a dollar bill in the host's pocket. He did tricks with cards and coins, and he told people about the characteristics and the habits of dress and speech of friends long dead. He even delivered messages from them to the living.

At the end of his séances he would go into some vacant room nearby, sink into a chair, and sit for a while with his hand over his eyes. He always looked very tired. After about half an hour he would shake

799

himself, drink a glass of water slowly, then eat something and go home.

Professor Gorylescu earned a good deal of money. His fee for a single performance was a flat hundred dollars, and he sometimes received that much again as a tip from a grateful host. But although he worked all during the season he spent everything he made and often asked for and received his fee in advance. All he earned went to women —to the support of a Rumanian wife in Bucharest, to an American one who lived somewhere in New Jersey, and to what must have been a considerable number of New York girls of all nationalities to whom he sent little gifts and flowers.

When he came to the hotel during the day, he would hang his cane on the doorknob outside the ballroom office, ask me for a cigarette, and after a while steal a look at the book in which the reservations for small dinners were recorded. Very casually, and while talking of other things, he would turn the leaves and say something like "Looks very nice for the next two months," and put the book back. It took only a few seconds, but in this time his trick mind had stored away all the names, addresses, dates, and telephone numbers in the book. He went home with this information, called up the prospective party-givers, and offered his services.

There was a strict rule that no one should be permitted to look at these reservations, certainly not Professor Gorylescu, but I liked him, and when I was on duty in the ballroom office I would pretend not to see him when he peeked in the book. I also gave him left-over *petits fours,* candies, and after-dinner mints, of which he was very fond. He stuffed them into his pockets without bothering to wrap them up. He would wave goodbye with his immense hands, ask me to visit him soon at his home, and suggest that I bring along some *marrons glacés,* pastry, nuts—anything like that—and then he would leave, a stooping, uncouth figure, bigger than our tallest doorman.

Maurice Gorylescu lived on one of the mediocre streets that run between Riverside Drive and West End Avenue. He had a room in one of the small marble mansions that are common in that neighborhood. The rooming house in which Gorylescu lived was outstanding even among the ornate buildings of that district. It was a sort of junior Frankenstein castle, bedecked with small turrets, loggias, and balconies. It faced the sidewalk across a kind of moat—an air shaft for the basement windows—traversed by a granite bridge. The door was hung on heavy iron hinges that reached all the way across.

The character of this house was, moreover, complemented by the woman who rented its rooms, a Mrs. Houlberg. She stood guard much of the time at the window next to the moat, looking out over a sign that read "Vacancies." She always covered three-quarters of her face with her right hand, a long hand that lay diagonally across her face, the palm over her mouth, the nails of the fingers stopping under the right eye. It looked like a mask, and as if she always had a toothache.

Gorylescu lived on the top-floor front and answered to four short rings and one long one of a shrill bell that was in Mrs. Houlberg's entrance hall. Badly worn banisters led up four flights of stairs. From the balcony of his room one could see the time flash on and off in Jersey and the searchlights of a battleship in the Hudson. The room was large and newly painted in a wet, loud red, the shade of the inside of a watermelon. A spotty chartreuse velvet coverlet decorated a studio couch. Facing this was a chair, a piece of furniture such as you see in hotel lobbies or club cars, covered with striped muslin and padded with down. There was also a Sheraton highboy, which stood near a door that led into an adjoining room which was not his. From the ceiling hung a cheap bazaar lamp with carmine glass panes behind filigree panels. On shelves and on a table were the photographs of many women; in a box, tied together with ribbons in various colors, he kept packets of letters, and in a particular drawer of the highboy was a woman's garter, an old girdle, and various other disorderly trophies.

Gorylescu reclined on the studio bed most of the time when he was at home. He wore a Russian blouse that buttoned under the left ear, and he smoked through a cigarette holder a foot long. One of his eyes was smaller and lower down in his face than the other, and between them rose a retroussé nose, a trumpet of a nose, with cavernous nostrils. Frequently and with great ceremony he sounded it into an immense handkerchief. His cigar-colored skin was spotted as if with a bluish kind of buckshot, and when he was happy he hummed through his nose, mostly the melody of a song whose title was "Tu Sais."

At home he was almost constantly in the company of women. He made the acquaintance of some of them at parties where he had entertained. They brought him gifts, and if they were fat and old, he read their minds and told them things of the past and future. At other times he went looking for girls along Riverside Drive, humming through his nose, and dragging after him a heavy cane whose handle was hooked into his coat pocket.

He went to various other places to find girls. He picked them up at dance halls in Harlem, on the subway, on roller coasters. He easily became acquainted with them anywhere, and they came to his room willingly and took their chances with him. I always thought I might find one of them, dead and naked, behind the Japanese screen, where he kept a rowing machine on which he built himself up. For the space of time that I knew him, love, murder, and that man seemed to be close together and that room the inevitable theatre for it.

The Professor gave me a series of lectures during my visits to his room in which he detailed for me the routines and the mechanisms of his untidy passions. He insisted during these long *études* that the most important piece of strategy was to get the subject to remove her shoes. "Once the shoes are off, the battle is already half won," he would say. "Get a woman to walk around without shoes, without heels—she looks a fool, she feels a fool, she is a fool. Without her shoes, she is lost. Take the soft instep in your hand, caress her ankles, her calf, her knee—the rest is child's play. But remember, first off with the shoes." While he talked, he would scratch his cat, which was part Siamese. The lecture was followed by a display of the collection of photographs he himself had taken, as evidence of the soundness of his theories.

When the Russian Ballet came to town, Professor Gorylescu was not to be had for any parties at the hotel. He went to all the performances, matinées and evenings alike, and he hummed then the music of "Puppenfee," "L'Après-Midi d'un Faune," and the various *divertissements,* and was completely broke. One day he was in a state of the highest elation because he had invited a ballet dancer to tea. He wanted me to come too because she had a friend, who would be an extra girl for me; both of them were exquisite creatures, he assured me, and I was to bring some tea, *marrons glacés, petits fours,* and ladyfingers.

I came early and I brought everything. He darkened the room, lit a brass samovar, laid out some cigarettes, sliced some lemons, hid the rowing machine under the studio couch, and with the Japanese silk screen divided the room into two separate camps. On one side was the couch, on the other the great chair. He buttoned his Russian blouse, blew his nose frequently, and hummed as he walked up and down. He brushed the cat and put away a Spanish costume doll that might have made his couch crowded. He arranged the *petits fours* in saucers, and when the bell rang four times short and one long, he put a Chopin record on his victrola. "Remember about the shoes," he told me over his shoulder, "and always play Chopin for ballet dancers." He quickly surveyed the room once more, turned on the bazaar lamp, and, humming, opened the door—and then stopped humming suddenly. He had invited two of the dancers, but up the stairs came a bouquet of girls, more than a dozen of them.

All at once it was the month of May in the dimmed room. The lovely guests complimented the samovar, the cat, the music, and the view from the balcony, to which they had opened the door, letting much fresh air come in, which intensified the new mood. Gorylescu's voice became metallic with introductions; he ran downstairs to get more glasses for tea and came back breathing heavily. All the girls, without being asked, took their shoes off immediately, explaining that their feet hurt from dancing. They arranged the shoes in an orderly row, as one does on entering a Japanese house or a mosque, then sat down on the floor in a circle. One of them even removed her stockings and put some slices of lemon between her toes. "Ah-h-h," she said.

There started after this a bewildering and alien conversation, a remote, foggy ritual, like a Shinto ceremonial. It consisted of the telling of ballet stories, and seemed to me a high, wild flight into a world closed to the outsider. The stories were told over and over until every detail was correct. In all of these stories appeared Anna Pavlova, who was referred to as "Madame"—what Madame had said, what Madame had done, what she had thought, what she had worn, how she had danced. There was an atmosphere of furious backstage patriotism. The teller of each story swayed and danced with hands, shoulders, and face. Every word was illustrated; for anything mentioned—color, light, time, and person—there was a surprisingly expressive and fitting gesture. The talker was rewarded with applause, with requests for repetition of this or that part again and again, and there swept over the group of girls waves of intimate, fervent emotion.

The Professor served tea on his hands and knees and retired to the shadows of his room. He sat for a while in the great chair like a bird with a wounded wing, and then, with his sagging and cumbersome gait, he wandered around the group of innocents, who sat straight as so many candles, all with their shoes off. The room was alive with young heads and throats and flanks.

The Professor succeeded finally in putting his head into the lap of the tallest, the most racy of the nymphs. She quickly kissed him, said "Sh-h-h-h, daaaahrling," and then caressed his features, the terrible nose, the eyebrows, the corrugated temples, and the great hands, with the professional detachment of a masseuse, while she related an episode in Cairo during a performance of "Giselle" when the apparatus that carried Pavlova up out of her grave to her lover got stuck halfway, and how Madame had cursed and what she had said after the performance and to whom she had said it. An indignant fire burned in all the narrowed eyes of the disciples as she talked.

Suddenly one of them looked at her watch, remembered a rehearsal, and the girls got up and remembered us. They all had Russian names, but all of them were English, as most ballet dancers are; in their best accents, they said their adieus. With individual graces, they arranged their hair, slipped into their shoes, and thanked Maurice. Each one of them said "Daaaahrling" to us and to each other. It was Madame Pavlova's form of address and her pronunciation.

All the girls kissed us, and it was as if we all had grown up in the same garden, as if they were all our sisters. The Professor said a few mouthfuls of gallant compliments, and when they were gone he fished the rowing machine out from under the couch, without a word, and carried it in back of the Japanese screen. Together, we rearranged the room. The *marrons glacés* and the ladyfingers were all gone, but the cigarettes were still there.

AUTHORS AND TITLES